ALGEBRA

and Trigonometry

ADDISON-WESLEY PUBLISHING COMPANY

Menlo Park, California • Reading, Massachusetts • London • Don Mills, Ontario

Secondary Mathematics Series

ALGEBRA
and Trigonometry

SECOND EDITION

RICHARD E. JOHNSON

The University of New Hampshire, Durham, New Hampshire

LONA LEE LENDSEY

Oak Park and River Forest High School, Oak Park, Illinois

WILLIAM E. SLESNICK

Dartmouth College, Hanover, New Hampshire

GRACE E. BATES

Mount Holyoke College, South Hadley, Massachusetts

THIS BOOK IS IN THE

Addison-Wesley
Secondary-Mathematics Series

CONSULTING EDITOR
Richard S. Pieters

ISBN 0-201-03423-9

ABCDEFGHIJKL-KP-787654

PREFACE

In this book, we assume that students are acquainted with the language of algebra, have an understanding of the structure of number systems, and have acquired some dexterity in the manipulation of algebraic expressions.

The mathematical goals of the various parts of this book can be briefly stated in the following manner. The first three chapters reintroduce students to the algebraic properties of the real number system, to equations, and to inequalities of the first and second degrees. After students have had the opportunity to observe that some second-degree equations have no solution in the real number system, we introduce (in Chapter 4) the complex number system in which every second-degree equation has a solution.

Conic sections are introduced in Chapter 5 in order to give a geometric application of quadratic equations in two variables. The discussion of conic sections is followed by Chapter 6 on functions, Chapter 7 on logarithms, and Chapter 8 on polynomials. All the elementary properties of the trigonometric functions are covered in Chapters 9 and 10. Students are thereby given the background in trigonometry that they will need in physics and more advanced mathematics courses.

Ways of counting the number of possible results of a sequence of actions are described in Chapter 11. Then in Chapter 12 these counting procedures are applied to elementary probability theory. Mathematical induction is introduced in Chapter 13, vectors in Chapter 14, and symbolic logic in Chapter 15.

The study of mathematics involves doing mathematics. Consequently, the exercises are designed to lead students to a successful solution of the type of problem under analysis. The exercises are separated into three levels, with many discovery exercises included in the third level. Additional aids to learning may be found in several historical notes, numerous starred sections, and the Extra sections.

The content of this book has been noticeably influenced by the report of the Commission on Mathematics of the College Entrance Examination Board and by the School Mathematics Study Group.

The authors wish to express their appreciation to their colleagues for suggestions and encouragement, to the teachers who so kindly gave their impressions of the book, and to the publishers for their untiring efforts to produce a superior book.

R.E.J.
L.L.L.
W.E.S.
G.E.B.

CONTENTS

The Real Number System

Objectives...

- To list the axioms for the real number system, and to give examples of their application.
- To demonstrate ability with the basic concepts and operations of elementary algebra.
- To give examples that differentiate between the rational number system and the real number system.
- To simplify expressions involving integral and rational exponents.
- To compute with expressions involving radicals.

1–1   FUNDAMENTAL AXIOMS

The axioms of the real number system are divided into two groups: those concerning addition and multiplication and those concerning order. In the first group, we have such familiar axioms as the commutative axioms, associative axioms, and the distributive axiom. Also in this group are the axioms concerning 0 and 1, and the axioms of negatives and reciprocals. The order axioms of the real number system are concerned with the relative sizes of numbers.

Chapter 1 is a review of the material studied in elementary algebra: the fundamental properties of the integers, rational numbers, and real numbers, and common mathematical notations such as exponents and radicals. Although your instructor may not assign this complete chapter, you should be certain that you understand all of the material covered.

The number system of elementary algebra is the *system of real numbers*. It consists of *rational numbers* and *irrational numbers*. From our previous work in algebra, we recall that quotients of integers, such as $-\frac{1}{3}$, $\frac{2}{7}$, $\frac{3}{1}$, and $\frac{876}{29}$, are called rational numbers. Real numbers, such as $\sqrt{3}$, π, and $\sqrt[3]{2} + \sqrt{29}$, which cannot be expressed as quotients of integers are called irrational numbers.

The two basic operations of the real number system are addition and multiplication. The real number system is closed with respect to the operations of addition and multiplication. In other words, if x and y are real numbers, then so are $x + y$ and $x \cdot y$.

Addition and multiplication are unique in the following way.

ADDITIVE AXIOM

$$\text{If } a = b \text{ and } c = d, \text{ then } a + c = b + d. \quad (Add\text{-}A)$$

1

Add =

In other words, if a and b have the same value and c and d have the same value, then $a + c$ has the same value as $b + d$.

MULTIPLICATIVE AXIOM

$$\text{If } a = b \text{ and } c = d, \text{ then } ac = bd. \qquad (Mult\text{-}=)$$

The Additive and Multiplicative Axioms are commonly called *Axioms of Equality*.

Addition and multiplication have the following five fundamental axioms.

COMMUTATIVE AXIOMS OF ADDITION AND MULTIPLICATION

The equations

$$x + y = y + x, \qquad (C\text{-}A)$$
$$x \cdot y = y \cdot x \qquad (C\text{-}M)$$

are true for all real numbers x and y.

ASSOCIATIVE AXIOMS OF ADDITION AND MULTIPLICATION

The equations

$$(x + y) + z = x + (y + z), \qquad (A\text{-}A)$$
$$(x \cdot y) \cdot z = x \cdot (y \cdot z) \qquad (A\text{-}M)$$

are true for all real numbers x, y, and z.

DISTRIBUTIVE AXIOM

The equations

$$x \cdot (y + z) = (x \cdot y) + (x \cdot z),$$
$$(y + z) \cdot x = (y \cdot x) + (z \cdot x) \qquad (D)$$

are true for all real numbers x, y, and z.

ADDITIVE AND MULTIPLICATIVE IDENTITY AXIOMS

The equations

$$x + 0 = x, \quad 0 + x = x, \qquad (Id\text{-}A)$$
$$x \cdot 1 = x, \quad 1 \cdot x = x \qquad (Id\text{-}M)$$

are true for every real number x.

ADDITIVE AND MULTIPLICATIVE INVERSE AXIOMS

Each real number x has a unique additive inverse, ^{-}x, called the negative of x such that

$$x + {}^{-}x = 0,$$
$${}^{-}x + x = 0. \qquad (Inv\text{-}A)$$

Each nonzero real number x has a unique multiplicative inverse, $1/x$, called the reciprocal of x such that

$$x \cdot \frac{1}{x} = 1,$$
$$\frac{1}{x} \cdot x = 1, \quad x \neq 0. \qquad (Inv\text{-}M)$$

These five axioms are assumptions that we make about the real number system, and they are not to be proved.

The following basic assumptions about the use of the equals sign, $=$, are also *Axioms of Equality.*

REFLEXIVE AXIOM

$$x = x \text{ for every real number } x \qquad (Ref\text{-}=)$$

SYMMETRIC AXIOM

If $x = y$, then $y = x$ for every pair x, y of real numbers. $(Sym\text{-}=)$

TRANSITIVE AXIOM

If $x = y$ and $y = z$, then $x = z$ for every triple x, y and z of real numbers. $(Trans\text{-}=)$

Another property, the *substitution principle,* is so elementary that it is used almost without mention. For example, in the equation $3x + 11 - 6 = 7$, we can write $3x + 5 = 7$ instead of $3x + 11 - 6 = 7$; 5 and $11 - 6$ are numerals for the same number and hence either can be *substituted* (Subst.) for the other.

Exercises

Perform the addition.

1. (a) $5 + {}^-2$ (b) ${}^-7 + 3$
2. (a) ${}^-6 + {}^-2$ (b) $3 + {}^-8$

Find the sum.

3. (a) $(7 + 8) + {}^-8$ (b) $7 + (8 + {}^-8)$
4. (a) $({}^-13 + 5) + {}^-5$ (b) ${}^-13 + (5 + {}^-5)$

Which of the following pairs of numbers are additive inverses of each other?

5. (a) $2, \frac{1}{2}$ (b) ${}^-3, \frac{27}{9}$
6. (a) ${}^-4, \frac{16}{4}$ (b) $1, 0$

Which of the following pairs of numbers are multiplicative inverses of each other?

7. (a) $5, {}^-5$ (b) $\frac{1}{7}, 7$
8. (a) $2, .5$ (b) ${}^-.125, {}^-8$

Which of the following pairs of numbers are additive inverses of each other and which are multiplicative inverses of each other?

9. (a) ${}^-3, 3$ (b) $3, \frac{1}{3}$
10. (a) $.5, \frac{1}{2}$ (b) $7, \frac{4}{28}$
11. (a) $.004, 250$ (b) x, y if $x + y = 1$
12. (a) $\frac{1}{3}, {}^-\frac{1}{3}$ (b) $.1, {}^-10$
13. (a) x, y if $x \cdot y = 0$ (b) $12, {}^-12$
14. Complete the arithmetic.
    (a) $16 \cdot 13 + 16 \cdot 17$ (b) $47 \cdot 23 + 53 \cdot 23$

State the axiom(s) of the real number system which makes each of the following equations true.

15. (a) $(21 + 6) + 2 = 21 + (6 + 2)$
    (b) $20 \cdot (5 \cdot 13) = (20 \cdot 5) \cdot 13$
16. (a) $(18 \cdot 23) + (18 \cdot 27) = 18(23 + 27)$
    (b) $16 \cdot 7 + 4 \cdot 7 = 20 \cdot 7$
17. (a) $17 + (8 + 9) = (17 + 9) + 8$
    (b) $(32 + 17) + {}^-17 = 32$

18. (a) $(83 \cdot \frac{57}{19}) \cdot \frac{1}{3} = 83$ (b) $(37 \cdot \frac{13}{91}) \cdot 7 = 37$

19. (a) $17(8 + 12) = (8 + 12)17$ (b) $(16 + 4) \cdot \frac{5}{2} = (4 + 16) \cdot \frac{5}{2}$

20. (a) If $10 = 2x$, why does $2x = 10$?
    (b) If $6 = 8 + x$, why does $8 + x = 6$?

21. (a) If $3x = 8 + 7$ and $8 + 7 = 15$, why does $3x = 15$?
    (b) If $x = 2y + 8$ and $2y = 12$, why does $x = 20$?

Tell which of the following equations are true and which are false. State the axiom(s) of the real number system that support each of your true answers.

22. $(18 \cdot 2)3 = 18(2 \cdot 3)$

23. $14 + (7 + 5) = (14 + 7) + 5$

24. $(30 \cdot 3)5 = 5(30 \cdot 3)$

25. $37(15 + 22) = (15 \cdot 37) + (22 \cdot 37)$

26. $(28 \cdot 7) \cdot 2 = 28 \cdot (7 \cdot 2)$

27. $19 \cdot (108 \cdot \frac{1}{19}) = (19 \cdot \frac{1}{19}) \cdot 108$

28. $(36 \cdot 17) + (64 \cdot 17) = 17(36 + 64)$

1-2 ADDITIONAL PROPERTIES

So far, we have discussed only the operations of addition and multiplication. The other common operations of arithmetic, subtraction and division, may be defined in terms of addition and multiplication. Hence, the properties of subtraction and division may be derived from the five axioms already given. We define subtraction and division in the following way.

Definition of subtraction

The equation

$$x - y = x + {}^-y \qquad\qquad (Def\text{-}Sub)$$

is true for all real numbers x and y.

Since by this definition $x + {}^-y$ is simply $x - y$, there should be no confusion in representing the negative of a number with a centered, rather than raised, negative sign. Hereafter the negative of a number will be denoted by $-x$ instead of ${}^-x$.

Definition of division

The equation

$$x \div y = x \cdot \frac{1}{y} \qquad\qquad (Def\text{-}Div)$$

is true for all real numbers x and y if y $\neq$ 0.

The notations

$$\frac{x}{y} \quad \text{and} \quad x/y$$

are also used for $x \div y$.

The following are examples of the way in which we use the definitions of subtraction and division.

$$7 - 4 = 7 + (-4), \quad \text{or } 3$$
$$13 - 17 = 13 + (-17), \quad \text{or } -4$$
$$9 \div 6 = 9 \cdot \tfrac{1}{6}, \quad \text{or } \tfrac{3}{2}$$
$$\tfrac{1}{3} \div \tfrac{7}{9} = \tfrac{1}{3} \cdot \tfrac{9}{7}, \quad \text{or } \tfrac{3}{7}$$

The real number system is also closed with respect to the operations of subtraction and division, with the exception that division by zero is not defined. Since subtraction is defined in terms of addition and division is defined in terms of multiplication, the additive and multiplicative axioms are valid for subtraction and division.

In the process of finding a sum of several numbers, we may make repeated use of the associative and commutative laws to move addends around in any way we wish. For example,

$$
\begin{aligned}
a + (b + c) &= a + (c + b) & \text{(C-A)}\\
&= (a + c) + b & \text{(A-A)}\\
&= (c + a) + b & \text{(C-A)}\\
&= c + (a + b) & \text{(A-A)}\\
&= c + (b + a). & \text{(C-A)}
\end{aligned}
$$

It is common practice to write

$$a + b + c$$

for either $a + (b + c)$ or $(a + b) + c$. Hence,

$$a + b + c = a + c + b = c + a + b = c + b + a,$$

and so on, by our argument above. If we continue our argument to include four or more addends, we can prove the following property.

REARRANGEMENT PROPERTY OF ADDITION

The terms of a sum may be rearranged in any way.   (R-A)

Since the commutative and associative axioms are also true for multiplication, the rearrangement property is true for multiplication.

REARRANGEMENT PROPERTY OF MULTIPLICATION

The factors of a product may be rearranged in any way.   (R-M)

The *cancellation laws* are, in a sense, converses of the additive and multiplicative axioms.

CANCELLATION LAW OF ADDITION

$$\text{If } x + z = y + z, \text{ then } x = y. \qquad (Can\text{-}A)$$

Proof.

$$
\begin{aligned}
x + z &= y + z &&\text{(hypothesis)} \\
x + z + (-z) &= y + z + (-z) &&\text{(Add-A)} \\
x + [z + (-z)] &= y + [z + (-z)] &&\text{(A-A)} \\
x + 0 &= y + 0 &&\text{(Inv-A)} \\
x &= y &&\text{(Id-A)}
\end{aligned}
$$

This proves that the cancellation law of addition is valid for all real numbers x, y, and z. The *cancellation law of multiplication* can be proved in a similar manner.

CANCELLATION LAW OF MULTIPLICATION

$$\text{If } x \cdot z = y \cdot z \text{ and } z \neq 0, \text{ then } x = y. \qquad (Can\text{-}M)$$

According to the following property, the product of any number and zero is always zero.

ZERO MULTIPLICATION

$$x \cdot 0 = 0 \quad \text{for every real number } x \qquad (Zero\text{-}M)$$

Proof. Since $0 + 0 = 0$,

$$
\begin{array}{rl}
x \cdot (0 + 0) = x \cdot 0, & \text{(Mult-A)} \\
(x \cdot 0) + (x \cdot 0) = x \cdot 0, & \text{(D)} \\
(x \cdot 0) + (x \cdot 0) = (x \cdot 0) + 0, & \text{(Id-A)} \\
x \cdot 0 = 0. & \text{(Can-A)}
\end{array}
$$

From an earlier algebra course, we recall that the product of a positive number and a negative number is a negative number. This is one example of the following property.

NEGATIVE MULTIPLICATION

$$
x \cdot (-y) = -(x \cdot y) \qquad (Neg\text{-}M)
$$

Proof.
$$
\begin{array}{rl}
[x \cdot (-y)] + (x \cdot y) = x \cdot (-y + y) & \text{(D)} \\
= x \cdot 0 & \text{(Inv-A)} \\
= 0 & \text{(Zero-M)} \\
= -(x \cdot y) + (x \cdot y) & \text{(Inv-A)}
\end{array}
$$

Hence,

$$
[x \cdot (-y)] + (x \cdot y) = -(x \cdot y) + (x \cdot y) \quad \text{(Trans-A)}
$$

and

$$
x \cdot (-y) = -(x \cdot y). \qquad \text{(Can-A)}
$$

In general,

$$
-(x \cdot y) = -x \cdot y = x \cdot (-y).
$$

Some examples of the use of negative multiplication are given below.

$$
\begin{array}{l}
-5 \cdot 4 = -(5 \cdot 4), \quad \text{or} \ -20 \\
\tfrac{2}{3} \cdot (-9) = -(\tfrac{2}{3} \cdot 9), \quad \text{or} \ -6
\end{array}
$$

Using the inverse axiom of addition, we can show that $-(-x) = x$. By this axiom, $-x + [-(-x)] = 0$. However, $-x + x = 0$, also, by the inverse axiom of addition. Hence,

$$
-x + [-(-x)] = -x + x \qquad \text{(Trans-A)}
$$

and

$$
-(-x) = x. \qquad \text{(Can-A)}
$$

In other words,

$$
-(-x) = x \quad \text{for every real number } x.
$$

For example, $-(-8) = 8$ and $-[-(-3)] = -3$.
If we use negative multiplication, we see that

$$
\begin{aligned}
(-8) \cdot (-5) &= -(-8 \cdot 5) &\text{(Neg-M)} \\
&= -(5 \cdot -8) &\text{(C-M)} \\
&= -[-(5 \cdot 8)] &\text{(Neg-M)} \\
&= 5 \cdot 8, \quad \text{or } 40.
\end{aligned}
$$

Exercises

Complete the arithmetic.

1. (a) $12 - 17$ (b) $12 - (-17)$
2. (a) $-13 - 4$ (b) $-13 - (-4)$
3. (a) $24 \div 10$ (b) $-36 \div 15$
4. (a) $\frac{3}{7} \div \frac{6}{35}$ (b) $\frac{4}{9} \div \frac{9}{4}$
5. (a) $(-57 \div -19) \cdot (-\frac{1}{3})$ (b) $(87 \div -3) \cdot (-2)$
6. (a) $(17 - 63) \cdot [31 + (-31)]$ (b) $(83 - 21) \cdot [57 + (-57)]$
7. (a) $(-7 \cdot 8) \cdot (-\frac{1}{7})$ (b) $(-12 \cdot 11) \cdot (-\frac{1}{12})$
8. (a) $-17 + 39 + (-83)$ (b) $25 \cdot 86 \cdot (-4)$
9. (a) $-93(-7 + 7)$ (b) $-76 \div (-2)$
10. (a) $32 - (-21) - 67$ (b) $(-17)(-3)$
11. (a) $-20 - 15 - 7$ (b) $[61(-5)] \div (-61)$
12. (a) $[207 \div (-23)] \cdot 23$ (b) $-8(7 - 19)$
13. (a) $(12 - 60) \div (-3)$ (b) $-34 + 71 - 37$

Give the reason or reasons why each of the following statements is true.

14. (a) If $5 + 2 = 7$, then $(5 + 2) + 8 = 7 + 8$.
    (b) If $9 = 18 \div 2$, then $2 \cdot 9 = 2(18 \div 2)$.

15. (a) If $12 + 9 = 21$ and $13 = 7 + 6$, then $(12 + 9) - 13 = 21 - (7 + 6)$.
    (b) If $\dfrac{x + 2}{3} = \dfrac{5}{3}$, then $x + 2 = 5$.

16. (a) If $7(2x - 3) = 7 \cdot 81$, then $2x - 3 = 81$.
    (b) If $2x + 27 = (x + 2) + 27$, then $2x = x + 2$.

17. (a) If $.04x + .05y = 23$, then $4x + 5y = 2300$.
    (b) $(8 \cdot 19) \cdot 25 = (25 \cdot 8) \cdot 19$

18. (a) If $(x + 2) + -2 = 8 + (-2)$, then $x + 2 = 8$.
    (b) If $2x - 3 = 5$, then $2x = 8$.

19. (a) If $5x + 10 = 30$, then $x + 2 = 6$.
    (b) If $-18x = 54$, then $x = -3$.

Complete each statement and name the axiom used.

20. (a) If $x + y = 9 + y$, then $x = $ __?__.

(b) If $\dfrac{x}{3} = \dfrac{20}{7}$, then $7x = $ __?__.

21. (a) If $3x - 12 = 17$, then $3x = $ __?__.

(b) If $\dfrac{4x}{5} = \dfrac{12}{25}$, then $x = $ __?__.

22. (a) If $53x = 53 \cdot \frac{9}{2}$, then $x = $ __?__.

(b) If $21x - 35 = 28x + 7$, then $3x - 5 = $ __?__.

23. (a) If $x - 2 = 0$, then $(x + 3)(x - 2) = $ __?__.

(b) If $7x + 5x = 36$, then $12x = $ __?__.

24. (a) If $x = 13$, what is $-x$? $-(-x)$?

(b) If $x = -17$, what is $-x$? $-(-x)$?

25. (a) Summarize the rules for adding signed numbers.

(b) Summarize the rules for multiplying signed numbers.

---

26. Give a reason for the key steps in the following multiplication problem.

$$
\begin{aligned}
(-4)(-3) &= -(4 \cdot -3) &&\text{__?__}\\
&= -(-3 \cdot 4) &&\text{__?__}\\
&= -[-(3 \cdot 4)] &&\text{__?__}\\
&= 3 \cdot 4, \quad \text{or } 12
\end{aligned}
$$

27. For every real number x, what is $-[-(-x)]$? Illustrate.

28. Is the following equation true for the given values of x and y?

$$-(x + y) = -x + (-y)$$

(a) 5, 3   (b) $-7, -9$

(c) $-12, 6$ (d) $-16, 23$

29. Do you think that the equation in Exercise 28 is true? Prove it.

30. Prove that the equation

$$-x \cdot (-y) = x \cdot y$$

is true for every pair x, y of real numbers. (Hint: Study Exercise 26.)

31. If subtraction is an associative operation, then the equation

$$x - (y - z) = (x - y) - z$$

must be true for every triple x, y, z of real numbers.

(a) Describe a set of number triples for which the equation is true.

(b) Give at least one triple of numbers for which the equation is false.

(c) Is subtraction associative?

1–3 ORDER AXIOMS

Every nonzero real number is either a *positive number* or a *negative number*. For example, 7 and $\pi - 3$ are positive numbers, and -5 and $\sqrt{15} - 4$ are negative numbers. There are three additional fundamental axioms of the real number system that apply to the set of all positive real numbers. They are called the *order axioms*. The order axioms, like the five fundamental axioms of Section 1–1, are basic assumptions which cannot be proved. If we denote the set of all positive real numbers by P, we can state these properties in the following manner.

CLOSURE OF P UNDER ADDITION

For every pair x, y of positive real numbers, $x + y$ is also a positive real number. (Clos-A)

CLOSURE OF P UNDER MULTIPLICATION

For every pair x, y of positive real numbers, $x \cdot y$ is also a positive real number. (Clos-M)

TRICHOTOMY AXIOM

For every real number x, one, and only one, of the following three statements is true:

$$x = 0, \quad x \text{ is positive}, \quad -x \text{ is positive}. \quad (Tri)$$

According to the trichotomy axiom, the system of real numbers consists of three kinds of numbers: positive numbers, negative numbers, and zero. If x is a positive number, then $-x$ is a negative number; if x is a negative number, then $-x$ is a positive number; if x is neither a positive number nor a negative number, then $x = 0$.

The order relations *greater than*, designated by $>$, and *less than*, designated by $<$, are defined in the following way.

Definition of greater than

$x > y$ *if, and only if,* $x - y$ *is a positive number*   *(Def >)*

Definition of less than

$x < y$ *if, and only if,* $y > x$ *(Def <)*

For example,

$11 > 9$,   since $11 - 9 = 2$, and 2 is positive;
$-7 < -4$, or $-4 > -7$,   since $-4 - (-7) = 3$ and 3 is positive.

Since $x - 0 = x$,

$x > 0$ if, and only if, x is a positive number.

Similarly,

$x < 0$ if, and only if, x is a negative number.

Using the order relations, we may express closure of P under addition, closure of P under multiplication, and the trichotomy axiom in the following condensed form.

If $x > 0$ and $y > 0$, then $x + y > 0$.   *(Clos-A)*
If $x > 0$ and $y > 0$, then $xy > 0$.   *(Clos-M)*
If x is a real number, then $x = 0$, $x > 0$, or $x < 0$.   *(Tri)*

We may derive other useful order properties of the real number system from the basic assumptions. The following are three such properties.

TRANSITIVE LAW OF INEQUALITIES

If $x > y$ and $y > z$, then $x > z$.   *(T >)*

TRANS >

ADDITIVE PROPERTY OF INEQUALITIES

If $x > y$, then $x + z > y + z$ for every real number z.   *(A >)*

ADD >

MULTIPLICATIVE PROPERTIES OF INEQUALITIES

mult >

If $x > y$, then $xz > yz$ for every positive number z.   *(M >)*
If $x > y$, then $xz < yz$ for every negative number z.   *(−M >)*

−mult >

We shall prove some of these properties, and leave the proofs of the others as exercises.

Proof of the transitive law

$$
\begin{array}{ll}
x > y \quad \text{and} \quad y > z & \text{(hypothesis)} \\
x - y > 0 \quad \text{and} \quad y - z > 0 & \text{(Def } >) \\
(x - y) + (y - z) > 0 & \text{(Clos-A)} \\
x + (-y + y) - z > 0 & \text{(Def-Sub), (A-A)} \\
x + 0 - z > 0 & \text{(Inv-A)} \\
x - z > 0 & \text{(Id-A)}
\end{array}
$$

Therefore,

$$x > z. \qquad \text{(Def } >)$$

Proof of the multiplicative property for positive numbers

$$
\begin{array}{ll}
x > y \quad \text{and} \quad z > 0 & \text{(hypothesis)} \\
x - y > 0 \quad \text{and} \quad z > 0 & \text{(Def } >) \\
(x - y)z > 0 & \text{(Clos-M)} \\
xz - yz > 0 & \text{(D)}
\end{array}
$$

Therefore,

$$xz > yz. \qquad \text{(Def } >)$$

In a similar way, we can show that the following properties are true: *the transitive law for less than, $(T <)$; the additive property for less than, $(A <)$; multiplication of positive numbers for less than, $(M <)$; and multiplication of negative numbers for less than, $(-M <)$.*

Exercises

Tell which statements are true and which are false. Correct the statements that you marked false.

1. (a) $3 > -4$ (b) $-5 > -6$
2. (a) $0 < -10$ (b) $0 > -1$
3. (a) $-\frac{1}{7} < -\frac{2}{7}$ (b) $-.33 > -.3$

Complete each of the expressions to make a true statement.

4. (a) Since $-12 - (-15) = 3$, __?__ > __?__.
   (b) Since $-7 - (-8) = 1$, __?__ > __?__.

5. (a) Since $-3 - (-12) = 9$, __?__ < __?__.
   (b) Since $0 - (-7) = 7$, __?__ < __?__.

6. (a) Since $-2 > -3$ and $-3 > -4$, __?__ > __?__.
   (b) Since $-1 < 0$ and $0 < \frac{1}{2}$, __?__ < __?__.

7. Verify (A >) with examples in which
   (a) x and y are positive, z is negative.
   (b) x and y are negative, z is positive.
   (c) x, y, z are all negative.

8. Verify (T >) with examples in which
   (a) x, y, z are all positive numbers.
   (b) x, y, z are all negative numbers.
   (c) one is positive and two are negative.
   (d) y is zero.

9. Verify (M >) with examples in which
   (a) x and y are both positive.
   (b) x and y are both negative.
   (c) x and y have opposite signs.

10. Verify ($-$M >) with examples in which
    (a) x and y are both positive.
    (b) x and y are both negative.
    (c) x and y have opposite signs.

11. State the reason for each step in the proof of the following implication:

    If $x > y$, then $x + z > y + z$ for every real number z.

    (a) If $x > y$, then $x - y$ is positive.
    (b) $(x + z) - (y + z) = x - y$
    (c) Since $(x + z) - (y + z)$ is positive, $(x + z) > (y + z)$.

12. If $a < b$, is $a < 2b$? Give some examples, using both positive and negative numbers.

13. Use (Tri), (Def >), and (Def <) to prove that for every pair of real numbers x and y, one, and only one, of the following three statements is true.

    $$x = y, \quad x > y, \quad x < y$$

14. Prove that if x and y are real numbers such that

    $$x > y,$$

    then

    $$x \cdot z < y \cdot z$$

    for every negative number z.

Before attempting to prove the following statements, use different numbers to give several examples which support each statement.

15. Prove that if x and y are real numbers such that $x > y$, then

$$x - z > y - z$$

for every real number z.

16. Prove that if z is positive, its reciprocal is positive, and if z is negative, its reciprocal is negative.

17. If x and y are both positive and $x > y$, state and prove the relationship which exists between $1/x$ and $1/y$.

18. Before attempting to prove the statements below, use different numbers to give several specific examples which support each statement.

    (a) Prove that if x and y are positive real numbers such that $x > y$, then $x^2 > y^2$.

    (b) Prove that if x and y are positive real numbers such that $x^2 > y^2$, then $x > y$.

    (c) Combine the statements in parts (a) and (b) into one statement.

19. Consider a number system S of ten elements, the ten digits of the real number system. Thus,

$$S = \{0, 1, 2, 3, 4, 5, 6, 7, 8, 9\}.$$

For $a \neq b$, define $a \delta b$ to be the larger of a and b. For $a = b$, define $a \delta b$ to be a. Thus, for example, $2 \delta 3 = 3$, $8 \delta 5 = 8$, $7 \delta 7 = 7$. Examine S for closure under δ, rearrangement properties of δ, identity element for δ, and inverse elements.

1–4   ADDITIONAL ORDER PROPERTIES

The order relation *greater than or equal to* is denoted by $\geq$.

Definition of greater than or equal to

      $x \geq y,$ *if and only if,* *either $x > y$ or $x = y$*   (*Def* $\geq$)

Similarly, the order relation *less than or equal to* is denoted by $\leq$.

Definition of less than or equal to

      $x \leq y$ *if, and only if,* $y \geq x$ (*Def* $\leq$)

For example,

$$7 \geqq 3 \quad \text{because} \quad 7 > 3,$$
$$-3 \geqq -3 \quad \text{because} \quad -3 = -3,$$
$$-4 \leqq -1 \quad \text{because} \quad -4 < -1,$$
$$\frac{1}{\sqrt{2}} \leqq \frac{\sqrt{2}}{2} \quad \text{because} \quad \frac{1}{\sqrt{2}} = \frac{\sqrt{2}}{2}.$$

If x, y, and z are three numbers such that $x < y$ and $y < z$, then we write

$$x < y < z.$$

This shows that y is a number *between* x and z. For example,

$$-1 < 2 < 5 \quad \text{because} \quad -1 < 2 \text{ and } 2 < 5.$$

Statements such as

$$x > y > z, \quad x \leqq y < z, \quad x < y \leqq z,$$

and so on, are also meaningful and are often used in mathematics.

We shall never contract a statement such as $0 < 2$ and $2 > -1$ to $0 < 2 > -1$, or $5 > 1$ and $1 < 3$ to $5 > 1 < 3$. We contract only when two order relations are of the same type and the contraction shows us at a glance that one number is between two other numbers.

Each real number x has associated with it a *nonnegative* number, called its *absolute value,* which is denoted by $|x|$.

Definition of absolute value

$$\textit{If } x \geqq 0, \textit{ then } |x| = x.$$

$$\textit{If } x < 0, \textit{ then } |x| = -x.$$

(Def $|x|$)

For example,

$$|7| = 7 \text{ and } |-7| = -(-7), \quad \text{or } 7,$$
$$|1 - \sqrt{2}| = -(1 - \sqrt{2}), \quad \text{or } \sqrt{2} - 1,$$
$$|0| = 0.$$

By the definition of absolute value,

$$|x| = |-x| \quad \text{for every real number } x.$$

The rules for multiplying positive and negative numbers are summarized below for easy reference.

If $x > 0$ and $y > 0$, then $xy > 0$.

If $x > 0$ and $y < 0$, or $x < 0$ and $y > 0$, then $xy < 0$.

If $x < 0$ and $y < 0$, then $xy > 0$.

Each of the rules above may be proved by using the property for multiplication of negative numbers for greater than, $(-M >)$. For example, if $x > 0$ and $y < 0$, then

$$x \cdot y < 0 \cdot y, \qquad\qquad (-M >)$$
$$x \cdot y < 0. \qquad\qquad (\text{Zero-M})$$

The actual product of a positive and a negative number or of two negative numbers may be found by first obtaining the product of their absolute values. For example,

$$-8 \cdot 7 = -(8 \cdot 7) \qquad\qquad (\text{Neg-M})$$
$$= -(|8| \cdot |7|), \quad \text{or} \ -56.$$

We may also use absolute value to give the rules for multiplying positive and negative numbers.

$$x \cdot y = -(|x| \cdot |y|) \qquad \text{if } x \text{ and } y \text{ have opposite signs}$$
$$x \cdot y = |x| \cdot |y| \qquad \text{if } x \text{ and } y \text{ have the same sign}$$

Exercises

Tell which of the following statements are true and which are false. Correct the statements that you marked false.

1. (a) $-8 \leqq -7$　　　　　　　　(b) $4 \geqq 4$

2. (a) $-2 \leqq -2 < 2$　　　　　　(b) $-5 < 5 \leqq 5$

3. (a) $|3 - \pi| = 3 - \pi$　　　　　(b) $|3 - 5| = 5 - 3$

4. (a) $-5 \cdot 3 = -(|-5| \cdot |3|)$　　(b) $(6)(-3) = |-6| \cdot |-3|$

5. (a) $|2 - \sqrt{3}| = -(\sqrt{3} - 2)$　(b) $\dfrac{1}{\sqrt{3}} \geqq \dfrac{\sqrt{3}}{3}$

6. (a) $|-7| > |-4|$　　　　　　　(b) $|2| \geqq |-8|$

Express each of the following numbers without using absolute-value signs.

7. (a) $|-5 - (-6)|$　　　　　　　(b) $|-5| - |-6|$

8. (a) $|-2| + |-4|$　　　　　　　(b) $|-2 + -4|$

9. (a) $|\sqrt{2} - 1.41|$ (b) $|\sqrt{15} - 4|$

10. (a) $|\frac{1}{3} - .333|$ (b) $\left|\frac{3}{4} - \frac{\pi}{4}\right|$

11. (a) $|12 + (-9)|$ (b) $|12| + |-9|$

12. (a) $|-5 - (-5)|$ (b) $|10^{-6}|$

Find all integral values of x that make each of the statements true if the set is finite. Otherwise, find six values.

13. $|x| = 4$ 14. $|x + 1| = 3$

15. $|x - 6| = 9$ 16. $|x| + 3 = 10$

17. $|x| < 5$ 18. $|x| > 5$

19. $|x - 1| < 6$ 20. $|x - 1| > 6$

21. $|2x + 1| \leq 21$ 22. $|2x + 1| > 21$

23. $12 > x + 1 > 2$ 24. $12 > |x + 1| > 2$

25. $|2 - x| \leq 7$ 26. $|2 - x| > 7$

27. $3 < |x| < 10$ 28. $3 < x < 10$

For each of the following pairs of values of x and y, compare the value of $|x| \cdot |y|$ with that of $|x \cdot y|$.

29. 5, 6   30. $-4, 3$

31. $7, -8$ 32. $-2, -10$

33. In general, is $|x| \cdot |y|$ greater than, equal to, or less than $|x \cdot y|$? (See Exercises 29–32.)

Compare the value of $|x| + |y|$ with the value of $|x + y|$ for each pair of values of x and y.

34. (7, 10)   35. $(-8, 6)$

36. $(9, -4)$ 37. (0, 12)

38. $(-5, -4)$

---

39. Use the results of Exercises 34–38 to answer each of the following questions.

(a) For what values of x and y is it true that

$$|x| + |y| = |x + y|?$$

(b) For what values of x and y is it true that

$$|x| + |y| > |x + y|?$$

(c) Are there any values of x and y for which it is true that

$$|x| + |y| < |x + y|?$$

(d) Make a general statement that is true for all real numbers x and y, comparing the value of $|x| + |y|$ with that of $|x + y|$.

1–5 THE INTEGERS AND THE RATIONAL NUMBERS

The system of integers is a subsystem of the real number system, and consists of positive integers, negative integers, and zero. If we imagine the integers arranged in a line as indicated below, they will extend endlessly in both directions.

$$\ldots, -10^9, \ldots, -4, -3, -2, -1, 0, 1, 2, 3, 4, \ldots, 10^9, \ldots$$

In this line, the positive integers are to the right of 0, and the negative integers are to the left of 0.

Because the system of integers is a subsystem of the real number system, we might suppose that the eight basic axioms of the real number system are also valid for the system of integers. This is almost, but not entirely, true. Clearly, the commutative, associative, and distributive axioms are true. Since the sum of two integers is always an integer, *the system of integers is closed with respect to addition.* It is also *closed with respect to multiplication,* because the product of two integers is always an integer. The identity elements of the real number system, 0 and 1, are also integers. Each integer has an additive inverse which is an integer. Thus, -8 is the additive inverse of 8, and 113 is the additive inverse of -113. However, not every nonzero integer has a multiplicative inverse which is an integer. For example, the multiplicative inverse of the integer 8 is $\frac{1}{8}$, and $\frac{1}{8}$ is not an integer. Therefore, the *multiplicative inverse axiom is not valid for the system of integers.* The order axioms are valid for this system. We conclude that, with the exception of the multiplicative inverse property, the eight basic axioms of the real number system are true for the system of integers.

In addition to these eight, there is one more property that applies exclusively to the system of integers. Roughly speaking, this is the property which says that every positive integer may be reached by starting with 1 and counting 2, 3, 4, and so on, in order up to the given integer. For example, we arrive at 9 by counting 1, 2, 3, 4, 5, 6, 7, 8, 9. By *counting*, we mean that after every integer n, we name its *successor*, $n + 1$. It would take a long time to count to the number 10^{100}, but we can imagine that it could be done. This new property is really a property of the set P of all positive integers. It is called the *induction property* and will be discussed later in the text.

Another important subsystem of the real number system is the rational number system. We recall that a number is called *rational* if it can be expressed as a quotient of two integers. For example, each of the numbers

$$\frac{3}{5}, \quad \frac{-6}{8}, \quad \frac{4}{3}, \quad \frac{-100}{-101}, \quad 3.14159$$

is rational. Each integer n is also a rational number since $n = n/1$. Consequently, the rational number system contains the system of integers.

Each rational number can be expressed in many different ways as a quotient of two integers. For example, $2/4$, $3/6$, $1/2$, and $13/26$ are different numerals for the same rational number, and $6/14$, $-15/-35$, $3/7$, $21/49$, and $-3/-7$ are different ways of representing the same rational number. If we are given two quotients of integers, we can tell whether they represent the same rational number by the following rule. If a, b, c, and d are integers with $b \neq 0$ and $d \neq 0$, then

$$\frac{a}{b} = \frac{c}{d} \quad \textit{if, and only if,} \quad a \cdot d = b \cdot c.$$

For example,

$$\frac{3}{7} = \frac{6}{14} \quad \text{since} \quad 3 \cdot 14 = 7 \cdot 6, \quad \text{or } 42.$$

A nonzero rational number a/b is said to be expressed in *simplest form* if $b > 0$ and the integers a and b are relatively prime, that is, if the greatest common divisor (g.c.d.) of a and b is 1. For example, the rational number $3/7$ is expressed in simplest form, since $7 > 0$ and the g.c.d. of 3 and 7 is 1. We shall not prove it here, but the simplest form of a rational number is *unique*. If a/b is the simplest form of a rational number, then any other representation has the form na/nb for some nonzero integer n.

The rational number system is *closed* with respect to the operations of addition, multiplication, subtraction, and division (except by zero). In other words, if a and b are rational numbers, then so are $a + b$, $a \cdot b$, $a - b$, and $a \div b$, if $b \neq 0$. Since the negative of each rational number is rational and the reciprocal of each nonzero rational number is also rational, the eight basic axioms of the real number system are also valid for the rational number system.

Exercises

Write each of the following rational numbers as a quotient of integers and express each answer in simplest form.

1. (a) $\frac{24}{64}$ (b) $\frac{98}{1008}$ 2. (a) 3.14   (b) 1.414

Perform the indicated operations, and express each answer in simplest form.

3. (a) $\frac{3}{4} - \frac{2}{3}$ (b) $\frac{4}{15} - \frac{7}{20}$

4. (a) $\frac{3}{4} \cdot (-\frac{2}{3})$ (b) $\frac{66}{65} \times \frac{13}{44}$

5. (a) $\frac{3}{4} \div (-\frac{2}{3})$ (b) $-\frac{38}{45} \div \frac{57}{70}$

6. (a) $\frac{4}{39} - \frac{5}{52} + \frac{6}{65}$ (b) $\frac{12}{75} - \frac{7}{60} - \frac{11}{30}$

7. (a) $(\frac{4}{5} + \frac{3}{15}) \div (-\frac{5}{9})$ (b) $(2\frac{1}{8} - 1\frac{5}{16}) \div 3$

8. (a) $(\frac{5}{2} - \frac{5}{3}) \times \frac{36}{15}$ (b) $(\frac{4}{17} \times \frac{85}{64}) + (\frac{111}{52} \times \frac{39}{74})$

9. (a) $\frac{7}{8}(\frac{19}{57} - \frac{1}{3})$ (b) $(\frac{17}{68} - \frac{1}{4}) \div (-\frac{13}{17})$

Which, if any, of the following systems are closed?

10. The set of positive integers with respect to subtraction
11. The set of integers with respect to subtraction
12. The set of negative integers with respect to addition
13. The set of negative integers with respect to multiplication
14. The set of integers with respect to division
15. The set of positive rational numbers with respect to division
16. The set of even integers with respect to addition
17. The set of odd integers with respect to multiplication
18. The set of positive rational numbers with respect to subtraction
19. The set of rational numbers with respect to subtraction
20. The set of negative rational numbers with respect to addition
21. The set of negative rational numbers with respect to multiplication
22. The set of rational numbers with respect to division
23. The set of nonzero rational numbers with respect to division
24. (a) Name six rational numbers between 0 and 1, between 0 and $\frac{1}{2}$, between 0 and $\frac{1}{4}$, between 0 and $\frac{1}{10}$, and between 0 and a when $a > 0$.
    (b) How many rational numbers are there between any two rational numbers?
25. (a) What is the largest integer that is less than $\frac{137}{56}$?
    (b) What is the smallest integer that is greater than $\frac{137}{56}$?
    (c) What integer is nearest to $\frac{137}{56}$?

26. (a) Can you find a largest rational number which is less than $\frac{137}{56}$? Explain your answer.

(b) Can you find a smallest rational number which is greater than $\frac{137}{56}$? Explain your answer.

27. Is the set $\{-1, 0, 1\}$ closed with respect to any of the operations of arithmetic? If so, name them.

28. For which operations of arithmetic is the set of multiples of 3 closed?

29. If $S = \{x \mid x = 3^n, n \text{ a positive integer}\}$, is S closed with respect to any arithmetic operations? If so, name them.

30. Describe a subset of the rational numbers which is closed

(a) under $+$, $-$, and $\times$, but not $\div$.

(b) under $\times$, but not $+$.

(c) under $+$ and $-$, but not $\times$.

Review for Sections 1–1 through 1–5.

Give the reason or reasons why each of the following equations is true.

1. $5 + 6 = 6 + 5$

2. $x = 12$ and $12 = 3 \cdot 4$; therefore $x = 3 \cdot 4$.

3. $20 - 7 = -7 + 20$

4. $84 \cdot 125 = 125 \cdot 84$

5. $m + 9 = 4 + 9$; therefore $m = 4$.

6. $(-71) \cdot (93) = (93) \cdot (-71)$

7. $(20)(.05) = 1$

8. $k > 5$ and $5 > 3$; therefore $k > 3$.

9. $-4 + \frac{8}{2} = 0$

10. $3 \cdot \frac{3}{3} = 3$

11. $4 > 3$; therefore $4(-2) < 3(-2)$.

12. $(.75)(\frac{4}{3}) = 1$

13. $76 + 0 = 76$

14. $3(7 - 2) = 3 \cdot 7 - 3 \cdot 2$

15. $(71 + 12) - 12 = 71$

16. $(39 \cdot 4) \cdot \frac{1}{4} = 39$

17. $67 + x - 67 = x$

18. $.5 \times y \times 2 = y$

19. $21 \times 33 \times 0 = 0$

20. $(-3 \times 5) \times [6 \times (-10)] = -15 \times (-60)$

Perform the indicated operations and express each answer in simplest form.

21. $\frac{7}{2} + (-\frac{2}{7} - \frac{3}{14})$

22. $|13 - 8| + |2 - 6|$

23. $15 \cdot (-3)$

24. $|5 - 7| - |4 - 10|$

25. $(-4)(-12)$

26. $(-\frac{5}{8} \times \frac{7}{9}) \div (-\frac{105}{216})$

27. $(2\frac{1}{5} + 1\frac{5}{6}) - (4 + \frac{1}{30})$

28. $(1\frac{2}{5} \div 3\frac{3}{4}) \div (2\frac{2}{3} \div 2\frac{1}{2})$

Which, if any, of the following sets are closed with respect to the given operation?

29. The set of odd integers, addition

30. The set of positive rational numbers, division

31. The set of even integers, multiplication

32. The set of positive even integers, subtraction

Tell whether each of the following pairs of numbers are multiplicative inverses or additive inverses of each other or neither.

33. $25, -\frac{50}{2}$

34. $3, -\frac{1}{3}$

35. $\frac{1}{2}, .5$

36. $15, \frac{1}{15}$

37. $4, -4$

38. $5, .2$

Answers to Review for Sections 1–1 through 1–5

1. (C-A) **2.** (Trans-A) **3.** (C-A) **4.** (C-M)

5. (Can-A) **6.** (C-M) **7.** (Inv-M) **8.** (T >)

9. (Inv-A) **10.** (Id-M) **11.** (−M >) **12.** (Inv-M)

13. (Id-A) **14.** (D)

15. (A-A), (Inv-A), (Id-A) **16.** (A-M), (Inv-M), (Id-M)

17. (R-A), (Inv-A), (Id-A) **18.** (R-M), (Inv-M), (Id-M)

19. (Zero-M) **20.** (Neg-M)

21. 3 **22.** 9

23. −45 **24.** −4

25. 48 **26.** 1

27. 0 **28.** $\frac{7}{20}$

29. Not Closed **30.** Closed

31. Closed **32.** Not Closed

33. Additive Inverses **34.** Neither

35. Neither **36.** Multiplicative Inverses

37. Additive Inverses **38.** Multiplicative Inverses

1-6   IRRATIONAL NUMBERS

There are many real numbers which cannot be expressed as a quotient of two integers. Such real numbers are called *irrational numbers.* For example, it may be shown that $\sqrt{2}$, π, $\sqrt[3]{7} - 3$, and $\sqrt{29}/4$ are irrational numbers.

We may obtain many irrational numbers by taking square roots, cube roots, and so on, of positive rational numbers. The real number y is called a *square root* of x if $y^2 = x$; a *cube root* of x if $y^3 = x$; and so on. Thus, since $4^2 = 16$, 4 is a square root of 16; and since $4^3 = 64$, 4 is a cube root of 64. One of the properties of the real number system is that every positive real number has a positive square root, cube root, and so on.

There is an interesting question about rational numbers: What positive rational numbers have *rational* square roots? In other words, under what conditions is a given rational number the square of another rational number? To answer this question, let a/b be a positive rational number expressed in simplest form. If there exists another positive rational number x/y, also in simplest form, such that

$$\left(\frac{x}{y}\right)^2 = \frac{a}{b},$$

then we must have

$$\frac{x^2}{y^2} = \frac{a}{b}.$$

Now, if the integers x and y are relatively prime, then so are the integers x^2 and y^2. Hence, the rational number x^2/y^2 is expressed in simplest form. Since x^2/y^2 and a/b are simplest forms for the same rational number, and the simplest form of a rational number is unique, we must have

$$x^2 = a \quad \text{and} \quad y^2 = b.$$

Therefore, we can make the following statement.

The positive rational number a/b, expressed in simplest form, is the square of another rational number if, and only if, the integers a and b are squares of integers.

The squares of the positive integers, in order, are

1, 4, 9, 16, 25, 36, 49, 64, 81, 100, 121, 144, ...

These numbers are called *perfect squares.* Hence, only rational numbers such as

$$\tfrac{4}{9}, \quad \tfrac{36}{81}, \quad \tfrac{121}{144}$$

have rational square roots.

Knowing which rational numbers have rational square roots, we can easily give examples of irrational numbers. All we need do is select a rational number in simplest form, such as $\tfrac{7}{3}$ or $\tfrac{5}{1}$, for which the two integers involved are not both perfect squares. Then the positive square root of the number must be irrational. For example,

$$\sqrt{\tfrac{7}{3}} \quad \text{and} \quad \sqrt{5}$$

are irrational numbers. We recall that for a positive number x, $\sqrt{x}$ designates the *positive square* root of x. (The negative square root of x is denoted $-\sqrt{x}$.) *Negative numbers do not have real square roots.*

If x is a rational number and y is an irrational number, then $x + y$ must be irrational. To see that this is so, let $z = x + y$. Then $y = z - x$, and y is rational if both z and x are rational, because the set of rational numbers is closed under subtraction. Since we assumed that y was irrational, z must be irrational. Similarly, if x is a nonzero rational number and y is irrational, then xy is irrational. Neither the sum nor the product of two irrational numbers need be irrational. For example, $3 - \sqrt{2}$ and $3 + \sqrt{2}$ are two irrational numbers whose sum and product are both rational:

$$(3 - \sqrt{2}) + (3 + \sqrt{2}) = 6,$$
$$(3 - \sqrt{2}) \times (3 + \sqrt{2}) = 3^2 - (\sqrt{2})^2, \quad \text{or } 7.$$

Hence, the set of irrational numbers is *not closed* under either addition or multiplication.

Since $(\sqrt{x}\,\sqrt{y})^2 = (\sqrt{x})^2\,(\sqrt{y})^2$, or xy, for every pair x, y of positive real numbers, it follows that

$$\sqrt{xy} = \sqrt{x}\,\sqrt{y}$$

for every pair x, y of positive real numbers. For example,

$$\sqrt{9 \times 2} = \sqrt{9}\,\sqrt{2}, \quad \text{or } 3\sqrt{2}.$$

Thus, $\sqrt{18} = 3\sqrt{2}$.

This example illustrates an interesting fact about the set of positive integers: Every positive integer can be expressed as a product of two integers; the first being a *perfect square* and the second a *square-free* integer. An integer is said to be square-free if none of its integral factors other than 1 is a perfect square. For example, 6 and 14 are square-free whereas 24 is not, since $24 = 4 \times 6$ and 4 is a perfect square.

We shall say that the square root of a positive integer is expressed in *simplest form* if it is expressed as the product of an integer and the square root of a square-free integer. For example, the simplest form of $\sqrt{18}$ is $3\sqrt{2}$, and the simplest form of $\sqrt{75} = 5\sqrt{3}$.

The positive rational numbers, on the other hand, have the property that every positive rational number can be expressed as the product of a perfect-square rational number and a square-free integer. We can then express the square root of a positive rational number as the product of a rational number and the square root of a square-free integer. When expressed this way, it is in simplest form. For example,

$$\sqrt{\tfrac{2}{3}} = \sqrt{\tfrac{6}{9}} = \sqrt{\tfrac{1}{9} \cdot 6} = \tfrac{1}{3}\sqrt{6}$$

and

$$\sqrt{\tfrac{8}{5}} = \sqrt{\tfrac{40}{25}} = \sqrt{\tfrac{4}{25} \cdot 10} = \tfrac{2}{5}\sqrt{10}.$$

Problem. Find the simplest form of $\sqrt{180}$.

Solution. Evidently 4 is a factor of 180 and $180 = 4 \times 45$. In turn, 9 is a factor of 45 and $180 = 4 \times 9 \times 5$. The remaining integer, 5, is square-free. Hence, $180 = 36 \times 5$ and $\sqrt{180} = 6\sqrt{5}$.

Another important property of the real number system is that *every real number other than an integer lies between two consecutive integers.* According to this property, if r is a real number that is not an integer, then there exists an integer n such that

$$n < r < n + 1.$$

The integer n is called the *greatest integer* in r. The notation $[r]$ is used in mathematics to designate the greatest integer in the real number r. Naturally, $[n] = n$ if n is an integer.

For example,

$$[\sqrt{2}] = 1, \quad \text{since} \quad 1 < \sqrt{2} < 2;$$
$$[\pi] = 3, \quad \text{since} \quad 3 < \pi < 4;$$
$$[4.95] = 4, \quad \text{since} \quad 4 < 4.95 < 5.$$

This new property of the real number system allows us to approximate every irrational number by a rational number with any desired degree of accuracy.

For example, either 1 or 2 is a rough approximation of $\sqrt{2}$, since $1 < \sqrt{2} < 2$. To obtain a better approximation of $\sqrt{2}$, consider the number $10\sqrt{2}$. What is $[10\sqrt{2}]$? To answer this question, we look at the integer $(10\sqrt{2})^2$, or 200. The largest perfect-square integer less than 200 is 196, which is 14^2. Hence,

$$14^2 < 200 < 15^2$$

and, taking square roots, we have

$$14 < 10\sqrt{2} < 15.$$

Finally, if we multiply each member of the inequality by $\frac{1}{10}$, we obtain

$$1.4 < \sqrt{2} < 1.5.$$

Therefore, either 1.4 or 1.5 is a one-decimal-place approximation of $\sqrt{2}$. To obtain a better approximation of $\sqrt{2}$, we find $[100\sqrt{2}]$. Obviously $(100\sqrt{2})^2 = 20{,}000$ and $140^2 < 20{,}000 < 150^2$, by our work above. It may be shown that the *largest* perfect-square integer less than 20,000 is 19,881, which is 141^2. Hence,

$$141^2 < 20{,}000 < 142^2,$$
$$141 < 100\sqrt{2} < 142,$$

and, finally,

$$1.41 < \sqrt{2} < 1.42.$$

Consequently, either 1.41 or 1.42 is a two-decimal-place approximation of $\sqrt{2}$.

Exercises

Use the fact that $\sqrt{x} \cdot \sqrt{y} = \sqrt{xy}$ to find the following products.

1. (a) $\sqrt{3} \cdot \sqrt{5}$ (b) $\sqrt{2} \cdot \sqrt{3}$
2. (a) $\sqrt{14} \cdot \sqrt{5}$ (b) $\sqrt{7} \cdot \sqrt{6}$

Use the fact that $\sqrt{xy} = \sqrt{x} \cdot \sqrt{y}$ to factor each square root and simplify.

3. (a) $\sqrt{45}$ (b) $\sqrt{20}$
4. (a) $\sqrt{80}$ (b) $\sqrt{125}$
5. (a) $\sqrt{12}$ (b) $\sqrt{27}$
6. (a) $\sqrt{48}$ (b) $\sqrt{75}$
7. (a) $\sqrt{98}$ (b) $\sqrt{847}$
8. (a) $\sqrt{180}$ (b) $\sqrt{210}$
9. (a) $\sqrt{2475}$ (b) $\sqrt{3872}$

Write each of the following square roots of rational numbers as a rational number times the square root of a square-free integer.

10. (a) $\sqrt{\frac{1}{5}}$ (b) $\sqrt{\frac{1}{6}}$

11. (a) $\sqrt{\frac{2}{11}}$ (b) $\sqrt{\frac{4}{7}}$

12. (a) $\sqrt{\frac{3}{8}}$ (b) $\sqrt{\frac{2}{27}}$

13. (a) $\sqrt{1\frac{3}{5}}$ (b) $\sqrt{\frac{148}{3}}$

14. (a) $\sqrt{\frac{7}{20}}$ (b) $\sqrt{\frac{35}{6}}$

15. (a) $\sqrt{\frac{49}{24}}$ (b) $\sqrt{\frac{169}{180}}$

Find the sum of each of the following pairs of irrational numbers.

16. (a) $5 + \sqrt{3},\ 5 - \sqrt{3}$

    (b) $3\sqrt{2} + \sqrt{7},\ 3\sqrt{2} - \sqrt{7}$

Find the product of each of the following pairs of irrational numbers.

17. (a) $5 + \sqrt{3},\ 5 - \sqrt{3}$

    (b) $\sqrt{2} - \sqrt{5},\ \sqrt{2} + \sqrt{5}$

Find the products.

18. (a) $3\sqrt{2} \cdot 5\sqrt{2}$ (b) $(4\sqrt{3})^2$

19. (a) $(3\sqrt{2})^3$ (b) $(2\sqrt{3})^3$

Find each of the following greatest integers.

20. (a) $[3 + \sqrt{5}]$ (b) $[-\sqrt{10}]$

21. (a) $[\sqrt{19}]$ (b) $\left[\frac{-17}{5}\right]$

---

22. (a) What is the largest integer that is less than $\sqrt{7}$?

    (b) What is the smallest integer that is greater than $\sqrt{7}$?

    (c) What integer is nearest to $\sqrt{7}$?

    (d) Can you find a largest rational number which is less than $\sqrt{7}$?

    (e) Can you find a smallest rational number which is greater than $\sqrt{7}$?

23. Find approximations to $\sqrt{3}$ by determining

    (a) the consecutive integers between which $\sqrt{3}$ lies.

    (b) the consecutive integers between which $10\sqrt{3}$ lies (the largest integer which has a square less than 300 and the smallest integer which has a square greater than 300).

    (c) the consecutive integers between which $100\sqrt{3}$ lies.

24. (a) Between which two consecutive integers does $-\sqrt[3]{100}$ lie?

    (b) What is the largest integer that is less than $-\sqrt[3]{100}$?

    (c) Is there a largest rational number which is less than $-\sqrt[3]{100}$?

25. Describe those numbers for which the *greatest* integer is also the *nearest* integer. Illustrate.

1-7 INTEGRAL EXPONENTS

In exponential notation, introduced into mathematics in the seventeenth century by the Frenchman René Descartes, x^6 designates the product $x \cdot x \cdot x \cdot x \cdot x \cdot x$. This notation allows the astronomer to express the approximate distance from the earth to the farthest visible star very simply as 6×10^{19} miles. Without exponential notation, this distance would have to be written as 60,000,000,000,000,000,000 (in words, 60 quintillion). Today's physicist is able to describe the diameter of an electron as

$$1 \times 10^{-13}, \quad \text{or} \quad \frac{1}{10^{13}} \text{ centimeter,}$$

instead of as .0000000000001 centimeter (1 ten-trillionth of a centimeter). By definition,

$$\overbrace{x^n = x \cdot x \cdot \ldots \cdot x}^{n \text{ factors}}, \quad n \text{ any positive integer,}$$

for every real number x. The number n is called the *exponent* of x in x^n, and x^n is called the nth power of x. For convenience, we define

$$x^0 = 1 \quad \textit{for every nonzero real number } x.$$

Negative exponents can be defined in the following manner.

Definition of negative exponents

The equation

$$x^{-n} = \frac{1}{x^n} \qquad\qquad \textit{(Def-Neg. Exp.)}$$

is true for every positive integer n and every nonzero real number x.

In other words, x^{-n} is the *reciprocal* of x^n. Since y/x is the reciprocal of x/y, it follows that

$$\left(\frac{x}{y}\right)^{-n} = \left(\frac{y}{x}\right)^n$$

for every integer n and all nonzero real numbers x and y. Therefore, we have defined the nth power of every nonzero real number for every integer n, whether n is positive, negative, or zero.

You are undoubtedly aware of certain basic rules for working with powers of numbers. These rules are called the *laws of exponents,* and may be stated in the following way.

LAWS OF EXPONENTS

$$x^m \cdot x^n = x^{m+n} \qquad\qquad (LE\text{-}1)$$

$$\frac{x^m}{x^n} = x^{m-n} \qquad\qquad (LE\text{-}2)$$

$$(x^m)^n = x^{mn} \qquad\qquad (LE\text{-}3)$$

$$(x \cdot y)^n = x^n \cdot y^n \qquad\qquad (LE\text{-}4)$$

$$\left(\frac{x}{y}\right)^n = \frac{x^n}{y^n} \qquad\qquad (LE\text{-}5)$$

The equations above are true for all integers m and n and all non-zero real numbers x and y.

We can sometimes use the laws of exponents to find simpler forms for algebraic expressions that have exponents. This process is illustrated in the following problem.

Problem. Simplify each of the following expressions.

(a) $\dfrac{2^6 \cdot 3^2}{2^4 \cdot 3^5}$ (b) $(a^{-3}b^2)^{-2}$ (c) $\left(\dfrac{5xy^3}{2x^5y^2}\right)^3$

Solution. We proceed in the following way.

(a)
$$\frac{2^6 \cdot 3^2}{2^4 \cdot 3^5} = \frac{2^6}{2^4} \cdot \frac{3^2}{3^5}$$

$$= 2^{6-4} \cdot 3^{2-5} \qquad\qquad (LE\text{-}2)$$

$$= 2^2 \cdot 3^{-3} \qquad\qquad (\text{Subst.})$$

$$= 2^2 \cdot \frac{1}{3^3} \qquad\qquad (\text{Def-Neg. Exp.})$$

$$= \frac{2^2}{3^3}, \quad \text{or} \quad \frac{4}{27} \qquad\qquad (\text{Def-Div.})$$

(b)
$$(a^{-3}b^2)^{-2} = (a^{-3})^{-2}(b^2)^{-2} \qquad\qquad (LE\text{-}4)$$

$$= a^6 b^{-4} \qquad\qquad (LE\text{-}3)$$

$$= \frac{a^6}{b^4} \qquad\qquad (\text{Def-Neg. Exp.})$$

(c)
$$\left(\frac{5xy^3}{2x^5y^2}\right)^3 = \left(\frac{5}{2}\cdot\frac{x}{x^5}\cdot\frac{y^3}{y^2}\right)^3$$

$$= \left(\frac{5}{2}x^{1-5}y^{3-2}\right)^3 \qquad \text{(LE-2)}$$

$$= \left(\frac{5}{2}x^{-4}y^1\right)^3 \qquad \text{(Subst.)}$$

$$= \left(\frac{5}{2}\right)^3 x^{-12}y^3 \qquad \text{(LE-3), (LE-4)}$$

$$= \frac{125}{8}\cdot\frac{1}{x^{12}}\cdot y^3 \qquad \text{(LE-5), (Def-Neg. Exp.)}$$

$$= \frac{125y^3}{8x^{12}}$$

Exercises

Use (LE-1) to perform each of the following multiplications.

1. (a) $3^7\cdot 3^0$ (b) $(-2)^3(-2)^0$

2. (a) $y^8\cdot y^0$ (b) $x^0\cdot x^5$

Use (LE-2) to perform each of the following divisions.

3. (a) $\dfrac{3^2}{3^2}$ (b) $\dfrac{2^4}{2^4}$

4. (a) $\dfrac{y^n}{y^n}$, $y\neq 0$ (b) $x^n \div x^n$, $x\neq 0$

Perform the indicated operations, and express each answer in simplest form. State the laws or definitions used.

5. (a) $7^2\cdot 7^6\cdot 7$ (b) $5\cdot 5^2\cdot 5^3$

6. (a) $1^0 + 2^0 + 3^0$ (b) $5^0 + 6^0 + 7^0$

7. (a) $\dfrac{5^6\cdot 2^4}{5^4\cdot 2^3}$ (b) $\dfrac{7^6\cdot 3^3}{7^8\cdot 3^2}$

8. (a) $\left(\dfrac{3x^2}{2y^3}\right)^4$ (b) $\left(-\dfrac{2a^2}{3b^4}\right)^2$

9. (a) $\left(\dfrac{2x^4\cdot x^7}{10y^3\cdot y}\right)^3$ (b) $-\left(\dfrac{2x}{y^2}\right)^5$

Assume that the value of any variable that appears in a denominator is a nonzero number, and simplify each of the following algebraic expressions. Give answers without negative exponents.

10. (a) $\dfrac{x^{-2}}{x^{-5}}$ (b) $\dfrac{2x^6}{6x^{12}}$

11. (a) $\dfrac{3^6}{2^3 + 2^0}$ (b) $\dfrac{49^3 \cdot 13 \cdot 49^{-3}}{5^2 + 5^0}$

Use (LE-3) to complete each statement.

12. (a) $4^8 = 2^?$ (b) $9^6 = 3^?$

Write the expressions with positive exponents only, and simplify.

13. (a) $3 + 3^{-1}$ (b) $x + x^{-1}$

14. (a) $x^{-2} + y^{-2}$ (b) $z^{-3} - y^{-1}$

15. (a) $(-5xy)^3$ (b) $(-3x^{-4})^2$

16. (a) $(a^{-2}b)^4$ (b) $(x^5x^{-5})^5$

17. (a) $\dfrac{2x^{-3}}{3y^{-2}}$ (b) $\dfrac{(x^{-3})^2 x^5}{x^{-1}}$

18. (a) $\dfrac{x^0}{y^3}$ (b) $0^1 \cdot 1^0$

19. (a) $\dfrac{(2 \cdot 10^2)^3 (4 \cdot 10^{-2})^2}{(2 \cdot 10^3)^{-1}}$ (b) $\dfrac{(3 \cdot 10^{-3})(4 \cdot 10^5)}{2 \cdot 10^4}$

20. (a) $\left(\dfrac{3xy^2}{5x^3y}\right)\left(\dfrac{10x^4}{21y^5}\right)$ (b) $\left(\dfrac{28a^4b}{7ab^4}\right)^2 \left(\dfrac{27ab^5}{54a^5b}\right)^3$

Use (LE-3) to complete each statement.

21. (a) $27^6 = 3^?$ (b) $8^5 = 2^?$

22. (a) $2^7 \cdot 4^3 = 2^?$ (b) $3^6 \cdot 81^2 = 3^?$

Express each number as a power of 2 and simplify.

23. (a) $[(\frac{1}{4})^6 \cdot 64]^{-3}(32)^{-2}$ (b) $\dfrac{16^3 - 32^4}{4^6 + 8^5}$

Express each number as a power of 3 and simplify.

24. (a) $243^6 \cdot 27^8 \div 81^2$ (b) $\dfrac{\frac{1}{27} + \frac{1}{81}}{\frac{1}{3} - \frac{1}{9}}$

---

25. Why is it convenient to define $x^0 = 1$, if $x \neq 0$? (See Exercises 1–4.)

26. If $y = \dfrac{1}{x}$, is $x = \dfrac{1}{y}$?

   If $7^{-1} = \dfrac{1}{7}$, is $7 = \dfrac{1}{7^{-1}}$?

27. (a) Is the statement

$$x^{-2} + y^{-2} = \dfrac{1}{x^2 + y^2}$$

true when $x = 3$ and $y = 4$? when $x = y = 1$?

(b) Are

$$x^{-2} + y^{-2} \quad \text{and} \quad \frac{1}{x^2 + y^2}$$

equivalent forms?

(c) Is the statement

$$x^{-2} + y^{-2} = \frac{x^2 + y^2}{x^2 y^2}$$

true when $x = 3$ and $y = 4$? when $x = y = 1$?

(d) Prove that

$$x^{-2} + y^{-2} = \frac{x^2 + y^2}{x^2 y^2}$$

is a true statement for all real numbers x and y, $x \neq 0$, $y \neq 0$.

Find an equivalent form with positive exponents for each of the following expressions and then simplify.

28. $x^{-1} - x$

29. $x^2 - y^{-2}$

30. $x^{-2} - y^{-2}$

31. $\dfrac{(2x - y)^{-1}}{2x + y}$

32. $\dfrac{3a - b}{(3a - b)^{-1}}$

33. $\dfrac{x - y}{x^{-1} - y^{-1}}$

34. $(x^{-2} + 3y^{-1})^{-1}$

1–8 RADICALS

Knowing that the area of a square is A square inches, we can find the length L, in inches, of a side of the square by the formula

$$L = \sqrt{A}.$$

Similarly, if the volume of a cube is V cubic inches, then the length E, in inches, of an edge of the cube is given by the formula

$$E = \sqrt[3]{V}.$$

We call L the positive square root of A, and E the positive cube root of V. Roots of real numbers are defined in the following way.

Definition of the nth root of a number

For every integer $n > 1$ and all real numbers x and y, the number y is called an nth root of x if, and only if,

$$y^n = x. \qquad \text{(Def-nth Rt.)}$$

If $x > 0$ and $y > 0$, then we write

$$y = \sqrt[n]{x}$$

to indicate that y is the positive nth root of x. In addition, if n is an odd integer, $x < 0$, and $y < 0$, then we write

$$y = \sqrt[n]{x}$$

to indicate that y is the negative nth root of x.

One of the unusual, but quite useful, properties of the real number system is that every positive real number x has a unique positive real nth root $\sqrt[n]{x}$. If n is an odd positive integer, every negative real number x has a unique negative real nth root $\sqrt[n]{x}$.

For example,

$$\sqrt{49} = 7, \quad \sqrt[3]{27} = 3, \quad \sqrt[4]{625} = 5, \quad \sqrt[5]{-32} = -2,$$

according to the definition of nth roots. Since an even power of a non-zero number is always positive, in the real number system negative numbers do not have square roots, fourth roots, or, in general, nth roots if n is even.

The following two laws are useful in working with algebraic expressions involving radicals.

LAWS OF RADICALS

$$\sqrt[n]{x \cdot y} = \sqrt[n]{x} \cdot \sqrt[n]{y} \qquad\qquad (LR\text{-}1)$$

$$\sqrt[n]{\frac{x}{y}} = \frac{\sqrt[n]{x}}{\sqrt[n]{y}} \qquad\qquad (LR\text{-}2)$$

These laws are valid for all integers $n > 1$ and all positive real numbers x and y. If n is odd, then they are true for all nonzero real numbers x and y.

The laws of radicals follow directly from the laws of exponents. For example,

$$(\sqrt[n]{x} \cdot \sqrt[n]{y})^n = (\sqrt[n]{x})^n \cdot (\sqrt[n]{y})^n \qquad\qquad (LE\text{-}4)$$

$$= x \cdot y. \qquad\qquad (\text{Def-}n\text{th Rt.})$$

Therefore, $\sqrt[n]{x} \cdot \sqrt[n]{y}$ is the nth root of $x \cdot y$. This proves the first law of radicals.

If c/d is a rational number expressed in simplest form, then $\sqrt{c/d}$ is also a rational number if, and only if, the integers c and d are perfect squares, that is, $\sqrt{c}$ and $\sqrt{d}$ are integers. It can be shown in the same way that $\sqrt[n]{c/d}$ is a rational number if, and only if, $\sqrt[n]{c}$ and $\sqrt[n]{d}$ are integers. In this case,

$$\sqrt[n]{\frac{c}{d}} = \frac{\sqrt[n]{c}}{\sqrt[n]{d}}$$

by the second law of radicals, (LR-2). For example,

$$\sqrt[3]{\frac{125}{27}} = \frac{\sqrt[3]{125}}{\sqrt[3]{27}}, \quad \text{or} \quad \frac{5}{3}.$$

We recall that every positive integer can be expressed as a product of a perfect-square integer and a square-free integer. Thus $40 = 4 \cdot 10$ and $17 = 1 \cdot 17$. In the same way, every positive integer can be expressed as a product of a perfect-cube integer and a cube-free integer, and so on. For example, $384 = 64 \times 6$, where $64 = 4^3$ and 6 has no positive perfect-cube factor other than 1. Therefore,

$$\sqrt[3]{384} = \sqrt[3]{64} \cdot \sqrt[3]{6}, \quad \text{or } 4\sqrt[3]{6}.$$

Again, we call $4\sqrt[3]{6}$ the *simplest form* for expressing the cube root of 384. The nth root of every integer can be expressed in a simplest form in this way.

Problem. Simplify each of the following expressions.

(a) $\sqrt[5]{1152}$

(b) $\sqrt[3]{81x^5y^{10}}$

(c) $\sqrt[3]{\dfrac{4a^5}{9b^7}}$

(d) $\dfrac{\sqrt{24}}{2 + \sqrt{3}}$

Solution
(a) We can factor 1152 as follows:

$$1152 = 2^7 \times 3^2 = 2^5 \times 2^2 \times 3^2.$$

This shows a fifth-power factor, hence

$$\sqrt[5]{1152} = \sqrt[5]{2^5} \times \sqrt[5]{2^2 \times 3^2}$$
$$= 2\sqrt[5]{36}.$$

Note that 36 contains no fifth-power factor.

(b) Factor $81x^5y^{10}$ into a third power times first or second powers.

$$\sqrt[3]{81x^5y^{10}} = \sqrt[3]{(3^3x^3y^9)(3x^2y)}$$
$$= \sqrt[3]{(3xy^3)^3} \cdot \sqrt[3]{3x^2y} \qquad \text{(LR-1)}$$
$$= 3xy^3 \sqrt[3]{3x^2y}$$

(c) Let us rationalize the denominator while simplifying. This may be accomplished by finding an equivalent algebraic expression which has a perfect-cube denominator. We want all exponents in the denominator to be divisible by 3. Thus,

$$\sqrt[3]{\frac{4a^5}{9b^7}} = \sqrt[3]{\frac{4a^5}{9b^7} \cdot \frac{3b^2}{3b^2}} \qquad \text{(Id-M)}$$

$$= \sqrt[3]{\frac{12a^5b^2}{27b^9}}$$

$$= \sqrt[3]{\frac{a^3}{27b^9} \cdot 12a^2b^2}$$

$$= \sqrt[3]{\frac{a^3}{27b^9}} \cdot \sqrt[3]{12a^2b^2} \qquad \text{(LR-1)}$$

$$= \frac{a}{3b^3} \sqrt[3]{12a^2b^2}, \quad \text{or} \quad \frac{a\sqrt[3]{12a^2b^2}}{3b^3}.$$

(d) A possible simplification is to rationalize the denominator. You should recall that $(x + y)(x - y) = x^2 - y^2$. We can use this fact to eliminate the radical from the denominator by multiplying the given expression by $\dfrac{2 - \sqrt{3}}{2 - \sqrt{3}}$.

$$\frac{\sqrt{24}}{2 + \sqrt{3}} = \frac{\sqrt{24}}{2 + \sqrt{3}} \times \frac{2 - \sqrt{3}}{2 - \sqrt{3}}$$

$$= \frac{2\sqrt{24} - \sqrt{3} \times \sqrt{24}}{4 - 3}$$

$$= \frac{2\sqrt{24} - \sqrt{72}}{1}, \quad \text{or} \quad 2\sqrt{24} - \sqrt{72}$$

This can be further simplified in the following way.

$$2\sqrt{24} - \sqrt{72} = 2\sqrt{4 \times 6} - \sqrt{36 \times 2}$$
$$= 2 \cdot 2\sqrt{6} - 6\sqrt{2}$$
$$= 4\sqrt{6} - 6\sqrt{2}$$

Thus,

$$\frac{\sqrt{24}}{2 + \sqrt{3}} = 4\sqrt{6} - 6\sqrt{2}.$$

Exercises

Simplify each of the following expressions.

1. (a) $\sqrt{175}$ (b) $\sqrt{108}$
2. (a) $\sqrt[3]{343}$ (b) $\sqrt[3]{-27}$
3. (a) $\sqrt{27x^4y^3}$ (b) $\sqrt[3]{27x^4y^3}$
4. (a) $\sqrt[5]{-96x^7y^5}$ (b) $\sqrt[5]{-243}$
5. (a) $\sqrt[3]{-250x^6y^8}$ (b) $\sqrt[3]{16xy}$
6. (a) $\sqrt[4]{48x^8y^{10}}$ (b) $\sqrt[4]{162x^6y^{12}}$

Complete each of the following simplifications.

7. (a) $\sqrt{\dfrac{12a^3}{5b^3}} = \sqrt{\dfrac{12a^3}{5b^3} \times \dfrac{5b}{5b}} = \sqrt{\dfrac{4a^2}{25b^4} \times \,?} = \,?\sqrt{?}$

   (b) $\sqrt{\dfrac{18a}{7b}} = \sqrt{\dfrac{18a}{7b} \times \dfrac{7b}{7b}} = \sqrt{\dfrac{9}{49b^2} \times \,?} = \,?\sqrt{?}$

8. (a) $\dfrac{5 + \sqrt{3}}{5 - \sqrt{3}} = \dfrac{5 + \sqrt{3}}{5 - \sqrt{3}} \cdot \dfrac{5 + \sqrt{3}}{5 + \sqrt{3}} = \dfrac{?}{?}$

   (b) $\dfrac{2\sqrt{3} - \sqrt{5}}{2\sqrt{3} + \sqrt{5}} = \dfrac{2\sqrt{3} - \sqrt{5}}{2\sqrt{3} + \sqrt{5}} \cdot \dfrac{2\sqrt{3} - \sqrt{5}}{2\sqrt{3} - \sqrt{5}} = \dfrac{?}{?}$

Perform the indicated operations and give each answer in simplest form.

9. (a) $\sqrt{3} \cdot \sqrt{6}$ (b) $\sqrt{7} \cdot \sqrt{35}$
10. (a) $\sqrt[3]{4} \cdot \sqrt[3]{10}$ (b) $\sqrt[4]{40} \cdot \sqrt[4]{14}$
11. (a) $\sqrt{6} \div \sqrt{12}$ (b) $\sqrt{7xy} \div \sqrt{14x^2y^2}$

---

12. (a) $\sqrt{\frac{3}{4}} \div \sqrt{\frac{5}{6}}$ (b) $\sqrt[3]{-5x^2y} \div \sqrt[3]{10xy^5}$
13. (a) $\dfrac{\sqrt[3]{16}}{\sqrt[3]{2}}$ (b) $\dfrac{\sqrt[5]{64}}{\sqrt[5]{3}}$
14. (a) $\sqrt{20x^3} \cdot \sqrt{30x^7}$ (b) $\sqrt[3]{-10x^7} \cdot \sqrt[3]{-4x^7}$
15. (a) $(5 + \sqrt{3})(5 - \sqrt{3})$ (b) $(2\sqrt{3} + 3\sqrt{2})^2$
16. (a) $(3 - \sqrt{5})^2 + \sqrt{180}$ (b) $(\sqrt{6x} - \sqrt{3x^3})^2$

Simplify each radical that is not in simplest form, and find the sum or difference.

17. $6\sqrt{12x} - 5\sqrt{27x^3}$ 18. $\sqrt[3]{24x^2} - 5\sqrt[3]{-81x^5}$

Simplify each of the following radicals.

19. (a) $\sqrt{\dfrac{2x^3}{5}}$ (b) $\sqrt[3]{\dfrac{2}{9x}}$ **20.** (a) $\sqrt[3]{\dfrac{8x^4y}{z^5}}$ (b) $\sqrt[5]{\dfrac{2a^6}{3b^7}}$

Rationalize the denominator of each fraction, and simplify.

21. $\dfrac{4}{\sqrt{3}-1}$ **22.** $\dfrac{\sqrt{2}+3}{\sqrt{2}-5}$

23. $\dfrac{16}{\sqrt{7}-\sqrt{3}}$ **24.** $\dfrac{\sqrt{7}-\sqrt{2}}{\sqrt{7}+\sqrt{2}}$

25. $\dfrac{\sqrt{x}+3\sqrt{y}}{\sqrt{x}-3\sqrt{y}}$

Simplify each radical that is not in simplest form, and perform the indicated operations.

26. $\sqrt{\dfrac{4}{15}}+3\sqrt{15}$ **27.** $\sqrt{\dfrac{1}{2}}-3\sqrt{\dfrac{2}{9}}$ **28.** $\sqrt[4]{32}-\sqrt[4]{2}$

29. $\sqrt{32}+\dfrac{1}{\sqrt{2}}-\sqrt{\dfrac{2}{9}}$

30. $\sqrt{8-\sqrt{15}}\cdot\sqrt{8+\sqrt{15}}$

31. $\sqrt{8x}+\sqrt{2x^3}$

32. $\sqrt{\dfrac{x}{2}}-\sqrt{\dfrac{2}{x}}$

33. $\left(\dfrac{1}{\sqrt{x}}-\sqrt{x}\right)^2$

34. $5\sqrt{72a}-2\sqrt{50a}+\sqrt{288a}-\sqrt{242a}$

35. Arrange the following numbers in order of increasing magnitude.

$$\sqrt{3},\quad \sqrt[4]{27},\quad \sqrt[6]{9}$$

36. Is the statement

$$\sqrt{x^2+y^2}=x+y$$

true when $x=3$, $y=4$? $x=y=1$? $x=y=0$?

37. Give a pair of values for x and y which makes the following statement false.

$$\sqrt{x-y}=\sqrt{x}-\sqrt{y}\quad\text{for every positive value of }x\text{ and }y.$$

38. (a) Give a counterexample to show that the following statement is false.

$$\sqrt{x^2 + 2xy + y^2} = x + y \quad \text{for every value of } x \text{ and } y.$$

(b) Prove that for every pair x, y of real numbers, where $x > 0$ and $y > 0$,

$$\sqrt{x^2 + 2xy + y^2} = x + y.$$

39. Prove the second law of radicals, (LR-2).

40. Find a fraction that has a rational denominator and is equivalent to the fraction

$$\frac{1}{\sqrt{5} - \sqrt{3} + \sqrt{2}}.$$

1-9 RATIONAL EXPONENTS

We have defined the exponential notation x^n for every integer n. It is natural to ask whether x^r can be defined for every rational number r. Of course, we would like to define x^r so that the laws of exponents continue to be valid for rational exponents.

For example, what is a reasonable definition of $x^{\frac{1}{3}}$? If the third law of exponents, (LE-3), is to be valid for rational exponents, then we must have

$$(x^{\frac{1}{3}})^3 = x^{\frac{1}{3} \cdot 3}, \quad \text{or } x.$$

Since $(\sqrt[3]{x})^3 = x$ for every real number x, a natural definition of $x^{\frac{1}{3}}$ is the cube root of x:

$$x^{\frac{1}{3}} = \sqrt[3]{x}.$$

With this example in mind, we define

$$x^{\frac{1}{n}} = \sqrt[n]{x}$$

for every positive integer n and for every real number x for which $\sqrt[n]{x}$ is real. Thus, for example,

$$4^{\frac{1}{2}} = \sqrt{4}, \quad \text{or } 2,$$
$$81^{\frac{1}{4}} = \sqrt[4]{81}, \quad \text{or } 3,$$
$$(-32)^{\frac{1}{5}} = \sqrt[5]{-32}, \quad \text{or } -2.$$

Now that we have defined the $(1/n)$-power of a real number, let us consider how we might define the (m/n)-power of a number. We first look at a special example, say $8^{\frac{2}{3}}$. If the third law of exponents, (LE-3), is to be valid, then we must have

$$8^{\frac{2}{3}} = (8^{\frac{1}{3}})^2$$
$$= (\sqrt[3]{8})^2$$
$$= 2^2, \quad \text{or } 4.$$

With this example in mind, we give the following definition.

Definition of rational exponents

For every pair of integers m and n, with $n > 1$, and for every real number x for which $(\sqrt[n]{x})^m$ is real, we define

$$x^{\frac{m}{n}} = (\sqrt[n]{x})^m. \qquad (\textit{Def-Rat. Exp.})$$

Returning to the example above, we might have computed $8^{\frac{2}{3}}$ as follows:

$$8^{\frac{2}{3}} = (8^2)^{\frac{1}{3}}$$
$$= \sqrt[3]{8^2}$$
$$= \sqrt[3]{64}, \quad \text{or } 4.$$

The fact that the answer is the same as before suggests that the following equation is true for all integers m and n, with $n > 0$, and all nonzero numbers x having a real number nth root.

$$(x^{\frac{1}{n}})^m = (x^m)^{\frac{1}{n}}$$

If $m > 0$, we can prove that this equation is true by proceeding as follows:

$$(\sqrt[n]{x})^m = \underbrace{\sqrt[n]{x} \cdot \sqrt[n]{x} \cdot \ldots \cdot \sqrt[n]{x}}_{m \text{ factors}} \qquad (\text{LE-1})$$

$$= \sqrt[n]{\underbrace{x \cdot x \cdot \ldots \cdot x}_{m \text{ factors}}} \qquad (\text{LR-1})$$

$$= \sqrt[n]{x^m}.$$

From the definition of zero and negative exponents, it follows that the equation above is also true when $m \leq 0$.

The truth of the above equation allows us to find $x^{\frac{m}{n}}$ in either one of two ways:

$$x^{\frac{m}{n}} = (x^{\frac{1}{n}})^m$$

or

$$x^{\frac{m}{n}} = (x^m)^{\frac{1}{n}}.$$

For example,

$$4^{\frac{3}{2}} = (\sqrt{4})^3 = 2^3, \quad \text{or } 8,$$
$$4^{\frac{3}{2}} = (4^3)^{\frac{1}{2}} = \sqrt{64}, \quad \text{or } 8.$$

It can be proved that the five laws of exponents are valid for rational exponents as well as for integral exponents. From now on, we shall assume that these laws are true for rational exponents, and we shall use them whenever necessary.

Problem 1. Simplify each of the following expressions.

(a) $2^{\frac{2}{3}} \cdot 4^{\frac{1}{6}}$

(b) $(x^{-\frac{5}{2}} \cdot y^{\frac{7}{3}})^6$

(c) $\sqrt[4]{25}$

Solution

(a)
$$2^{\frac{2}{3}} \cdot 4^{\frac{1}{6}} = 2^{\frac{2}{3}} \cdot (2^2)^{\frac{1}{6}}$$
$$= 2^{\frac{2}{3}} \cdot 2^{\frac{2}{6}} \quad \text{or } 2^{\frac{2}{3}} \cdot 2^{\frac{1}{3}} \qquad \text{(LE-3)}$$
$$= 2^{\frac{2}{3}+\frac{1}{3}} \qquad \text{(LE-1)}$$
$$= 2$$

(b)
$$(x^{-\frac{5}{2}} \cdot y^{\frac{7}{3}})^6 = (x^{-\frac{5}{2}})^6 \cdot (y^{\frac{7}{3}})^6 \qquad \text{(LE-4)}$$
$$= x^{-15} \cdot y^{14} \qquad \text{(LE-3)}$$
$$= \frac{y^{14}}{x^{15}}$$

(c)
$$\sqrt[4]{25} = \sqrt[4]{5^2}$$
$$= 5^{\frac{2}{4}} \qquad \text{(Def-Rat. Exp.)}$$
$$= 5^{\frac{1}{2}} \quad \text{or } \sqrt{5}$$

Problem 2. Simplify $\dfrac{\sqrt{10x}}{\sqrt[3]{20x^2}}$.

Solution. Neither (LR-1) nor (LR-2) apply because the radicals are of different orders. Let us see if the laws of exponents apply.

$$\frac{\sqrt{10x}}{\sqrt[3]{20x^2}} = \frac{(10x)^{\frac{1}{2}}}{(20x^2)^{\frac{1}{3}}} \qquad \text{(Def-Rat. Exp.)}$$

$$= \frac{10^{\frac{1}{2}}x^{\frac{1}{2}}}{20^{\frac{1}{3}}x^{\frac{2}{3}}} \qquad \text{(LE-4)}$$

$$= \frac{10^{\frac{3}{6}}}{20^{\frac{2}{6}}} \cdot x^{\frac{3}{6}-\frac{4}{6}} \qquad \text{(LE-2)}$$

$$= \frac{10^{\frac{3}{6}}}{20^{\frac{2}{6}}} \cdot x^{-\frac{1}{6}}$$

$$= \sqrt[6]{\frac{10^3}{20^2 x}} \qquad \text{(Def-Rat. Exp.)}$$

$$= \sqrt[6]{\frac{2 \cdot 5 \cdot 2 \cdot 5 \cdot 2 \cdot 5}{2 \cdot 2 \cdot 5 \cdot 2 \cdot 2 \cdot 5x}}$$

$$= \sqrt[6]{\frac{5}{2x}}$$

To rationalize the denominator, multiply $\dfrac{5}{2x}$ by $\dfrac{2^5 x^5}{2^5 x^5}$.

$$= \sqrt[6]{\frac{5}{2x} \cdot \frac{2^5 x^5}{2^5 x^5}} \qquad \text{(Id-M)}$$

$$= \sqrt[6]{\frac{1}{2^6 x^6} \cdot (5 \cdot 2^5 \cdot x^5)} \qquad \text{(Def.-Div)}$$

$$= \frac{1}{2x} \sqrt[6]{160x^5}$$

Exercises

Simplify each of the following expressions.

1. (a) $9^{\frac{1}{2}}$ (b) $27^{\frac{2}{3}}$ 2. (a) $9^{-\frac{1}{2}}$ (b) $27^{-\frac{2}{3}}$

3. (a) $64^{\frac{5}{6}}$ (b) $32^{-\frac{2}{5}}$ 4. (a) $16^{\frac{3}{2}}$ (b) $8^{-\frac{2}{3}}$

5. (a) $3^{\frac{1}{2}} \cdot 3^{\frac{3}{2}}$ (b) $\dfrac{27^{\frac{2}{3}} - 27^{-\frac{2}{3}}}{9}$

Rewrite each expression, using fractional exponents instead of radicals.

6. (a) $-2\sqrt{y}$ (b) $-x\sqrt{x}$

7. (a) $3\sqrt[4]{4x^3y}$ (b) $2\sqrt[3]{2x^2y}$

8. (a) $\sqrt[3]{(x-y)^2}$ (b) $\sqrt[4]{(x-2y)^5}$

Rewrite each expression, using radicals instead of fractional exponents. Simplify when possible.

9. (a) $(2x)^{\frac{4}{5}}$ (b) $y^{\frac{2}{3}}$

10. (a) $-3x^{\frac{4}{5}}$ (b) $(-3x)^{\frac{4}{5}}$

11. (a) $x^{\frac{1}{3}} - y^{\frac{1}{3}}$ (b) $(x+y)^{\frac{1}{3}}$

Simplify each of the following expressions.

12. $(10^{\frac{1}{3}} \cdot 10^{-\frac{1}{6}})^6$ **13.** $(10^{\frac{1}{3}})^6 + (10^{-\frac{1}{3}})^6$

14. $9^{\frac{2}{3}} \cdot 27^{\frac{2}{9}}$ **15.** $8^{\frac{3}{2}} \cdot 4^{\frac{1}{4}}$

16. $(64x^9)^{\frac{2}{3}}$ **17.** $(36x^2)^{-\frac{3}{2}}$

18. $(x^{\frac{1}{2}} + y^{\frac{1}{2}})(x^{\frac{1}{2}} - y^{\frac{1}{2}})$ **19.** $(e^x - e^{-x})^2$

20. $\left(\dfrac{-x^{\frac{1}{2}}y^{\frac{2}{3}}}{x^{\frac{3}{4}}y^{\frac{1}{6}}}\right)^{12}$

21. In the following solution, radicals with different indices are multiplied. Replace each question mark by an exponent to make the equation true.

$$\sqrt{xy^3} \cdot \sqrt[3]{x^2y} = (xy^3)^? \cdot (x^2y)^?$$
$$= (xy^3)^{\frac{3}{6}} \cdot (x^2y)^{\frac{2}{6}}$$
$$= (x^?y^?)^{\frac{1}{6}} \cdot (x^?y^?)^{\frac{1}{6}}$$
$$= \sqrt[6]{x^?y^?}$$
$$= ?\sqrt[6]{xy^5}$$

In Exercises 22 and 23, simplify the expression, following the method of Exercise 21.

22. $(\sqrt{x^3y^2})(\sqrt[3]{xy})$ **23.** $\dfrac{\sqrt[3]{a^2b}}{\sqrt{ab^3}}$

Simplify.

24. $\sqrt[4]{a^2b} - b\sqrt{a}$ **25.** $\sqrt[6]{27x^3} - \sqrt{3x}$

26. $\sqrt[3]{16} \cdot \sqrt[6]{4}$ **27.** $\sqrt{2}\,\sqrt[3]{3}$

28. $\sqrt[6]{8} \div \sqrt[4]{25}$ **29.** $\sqrt[3]{\sqrt{8}}$

30. $\sqrt[3]{\sqrt{2\sqrt{2}}}$ **31.** $\sqrt[3]{\sqrt[5]{64}}$

32. Use fractional exponents to show that $\sqrt[4]{9} = \sqrt{3}$.

33. Show that $\sqrt[6]{x^3} = \sqrt[4]{x^2}$, x non-negative. Find another way to express this number.

The *index* of the radical $\sqrt[n]{a}$ is the integer *n*. Use fractional exponents to express each of the following as a single radical with the smallest possible index.

34. (a) $\sqrt[4]{49}$ (b) $\sqrt[8]{25}$ (c) $\sqrt[6]{125}$ (d) $\sqrt[6]{4}$

1-10 NUMBER LINES

An interesting feature of the real number system is that it may be used as a scale on a line. Thus, if we choose a unit of length, such as an inch or a centimeter, we may represent the integers as equispaced points (the chosen unit apart) on a line. (See Fig. 1–1.) By bisecting, trisecting, and so on, each unit segment, the rational numbers may also be assigned to points on the line. For example, $\frac{1}{2}$ is assigned to the point halfway between 0 and 1; $-\frac{5}{3}$ is assigned to the point two-thirds of the way from -1 to -2; $\frac{12}{5}$ is assigned to the point two-fifths of the way from 2 to 3; and so on. The point *O*, which has zero assigned to it, is called the *origin*.

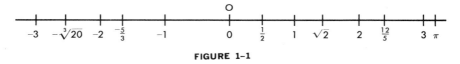

FIGURE 1–1

Each irrational number can also be assigned to a point on the line. For example, we may find the point having $\sqrt{2}$ assigned to it in the way indicated in Fig. 1–2. In this figure, the partially drawn circle has its center at the origin and a radius of $\sqrt{2}$. Hence, it will intersect the given line at the point having $\sqrt{2}$ assigned to it.

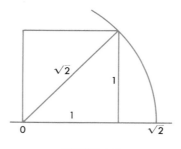

FIGURE 1–2

It is not possible to construct the point assigned to every real number by the method used for $\sqrt{2}$. For example, it is impossible (by means of straightedge and compass alone) to construct the point assigned to the irrational number π. However, we can imagine that there is a point representing π.

Each real number is assigned to a unique point on the line, and each point on the line has a unique real number assigned to it. A line having a real-number scale on it is called a *number line*. The number assigned to a point on the number line is called the *coordinate* of the point.

A number line may be assigned a *direction*. We shall always take the direction as that from the origin, O, toward the point with coordinate 1. Thus, if we imagine ourselves walking from left to right along the number line in Fig. 1–3, we are walking in the direction of the line, called the *positive direction*. We would be walking counter to the direction of the line, or in the *negative direction,* if we walked from right to left. The direction of a number line is indicated by an arrowhead as shown in Fig. 1–3. If point A on the line has coordinate a, then A is to the *right* of the origin O if, and only if, $a > 0$. Similarly, point B with coordinate b is to the *left* of O if, and only if, $b < 0$.

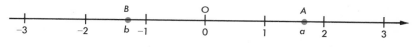

FIGURE 1–3

The distance between two points on a yardstick may be found by subtracting the coordinates of the two points. For example, the distance between points A and B on the yardstick of Fig. 1–4 is $29 - 21$, or 8 inches. It is possible to find the distance between any two points on a number line in the same way if the two points are on the same side of the origin. This situation is similar to our yardstick in Fig. 1–4.

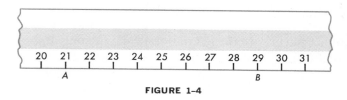

FIGURE 1–4

If two points are on opposite sides of the origin, as are C and D in Fig. 1–5, then how do we find the distance between them? By counting

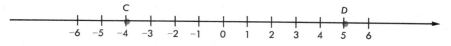

FIGURE 1–5

unit intervals we see that the distance between C and D is 9. If we subtract the coordinate of C from that of D, we get

$$5 - (-4) = 5 + 4, \quad \text{or } 9.$$

Thus, we see that the distance between two points on opposite sides of the origin may also be found by subtracting their coordinates.

If we subtract coordinates in the opposite order in each of the cases above, we obtain $21 - 29$, or -8, for the distance between points A and B on the yardstick and $-4 - 5$, or -9, for the distance between points C and D on the number line. Each of these negative numbers is a *directed distance* as defined below.

Definition of directed distance

If points A and B on a number line have respective coordinates a and b, the directed distance from A to B is designated by d(AB) and is defined as

$$d(AB) = b - a.$$

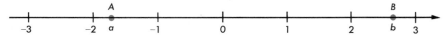

FIGURE 1-6

If a number line is directed toward the right, as in Fig. 1-6, then point B is to the right of point A if, and only if, the coordinate of B is greater than the coordinate of A, that is, $b > a$. In this case, the directed distance from A to B is $b - a$, a positive number. On the other hand, point A is to the left of point B if, and only if, $a < b$. Then the directed distance from B to A is $a - b$, a negative number.

In either case, the distance or non-directed distance between points A and B, AB, is the absolute value of the difference of their coordinates, a and b.

$$AB = |a - b|$$

FIGURE 1-7

Knowing the directed distance between two points, we not only know the distance between the points, but we also know the direction from one point to the other.

To illustrate these ideas, consider the number line with points O, A, B, C, and D having the coordinates shown in Fig. 1–7. Then

$$d(OA) = 2 - 0, \quad \text{or } 2; \qquad d(AD) = -5 - 2, \quad \text{or } -7;$$
$$d(OB) = -2 - 0, \quad \text{or } -2; \qquad d(DA) = 2 - (-5), \quad \text{or } 7;$$
$$d(BC) = 5 - (-2), \quad \text{or } 7; \qquad d(DC) = 5 - (-5), \quad \text{or } 10.$$

Note that $d(OA) > 0$, and A is to the right of O; $d(OB) < 0$, and B is to the left of O; $d(BC) > 0$, and C is to the right of B; $d(AD) < 0$, and D is to the left of A.

For any three points A, B, and C on a number line, it is true that

$$d(AB) = -d(BA) \tag{1}$$

and

$$d(AB) + d(BC) = d(AC). \tag{2}$$

We can prove this in the following way. If A, B, and C have respective coordinates a, b, and c, then

$$d(AB) = b - a, \quad d(BA) = a - b,$$

and the first equation is true because

$$b - a = -(a - b).$$

Since $d(AB) = b - a$, $d(BC) = c - b$, and $d(AC) = c - a$, the second equation is true because

$$(b - a) + (c - b) = c - a.$$

If point C is the midpoint of the segment $\overline{AB}$, then $d(AC) = d(CB)$. Hence,

$$c - a = b - c,$$
$$2c = a + b,$$

and

$$c = \tfrac{1}{2}(a + b).$$

If we recall that one-half the sum of two numbers is called the *arithmetic mean* of the two numbers, then we have proved the following statement.

The coordinate of the midpoint of a segment of a number line is the arithmetic mean of the coordinates of the endpoints of the segment.

For example, if A has coordinate 2 and D has coordinate -5, as shown in Fig. 1–7, the coordinate of the midpoint of segment $\overline{AD}$ is

$$\tfrac{1}{2}[2 + (-5)], \quad \text{or} \quad -\tfrac{3}{2}.$$

Exercises

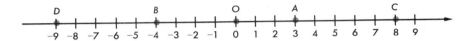

Refer to the figure to find each of the following directed distances.

1. (a) $d(OB)$ (b) $d(OA)$

2. (a) $d(BA)$ (b) $d(AB)$

3. (a) $d(AB) + d(BC)$ (b) $d(CB) + d(BA)$

4. (a) $d(BA) + d(AD)$ (b) $d(BA) + d(AC)$

Refer to the figure to find the coordinate of the midpoint of each of the following segments.

5. (a) $\overline{OC}$ (b) $\overline{OB}$ **6.** (a) $\overline{BC}$ (b) $\overline{AB}$

Draw a number line, and on it, indicate points $O, A, B, C, D, E,$ and F which have respective coordinates $0, -\tfrac{1}{2}, -4, \sqrt{2}, 2\sqrt{3}, -6,$ and 5. Find the following directed distances.

7. (a) $d(OB)$ (b) $d(OC)$

8. (a) $d(AF) - d(FA)$ (b) $d(AB) + d(BA)$

9. (a) $d(EC) + d(CB) + d(EB)$ (b) $d(CD) + d(DO) + d(OC$

10. Refer to the number line that you drew for Exercises 7–9 to find each of the following.
     (a) The coordinates of the points midway between A and B and midway between A and D
     (b) The midpoint of segment $\overline{PQ}$ if P is the midpoint of segment $\overline{AF}$ and Q is the midpoint of segment $\overline{AB}$

11. Verify that the equation $d(AB) + d(BC) + d(CD) = d(AD)$ is true for points $A, B, C,$ and D which have the following coordinates respectively.
     (a) $-5, -1, 6, 8$ (b) $-2, -10, 6, -5$

12. Prove that the equation in Exercise 11 is true for any four points $A, B, C,$ and D arranged in any order on a coordinate line by using $a, b, c,$ and d to designate the coordinates of the four points.

13. Let A and B designate points on a number line with known coordinates a and b, respectively. For this exercise, A and B are considered fixed. Let P denote a variable point with unknown coordinate x.
   (a) Given that $d(AP)/d(PB) = \frac{2}{1}$, find a formula for x in terms of a and b.
   (b) Find a formula for x if $d(AP)/d(PB) = \frac{3}{1}$.
   (c) Find a formula for x if $d(AP)/d(PB) = \frac{3}{2}$.
   (d) Find x if P divides $\overline{AB}$ into two segments in the ratio of $r : s$.

14. Find the coordinates of the trisection points of $\overline{AB}$ if A has coordinate -6 and B has coordinate 5. (Hint: See Exercise 13(a).)

15. After 0 and 1 have been located on a number line, can you suggest a ruler and compass method for locating the points corresponding to $\frac{1}{3}$ and $\frac{2}{3}$? Can you find $\frac{1}{4}$, $\frac{2}{4}$, and $\frac{3}{4}$? Can you find $\frac{1}{5}$, $\frac{2}{5}$, $\frac{3}{5}$, and $\frac{4}{5}$? Assuming this could be done, how would you find $\frac{8}{5}$?

HISTORICAL NOTE

The classic Greek scholars made a major contribution to mathematics by proving the existence of irrational numbers. Eudoxus (408–355 B.C.) developed a theory of the real number system which probably influenced Euclid to include number theory in his *Elements*. The proof of the irrationality of $\sqrt{2}$ dates back to at least the time of Pythagoras (circa 500 B.C.).

The Greek concept of real numbers was generally accepted in mathematics until the nineteenth century. After the great advances made in mathematics in the seventeenth and eighteenth centuries, mathematicians felt the need for a more precise statement of the fundamental properties of real numbers. Two German mathematicians, Cantor and Dedekind, are primarily responsible for the modern description of the system of real numbers.

In the nineteenth century, mathematicians discovered that there are two different kinds of irrational numbers: algebraic numbers and transcendental numbers. The number $\sqrt{2}$ is algebraic because it is a solution of the equation

$$x^2 - 2 = 0$$

having integral coefficients. Similarly, the number $\sqrt{5} - \sqrt{3}$ is algebraic because it is a solution of the equation

$$x^4 - 16x^2 + 4 = 0.$$

It is natural to wonder whether π is an algebraic number. In other words, does there exist an equation of the form

$$a_n x^n + a_{n-1} x^{n-1} + \ldots + a_1 x + a_0 = 0,$$

where $a_0, a_1, \ldots, a_{n-1}, a_n$ are integers and n is a positive integer, having π as a solution? This question was not answered until 1882, when the German mathematician Lindemann proved that π is not an algebraic number. Nonalgebraic real numbers, such as π, are called transcendental numbers.

KEY IDEAS AND KEY WORDS

The following are the fundamental axioms and properties of the real number system.

Commutative axioms

  The equations

$$x + y = y + x, \tag{C-A}$$
$$xy = yx \tag{C-M}$$

  are true for all real numbers x and y.

Associative axioms

  The equations

$$(x + y) + z = x + (y + z), \tag{A-A}$$
$$(xy)z = x(yz) \tag{A-M}$$

  are true for all real numbers x, y, and z.

Distributive axiom

  The equation

$$x(y + z) = xy + xz \tag{D}$$

  is true for all real numbers x, y, and z.

Identity elements

$$x + 0 = x \tag{Id-A}$$
$$x \cdot 1 = x \tag{Id-M}$$

Inverse elements

$$x + (-x) = 0 \tag{Inv-A}$$
$$x \cdot \frac{1}{x} = 1, \quad \text{if } x \neq 0 \tag{Inv-M}$$

The following fundamental axioms of the real number system are called *Axioms of Equality*.

Additive Axiom

$$\text{If } a = b \text{ and } c = d, \text{ then } a + c = b + d. \tag{Add-A}$$

Multiplicative Axiom

$$\text{If } a = b \text{ and } c = d, \text{ then } ac = bd. \qquad \text{(Mult-A)}$$

Reflexive Axiom

$$x = x \text{ for every real number } x \qquad \text{(Ref-A)}$$

Symmetric Axiom

$$\text{If } x = y, \text{ then } y = x \text{ for all real numbers } x \text{ and } y. \qquad \text{(Sym-A)}$$

Transitive Axiom

If $x = y$ and $y = z$, then $x = z$ for all real numbers $x, y, z.$ (Trans-A)

Order axioms

If $x > 0$ and $y > 0$, then $x + y > 0.$ (Clos-A)

If $x > 0$ and $y > 0$, then $xy > 0.$ (Clos-M)

If x is a real number, then $x = 0$, $x > 0$, or $x < 0.$ (Tri)

The following are some definitions that are valid for the real number system.

Definition of subtraction

$$x - y = x + (-y) \qquad \text{(Def-Sub)}$$

Definition of division

$$x \div y = x \cdot \frac{1}{y}, \quad \text{if } y \neq 0 \qquad \text{(Def-Div)}$$

Definition of greater than

$$x > y \quad \text{if, and only if,} \quad x - y \text{ is positive} \qquad (\text{Def} >)$$

Definition of less than

$$x < y \quad \text{if, and only if,} \quad y > x \qquad (\text{Def} <)$$

Definition of greater than or equal to

$$x \geq y \quad \text{if, and only if,} \quad \text{either } x > y \text{ or } x = y \qquad (\text{Def} \geq)$$

Definition of less than or equal to

$$x \leq y \quad \text{if, and only if,} \quad y \geq x \qquad (\text{Def} \leq)$$

Definition of absolute value

$$|x| = x, \qquad \text{if } x \geq 0 \qquad (\text{Def } |x|)$$
$$|x| = -x, \quad \text{if } x < 0$$

The following are properties which may be proved from the fundamental axioms.

Rearrangement property of addition

The terms of a sum may be rearranged in any way. (R-A)

Rearrangement property of multiplication

The factors of a product may be rearranged in any way. (R-M)

Cancellation law of addition

If $x + z = y + z$, then $x = y$. (Can-A)

Cancellation law of multiplication

If $xz = yz$ and $z \neq 0$, then $x = y$. (Can-M)

Zero multiplication

$x \cdot 0 = 0$ for every real number x (Zero-M)

Negative multiplication

$x \cdot (-y) = -(x \cdot y)$ (Neg-M)

Transitive law of inequalities

If $x > y$ and $y > z$, then $x > z$. (T >)

Additive property of inequalities

If $x > y$, then $x + z > y + z$ for every real number z. (A >)

Multiplicative properties of inequalities

If $x > y$, then $xz > yz$ for every positive real number z. (M >)
If $x > y$, then $xz < yz$ for every negative real number z. (−M >)

A nonzero rational number a/b is expressed in **simplest form** if $b > 0$ and the integers a and b are relatively prime.

We define

$$x^0 = 1 \quad \text{for every nonzero number } x.$$

If n is a positive integer, then we define

$$x^n = \overbrace{x \cdot x \cdot \ldots \cdot x}^{n \text{ factors}}$$

and

$$x^{-n} = \frac{1}{x^n}, \quad \text{if } x \neq 0.$$

The **laws of exponents** are as follows. They are true for all integers m and n and all nonzero real numbers x and y.

$$x^m \cdot x^n = x^{m+n} \qquad \text{(LE-1)}$$

$$\frac{x^m}{x^n} = x^{m-n} \qquad \text{(LE-2)}$$

$$(x^m)^n = x^{mn} \qquad \text{(LE-3)}$$

$$(x \cdot y)^n = x^n \cdot y^n \qquad \text{(LE-4)}$$

$$\left(\frac{x}{y}\right)^n = \frac{x^n}{y^n} \qquad \text{(LE-5)}$$

For every integer $n > 1$ and all real numbers x and y, the number y is called an **nth root** of x if, and only if,

$$y^n = x. \qquad \text{(Def-}n\text{th Rt.)}$$

The following are the **laws of radicals.** They are true for every integer $n > 1$ and all positive real numbers x and y and for all nonzero numbers x and y, if n is odd.

$$\sqrt[n]{x \cdot y} = \sqrt[n]{x} \cdot \sqrt[n]{y} \qquad \text{(LR-1)}$$

$$\sqrt[n]{\frac{x}{y}} = \frac{\sqrt[n]{x}}{\sqrt[n]{y}} \qquad \text{(LR-2)}$$

We define **rational exponents**

$$x^{\frac{m}{n}} = (\sqrt[n]{x})^m, \quad \text{or} \quad \sqrt[n]{x^m}, \qquad \text{(Def-Rat. Exp.)}$$

for all integers m and n, with $n > 1$, and every positive real number x. If n is odd, x may also be a negative number. The laws of exponents are true for rational exponents as well as for integral exponents.

If points A and B on a number line have respectively coordinates a and b, then the **directed distance** from A to B is denoted by $d(AB)$ and defined by $d(AB) = b - a$. The **midpoint** of segment $\overline{AB}$ has coordinate $(a + b)/2$.

CHAPTER REVIEW

Give the reason or reasons why each of the following statements is true.

1. $x + (9 \cdot 5) = (5 \cdot 9) + x$
2. $(x - 3) + 3 = x + (-3 + 3)$
3. $x + ax = x(1 + a)$

4. If $\dfrac{x}{5} = \dfrac{3}{4} + \dfrac{x}{2}$, then $4x = 15 + 10x$.

5. If $\dfrac{x}{5} + 19 = 3x + 19$, then $\dfrac{x}{5} = 3x$.

6. If $2x + 1 = 0$, then $x(2x + 1) = 0$.

7. If $8x + 12 = 5$, then $8x = -7$.

8. If $-3x > 5$, then $x < -\frac{5}{3}$.

9. If $\frac{2}{3}x \geqq 10$, then $x \geqq 15$.

10. If $x + 3 < 0$, then $|x + 3| = -(x + 3)$.

Perform the indicated operations.

11. $|5 - 7| - |7 - 5|$

12. $-|-18 \cdot 19| \div |-19 \cdot 18|$

13. $8 - 12 - 13$

14. $(-\frac{4}{5})(-\frac{20}{7})$

15. $(7 - 10) \div (20 - 26)$

16. $\sqrt{2} \cdot \sqrt{5}$

17. $\sqrt[3]{-125} \div \sqrt[3]{8}$

18. $16^{-\frac{5}{4}} + 16^0$

19. $\dfrac{1}{2^{-1} + 3^{-1}}$

20. $(8^0 + 8)^{\frac{1}{2}}$

In Exercises 21–30, perform the indicated operations and express each answer in simplest form.

21. $\sqrt{35} \cdot \sqrt{10}$

22. $\sqrt{\frac{8}{7}} \div \sqrt{\frac{5}{14}}$

23. $\frac{2}{3} - \frac{5}{2} - \frac{9}{5}$

24. $\dfrac{7^5 \cdot 6^8}{7 \cdot 6^{12}}$

25. $\left(\dfrac{4}{5}\right)^{-2} \left(\dfrac{8x^2y}{15xy^3}\right)^2$

26. $5^3 \cdot 125^7 \div 25^4$

27. $\sqrt{12} \cdot \sqrt{50} \div \sqrt{63}$

28. $(3x^{-2}y^4)^{-3}$

29. $2x^{-3} \div 5b^{-4}$

30. $x^{-12} \div x^{-15}$

31. Write each of the following expressions with positive exponents.

    (a) $x^{-2} + y^2$

    (b) $x^{-2} - y^{-2}$

For each expression, find an equivalent fraction with a rational denominator.

32. $\dfrac{6}{\sqrt{5}}$

33. $\dfrac{7}{\sqrt{14}}$

34. $\dfrac{8}{\sqrt{5} - 4}$

35. $\dfrac{\sqrt{5} - 2\sqrt{3}}{\sqrt{5} + 2\sqrt{3}}$

36. $\dfrac{1}{3\sqrt{3} - 2\sqrt{2} + \sqrt{5}}$

37. $\dfrac{4 + \sqrt{12} - \sqrt{27}}{2 + \sqrt{75}}$

In Exercises 38–45, perform the indicated operations and simplify.

38. $\sqrt[3]{-16x^5y^9} - y\sqrt[3]{54x^2y^6}$

39. $\sqrt[4]{\dfrac{32p^9}{27q^2}} + \sqrt[4]{6pq^6}$

40. $\sqrt{18x} - \sqrt{50x^3}$

41. $\left(\dfrac{3}{\sqrt{2x}} - \dfrac{\sqrt{2x}}{3}\right)^2$

42. $5^{\frac{2}{3}} \cdot 5^{\frac{7}{3}}$

43. $27^{\frac{4}{3}} \cdot 9^{\frac{3}{2}}$

44. $\sqrt{2xy} \cdot \sqrt[3]{5x^2y^2}$

45. $\sqrt[3]{-24x^4} - \sqrt[3]{81x^7}$

46. If x and y are real numbers such that $x > y$ and z is any real number, what relation must exist between $z - x$ and $z - y$? Prove that your statement is true.

47. If $x > y$ and $xy < 0$, state and prove the relation which exists between $1/x$ and $1/y$.

48. If x, y, z, and w are positive real numbers such that $x > y$ and $z > w$, prove that $xz > yw$. (Hint: By the multiplicative property, if $x > y$, then $x \cdot z > y \cdot z$ for z positive. Now start with $z > w$ and use the multiplier y.)

49. Prove that the equation

$$d(DA)^2 \cdot d(BC) + d(DB)^2 \cdot d(CA) + d(DC)^2 \cdot d(AB)$$
$$= d(AB) \cdot d(BC) \cdot d(AC)$$

is true for any four points A, B, C, and D arranged in any order on a coordinate line.

In Exercises 50–56, draw a number line and indicate on it points O, R, S, T, P, and Q having respective coordinates 0, 5, -3, 12, $-4\frac{1}{2}$, and 20. Find each of the following directed distances.

50. $d(SR)$

51. $d(PS)$

52. $d(RO)$

53. $d(PR) + d(RT)$

54. $d(SR) + d(RP)$

55. $d(RT) - d(TR)$

56. $d(PS) + d(SP)$

57. Refer to the directions for Exercises 50–56 to find the coordinates of the midpoint of each of the following line segments.

    (a) $\overline{OT}$ (b) $\overline{SR}$ (c) $\overline{PS}$ (d) $\overline{TQ}$

58. Is

$$\left\{\frac{1}{x} \mid x \text{ is a nonzero integer}\right\}$$

closed with respect to multiplication? Why?

59. Is the set of multiples of 7 closed with respect to division? Why?

60. Is the set of positive integral powers of 2 closed with respect to subtraction? Why?

61. If $\{x \mid x = r\sqrt{3}, r$ any rational number$\}$ closed with respect to addition?

62. In each expression, find all integral values of x for which the expression is true.

(a) $|x + 7| = -9$ (b) $|x - 3| \leq 7$

(c) $1 < |x + 2| < 8$ (d) $|x| + 5 = 8$

CHAPTER TEST

In Exercises 1–6, name the property of the real number system which justifies each statement.

1. $97(23 \cdot 31) = (97 \cdot 23) \cdot 31$

2. $(83 + 43) + (95 + 73) = (95 + 73) + (83 + 43)$

3. $74(6 + 4) = 74 \cdot 6 + 74 \cdot 4$

4. If $19 \cdot x = 19 \cdot (2x + 5)$, then $x = 2x + 5$.

5. If $17x + 3 = 5 + x$, then $17x = 2 + x$.

6. If $-3x > 12$, then $x < -4$.

7. In each expression, find all integral values of x for which the expression is true.

(a) $|x - 4| = 10$ (b) $|x + 4| \leq 3$ (c) $3 \leq |x| \leq 6$

Perform the indicated operations and express each answer in simplest form.

8. $\sqrt{33} \cdot \sqrt{22}$ **9.** $\sqrt{\dfrac{5x}{3y}} \div \sqrt{\dfrac{35x^2}{12y^6}}$

10. $\sqrt{50x^3y} - \sqrt{98xy^3}$ **11.** $\sqrt{6} \cdot \sqrt[3]{36}$

12. $\left(\dfrac{\sqrt{x}}{5} - \dfrac{5}{\sqrt{x}}\right)^2$ **13.** $\sqrt[3]{-6x^2y^5} \cdot \sqrt[3]{72x^5y}$

For each of the following expressions, find an equivalent fraction with a rational denominator.

14. $\dfrac{2}{\sqrt{3}}$ **15.** $\dfrac{5}{\sqrt{2} - 3}$

16. $\dfrac{4}{\sqrt{5} - \sqrt{7}}$

In Exercises 17–20, perform the indicated operations.

17. $9^{\frac{3}{2}} - 27^0 + 8^{-\frac{1}{3}}$ **18.** $7^{\frac{3}{5}} \cdot 7^{\frac{2}{5}} \div 7^{-2}$

19. $\dfrac{2}{3^{-1} + 5^{-1}}$ **20.** $\sqrt[4]{9} \cdot \sqrt{3}$

21. (a) If A, B, and C are points on a number line with respective coordinates -10, -6, and 7, find the following directed distances.

$$d(BC) \quad \text{and} \quad d(CB) + d(BA)$$

(b) Find the midpoint of segment $\overline{AC}$.

*22. Use the properties of the real number system to prove that if $a < b$ and $c < d$, then $ac < bd$, when a, b, c, and d are positive real numbers.

CHAPTER 2

First-degree Equations and Inequalities

Objectives . . .

- To solve linear equations and inequalities.
- To graph linear equations and inequalities.
- To solve and apply systems of equations in two variables.
- To use determinants and matrices in the solution of systems of equations.

2-1 EQUATIONS IN ONE VARIABLE

Each of the algebraic expressions

$$3x - 7, \quad 11x + 33, \quad 4x, \quad -2, \quad 0$$

is called a linear form in the variable x. Thus, a *linear form in the variable* x is an algebraic expression of the type

$$ax + b,$$

where a and b are real numbers. Of course, there are linear forms in other variables. For example, $7y - 11$ is a linear form in the variable y.

If, in a linear form, we give the variable a value, the resulting number is called a *value* of the linear form. For example, the linear form $3x - 7$ has the value $(3 \cdot 5) - 7$, or 8, when $x = 5$.

If two linear forms in the same variable are connected by an equals sign, the resulting algebraic statement is called a *first-degree equation,* or *linear equation,* in that variable. For example,

$$3x - 7 = 11x + 33$$

is a first-degree equation in the variable x.

A number is called a *solution* of an equation in one variable if a true equation is obtained when we give the variable the value of the number. For example, 2 is a solution of the equation $3x - 1 = 7 - x$ since the equation obtained by letting $x = 2$ is true:

$$(3 \cdot 2) - 1 = 7 - 2, \quad \text{or } 5 = 5.$$

On the other hand, 3 is not a solution of this equation since the equation obtained by letting $x = 3$ is false:

$$(3 \cdot 3) - 1 = 7 - 3, \quad \text{or } 8 = 4.$$

59

If an equation has any solutions, then the set of all its solutions is called the *solution set of the equation.* If an equation has no solution, then its solution set is the empty set, ∅. When we *solve* an equation, we find its solution set.

Two or more equations in a variable are said to be *equivalent equations* if they have the same solution set. The process of solving an equation involves replacing the given equation by a succession of equivalent equations until we obtain an equation with an obvious solution set. For example, the given equation might be

$$2(x - 4) + 2x + 27 = 3(x + 7),$$

and the final equivalent one might be $x = 2$. Since $\{2\}$ is the solution set of the final equation, $\{2\}$ is also the solution set of the given equation.

We can use various axioms and properties, such as the additive and multiplicative axioms and the cancellation axioms of addition and multiplication, to derive equivalent equations from a given equation. Several of these axioms and properties are used in the following problems.

Problem 1. Solve the equation $3x - 7 = 11x + 33$.

Solution. Each of the following equations is equivalent to the preceding one for the reason given.

$$3x - 7 = 11x + 33$$
$$(3x - 7) + (-11x + 7) = (11x + 33) + (-11x + 7) \quad \text{(Add-A)}$$
$$-8x = 40 \quad \text{(R-A)}$$
$$(-\tfrac{1}{8})(-8x) = (-\tfrac{1}{8}) \cdot 40 \quad \text{(Mult-A)}$$
$$x = -5 \quad \text{(Inv-M)}$$

Thus, $\{-5\}$ is the solution set of the given equation.

Check.
$$[3 \cdot (-5)] - 7 \overset{?}{=} [11 \cdot (-5)] + 33$$
$$-15 - 7 \overset{?}{=} -55 + 33$$
$$-22 \overset{\vee}{=} -22$$

We check the solution to catch possible computational errors and to be certain that no errors have been made in forming each equivalent equation. If no errors have been made, the solution set of the final equation must be the solution set of the given equation.

Problem 2. Solve the equation $\frac{1}{3}y - 12 = 4 - \frac{3}{5}y$.

Solution. As before, we proceed by finding equivalent equations.

$$\frac{1}{3}y - 12 = 4 - \frac{3}{5}y$$

$$(\frac{1}{3}y - 12) + (\frac{3}{5}y + 12) = (4 - \frac{3}{5}y) + (\frac{3}{5}y + 12)$$

$$\frac{1}{3}y + \frac{3}{5}y = 4 + 12$$

$$(\frac{1}{3} + \frac{3}{5})y = 16$$

$$\frac{14}{15}y = 16$$

$$\frac{15}{14} \cdot \frac{14}{15}y = \frac{15}{14} \cdot 16$$

$$y = \frac{120}{7}$$

Thus, $\{17\frac{1}{7}\}$ is the solution set of the given equation.

Check.

$$(\frac{1}{3} \cdot \frac{120}{7}) - 12 \overset{?}{=} 4 - (\frac{3}{5} \cdot \frac{120}{7})$$

$$\frac{40}{7} - 12 \overset{?}{=} 4 - \frac{72}{7}$$

$$\frac{40 - 84}{7} \overset{?}{=} \frac{28 - 72}{7}$$

$$\frac{-44}{7} \overset{\checkmark}{=} \frac{-44}{7}$$

Exercises

In Exercises 1 and 2, test the solution of the second equation in the first equation to see whether or not the two equations are equivalent. If they are not equivalent, change the second equation to make it equivalent to the first.

1. (a) $\dfrac{x}{2} - \dfrac{x}{3} = 5$ (b) $\dfrac{x}{7} = 42$

 $3x - 2x = 30$ $x = 6$

2. (a) $5x - 6 = 17$ (b) $3x = 15$

 $5x = 11$ $x = 12$

Solve each of the following equations by writing a succession of equivalent equations, and check each solution.

3. (a) $3x + 4 = x + 12$ (b) $3 - 7x = 4x - 30$

4. (a) $5z + \frac{1}{3} = 2z - \frac{3}{2}$ (b) $\frac{1}{2}x - \frac{6}{5} = 12 - \frac{3}{2}x$

5. (a) $3(x - 3) = 7(2x + 1)$ (b) $2(3x + 2) - 12 = 3x - 11$

6. (a) $\frac{1}{5}(x + 1) = \frac{2}{3} + \frac{1}{9}(x - 1)$ (b) $\frac{1}{5}(x + 2) = \frac{2}{3} + \frac{1}{9}x$

7. (a) $.13y + 1.17 = 1.23y - .04$ (b) $6.1 - 5w = 4.6w + 3.22$

8. (a) $\dfrac{x - 13}{3} = \dfrac{78 - x}{10}$ (b) $\dfrac{x - 4}{3} = \dfrac{69 - x}{10}$

Tell whether or not the two equations of each given pair are equivalent. If not, change the second equation to make it equivalent to the first.

9. $\dfrac{x-3}{5} + \dfrac{3}{2} = 4 + \dfrac{5-x}{10}$, $2x - 6 + 15 = 40 + 5 - x$

10. $\dfrac{6x-1}{5} - 3x = \dfrac{12x-16}{15}$, $18x - 3 - 3x = 12x - 16$

11. $3(x-2) - 5 = 8 - 2(x-4)$, $3x - 6 - 5 = 8 - 2x - 8$

12. $4 - \dfrac{2x+1}{4} = \dfrac{1}{2} - \dfrac{9x+9}{8}$, $32 - 4x - 2 = 4 - 9x + 9$

Solve each of the following equations by writing a succession of equivalent equations, and check each solution.

13. $\dfrac{x+3}{5} - 2 = \dfrac{3x+2}{4} - 3$

14. $\dfrac{6y-1}{5} - 3y = \dfrac{12y-16}{15}$

15. $5\left(\dfrac{x+2}{3}\right) - x = \dfrac{20}{3}$

16. $5z - \frac{1}{5} = 3(z + \frac{13}{15})$

17. $t + 13 = 3 - 2(1 + t)$

18. $.6(1 - .8x) = .5 - .4(2 - 1.8x)$

19. $\frac{1}{3}(u + 8) - \frac{1}{4}(3 - 2u) = \frac{1}{6}$

20. $4 - \dfrac{2x-1}{4} = \dfrac{1}{2} - \dfrac{9x}{8}$

21. $\dfrac{w}{3} - \dfrac{4w+1}{2} = w - \dfrac{5}{6}$

22. $4 - \dfrac{2x+1}{4} = \dfrac{1}{2} - \dfrac{9x+9}{8}$

23. $2 + \dfrac{3w+1}{6} = \dfrac{4w-3}{2} - \dfrac{5w-9}{3}$

24. For what value of x does the linear form $3x + 7$ have the same value as the linear form $5x - 3$? Is there more than one such value?

25. (a) Compare the values of $6 - 2x$ and $-2(x - 3)$ for $x = 3, -3, 0, \frac{1}{2}$.
   (b) If two linear forms in x have the same value for more than one value of x, for how many values of x do you suspect that they will have the same value?

26. Are the equations $x = 3$ and $x^2 = 3x$ equivalent? Why?

2–2 WORD PROBLEMS

As the following examples show, we can use linear equations in one variable to solve many kinds of word problems.

Problem 1. It takes a man 2 hours to drive a distance of 100 miles. If he averages 60 miles per hour in the country and 30 miles per hour in each city he passes through, how great a part of the trip does he spend in the country?

Solution. If we let t designate the number of hours he spends driving in the country, then $2 - t$ is the number of hours he spends driving in cities. The formula relating distance, d, rate, r, and time, t, is

$$d = rt.$$

Thus, the man drives a distance of $30(2 - t)$ miles in cities and $60t$ miles in the country. It is given that the sum of these distances is 100 miles:

$$60t + 30(2 - t) = 100.$$

We can solve the problem by solving the above first-degree equation in t. Let us proceed as follows:

$$60t + 60 - 30t = 100,$$
$$30t + 60 = 100,$$
$$(30t + 60) - 60 = 100 - 60,$$
$$30t = 40,$$
$$t = \tfrac{4}{3}.$$

Thus, the man spends $\tfrac{4}{3}$ hours, or 1 hour and 20 minutes, driving in the country and $2 - \tfrac{4}{3}$ hours, or 40 minutes, driving in cities. He drives a distance of

$$60 \cdot \tfrac{4}{3}, \quad \text{or } 80,$$

miles in the country and $30 \cdot \tfrac{2}{3}$, or 20, miles in cities. Since

$$80 + 20 = 100,$$

these answers are correct.

An interesting type of problem involves the mixing of two substances in order to form a prescribed mixture. We can use first-degree equations to solve these problems also.

Problem 2. If a certain sample of sea water contains 8% salt, how much fresh water must we add to 40 pounds of the sea water so that the mixture contains only 5% salt?

Solution. In the 40 pounds of sea water, there are .08 × 40, or 3.2, pounds of salt. If we add N pounds of fresh water to the 40 pounds of sea water, we can obtain $N + 40$ pounds of water. We add only fresh water to the salt water. Therefore, the amount of salt in our mixture remains the same. Since we want 5% of the mixture to be salt, we must have

$$.05(N + 40) = 3.2.$$

We may solve the above first-degree equation in N as follows:

$$.05N + 2 = 3.2,$$
$$(.05N + 2) - 2 = 3.2 - 2,$$
$$.05N = 1.2,$$
$$N = \frac{1.2}{.05},$$
$$N = 24.$$

Thus, we must add 24 pounds of fresh water.

Check. $.05(24 + 40) \overset{?}{=} 3.2$
$$.05 \times 64 \overset{\vee}{=} 3.2$$

Problem 3. Tickets at a theater sell for $5.50 on the main floor and $3.25 in the balcony. If $8550 is collected for 1800 tickets, how many of each kind are sold?

Solution. Let x denote the number of main floor tickets.
Then $1800 - x$ denotes the number of balcony tickets.

$5.50x$ (the price per ticket times the number of tickets) denotes the money collected for main floor seats.

$3.25(1800 - x)$ denotes money collected for balcony seats.

$5.50x + 3.25(1800 - x)$ denotes total receipts for all tickets

Hence, from the information given in the problem, we know that

$$5.50x + 3.25(1800 - x) = 8550.$$

Solving this equation,

$$5.50x + (3.25)(1800) - 3.25x = 8550,$$
$$5.50x + 5850 - 3.25x = 8550,$$
$$5.50x - 3.25x + 5850 - 5850 = 8550 - 5850,$$
$$2.25x = 2700,$$
$$x = \frac{2700}{2.25} = 1200.$$

Thus, $1800 - x = 600$. There are 1200 tickets sold for the main floor and 600 tickets sold for the balcony.

$$1200(5.5) + 600(3.25) \overset{?}{=} 8550$$
$$6600 + 1950 \overset{\checkmark}{=} 8550$$

Exercises

Let x denote an arbitrary integer, and write an algebraic expression for each of the following phrases.

1. (a) The sum of four consecutive integers
   (b) The sum of five consecutive integers

2. (a) The sum of three consecutive odd integers
   (b) The sum of five consecutive even integers

Let x denote the number of 6¢ stamps in a collection that contains both 6¢ and 10¢ stamps. Write an algebraic expression for each of the following phrases.

3. (a) The cost of the 6¢ stamps
   (b) The cost of the 10¢ stamps if there are twice as many 10¢ as 6¢ stamps

4. (a) The number of 10¢ stamps if it is known that there are three times as many 10¢ as 6¢ stamps
   (b) The number of 10¢ stamps if there are 100 stamps in the collection

5. (a) The cost of the collection if there are 100 stamps in the collection
   (b) The cost of the collection if there are 60 stamps in the collection

Write an algebraic expression for each of the following phrases.

6. (a) The distance between two trains at the end of t hours if they left the same station at the same time, were headed in the same direction, and one was traveling at a rate of 50 miles per hour and the other at 70 miles per hour
   (b) The distance between the trains in part (a) if they were headed in opposite directions

7. (a) The distance separating two boys h hours after the first boy leaves camp, walking $2\frac{1}{2}$ miles per hour, if the second boy leaves camp three hours later, walking $3\frac{1}{2}$ miles per hour in the same direction

(b) The distance between the two boys in part (a) if they were headed in opposite directions

Let x denote Jane's present age in years, and write an algebraic expression for each of the following phrases.

8. (a) Twice Jane's age next year

(b) Four times Jane's age 3 years ago

9. (a) The present age of Jane's mother if her mother is now twice as old as Jane will be 3 years from now

(b) The present age of Jane's father if his age is now 3 years less than 4 times Jane's age 7 years ago

Write an algebraic expression for each of the following phrases, and simplify it.

10. (a) The cost of 10 pounds of candy if some of it costs $1.69 a pound and the rest costs $1.98 a pound

(b) The cost of 25 tickets to a football game if some of the tickets cost $3.00 and the rest cost $3.50.

11. (a) The amount of alcohol in a mixture after x ounces of a solution which is 65% alcohol is added to 15 ounces of a solution which is 75% alcohol

(b) The income from two investments totaling $10,000 if part of it is invested at $3\frac{1}{2}\%$ simple interest and the rest is invested at $4\frac{3}{4}\%$ simple interest.

12. These early questions in algebra come from the Rhind papyrus, dated about 1600–1800 B.C. An Egyptian teacher put them to his pupil.

(a) "Heap" and twice the "heap"; the total is 18. Tell me, my young friend, what is the "heap"?

(b) "Heap" and one-fifth the "heap," take away three; the result is 21. What is the "heap"?

Write an equation for each of the following problems, and solve it. In each case, tell what is denoted by the variable that you use.

13. Find three consecutive even integers whose sum is 126.

14. Find four consecutive odd integers whose sum is 136.

15. If 3 times a number is added to 5 times the negative of the number, the sum is 12. Find the number.

16. There are 40 coins in a collection of nickels and quarters, and the collection is worth $5.40. How many nickels are there?

17. A newsboy collects $6.30 in nickels, dimes, and quarters. He has 4 more dimes than quarters and the number of nickels is 2 more than twice the number of dimes. How many coins of each type does he have?

✗ **18.** In a local election, two-fifths of the eligible voters voted to retain Mayor Mills, three-eighths voted for his opponent, and the remaining 90 of those eligible did not vote. How many eligible voters were there in all?

19. Two years ago a man was 7 times as old as his son, but in 3 years he will only be 4 times as old as the boy. How old is each now?

20. Chuck's present age is $\frac{5}{8}$ that of John's age. In two years Chuck's age will be $\frac{2}{3}$ of John's. How old is Chuck now?

✓ **21.** How many pounds of almonds which regularly sell for $1.10 per pound should be added to 10 pounds of peanuts which sell for 60¢ per pound if the resultant mixture should sell at 90¢ per pound?

22. Two men start at the same time from towns 19 miles apart and walk toward each other. One walks $2\frac{1}{2}$ miles per hour while the other covers $3\frac{1}{2}$ miles per hour. How long do they walk before meeting? How far has each man walked when they meet?

23. A man who walks $3\frac{1}{2}$ miles per hour sets out, from the same spot, to overtake a man who walks $2\frac{1}{2}$ miles per hour and who left $1\frac{1}{2}$ hours earlier. How long will it take the first walker to overtake the second one? How far has each man walked when the second one overtakes the first one?

✗ **24.** What quantity of a solution which is to be 15% alcohol can be made from 7.5 quarts of pure alcohol?

✓ **25.** How much water must be evaporated from 6 gallons of a 15%-salt solution if the residual solution is to contain 25% salt?

26. How much of the mixture in an 8-quart radiator should be drained and replaced with pure antifreeze if the mixture now consists of 75% antifreeze, and it is desired that the resultant mixture contain 90% antifreeze?

Preparation for Section 2-3

Give the reason that makes each of the following true.

1. If x is positive, then $3x > x$.   **2.** $-3 + a > -5 + a$

3. If x is negative, then $21x < 5x$.   **4.** If $7 > x$, then $10 > x$.

5. $-7 + x < 3 + x$

6. If $x < 2$, then $x < 12$.

2-3   INEQUALITIES IN ONE VARIABLE

A statement, such as

$$13x - 12 < 28 - 7x,$$

consisting of two linear forms in a variable connected by an order relation is called a *first-degree inequality*, or *linear inequality*, in the variable.

A number is called a solution of an inequality in one variable if a true statement is obtained when we give the variable the value of the number. The set of all solutions of an inequality is called the solution set of the inequality. If an inequality has no solution, its solution set is the empty set, $\emptyset$.

For example, let us determine which, if any, of the numbers $-2, 0, 2$, and 4 are solutions of the inequality above. If we let $x = -2$, we obtain

$$[13 \cdot (-2)] - 12 < 28 - [7 \cdot (-2)], \quad \text{or} \quad -38 < 42.$$

Since this is a true statement, -2 is in the solution set of the given inequality. If we let x equal 0, 2, and 4, in turn, we obtain the following statements:

$$(13 \cdot 0) - 12 < 28 - (7 \cdot 0), \quad \text{or} \quad -12 < 28,$$
$$(13 \cdot 2) - 12 < 28 - (7 \cdot 2), \quad \text{or} \quad 14 < 14,$$
$$(13 \cdot 4) - 12 < 28 - (7 \cdot 4), \quad \text{or} \quad 40 < 0.$$

Since the first statement is true and the last two are false, we conclude that 0 is in the solution set and that 2 and 4 are not in the solution set of the given inequality.

We solve an inequality as we solve an equation; that is, we find its solution set in a similar way. Two inequalities in a variable are said to be *equivalent* if they have the same solution set. Thus, we try to find an equivalent inequality with an obvious solution set. For example, if the inequalities

$$\tfrac{1}{2}(5x - 6) < \tfrac{1}{6}(108 - 3x)$$

and

$$x < 7$$

are equivalent, then we can tell from the second inequality that the solution set of both inequalities is the set of all real numbers less than 7.

In the solution of the following inequalities, we shall use several of the axioms and properties discussed in Chapter 1.

Problem 1. Solve the inequality $13x - 12 < 28 - 7x$.

Solution. Each of the following inequalities is equivalent to the preceding one for the reason given.

$$13x - 12 < 28 - 7x$$
$$13x - 12 + (7x + 12) < 28 - 7x + (7x + 12) \qquad \text{(A <)}$$
$$(13x + 7x) + (12 - 12) < (28 + 12) + (7x - 7x) \qquad \text{(R-A)}$$
$$20x + 0 < 40 + 0 \qquad \text{(Inv-A)}$$
$$20x < 40 \qquad \text{(Id-A)}$$
$$\tfrac{1}{20} \cdot 20x < \tfrac{1}{20} \cdot 40 \qquad \text{(M <)}$$
$$x < 2$$

We shall let you verify that the solution set of the given inequality is the set of all real numbers less than 2: $\{x \mid x < 2\}$.

The *graph* of an equation or inequality in one variable is the set of all points on a number line whose coordinates are solutions of the given equation or inequality. Since a first-degree equation in one variable usually has a single solution, its graph consists of a single point. On the other hand, the graph of an inequality often consists of more than one point.

For example, the graph of the inequality of Problem 1 is the set of all points on a number line having coordinates less than 2. This graph is an *open ray,* as indicated in Fig. 2–1. The hollow dot at 2 indicates that 2 is not part of the graph. The figure is incomplete, because the open ray extends infinitely far to the left.

FIGURE 2–1

Problem 2. Solve the inequality $\tfrac{11}{3}x + 2 \geq \tfrac{7}{6}x - 8$.

Solution.
$$\tfrac{11}{3}x + 2 \geq \tfrac{7}{6}x - 8$$
$$\tfrac{11}{3}x + 2 + (-\tfrac{7}{6}x - 2) \geq \tfrac{7}{6}x - 8 + (-\tfrac{7}{6}x - 2)$$
$$\tfrac{11}{3}x + (-\tfrac{7}{6}x) \geq -8 - 2$$
$$\tfrac{15}{6}x \geq -10$$
$$\tfrac{6}{15} \cdot \tfrac{15}{6}x \geq \tfrac{6}{15} \cdot (-10)$$
$$x \geq -4$$

Thus, the set of all numbers greater than or equal to -4, designated by

$$\{x \mid x \geqq -4\},$$

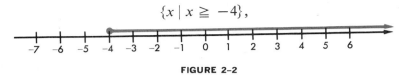

FIGURE 2-2

is the solution set of the given inequality. Its graph is the ray indicated in Fig. 2–2. The solid dot at -4 shows that -4 is part of the graph.

The graphs of the solution sets of two different inequalities may overlap, or intersect. For example, the solution set of the inequality $x + 1 < 4$ is the set of real numbers less than 3, or $\{x \mid x < 3\}$. The solution set of the inequality $2x > -4$ is the set of real numbers greater than -2, or $\{x \mid x > -2\}$. Those numbers which are greater than -2 and also less than 3, or $\{x \mid -2 < x < 3\}$, are in the solution set of both inequalities. The symbol $\cap$ is placed between two sets to indicate the set which is their *intersection*. Thus, we may write

$$\{x \mid x + 1 < 4\} \cap \{x \mid 2x > -4\} = \{x \mid -2 < x < 3\}.$$

The graph of the solution set of each of these two inequalities is an open ray, and the graph of the intersection of the two sets is an open interval, as shown in Fig. 2–3.

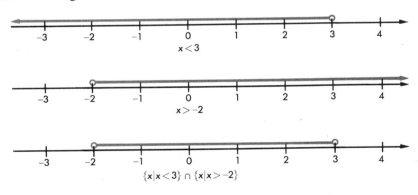

FIGURE 2-3

The *union* of two sets is the set consisting of all elements in either set. The symbol $\cup$ is used to denote the union of two sets. For example, the union of the closed intervals $\{x \mid -1 \leqq x \leqq 2\}$ and $\{x \mid 1 \leqq x \leqq 5\}$ is the closed interval $\{x \mid -1 \leqq x \leqq 5\}$:

$$\{x \mid -1 \leqq x \leqq 2\} \cup \{x \mid 1 \leqq x \leqq 5\} = \{x \mid -1 \leqq x \leqq 5\},$$

as shown in Fig. 2–4.

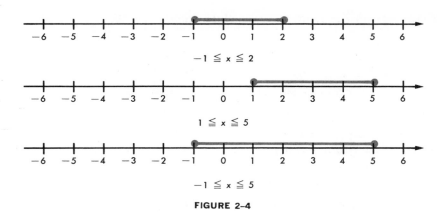

FIGURE 2-4

The *empty set*, denoted by ∅, is the set having no elements. For example,

$$\{x \mid x \leqq -2\} \cap \{x \mid x \geqq 3\} = \emptyset.$$

A bar drawn through a relation sign negates the relation. Thus,

$x \neq y$ means x is not equal to y,

$x \nless y$ means x is not less than y,

$x \ngeqq y$ means x is not greater than or equal to y.

Exercises

1. Tell which of the numbers

$$-8, 8, -5, 3, 0, 1.5, -1.5, 10, 1.6$$

are in the solution set of the following inequalities.

(a) $2x - 5 > 7 - 6x$ (b) $2x - 5 \leqq 7 - 6x$

Tell which of the numbers

$$0, -4, 5, -2, -3, 1, 3, -2.9, -3.1$$

are in the solution set of the inequalities in Exercises 2 and 3.

2. (a) $7 < 2x - 1$ (b) $2x - 1 < 5$

3. (a) $2x - 1 > 5$ (b) $2x - 1 < -7$

4. Tell which of the numbers

$$10, -2, 0, -1.5, -.5, 1, -1, 3$$

are in the solution set of the following inequalities.

(a) $4 - 5x \leqq 7 - 2x$ (b) $4 - 5x > 7 - 2x$

Solve each of the following inequalities, and graph its solution set on a number line.

5. (a) $x + 3 > 2$ (b) $x - 2 < 5$

6. (a) $x + 1 \geq -2$ (b) $2x - 3 \leq 7$

7. (a) $4x + 7 \geq x - 11$ (b) $\frac{1}{2}x + \frac{1}{3} \geq 3 - \frac{1}{6}x$

8. (a) $\frac{3}{5}x - \frac{1}{4} < \frac{49}{40} - \frac{7}{8}x$ (b) $3(x + 1) \geq 2(5 - x)$

9. (a) $\frac{3}{2}x - 2 < 2x + \frac{1}{3}$ (b) $-3(x + 2) > -9$

10. For each pair of inequalities, graph the two solution sets and show their intersection.

(a) $x > -3,\ x < 5$ (b) $x \geq -2,\ x \leq 2$

11. For each pair of inequalities, graph the two solution sets and describe their intersection.

(a) $x > 3,\ x > -1$ (b) $x < 5,\ x < -4$

12. Describe the intersections.

(a) $\{x \mid x > 3\} \cap \{x \mid x < 1\}$ (b) $\{x \mid x \leq 2\} \cap \{x \mid x > 2\}$

13. Graph each of the following sets.

(a) $\{x \mid x > 1\} \cup \{x \mid x < -1\}$ (b) $\{x \mid x \geq 3\} \cup \{x \mid x \leq 1\}$

---

14. Graph each of the following sets.

$$\{x \mid x + 3 > 0\} \cap \{x \mid x - 3 < 0\},\ \{x \mid |x| > 3\}$$

15. Graph each of the following sets.

$$\{x \mid x \geq 3\} \cup \{x \mid x \leq -3\},\ \{x \mid |x| \geq 3\}$$

16. Determine which of the numbers

$$10,\ 8,\ 6,\ 4,\ 3,\ 2,\ 0,\ -4,\ -9,\ -10$$

are in the solution set of the inequalities.

(a) $x > 4$ (b) $-2x > -8$

(c) Describe $\{x \mid x > 4\} \cap \{x \mid -2x > -8\}$ and $\{x \mid x > 4\} \cup \{x \mid -2x > -8\}$.

17. (a) Graph each of the following inequalities. Then give four elements of each solution set.

$$x < 3,\quad 2x < -6,\quad -2x > -6$$

(b) Are any of the inequalities in part (a) equivalent?

Solve each inequality of the following pairs of inequalities, and find the intersection of the solution sets of each pair. For each pair, graph both solution sets and their intersection.

18. $2x + 1 < 7$ and $3x - 1 > 2$

19. $x + 1 < 2x - 4$ and $3x - 2 > 1$

20. $2x + 3 \geqq 15 - 4x$ and $x - \frac{1}{3} > \frac{1}{6}x - 2$

21. $\frac{5}{4}x > 1 + x$ and $x + 2 < \frac{14}{5}$

22. (a) Write an inequality that has the same solution set as the inequality $x \not\gtrless 6$.

    (b) Write an inequality that has the same solution set as $x \not\lessdot -\frac{13}{5}$.

Two sets of real numbers are described below. Give three specific members of each set, and tell how the two sets are related to each other.

23. $A = \{x \mid x > -1\}$ and $B = \{x \mid x \not\gtrless -1\}$

24. $A = \{x \mid 5x - 1 \not\lessdot 2\}$ and $B = \{x \mid 5x - 1 \not\gtrless 2\}$

25. $A = \{x \mid 2x + 1 > 3\}$ and $B = \{x \mid 2x + 1 \not\lessgtr 3\}$

---

26. A football team has won 5 out of 7 games played. If there are 8 games remaining, how many more games must be won to give the team a season record of at least 60% games won out of all games played?

27. Johnny starts with the fraction $\frac{1}{2}$ and considers adding the same number x to both the numerator and the denominator. For what positive values of x will he obtain a number greater than or equal to $\frac{3}{4}$?

2-4   EQUATIONS IN TWO VARIABLES

An algebraic expression such as

$$3x - 2y + 4$$

is called a *linear form* in the two variables x and y. Every linear form in x and y is of the type

$$ax + by + c$$

for some real numbers a, b, and c. Note that

$$0x - 3y + 8, \quad \text{or} \quad -3y + 8,$$

may be considered to be a linear form in x and y although the variable x does not appear. Of course, $-3y + 8$ is also a linear form in the one variable y.

If values are given to the variables in a linear form, the resulting number is called a *value* of the linear form. For example, the linear form $3x - 2y + 4$ has the value

$$(3 \cdot 3) - 2 \cdot (-5) + 4, \quad \text{or } 23,$$

when $x = 3$ and $y = -5$. If we let $x = 17$ and $y = 3$ in the linear form $-3y + 8$, its value is $(-3 \cdot 3) + 8$, or -1. As long as we let $y = 3$, the value of this linear form is -1 for any value given to x.

A statement consisting of two linear forms in x and y connected by an equals sign is called a *first-degree equation*, or *linear equation*, in the variables x and y.
Consider

$$3x - 2y + 4 = -3y + 8$$

as an example of a first-degree equation in x and y. If we let $x = -1$ and $y = 7$ in this equation, we obtain the *true* equation

$$-3 - 14 + 4 = -21 + 8.$$

Therefore, the ordered pair $(-1, 7)$ is a *solution* of the given equation. On the other hand, the ordered pair $(3, 6)$ is *not a solution* since the equation obtained by letting $x = 3$ and $y = 6$ is false.

$$9 - 12 + 4 = -18 + 8$$

An ordered pair (a, b) is called a solution of an equation in x and y if, and only if, a true equation results when we let $x = a$ and $y = b$. The set of all solutions of an equation in x and y is called the solution set of the equation. If an equation has no solution, its solution set is the empty set, $\emptyset$.

We recall that a first-degree equation in one variable usually has only one solution. A first-degree equation in two variables, on the other hand, usually has an infinite number of solutions. A convenient method of finding solutions of a first-degree equation in two variables is to solve the given equation for one variable in terms of the other.

Problem. Solve the following equation for y in terms of x.

Solution.
$$3x - 2y + 4 = -3y + 8$$
$$(3y - 3x - 4) + 3x - 2y + 4 = -3y + 8 + (3y - 3x - 4)$$
$$y = -3x + 4$$

This final equation is equivalent to the given one. Hence, the solution set of the given equation may be described as follows:

$$\{(x, y) \mid y = -3x + 4\}.$$

By giving different values to x, we can find as many ordered pairs in the solution set of the given equation as we wish. For example, if we let $x = 3$, we obtain

$$y = (-3 \cdot 3) + 4, \text{ or } -5.$$

Thus, the ordered pair $(3, -5)$ is in the solution set. The following elements of the solution set were found in the same way.

$$(0, 4), \quad (1, 1), \quad (-1, 7), \quad (\tfrac{4}{3}, 0), \quad (2, -2), \quad (100, -296)$$

Exercises

1. (a) Tell which of the following ordered pairs are elements of the solution set of the equation $5x + 3y + 1 = 8x + 2y - 4$.

$$(\tfrac{1}{3}, -4), \ (3, 3), \ (0, -5), \ (\tfrac{1}{2}, \tfrac{7}{2}), \ (\tfrac{5}{3}, 0)$$

(b) Tell which of the following ordered pairs are elements of the solution set of the equation $4x + 2y + 20 = 3x + y + 15$.

$$(0, -5), \ (\tfrac{1}{2}, -4\tfrac{1}{2}), \ (-3, -2), \ (-1, -4), \ (4, 1)$$

2. Solve the equations for y in terms of x.
   (a) $3(2y - 1) - (x - 3) = 3x - y - 5$
   (b) $x - 3(x - 2y - 4) = 6 - (4x - y - 5)$

3. (a) Solve the equation in Exercise 2(a) for x in terms of y.
   (b) Solve the equation in Exercise 2(b) for x in terms of y.

Find five elements of the solution set of each of the following equations.

4. (a) $x + y + 8 = 0$ (b) $3x + y - 10 = 0$

5. (a) $x - 2y - 8 = 0$ (b) $\tfrac{1}{2}x + \tfrac{1}{4}y + 2 = 0$

Solve each of the following equations for y in terms of x. Find three ordered pairs that are elements of each solution set. Then check these solutions in the given equation.

6. (a) $3y - 2x + 4 = 8 - 3x$ (b) $5x - 6y - 9 = 2x + 4y - 3$

7. (a) $\dfrac{x}{5} - \dfrac{y}{6} + \dfrac{1}{2} = x + \dfrac{y}{3} - \dfrac{1}{10}$ (b) $\dfrac{1}{2}x + \dfrac{3}{10}y = \dfrac{4}{5}x + \dfrac{1}{5}y - \dfrac{1}{2}$

8. (a) Solve each equation in Exercises 6(a) and 7(a) for x in terms of y.
   (b) Solve each equation in Exercises 6(b) and 7(b) for x in terms of y.

9. Given the equation $x + y = 8$:
   (a) are there solutions with $x > 0$ and $y < 0$?
   (b) are there solutions with $x < 0$ and $y < 0$?

In each case, if your answer is yes, find three solutions.

10. Are there solutions of the equation $2x + y + 10 = 0$ with:
   (a) $x < 0$ and $y > 0$?
   (b) $x > 0$ and $y > 0$?

In each case, if your answer is yes, find three solutions.

---

11. Let sets R, S, and M be defined by

$$R = \{(x, y) \mid 2x - y = 1\},$$
$$S = \{(x, y) \mid 2x - y = -1\},$$
$$M = \{(x, y) \mid |2x - y| = 1\}.$$

   (a) Is $(3, 5)$ in R? S? M?
   (b) Is $(4, 9)$ in R? S? M?
   (c) Find two elements of R having $x < 0$. Do they also belong to S? M?
   (d) Find two elements of S having $x < 0$. Do they also belong to R? M?
   (e) How is set R related to set S?
   (f) What is the relationship of M to R and S?

12. Use the results of Exercise 11 to list two linear equations in x and y such that the union of their solution sets is the same as the solution set of the single equation $|x + y| = 3$.

13. List two linear equations in x and y such that the union of their solution sets is the same as the solution set of the single equation

$$|2x - 3y| = 10.$$

14. Find a single equation in x and y whose solution set is equal to the union of the solution sets described below.

$$\{(x, y) \mid 3y - 16 = 5y - x - 12\}, \quad \{(x, y) \mid 2x = 4y + 8\}$$

---

15. (a) What is the largest possible value for x in a solution of the equation $|x| + |y| = 2$? for y?
   (b) Give four solutions of the equation $|x| + |y| = 2$ with $x > 0$ and $y > 0$. What linear equation also has these solutions?
   (c) Give four solutions of $|x| + |y| = 2$ with $x < 0$ and $y < 0$. What linear equation also has these solutions?
   (d) Give four solutions of $|x| + |y| = 2$ with $x < 0$ and $y > 0$. What linear equation also has these solutions?
   (e) Give four solutions of $|x| + |y| = 2$ with $x > 0$ and $y < 0$. What linear equation also has these solutions?
   (f) Describe the solution set of the equation $|x| + |y| = 2$.

Review for Sections 2–1 through 2–4

Solve each of the following equations and inequalities by writing a succession of equivalent ones. Check each solution.

1. $3m - 3 = 5 + m$ **2.** $2(p + 1) + 5 > 6$

3. $\dfrac{4(6 + x)}{3} < 4$ **4.** $4(3y + 5) + 1 = 1 + 8y$

5. $3(4x + 3) = 3x + 15$ **6.** $3(k + 5) > k - 3$

7. $2(9n - 3) + 4 = 2(n + 3) + 2$

8. $\dfrac{3m + 4}{2} < m + 3$ **9.** $\dfrac{3(2x + 1) - 4}{2} = -2$

10. $4t - 13 = 2(t + 13) - t$

11. $\dfrac{4(2y + 1)}{3} > y + 1$ **12.** $2(2x - 7) + 3 = 10 + x$

13. $4(n + 1) < n$ **14.** $2x - 6 = 3(2x + 6)$

15. $\dfrac{6k + 7}{2} > 5 - k$ **16.** $\dfrac{4(2m + 3)}{3} > \dfrac{80}{4}$

Using m for your variable, write an algebraic expression for each of the following phrases.

17. The product of two consecutive even integers

18. Three times Martin's age 4 years ago

19. The cost of a dozen candy bars when some cost 6¢ and the rest cost 12¢

20. The sum of three consecutive integers

Write an equation for each of the following problems and solve it.

21. Find four consecutive integers whose sum is 90

22. Sue is three times as old as Mary was four years ago. Sue is two years older than Mary. How old are Sue and Mary?

23. There are 30 coins in a collection of nickels and dimes and the collection has a face value of $2.15. How many nickels and how many dimes are there?

Graph each of the following sets.

24. $\{x \mid x + 4 > 2\} \cap \{x \mid x - 3 < 0\}$

25. $\{x \mid x - 2 < 0\} \cap \{x \mid x + 5 \geqq 0\}$

Solve each of the following equations for y in terms of x and then tell which of the ordered pairs are elements of the solution set for each.

26. $2(x + y) + 1 = 5x + y + 3$; $(0, 2)$, $(1, 0)$, $(3, 7)$, $(-2, -4)$

27. $5y + x = y + 2(x + 1)$; $(4, 1)$, $(2, 1)$, $(-6, -1)$, $(0, 0)$

28. $3x + 3y = 2(x + y) + 5$; $(3, 8)$, $(1, 4)$, $(-1, -4)$, $(5, 0)$

29. $3(x + y + 1) = 2(3x + y) - 1$; $(1, -1), (0, 4), (2, 2), (-1, 1)$

30. $x + 3y - 4 = 2(x + 7)$; $(1, 7), (0, 6), (2, 8), (6, 8)$

Answers to Review for Sections 2–1 through 2–4

1. $\{4\}$ **2.** $\{p \mid p > -\frac{1}{2}\}$ **3.** $\{x \mid x < -3\}$

4. $\{-5\}$ **5.** $\{\frac{2}{3}\}$ **6.** $\{k \mid k > -9\}$

7. $\{\frac{5}{8}\}$ **8.** $\{m \mid m < 2\}$ **9.** $\{-\frac{1}{2}\}$

10. $\{13\}$ **11.** $\{y \mid y > -\frac{1}{5}\}$ **12.** $\{7\}$

13. $\{n \mid n < -\frac{4}{3}\}$ **14.** $\{-6\}$ **15.** $\{k \mid k > \frac{3}{8}\}$

16. $\{m \mid m > 6\}$ **17.** $2m(2m + 2)$ **18.** $3(m - 4)$

19. $.06m + .12(12 - m)$ or $.12m + .06(12 - m)$

20. $m + (m + 1) + (m + 2)$ or $3(m + 1)$

21. $x + (x + 1) + (x + 2) + (x + 3) = 90$;
$x = 21$, $x + 1 = 22$, $x + 2 = 23$, $x + 3 = 24$

22. $m + 2 = 3(m - 4)$; Mary is 7 years old, Sue is 9 years old.

23. $.05x + .10(30 - x) = \$2.15$; there are 17 nickels and 13 dimes.

24.

25.

26. $y = 3x + 2$; $(0, 2), (-2, -4)$

27. $y = \dfrac{x + 2}{4}$; $(2, 1), (-6, -1)$

28. $y = 5 - x$; $(1, 4), (5, 0)$

29. $y = 3x - 4$; $(1, -1), (2, 2)$

30. $y = 6 + \dfrac{x}{3}$; $(0, 6), (6, 8)$

2–5   THE GRAPH OF A FIRST-DEGREE EQUATION IN TWO VARIABLES

If we wish to construct a rectangular *cartesian coordinate system* in a plane, we select two perpendicular lines in the plane. Then we put a number scale on each line, in each case placing the origin at the point of intersection of the lines. Unless we are given a statement to the contrary, we use the same unit of length on both lines. The two resulting number lines are customarily called the x-axis and the y-axis, and we usually place and direct them as shown in Fig. 2–5.

We assign to each point an ordered pair of real numbers; this ordered pair describes the position of the point relative to the axes. Conversely,

each ordered pair is a pair of coordinates of some point in the plane.
Some examples of points and their
coordinates in the plane are given
in Fig. 2–5. Since each ordered pair
determines a point in the plane, a
set of ordered pairs determines a
set of points in the plane. This set
of points is called the *graph of the
set of ordered pairs*.

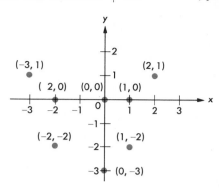

FIGURE 2–5

If the solution set of an equation
in x and y is not the empty set,
it is an example of a set of ordered pairs. The graph of the solution
set is called the graph of the given equation. A first-degree equation
in x and y has a straight line as its graph. In other words, its graph is
the set of all the points on some straight line. It is for this reason that
a first-degree equation in x and y is called a *linear equation*. Some
examples of linear equations and their graphs are given in the following
problems.

Problem 1. Graph the first-degree equation $3x - 2y + 4 = 0$.

Solution. When we solve the given equation for y, we obtain the
equivalent equation

$$2y = 3x + 4,$$

or

$$y = \tfrac{3}{2}x + 2.$$

Thus,

$$\{(x, y) \mid y = \tfrac{3}{2}x + 2\}$$

is the solution set of the given equation. Several elements of the solution set are given below.

$(0, 2), \quad (2, 5), \quad (-1, \tfrac{1}{2}), \quad (-4, -4)$

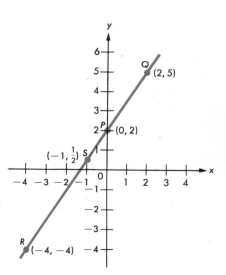

These ordered pairs are graphed in
Fig. 2–6. The straight line containing these points is the graph of the
given equation.

FIGURE 2–6

You might recall that each non-vertical straight line has a *slope* which we define as the ratio of the rise to the run of the line.

$$\text{slope} = \frac{\text{rise}}{\text{run}} \quad \text{or} \quad \frac{\text{change in ordinate}}{\text{change in abscissa}}$$

Any two points of the graph may be used to determine the slope. Thus, going from $P(0, 2)$ to $Q(2, 5)$,

$$\text{slope} = \frac{5 - 2}{2 - 0} \quad \text{or} \quad \frac{3}{2}.$$

Going from $S(-1, \frac{1}{2})$ to $P(0, 2)$,

$$\text{slope} = \frac{2 - \frac{1}{2}}{0 - (-1)} = \frac{\frac{3}{2}}{1} \quad \text{or} \quad \frac{3}{2}.$$

In both of these cases, rise and run are each positive, rise being "up" and run being "to the right." However, going from $S(-1, \frac{1}{2})$ to $R(-4, -4)$,

$$\text{slope} = \frac{-4 - \frac{1}{2}}{-4 - (-1)} = \frac{-\frac{9}{2}}{-3} = \left(-\frac{9}{2}\right)\cdot\left(-\frac{1}{3}\right) \quad \text{or} \quad \frac{3}{2}.$$

Here, rise and run are both negative, rise being "down" and run being "to the left." In general, if $P(x_1, y_1)$ and $Q(x_2, y_2)$ are two points on a line, then we define

$$\text{slope} = \frac{y_2 - y_1}{x_2 - x_1} \quad \text{or} \quad \frac{y_1 - y_2}{x_1 - x_2}, \quad x_1 \neq x_2.$$

Notice that the slope of the line in Fig. 2–6 is $\frac{3}{2}$ and an equation of the line is $y = \frac{3}{2}x + 2$. It is not an accident that the coefficient of x is the same as the slope of the line. Whenever a first-degree equation in x and y is solved for y and written in the form

$$y = mx + b,$$

where m and b are real numbers, the coefficient of x (that is, m) is the slope of the straight line which is the graph of the equation. (See Fig. 2–7.) We can prove that m is the slope by noting that the point $(0, b)$ and $(1, m + b)$ are on the line, and that the rise is m and the run is 1 from $(0, b)$ to $(1, m + b)$.

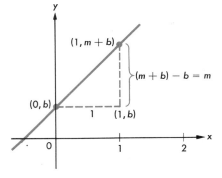

FIGURE 2-7

Since b is the y-coordinate of the point where the line crosses the y-axis, b is called the *y-intercept* of the line.

Problem 2. Graph the first-degree equation

$$3x - 2y + 4 = -3y + 8.$$

Solution. In Section 2–4, we saw that this equation is equivalent to

$$y = -3x + 4$$

and that $(0, 4)$, $(1, 1)$, $(-1, 7)$, and $(2, -2)$ are points on the line. The line L is graphed in Fig. 2–8. From the point $(0, 4)$ to the point $(2, -2)$, the line has a rise of $-2 - 4$, or -6, and a run of $2 - 0$, or 2. Thus, its slope is $-\frac{6}{2}$, or -3. Of course, when we say that the line has a rise of -6, we actually mean that the line is *falling* six units from $(0, 4)$ to $(2, -2)$.

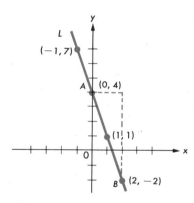

FIGURE 2–8

Using points $A(0, 4)$ and $B(2, -2)$,

$$\text{slope} = \frac{4 - (-2)}{0 - 2} = \frac{6}{-2} \quad \text{or} \quad -3.$$

We could have predicted this from the equation $y = -3x + 4$ where -3 is the coefficient of x.

Problem 3. Consider $2x + 3 = 0$ as an equation in x and y, and draw its graph.

Solution. The given equation is equivalent to the equation $x = -\frac{3}{2}$. Thus, every ordered pair of the type $(-\frac{3}{2}, y)$ is in the solution set of the given equation. In other words, $\{(-\frac{3}{2}, y) \mid y$ a real number$\}$ is the solution set of this equation. The graph of the given equation is the vertical line drawn in Fig. 2–9. Some points on the graph are $(-\frac{3}{2}, 0)$, $(-\frac{3}{2}, 2)$, and $(-\frac{3}{2}, -1)$.

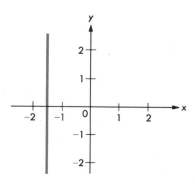

FIGURE 2–9

Since there is no run from one point to another point on this line, the slope is not defined for this line.

Every linear equation has a straight line as its graph. It is true, conversely, that every straight line is the graph of some linear equation. For example, the line drawn through the points $A(-2, 3)$ and $B(4, -1)$ has

$$\text{slope} = \frac{3 - (-1)}{-2 - 4} = \frac{4}{-6} = -\frac{2}{3}.$$

A point $P(x, y)$ other than A is on this line if, and only if, the slope of the line drawn through A and P is $-\frac{2}{3}$; that is,

$$\frac{y - 3}{x - (-2)} = -\frac{2}{3}.$$

Simplifying this equation, we obtain

$$y - 3 = -\tfrac{2}{3}(x + 2),$$

or

$$y = -\tfrac{2}{3}x + \tfrac{5}{3}.$$

This linear equation has the line drawn through the points A and B as its graph.

Check. Is $A(-2, 3)$ on the graph of this equation?

$$3 \stackrel{?}{=} -\tfrac{2}{3}(-2) + \tfrac{5}{3}$$
$$3 \stackrel{\checkmark}{=} \tfrac{4}{3} + \tfrac{5}{3}$$

Is $B(4, -1)$ on the graph?

$$-1 \stackrel{?}{=} -\tfrac{2}{3}(4) + \tfrac{5}{3}$$
$$-1 \stackrel{\checkmark}{=} -\tfrac{8}{3} + \tfrac{5}{3}$$

More generally, if $A(x_1, y_1)$ and $B(x_2, y_2)$ are two points not lying on a vertical line (that is, if $x_1 \neq x_2$), then the line drawn through A and B has slope m given by

$$m = \frac{y_2 - y_1}{x_2 - x_1}$$

and equation

$$y - y_1 = m(x - x_1).$$

Problem 4. Find an equation of the line through $A(3, 4)$ and $B(-2, -6)$.

Solution. The slope of the line is given by

$$m = \frac{4 - (-6)}{3 - (-2)} = \frac{10}{5} = 2.$$

Letting $(3, 4) = (x_1, y_1)$, we have

$$y - 4 = 2(x - 3)$$

as an equation of the line. Simplifying,

$$y - 4 = 2x - 6,$$
$$y = 2x - 2.$$

We could just as easily have let $(-2, -6) = (x_1, y_1)$. Then the equation would have been

$$y + 6 = 2(x + 2).$$

Simplifying, we get

$$y = 2x - 2$$

as before.

Exercises

1. What is the slope of a line through the points
   (a) $(-2, -3)$ and $(7, 9)$?
   (b) $(-4, 5)$ and $(6, -3)$?

Plot each pair of points below, draw the straight line through them, and determine the slope of the line.

2. (a) $(-2, 3)$, $(5, -6)$
   (b) $(-4, -1)$, $(3, 5)$

3. (a) $(2, -1)$, $(-2, -4)$
   (b) $(6, 2)$, $(-3, -4)$

4. (a) What is the slope of a line through the points $(-1, 3)$ and $(5, 3)$?
   (b) What is the slope of any line parallel to the x-axis?

5. (a) Does the line through $(-1, 3)$ and $(-1, 5)$ have a slope? Why?
   (b) How can you describe the set of all lines for which the slope is not defined?

6. Graph each of the following linear equations on a cartesian coordinate system in a plane. Give the slope and the y-intercept of each line.

(a) $x - y - 2 = 0$

(b) $\frac{1}{2}x + y = 3$

In Exercises 7–10, graph each of the linear equations on a cartesian coordinate system in a plane. Give first the slope and then the y-intercept of each line (if they exist).

7. (a) $2x + 5y = 10$

(b) $\frac{1}{2}x + \frac{1}{4}y = 1$

8. (a) $5y + 15 = 0$

(b) $\frac{1}{5}y = 0$

9. (a) $3x + 6 = 0$

(b) $2x = 0$

10. (a) $2x - \frac{1}{3}y = 0$

(b) $2x + 3y = 0$

---

11. (a) Graph each of the following equations on the same coordinate system.

$$y = 2x + 4, \quad y = 2x, \quad y = 2x - 3$$

(b) What do the three graphs in part (a) have in common?

(c) What do the three equations in part (a) have in common?

12. (a) Graph each of the following equations on the same coordinate system.

$$y = 2x + 4, \quad y = 4, \quad y = -x + 4, \quad y = \frac{1}{3}x + 4$$

(b) What do the four graphs in part (a) have in common?

(c) What do the four equations in part (a) have in common?

Find the slope and write an equation of the line through

13. $(-6, 5)$, $(-7, -2)$.   **14.** $(3, 1)$, $(7, -3)$.

Draw the line through the given point with the given slope m, and write an equation of the line.

15. $(-3, -2)$, $m = -\frac{1}{3}$

16. $(0, 4)$, $m = -\frac{2}{3}$

17. $(-2, 3)$, $m = 0$

18. $(4, 5)$, m undefined

19. Through the given point, draw the line with the given slope m.

(a) $(1, -3)$, $m = \frac{1}{2}$ (b) $(1, -3)$, $m = -2$

Write an equation for each of the lines graphed below.

20.

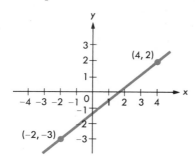

21.

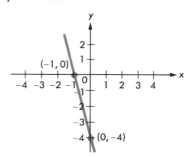

22.

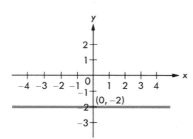

23.

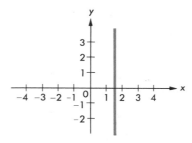

24.

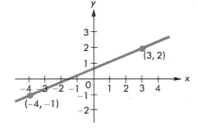

25.

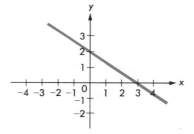

26. Show that three points

$$(4, 0), \ (8, -5), \ (0, 5)$$

are collinear (lie on the same line) by showing that the slope of the line drawn between any two of them is the same as the slope of the line drawn between any other two of them.

27. Are the following sets of points collinear? Why?

(a) $(2, -5)$, $(4, 0)$, $(7, 6)$

(b) $(0, 2)$, $(3, 0)$, $(1, 1)$

28. (a) Graph each of the following equations on the same set of axes.

$$\frac{x}{2} + \frac{y}{3} = 1, \quad \frac{x}{4} + \frac{y}{-6} = 1, \quad \frac{x}{-3} + \frac{y}{5} = 1$$

(b) Tell at what point each line graphed in part (a) cuts the x-axis and at what point it cuts the y-axis. Do the equations make these intercepts obvious?

(c) Give the x- and the y-intercept for the line with equation

$$\frac{x}{a} + \frac{y}{b} = 1.$$

(d) Write an equation of the line with x-intercept -2 and y-intercept 2.

---

29. (a) Graph $y = 3x - 1$ and $x = 3y - 1$ on the same cartesian coordinate system.

(b) How do you think the graphs of $y = rx + s$ and $x = ry + s$ will compare? In other words, find the slope and the y-intercept of the graph of each equation.

30. The equation $y = mx - 1$ represents a *family of lines*. Each value given m corresponds to a particular member of the family.

(a) Graph the member for which $m = 2$ (that is, $y = 2x - 1$).

(b) Graph the member for which $m = 3$.

(c) What do the members of the family of lines which have the equation $y = mx - 1$ have in common?

31. The equation $y = -x + b$ represents a *family of lines*. Each value given b corresponds to a particular member of the family.

(a) Graph the member for which $b = 2$ (that is, $y = -x + 2$).

(b) Graph the member for which $b = -2$.

(c) What do the members of the family of lines which have the equation $y = -x + b$ have in common? In what way do the members of this family differ?

32. (a) Draw three members of the family of lines represented by the equation

$$y + 1 = m(x + 1),$$

giving m the values -2, 4, and 0 in turn.

(b) Describe the family of lines which have the equation $y + 1 = m(x + 1)$, telling in what way they are alike and in what way different.

33. (a) Write an equation of the line with a slope of $\frac{1}{2}$ and a y-intercept of 3.

(b) Write an equation for the family of lines with a slope of $\frac{1}{2}$.

(c) Write an equation of the line passing through $(2, 3)$ with a slope of $\frac{1}{2}$.

34. Write an equation of a family or set of lines with slope $\frac{3}{4}$. Write an equation of the line in this set that passes through the point $(-5, 2)$.

35. Write an equation of a family or set of lines with y-intercept -5.

2-6 INEQUALITIES IN TWO VARIABLES

If two linear forms in x and y are connected by one of the order relations, the resulting statement is called a *first-degree inequality,* or *linear inequality,* in x and y. The solution set and graph of a linear inequality are defined as they were for a linear equation. To solve a linear inequality, we try to find an equivalent linear inequality with an obvious solution set.

Problem 1. Discuss the solution set and draw the graph of the inequality

$$2x - 2y + 9 > 3x - 3y + 8.$$

Solution. By adding $-2x + 3y - 9$ to each side of the given inequality, we obtain the equivalent inequality

$$y > x - 1.$$

Hence, the solution set of the given inequality is

$$\{(x, y) \mid y > x - 1\}.$$

To see what the graph of the inequality $y > x - 1$ is, sketch the graph of the *related equation* $y = x - 1$. The graph of this equation is the line L with slope $m = 1$ and y-intercept $b = -1$ shown in Fig. 2–10.

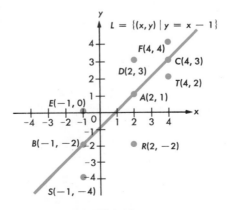

FIGURE 2–10

Any line divides a plane into three sets of points, those on the line and those on either side of the line. A point (x, y) is *on* the line L if, and only if, $y = x - 1$.

Thus,

> A (2, 1) is on L, since $1 = 2 - 1$;
> B (−1, −2) is on L, since $-2 = -1 - 1$;
> C (4, 3) is on L, since $3 = 4 - 1$.

A point (x, y) is *above* the line L if, and only if, $y > x - 1$.

Thus,

> D (2, 3) is above L, since $3 > 2 - 1$;
> E (−1, 0) is above L, since $0 > -1 - 1$;
> F (4, 4) is above L, since $4 > 4 - 1$.

Hence, the graph of the inequality $y > x - 1$ is the entire set of points *above* the line L. A portion of the graph is the shaded region in Fig. 2–11. Such a region is called a *half-plane*. The line L in the figure is broken to indicate that it is not part of the graph.

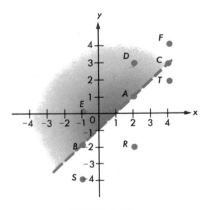

FIGURE 2–11

A point (x, y) is *below* the line L if, and only if, $y < x - 1$.

Thus,

> R (2, −2) is below L, since $-2 < 2 - 1$;
> S (−1, −4) is below L, since $-4 < -1 - 1$;
> T (4, 2) is below L, since $2 < 4 - 1$.

Hence, the graph of the inequality $y < x - 1$ is the half-plane below the line L. This region is infinite in extent. A portion of it is shaded in Fig. 2–12.

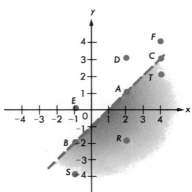

FIGURE 2-12

Problem 2. Discuss the solution set and draw the graph of the inequality

$$x - 2y - 3 < 0.$$

Solution. Upon adding $2y + 3$ to each side of the given inequality, we obtain the equivalent inequality

$$x < 2y + 3.$$

Hence,

$$\{(x, y) \mid x < 2y + 3\}$$

is the solution set of the given inequality.

To graph the inequality $x < 2y + 3$, first graph the related equation $x = 2y + 3$. The graph of $x = 2y + 3$ is the line K with slope $m = \frac{1}{2}$ and y-intercept $b = -\frac{3}{2}$ shown in Figure 2–13.

A point (x, y) is on K if, and only if, $x = 2y + 3$. For example, $A(5, 1)$ and $B(-1, -2)$ are on K.

A point (x, y) is *to the left* of K if, and only if, $x < 2y + 3$. For example,

C (2, 1) is to the left of K, since $2 < 2 \cdot 1 + 3$;
D (−3, −2) is to the left of K, since $-3 < 2 \cdot (-2) + 3$.

In other words, the graph of the inequality $x < 2y + 3$ is the half-plane to the left of K, a portion of which is shaded in Figure 2–13.

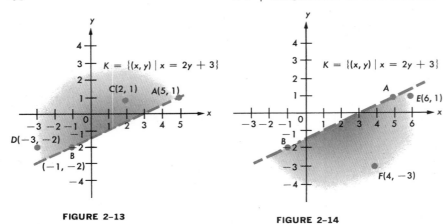

FIGURE 2–13   FIGURE 2–14

Similarly, you should see that the graph of the inequality $x > 2y + 3$ is the half-plane to the right of K, indicated in Figure 2–14.

Problem 3. Discuss the solution set and draw the graph of the inequality

$$2x + 3 \geq 0.$$

Solution. Since the given inequality is equivalent to the inequality

$$x \geq -\tfrac{3}{2},$$

the solution set is given by

$$\{(x, y) \mid x \geq -\tfrac{3}{2}\}.$$

Clearly, the graph of this set is the shaded *half-plane and its edge,* as shown in Fig. 2–15. The line $x = -\tfrac{3}{2}$ is solid to indicate that it is part of the graph of the inequality.

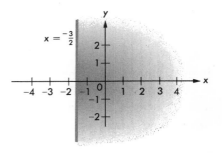

FIGURE 2–15

Exercises

Draw the graph of each inequality. If possible, give the slope and y-intercept of the line bounding each region.

1. (a) $y > 3$ (b) $y \leq 1$
2. (a) $x < -2$ (b) $x \geq 0$
3. (a) $y > -x + 2$ (b) $y < \tfrac{5}{2}x - 2$
4. (a) $x \geq y + 2$ (b) $x < -y + 2$

Find the solution set of each inequality and draw the graph.

5. (a) $2x + y - 1 < 2y - x + 1$

    (b) $3x + 2y - 2 \leqq x - y - 8$

6. (a) $\dfrac{x}{2} - \dfrac{1}{3} \geqq \dfrac{x}{3} - y$

    (b) $\dfrac{x}{2} - 1 > \dfrac{y}{4} + \dfrac{x}{5}$

7. (a) $2x + 1 - y > x + 2y + 1$

    (b) $x + 1 < \frac{1}{2}(y + x + 1)$

Find an inequality whose solution set has the given graph. (Hint: First obtain an equation of the bounding line.)

8.

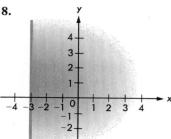

9.

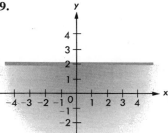

10.

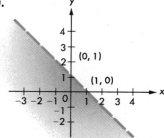

11.

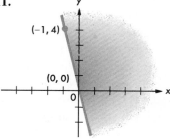

12. (a) Graph the inequality

$$y > -3x + 4.$$

   (b) Which of the ordered pairs

$$(-1, \tfrac{1}{2}), \ (-1, 1), \ (-1, 2), \ (2, -1), \ (2, -2), \ (2, -3)$$

   are elements of the solution set of the inequality $y > -3x + 4$?

   (c) Which of the points in 10(b) are above and which are below the line $y = -3x + 4$?

13. (a) Graph the inequality

$$x < 2y + 3.$$

(b) Tell which of the points

$$(3, 0), \quad (2, 0), \quad (\tfrac{7}{2}, 0), \quad (6, 1), \quad (5, 1),$$
$$(4, 1), \quad (0, -2), \quad (-2, -2), \quad (-1, -2)$$

lie to the left of the line $x = 2y + 3$.

14. (a) Give the slope and y-intercept of the line bounding the graph of $y < 2x - 3$.
(b) Draw the graph of $y < 2x - 3$.
(c) Does the inequality $y < 2x - 3$, with $x > 0$ and $y < 0$, have a solution in which both variables are integers?

15. If $(-1, b)$ is in the solution set of $x \geq -3y + 6$, what is the smallest integral value possible for b?

16. Find a pair of positive integers a and b such that (a, b) is in the solution set of $x \geq -3y + 6$ and $a + b$ has the smallest possible value.

2-7 SYSTEMS OF EQUATIONS IN TWO VARIABLES

Suppose we are asked how many boys and how many girls there are in a certain algebra class. Can we answer the question if all we know is that the total class size is 32? This is a problem involving two variables, say x boys and y girls, which our information says are related by the first-degree equation $x + y = 32$. Clearly, from this equation above we can only say that if $x = 15$, then $y = 17$; if $x = 20$, then $y = 12$, and so on. No single answer can be decided upon, and yet there is only one answer to the question "How many boys are in the algebra class?" With more information perhaps we can find a unique answer. For instance, suppose we learn that there are four more boys, than girls. This tells us x and y are also related by another first-degree equation,

$$x = y + 4,$$

from which we conclude that if $y = 12$, then $x = 16$ and if $y = 17$, then $x = 21$; once again we have an infinite set of choices.

The single answer we seek can be found by solving the system of first-degree equations

$$\begin{cases} x + y = 32, \\ \quad\; x = y + 4. \end{cases}$$

The graphs of these two first-degree equations are nonparallel lines, and their point of intersection is the graph of the unique solution of the problem.

In Figure 2-16,

$$S = \{(x, y) \mid x + y = 32\},$$
$$T = \{(x, y) \mid x = y + 4\},$$

and $S \cap T$ consists of the point $P(18, 14)$.   Hence, if $x = 18$ and $y = 14$, both statements

$$\begin{cases} x + y = 32, \\ \qquad x = y + 4, \end{cases}$$

are true. We now know there are 18 boys and 14 girls in the class of 32 having four more boys than girls.

An ordered pair is a *solution* of a system of equations in x and y if it is a solution of *every* equation of the system. The set of all solutions of the system is again called the *solution set* of the system. Knowing the solution set of each equation of the system, we find the solution set of the system to be the *intersection* of the solution sets of the individual equations.

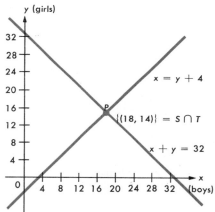

FIGURE 2-16

Problem 1. Solve the system of equations

$$\begin{cases} \qquad x = 3, \\ 7x + 9y = -15. \end{cases}$$

Solution. The solution set is given by

$$\{(x, y) \mid x = 3\} \cap \{(x, y) \mid 7x + 9y = -15\}.$$

All elements of the first set are ordered pairs of the form $(3, y)$, and therefore, the intersection contains ordered pairs of this form. However, the ordered pair $(3, y)$ is in the second set if, and only if,

$$(7 \cdot 3) + 9y = -15.$$

We solve this first-degree equation in one variable as follows:

$$21 + 9y = -15,$$
$$9y = -36,$$
$$y = -4.$$

Hence,

$$\{(3, -4)\}$$

is the solution set of the given system. The graphs of the equations of the system and of the solution set of the system are shown in Fig. 2–17.

Check. $\qquad 3 \overset{\vee}{=} 3 \qquad (7 \cdot 3) + [9 \cdot (-4)] \overset{?}{=} -15$
$$21 - 36 \overset{\vee}{=} -15$$

We solve a system of two first-degree equations in two variables by reducing the system to an equivalent system of the type in Problem 1. Two systems are said to be *equivalent systems* if they have the same solution set. You probably learned several methods of reducing a system of equations in your previous algebra course. A very effective way is the *substitution method,* which we shall use in the next problem.

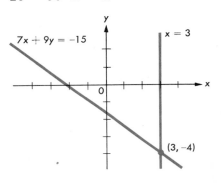

FIGURE 2–17

Problem 2. Solve the system of equations

$$\begin{cases} 3x - 2y = 19, \\ x + y = 23. \end{cases} \qquad (1)$$

Solution. System (1) is equivalent to system (2) by the additive axiom.

$$\begin{cases} 3x - 2y = 19 \\ \qquad y = 23 - x \end{cases} \qquad (2)$$

Since (x, y) is a solution of the second equation of (2) if, and only if, $y = 23 - x$, then (x, y) is a solution of both equations of (2) if, and only if, $y = 23 - x$ and $3x - 2(23 - x) = 19$. In other words, (2) is equivalent to the system

$$\begin{cases} 3x - 2(23 - x) = 19, \\ \qquad\qquad y = 23 - x. \end{cases} \qquad (3)$$

The first equation of (3) is equivalent to each of the following equations:

$$3x - 46 + 2x = 19,$$
$$5x = 65,$$
$$x = 13.$$

Therefore, (3) is equivalent to the system

$$\begin{cases} x = 13, \\ y = 23 - x. \end{cases} \tag{4}$$

The only solution of (4) is (13, 10). Hence,

$$\{(13, 10)\}$$

is the solution set of (1), the given system.

Check. $\qquad\qquad (3 \cdot 13) - (2 \vdots 10) \overset{?}{=} 19$
$$39 - 20 \overset{\vee}{=} 19$$

$$13 + 10 \overset{\vee}{=} 23$$

A linear equation in x and y has a straight line graph. Two linear equations in x and y have two straight line graphs. This pair of lines may be parallel, having no point in common, so that the system of equations has an empty solution set. Such equations are called *inconsistent.* See Fig. 2–18.

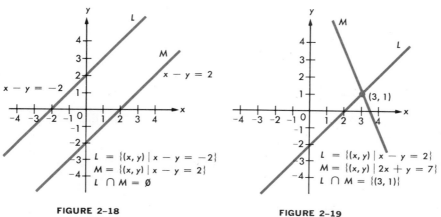

L = {(x, y) | x − y = −2}
M = {(x, y) | x − y = 2}
L ∩ M = ∅

FIGURE 2–18

L = {(x, y) | x − y = 2}
M = {(x, y) | 2x + y = 7}
L ∩ M = {(3, 1)}

FIGURE 2–19

If the pair of lines intersect in one point, the solution set of the system has exactly one member, an ordered number pair. Such equations are called *independent* and *consistent.* See Fig. 2–19.

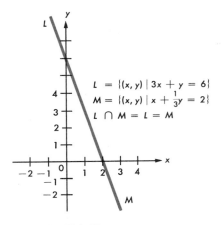

$$L = \{(x, y) \mid 3x + y = 6\}$$
$$M = \{(x, y) \mid x + \tfrac{1}{3}y = 2\}$$
$$L \cap M = L = M$$

FIGURE 2-20

If the graphs of the two equations coincide, then the solution set of the system is infinite. Such equations are called *dependent* but *consistent*. See Fig. 2–20.

Exercises

Graph each equation in the following systems, and from your graph, find the solution set of each system.

1. (a) $\begin{cases} x - 3 = 0 \\ y - 4 = 0 \end{cases}$ (b) $\begin{cases} 2x + 5 = 0 \\ 3y + 6 = 0 \end{cases}$

2. (a) $\begin{cases} y = x \\ y + 2 = 0 \end{cases}$ (b) $\begin{cases} x + y = 0 \\ x + 3 = 0 \end{cases}$

3. (a) $\begin{cases} 2x + y = 1 \\ y - x = 4 \end{cases}$ (b) $\begin{cases} 2x - y + 6 = 0 \\ y + 2x = 0 \end{cases}$

Graph the systems, and tell if each system is dependent, independent, or inconsistent.

4. $\begin{cases} 3x - y = 6 \\ y = 3x + 2 \end{cases}$ 5. $\begin{cases} x - y - 1 = 0 \\ x - y + 2 = 0 \end{cases}$

6. $\begin{cases} -2x + 2y - 2 = 0 \\ x - y + 1 = 0 \end{cases}$ 7. $\begin{cases} 2x - 3y = 12 \\ 4 + y = \tfrac{2}{3}x \end{cases}$

8. $\begin{cases} x - y - 1 = 0 \\ 2x + y + 4 = 0 \end{cases}$ 9. $\begin{cases} y - 2x = 4 \\ 2x + y + 2 = 0 \end{cases}$

Use the substitution method to solve each of the following systems.

10. $\begin{cases} x + 2y = 8 \\ x = 10 - 4y \end{cases}$ 11. $\begin{cases} p = 5 + 4q \\ 3p + 2q = 17 \end{cases}$

12. $\begin{cases} x - y = 4 \\ 3x + 4y = 12 \end{cases}$ **13.** $\begin{cases} 4x - y = 3 \\ 2x + 7y = 9 \end{cases}$

14. $\begin{cases} y + x = 3 \\ 3x - y = 1 \end{cases}$ **15.** $\begin{cases} y - x = 5 \\ 4x - y = 10 \end{cases}$

16. $\begin{cases} u - 2v = 12 \\ v = 7u + 6 \end{cases}$ **17.** $\begin{cases} u - (v - 2) = 2 \\ v = 2u \end{cases}$

---

18. Try to solve the system

$$\begin{cases} 2x + 3y - 5 = 0, \\ 2x + 3y + 10 = 0 \end{cases}$$

(a) by the substitution method.
(b) by graphing.
(c) Explain what happend in part (a).

19. (a) Graph the system

$$\begin{cases} 2x + 3y + 1 = 0, \\ 2kx + 3ky + k = 0. \end{cases}$$
$$(k = 1, 2, 3, \ldots)$$

(b) Try to solve the system by substitution and explain what happens.

2-8   MORE ON SYSTEMS OF EQUATIONS

Before solving more systems of linear equations, let us make some general observations about equivalent systems. In the first place, two systems are equivalent if each equation of one system is equivalent to the corresponding equation of the other system. For example, the two systems

$$\begin{cases} 4x + y - 7 = 0, \\ 2x + 3y = 5 \end{cases} \quad \text{and} \quad \begin{cases} y = 7 - 4x, \\ 3y = 5 - 2x \end{cases}$$

are equivalent, because the first equations of each system are equivalent and the second equations are also equivalent.

Next, if a system has the form

$$\begin{cases} F_1 = G_1, \\ F_2 = G_2 \end{cases} \tag{1}$$

where F_1, G_1, F_2, and G_2 designate linear forms in x and y, then

$$\begin{cases} F_1 = G_1, \\ F_1 + F_2 = G_1 + G_2 \end{cases} \tag{2}$$

is an equivalent system. To see this, let L_1 and R_1 be the respective values of F_1 and G_1, and let L_2 and R_2 be the respective values of F_2 and G_2 when $x = a$ and $y = b$.

If (a, b) is a solution of system (1), so that

$$\begin{cases} L_1 = R_1, \\ L_2 = R_2 \end{cases}$$

are true equations, then

$$\begin{cases} L_1 = R_1, \\ L_1 + L_2 = R_1 + R_2 \end{cases}$$

are also true by the additive property of equals. Hence, (a, b) is a solution of system (2).

Conversely, if (a, b) is a solution of system (2), so that the two equations

$$\begin{cases} L_1 = R_1, \\ L_1 + L_2 = R_1 + R_2 \end{cases}$$

are true, then

$$\begin{cases} L_1 = R_1, \\ (L_1 + L_2) - L_1 = (R_1 + R_2) - R_1, \end{cases}$$

or

$$\begin{cases} L_1 = R_1, \\ L_2 = R_2, \end{cases}$$

are also true by the additive property of equals. Hence, (a, b) is also a solution of system (1). We conclude that systems (1) and (2) are equivalent.

The method described above for finding equivalent systems of equations is called the *addition method*. We illustrate its use in the following problems.

Problem 1. Solve the system of equations

$$\begin{cases} x - 2y = 13, \qquad & (L_1 = R_1) \\ 5x + 2y = 5. \qquad & (L_2 = R_2) \end{cases} \tag{1}$$

Solution. Note that the coefficients of y are negatives of each other in the two equations of (1). The first equation of system (2),

$$\begin{cases} x - 2y = 13, \qquad & (L_1 = R_1) \\ (x - 2y) + (5x + 2y) = 13 + 5, \qquad & (L_1 + L_2 = R_1 + R_2) \end{cases} \tag{2}$$

is the same as the first equation of (1), while the second equation of (2) is obtained from (1) by adding the corresponding sides of the two equations of (1). Hence, (2) is equivalent to (1) by the addition method described above. On simplifying the second equation of (2), we obtain the equivalent system

$$\begin{cases} x - 2y = 13, \\ 6x = 18. \end{cases} \tag{3}$$

Thus, $x = 3$ by the second equation, and

$$3 - 2y = 13, \quad -2y = 10, \quad y = -5$$

from the first equation. Hence,

$$\{(3, -5)\}$$

is the solution set of the given system.

Check.
$$3 - [2 \cdot (-5)] \overset{?}{=} 13$$
$$3 + 10 \overset{\checkmark}{=} 13$$

$$(5 \cdot 3) + [2 \cdot (-5)] \overset{?}{=} 5$$
$$15 + (-10) \overset{\checkmark}{=} 5$$

Problem 2. Solve the system of equations

$$\begin{cases} 2x - 5y = -6, & (L_1 = R_1) \\ 3x + 2y = 29. & (L_2 = R_2) \end{cases} \tag{1}$$

Solution. The coefficients of x (2 and 3) are not negatives of each other. The coefficients of y (-5 and 2) are not negatives. Hence, adding corresponding sides of the two equations would not eliminate either variable. If we decide to eliminate y, we can multiply each side of the first equation by 2 and each side of the second equation by 5, obtaining an equivalent system with the coefficients of y being additive inverses, -10 and 10. Thus,

$$\begin{cases} 4x - 10y = -12, & (2L_1 = 2R_1) \\ 15x + 10y = 145. & (5L_2 = 5R_2) \end{cases} \tag{2}$$

By the addition method, the system

$$\begin{cases} 4x - 10y = -12, & (2L_1 = 2R_1) \\ 19x = 133 & (2L_1 + 5L_2 = 2R_1 + 5R_2) \end{cases} \tag{3}$$

is equivalent to (2). From the second equation of (3), $x = 7$, and hence, from the first equation of (3),

$$(4 \cdot 7) - 10y = -12,$$
$$-10y = -40,$$
$$y = 4.$$

Therefore,

$$\{(7, 4)\}$$

is the solution set of system (1).

Check.

$$(2 \cdot 7) - (5 \cdot 4) \overset{?}{=} -6$$
$$14 - 20 \overset{\checkmark}{=} -6$$

$$(3 \cdot 7) + (2 \cdot 4) \overset{?}{=} 29$$
$$21 + 8 \overset{\checkmark}{=} 29$$

Exercises

Solve the given system of equations by the addition method and check each solution.

1. (a) $\begin{cases} 4x + y = 17 \\ 3x - y = 4 \end{cases}$ (b) $\begin{cases} x - 2y = 3 \\ x + 2y = -5 \end{cases}$

2. (a) $\begin{cases} 3x - y = 5 \\ 4x - y = 7 \end{cases}$ (b) $\begin{cases} 2x - y = 16 \\ x - y = 7 \end{cases}$

3. (a) $\begin{cases} 3m - 2n = -10 \\ 4m + n = 49 \end{cases}$ (b) $\begin{cases} u - v = -1 \\ 10u - 8v = -7 \end{cases}$

Start with the system of equations

$$\begin{cases} 2x - 5y = 9, \\ 3x + 4y = 8, \end{cases}$$

and write an equivalent system in which

4. (a) the coefficients of x are the same.
   (b) the coefficients of x are negatives, or additive inverses, of each other.
5. (a) the coefficients of y are negatives, or additive inverses, of each other.
   (b) the coefficients of y are the same.

Solve each system of equations by the addition method, and check each solution.

6. (a) $\begin{cases} 2x - 5y = 9 \\ 3x + 4y = 25 \end{cases}$ (b) $\begin{cases} x + 2y = 14 \\ 4x - 5y = 43 \end{cases}$

7. (a) $\begin{cases} y + 2x - 4 = 0 \\ \frac{5}{2}y = 13x + 10 \end{cases}$

(b) $\begin{cases} \frac{2}{7}x + \frac{1}{8}y = 0 \\ \frac{3}{4}x - \frac{1}{3}y = 0 \end{cases}$

8. (a) $\begin{cases} x + 3y = 11 \\ x - y = 17 \end{cases}$

(b) $\begin{cases} 8p + 4q = 3 \\ 2p - 8q = -3.75 \end{cases}$

Use any method to solve each of the following systems of equations.

9. (a) $\begin{cases} p + 3(1 - q) = 0 \\ 3q - 2(6 - p) = 0 \end{cases}$

(b) $\begin{cases} \dfrac{x + y}{4} + \dfrac{x - y}{2} = 1 \\ \dfrac{3x - y}{4} + \dfrac{4x + 2y}{11} = 3 \end{cases}$

10. (a) $\begin{cases} 3x - y = 6 + x + 2y \\ 3(y - 2) = 2(x + 1) - 10 \end{cases}$

(b) $\begin{cases} 2p + q + 14 = 7(p - 4q + 2) \\ 3(2p - 3q + 4) = 5p + 12 \end{cases}$

11. (a) $\begin{cases} x + 2y - 1 = \dfrac{x + y}{5} \\ 2x - y = \dfrac{5 - 2x}{6} \end{cases}$

(b) $\begin{cases} .07n - .04m = .01 \\ .2n - .05m = .035 \end{cases}$

12. Try to solve the system of equations

$$\begin{cases} 5x + 2y = 10, \\ 3 - 5x = 2y \end{cases}$$

by the addition method. What is your conclusion about the solution set of this system? What can you say about the graphs of these two equations?

Review for Sections 2–5 through 2–8

Find the slope for each of the following lines.
1. $y + 3x = 2$
2. $2y + 3 = 5x$
3. $3y = 3x + 4$
4. $4y + x - 7 = 0$
5. The line through $(2, 3)$ and $(-2, 2)$
6. The line through $(1, 4)$ and $(5, -3)$

Graph each of the linear equations and inequalities on separate cartesian coordinate systems.

7. $2x + 3y = 6$

8. $y > 6x + 1$

9. $2y \leq 4x + 6$

10. $3y = 2x + 6$

11. $3y + x < 0$

12. $3x + 2y - 1 = 2x + y$

Write an equation for the lines passing through the following points.

13. $(0, 4)$ and $(2, -3)$

14. $(5, 2)$ and $(-3, -3)$

15. $(2, 4)$ and $(-3, 5)$

If possible, solve each of the following linear systems using any of the methods presented. Tell which, if any, are inconsistent.

16. $\begin{cases} 3y + 2x = 6 \\ 3y - 2x = 6 \end{cases}$

17. $\begin{cases} 5y - 3x = 2 \\ 2y + x = 1 \end{cases}$

18. $\begin{cases} 2y + 3x = 5 \\ 4y + 6x = 7 \end{cases}$

19. $\begin{cases} 4y - 2x + 6 = 0 \\ 5y + x - 3 = 0 \end{cases}$

Answers to Review for Sections 2-5 through 2-8

1. $m = -3$ **2.** $m = \frac{5}{2}$ **3.** $m = 1$

4. $m = -\frac{1}{4}$ **5.** $m = \frac{1}{4}$ **6.** $m = -\frac{7}{4}$

7.

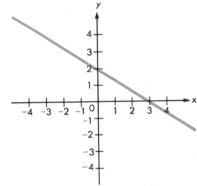

8.

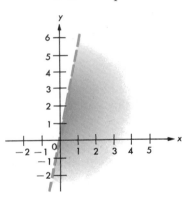

9.

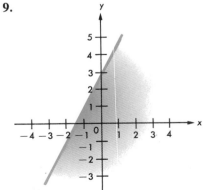

10.

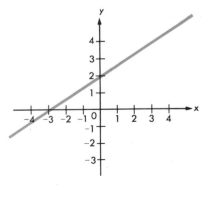

11.

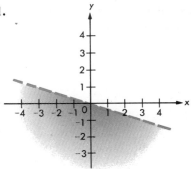

12.

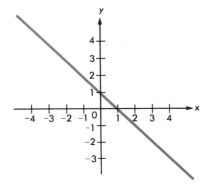

13. $2y = -7x + 8$

14. $8y = 5x - 9$

15. $5y = -x + 22$

16. $\{(0, 2)\}$

17. $\{(\frac{1}{11}, \frac{5}{11})\}$

18. Inconsistent

19. $\{(3, 0)\}$

2–9　APPLICATIONS

We can solve many word problems by writing and solving systems of linear equations. Consider, for example, the following problems.

Problem 1. A football game was attended by 4730 people, some paying $1.50 each for reserved seats and the rest paying 90¢ each for general admission. If the total receipts for the game were $5172, how many tickets of each kind were sold?

Solution. Let r designate the number of reserved-seat tickets and g the number of general-admission tickets sold. Since 4730 tickets were sold,

$$r + g = 4730.$$

The amount of money, in dollars, received from the sale of reserved-seat tickets was $1.50r$; that received from the sale of general-admission tickets was $.90g$. Since the total receipts were $5172,

$$1.50r + .90g = 5172.$$

Thus, the solution of the given problem is the solution of the system of equations

$$\begin{cases} r + g = 4730, \\ 1.50r + .90g = 5172. \end{cases} \tag{1}$$

Let us use the substitution method to solve system (1). If we solve the first equation for g in terms of r and substitute the result in the second equation, we obtain the equivalent system

$$\begin{cases} r + g = 4730, \\ 1.50r + .90(4730 - r) = 5172. \end{cases} \qquad (2)$$

The second equation of (2) may be simplified as follows:

$$\begin{aligned} 1.50r + 4257 - .90r &= 5172, \\ .60r &= 915, \\ r &= 1525. \end{aligned}$$

Thus, system (2) is equivalent to the system

$$\begin{cases} r + g = 4730, \\ r = 1525. \end{cases} \qquad (3)$$

System (3) is easily solved, yielding

$$r = 1525, \quad g = 3205.$$

Check. $1525 + 3205 \overset{\vee}{=} 4730$ $(1.50 \cdot 1525) + (.90 \cdot 3205) \overset{?}{=} 5172$

$2287.50 + 2884.50 \overset{\vee}{=} 5172$

Problem 2. An airplane carries enough gas for 10 hours of flight. Suppose that its speed in still air is 530 miles per hour. If it flies against a wind of 30 miles per hour on its outbound trip and with a wind of 30 miles per hour on the return trip, how far can it fly without refueling?

Solution. The speed of the outbound plane is $530 - 30$, or 500, miles per hour, and the speed on the return flight is $530 + 30$, or 560, miles per hour. Let x denote the distance, in miles, the plane travels from its base, and t the time, in hours, it takes for the outbound journey. Since the product of rate and time is distance, our first equation is

$$500t = x.$$

Our second equation relating x and t describes the return flight. Since the total time of the flight is 10 hours, and the flight out takes t hours, the flight back takes $10 - t$ hours. We have found that the speed on the return trip was 560 miles per hour and since the distance out is the same as the distance back, the equation

$$560(10 - t) = x$$

describes the flight back.

'The solution of the given problem is the same as the solution of the system of equations

$$\begin{cases} 500t = x, \\ 560(10 - t) = x. \end{cases}$$

You may easily verify that the following system is equivalent to the one above.

$$\begin{cases} 500t = x \\ t = \frac{280}{53} \end{cases}$$

Hence, the solution is

$$t = \frac{280}{53}, \quad x = \frac{140{,}000}{53}.$$

Thus, the airplane can fly approximately 2640 miles from its base and return without refueling. Does this answer check?

Exercises

1. How far can the airplane of Problem 2 fly without refueling
   (a) if there is no wind during the 10-hour flight?
   (b) if there is a wind of 50 miles per hour?

2. (a) Find two integers whose sum is 55 and whose difference is 9.
   (b) Find two numbers whose difference is 16 and whose sum is 73.

3. (a) A sum of money amounting to \$4.15 consists of dimes and quarters. If there are 19 coins in all, how many quarters are there?
   (b) John's bank contains some quarters and 3 times as many dimes as nickels. If there are 26 coins totaling \$3.90 in the bank, how many of each kind of coin does the bank contain?

4. (a) The initial investments of two partners in a business were \$50,000 and \$70,000. The partners agree to divide profits in the same ratio as their relative investments. How much does each partner receive if the first year's profits amount to \$15,000?
   (b) A jet plane makes a 3000-mile trip to Europe in 5 hours, but takes 6 hours for the return trip. If the speed of the wind is constant throughout the trip, what is the speed of the wind and what is the average speed of the plane in still air?

5. (a) State the conditions on the integers d and s, given that there are two integers whose difference is d and whose sum is s.
   (b) The sum of the digits of a two-digit number is one-half the number. Show that this property characterizes the number completely because there is one, and only one, number with this property. (Hint: Recall

that in our decimal system an expression for the two-digit number with tens' digit, t, and units' digit, u, is $10t + u$.)

6. (a) The sum of the digits of a two-digit number is one-seventh the number. Find all numbers having this property.

   (b) Divide 240 into two parts such that the ratio of the larger to the smaller part is 17 : 13. (Hint: The equation $x/y = 17/13$, or the equivalent linear equation $13x = 17y$, may be used to express the fact that x and y are in the ratio 17 : 13.)

7. (a) A linear form

$$ax + by$$

   is known to have value 21 when $x = 3$ and $y = 2$, and to have value 65 when $x = 7$ and $y = 10$. Find the coefficients a and b of this linear form.

   (b) A linear form

$$ax + by$$

   is known to have value 2 when $x = 5$ and $y = 9$, and to have value 15 when $x = 3$ and $y = 10$. Find the coefficients a and b of this linear form.

---

8. Two machines A and B produce items at the constant rate of 50 and 40 items per hour, respectively. An order for 1000 items is to be filled.

   (a) If the total number of machine-hours of operation used is exactly 24, show that to fill the order, there is one, and only one, way of assigning a number of hours of operation to each machine.

   (b) If it costs $10 per hour to operate machine A and $7 per hour to operate machine B, what is the total cost of the production that satisfies the specifications in part (a)?

   (c) If the total number of machine-hours of operation used is to be *at most* 24 (instead of exactly 24), the entire order for 1000 items could be handled by machine A. Find the cost of production under such a scheme, and compare it with the cost of the production plan in part (a).

   (d) If the hourly costs are $10 for machine A and $9 for machine B, compare the production costs under the plan in part (a) with that of the plan in part (c).

---

9. A system of equations such as

$$\begin{cases} \dfrac{10}{x} + \dfrac{3}{y} = 1, \\[2mm] \dfrac{8}{x} + \dfrac{6}{y} = 1 \end{cases}$$

   (1)

is not linear in x and y. However, if we replace $\dfrac{1}{x}$ by a and $\dfrac{1}{y}$ by b the resulting system is linear in a and b.

$$\begin{cases} 10a + 3b = 1 \\ 8a + 6b = 1 \end{cases} \tag{2}$$

System (2) can be solved by the addition method (or by substitution) showing $a = \frac{1}{12}$, $b = \frac{1}{18}$. Since $a = \dfrac{1}{x}$, $b = \dfrac{1}{y}$, we see that $x = 12$, $y = 18$.

Use this method to solve the following systems of equations.

(a) $\begin{cases} \dfrac{8}{x} + \dfrac{4}{y} = 3 \\ \dfrac{2}{x} - \dfrac{8}{y} = -\dfrac{15}{4} \end{cases}$
   (b) $\begin{cases} \dfrac{1}{x} - \dfrac{1}{y} + 1 = 0 \\ \dfrac{10}{x} - \dfrac{8}{y} + 7 = 0 \end{cases}$

10. Find two numbers such that the reciprocal of the first added to 6 times the reciprocal of the second is 1, while the reciprocal of the second number added to twice the reciprocal of the first gives $\frac{5}{8}$.

11. Machines A and B each produce items at a constant rate characteristic of the particular machine. If A produces 400 items and B produces 600 items, a total of 23 machine-hours is spent. If A produces 600 and B produces 400 items, a total of 22 machine-hours is spent. Find each machine's rate.

12. Working together, Smith and Jones can finish a job in 4 days. Smith does twice as much work in 1 day as Jones does. How long would it take Smith working alone to do the job?

*13. A rifleman standing 1000 yards from his target hears the bullet strike 4 seconds after he fires. An observer 800 yards from the target and 550 yards from the rifleman hears the bullet strike 2 seconds after he hears the report of the rifle. Find the velocity of sound and the velocity of the bullet.

Preparation for Section 2–10

Graph each of the following pairs of inequalities on the same coordinate plane

1. $x + 1 > 5$, $y < 0$
2. $x > 6$, $y \leq 3$
3. $x - 3 \leq 7$, $y + 4 \geq 0$
4. $x \leq 0$, $y - 5 > 1$

2–10 SYSTEMS OF INEQUALITIES IN TWO VARIABLES

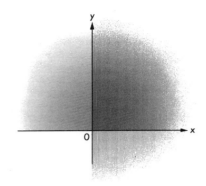

The solution set of a system of inequalities is the *intersection* of the solution sets of the individual inequalities of the system. For example, the system

$$\begin{cases} x > 0, \\ y > 0 \end{cases}$$

has as its solution the set of all number pairs (x, y) for which $x > 0$ and $y > 0$. In set notation, the solution set is given by

FIGURE 2–21

$$\{(x, y) \mid x > 0\} \cap \{(x, y) \mid y > 0\}.$$

The graph of this set is the set of all points in the first quadrant (the doubly shaded region of Fig. 2–21).

Problem 1. Describe the solution set and draw the graph of the system

$$\begin{cases} x - y - 2 < 0, \\ x + 2y - 8 > 0. \end{cases}$$

Solution. Each inequality of the system is simplified in the following way.

$$x - y - 2 < 0$$
$$(x - y - 2) + y < y$$
$$x - 2 < y, \quad \text{or } y > x - 2$$

$$x + 2y - 8 > 0$$
$$(x + 2y - 8) + (-x) + 8 > -x + 8$$
$$2y > -x + 8$$
$$y > -\tfrac{1}{2}x + 4$$

Thus, the given system is equivalent to the system

$$\begin{cases} y > x - 2, \\ y > -\tfrac{1}{2}x + 4, \end{cases}$$

and its solution set S is given by

$$S = \{(x, y) \mid y > x - 2\} \cap \{(x, y) \mid y > -\tfrac{1}{2}x + 4\}.$$

The line L of Fig. 2–22 is the graph of the equation $y = x - 2$. Therefore, the graph of the set $\{(x, y) \mid y > x - 2\}$ is the half-plane above L. In turn, the graph of the equation $y = -\frac{1}{2}x + 4$ is the line K of Fig. 2–22, and the graph of the set $\{(x, y) \mid y > -\frac{1}{2}x + 4\}$ is the half-plane above K. The intersection of these two half-planes is the graph of the solution set S. Thus, the graph of S is the doubly shaded region of Fig. 2–22. Such a region is called a *quarter-plane*.

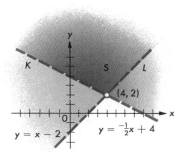

FIGURE 2–22

Problem 2. Describe the solution set and draw the graph of the system

$$\begin{cases} x - y - 2 < 0, \\ x + 2y - 8 > 0, \\ \qquad\quad y < 7. \end{cases}$$

Solution. The solution set T consists of all points (x, y) of set S (in Problem 1) for which $y < 7$, that is,

$$T = S \cap \{(x, y) \mid y < 7\}.$$

The graph of T is the set of all points *inside* the triangle ABC (the triply shaded region of Fig. 2–23).

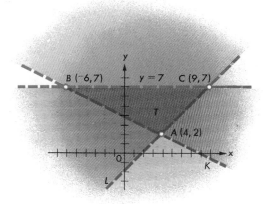

FIGURE 2–23

Problem 3. The shaded region of Fig. 2–24 lies between the two parallel lines with equations

$$x + y = 0,$$
$$x + y = 2.$$

Describe this shaded region as the graph of a system of inequalities.

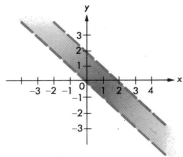

Solution. The shaded region is *above* the line with equation

$$x + y = 0, \quad \text{or } y = -x,$$

and *below* the line with equation

$$x + y = 2, \quad \text{or } y = -x + 2.$$

FIGURE 2-24

Thus, the shaded region is the graph of the set

$$\{(x, y) \mid y > -x\} \cap \{(x, y) \mid y < -x + 2\},$$

and hence of the system

$$\begin{cases} y > -x, \\ y < -x + 2. \end{cases}$$

Exercises

Describe the solution set and draw the graph of each of the following systems of inequalities.

1. (a) $\begin{cases} x < 0 \\ y < 0 \end{cases}$ (b) $\begin{cases} x \geq 0 \\ y \geq 0 \end{cases}$

2. (a) $\begin{cases} y < 2x \\ 2x + y < 12 \end{cases}$ (b) $\begin{cases} y > 3x \\ y < 5 - 3x \end{cases}$

3. (a) $\begin{cases} 2x + y > 3 \\ y < 5 - 2x \end{cases}$ (b) $\begin{cases} y < x + 2 \\ y > x - 4 \end{cases}$

4. (a) $\begin{cases} y < 2x \\ 2x + y < 12 \\ y > 2 \end{cases}$ (b) $\begin{cases} 3x + 4y \leq 12 \\ x \leq 4 \\ y \leq 3 \end{cases}$

Graph each of the following systems. In each case, list the positive integral solutions of the system.

5. (a) $\begin{cases} 3x + 4y \leq 12 \\ 4y \geq 3x \\ x \geq 0 \end{cases}$ (b) $\begin{cases} 50x + 40y \geq 1000 \\ x + y \leq 24 \\ y \geq 0 \end{cases}$

6. Give a system of inequalities for which the graph is the intersection of the half-planes below the graph of $x + y + 2 = 0$ and to the left of $2x - y = 4$. Draw the graph.

7. Give a system of inequalities for which the graph is the region which lies between the graphs of $x - 2y + 6 = 0$ and $x - 2y = 4$. Draw the graph.

Describe the region bounded by the graphs of each of the following systems of inequalities by giving its shape (triangle, pentagon, and so on) and the coordinates of the vertices of its boundary.

8. $\begin{cases} x > 0 \\ y > 0 \\ x < 5 \\ y < 7 \\ x + y \le 8 \end{cases}$

9. $\begin{cases} x \ge 3 \\ x \le 15 \\ y \ge 0 \\ y \le 22 \\ x + y \le 30 \end{cases}$

10. $\begin{cases} y \ge 0 \\ y \le 3 \\ 2y - x \le 0 \\ y \le 16 - 2x \end{cases}$

11. $\begin{cases} 2x + y \ge 8 \\ x + 3y \ge 9 \\ 3x + 4y \ge 22 \\ x \le 9 \\ y \le 8 \end{cases}$

12. $\begin{cases} .9x + .6y \ge 1 \\ .1x + .4y \ge .4 \\ x \le 4 \\ y \le \frac{5}{3} \end{cases}$

13. $\begin{cases} 2x + y + 9 \ge 0 \\ -x + 3y + 6 \ge 0 \\ x + 2y - 3 \le 0 \\ x + y \le 0 \end{cases}$

14. Give a system of inequalities for which the graph is the intersection of the half-planes above the graph of $3x + 2y = 12$ and below the graph of $2x - 3y + 18 = 0$. Draw the graph.

15. Given that

$$A = \{(x, y) \mid 2x - y \le 8\},$$
$$B = \{(x, y) \mid 2x + y \le 4\},$$
$$C = \{(x, y) \mid x \ge 0\},$$

draw the graph of each of the following.
(a) $A \cap B$ (b) $A \cap C$ (c) $B \cap C$ (d) $A \cap B \cap C$
(e) Describe the region $A \cap B \cap C$ by naming its shape and giving the coordinates of the vertices of its boundary.
(f) List all the points of $A \cap B \cap C$ with integral coordinates.

16. Graph the following system of inequalities, and list the positive integral solutions of the system. Where are the corners of the graph?

$$\begin{cases} 2x - y \le 6 \\ 2x + y \le 4 \\ x \ge 0 \end{cases}$$

17. Describe the solution set and draw the graph of the system

$$\begin{cases} 5x - 3y - 9 < 0, \\ 2x + 3y - 12 > 0. \end{cases}$$

Is there a point where y is least? Why?

---

18. The following table gives percentages of protein and fat contained in one gram of each of two foods.

	Protein	Fat
Bread	8%	1%
Butter	2%	80%

(a) Write a system of inequalities involving the two unknowns x and y (number of grams of bread and of butter, respectively) which expresses the fact that these two foods together are to supply daily at least 82 grams of protein and 90 grams of fat.

(b) Graph the solution set of your system in the region $x \geqq 0$ and $y \geqq 0$, and give the coordinates of the corner points.

(c) Give at least three solutions to the problem of meeting the daily minimum requirements of protein and fat.

2–11 SYSTEMS OF EQUATIONS IN THREE OR MORE VARIABLES

In modern applications of mathematics, systems of three or more first-degree equations in three or more variables are very common. It is not unusual for scientists working in economic theory to have to solve a system of fifty first-degree equations in fifty variables. Quite naturally, high-speed electronic computers are used to perform the necessary arithmetical operations. Let us look at some systems of first-degree equations in three variables.

Problem 1. Solve the system

$$\begin{cases} x - 5 = 0, \\ 3x - y - 8 = 0, \\ 7x + 4y + \frac{63}{11}z - 63 = 0. \end{cases}$$

Solution. Clearly, $x = 5$ from the first equation. Giving x the value 5 in the second equation, we see that

$$15 - y - 8 = 0,$$
$$y = 7.$$

Finally, giving x the value 5 and y the value 7 in the third equation, we get

$$35 + 28 + \tfrac{63}{11}z - 63 = 0,$$
$$\tfrac{63}{11}z = 0,$$
$$z = 0.$$

Thus, the ordered number triple $(5, 7, 0)$ is the solution of the given system.

Check. $5 - 5 \overset{\checkmark}{=} 0$ $(3 \cdot 5) - 7 - 8 \overset{\checkmark}{=} 0$
$$(7 \cdot 5) + (4 \cdot 7) + (\tfrac{63}{11} \cdot 0) - 63 \overset{?}{=} 0$$
$$35 + 28 - 63 \overset{\checkmark}{=} 0$$

The system of Problem 1 is easily solved, because only the variable x occurs in the first equation and only x and y occur in the second equation. Let us try to solve the system obtained in the following problem by changing it into an equivalent system of the type of Problem 1.

Problem 2. A steel company has three blast furnaces of varying sizes. If furnaces A, B, and C are used full time, 800 tons of steel are produced per day. If A and B are used half time and C full time, 545 tons are produced. If A is not used, B is used full time, and C half time, 410 tons are produced. How many tons per day does each furnace produce?

Solution. Let a, b, and c designate the number of tons of steel produced each day by furnaces A, B, and C, respectively, when they are used full time. Then the three given conditions yield the following system of equations.

$$\begin{cases} a + b + c = 800 & (1) \\ \tfrac{1}{2}a + \tfrac{1}{2}b + c = 545 & (2) \\ b + \tfrac{1}{2}c = 410 & (3) \end{cases}$$

An equivalent system is

$$\begin{cases} a + b + c = 800, & (1) \\ -a - b - 2c = -1090, & (2) \\ 2b + c = 820. & (3) \end{cases}$$

By the addition method, we see that the above system is equivalent to

$$\begin{cases} a + b + c = 800, & (1) \\ (a + b + c) + (-a - b - 2c) = 800 + (-1090), & (1) + (2) \\ 2b + c = 820, & (3) \end{cases}$$

or

$$\begin{cases} a + b + c = 800, \\ \quad\quad\quad -c = -290, \\ \quad\quad 2b + c = 820. \end{cases}$$

Thus, $c = 290$ from the second equation, and

$$2b + 290 = 820,$$
$$2b = 530,$$
$$b = 265$$

from the third equation. Hence,

$$a + 265 + 290 = 800,$$

or

$$a = 245$$

from the first equation.

We conclude that, working full time, furnace A produces 245 tons per day, B produces 265 tons, and C produces 290 tons.

Check.

$$245 + 265 + 290 \overset{\checkmark}{=} 800 \qquad (\tfrac{1}{2} \cdot 245) + (\tfrac{1}{2} \cdot 265) + 290 \overset{?}{=} 545$$
$$(\tfrac{1}{2} \cdot 510) + 290 \overset{?}{=} 545$$
$$255 + 290 \overset{\checkmark}{=} 545$$

$$265 + (\tfrac{1}{2} \cdot 290) \overset{?}{=} 410$$
$$265 + 145 \overset{\checkmark}{=} 410$$

Exercises

Solve each of the following systems of linear equations.

1. (a) $\begin{cases} x - 3y - 2z + 4 = 0 \\ 2x - 5y + 19 = 0 \\ x - 3 = 0 \end{cases}$ (b) $\begin{cases} 3x - 2y + 4z = 19 \\ 3y + z = -3 \\ z = 3 \end{cases}$

2. (a) $\begin{cases} 2x - y - 4z = 8 \\ 3x + 2y = 1 \\ x + y = 1 \end{cases}$ (b) $\begin{cases} 2x + y - z = 5 \\ y - 2z = 7 \\ 2y + 3z = 0 \end{cases}$

3. (a) $\begin{cases} 2x - 3y + 5z = 5 \\ x + y + z = 6 \\ x - y = 1 \end{cases}$ (b) $\begin{cases} x + y + z = 1 \\ x = y + z \\ z = .2 \end{cases}$

4. (a) $\begin{cases} 3x - 4y + 10z = -7 \\ 2x - 3y - z = -21 \\ x + y + z = 0 \end{cases}$ **(b)** $\begin{cases} x + y - z = 0 \\ \frac{1}{2}x + y + z = 11 \\ 2x - y + \frac{1}{3}z = 2 \end{cases}$

5. (a) $\begin{cases} 5x + 3y + 2z = 1 \\ 2x - y + z = -1 \\ -2x + 2y - z = 2 \end{cases}$ **(b)** $\begin{cases} 2x + y + z = 8 \\ 4x - y + 2z = 9 \\ x + \frac{1}{2}y - z = -2 \end{cases}$

6. (a) $\begin{cases} .3x + .2y = 1.3 \\ .2x + .3y + .1z = .5 \\ x + y + z = -2 \end{cases}$ **(b)** $\begin{cases} \dfrac{2}{x} + \dfrac{3}{y} + \dfrac{4}{z} = 3 \\ \dfrac{1}{x} - \dfrac{2}{z} = 0 \\ \dfrac{6}{x} - \dfrac{6}{y} = 8 \end{cases}$

$$\left(\text{Hint: Let } \frac{1}{x} = a, \ \frac{1}{y} = b, \ \frac{1}{z} = c. \right)$$

7. A bank contains 24 coins which are worth $3.00. If there are only nickels, dimes, and quarters, and the number of dimes is one-half the number of nickels and quarters combined, how many coins of each kind are there in the bank?

8. A, B, and C working together complete a job in 6 days; A and B working as a pair finish it in 7 days; B does twice as much work as C. How long would it take each of them working alone to do the job?

9. The sum of the angles of a triangle is 180°. The angle at B is twice as large as the angle at A, and the angle at C is 12° less than the sum of the other two angles. Find the angles.

10. Find three numbers which satisfy all of three conditions in part (a).
    (a) The sum of the three numbers is 72.
        The sum of two of the numbers is twice the third number.
        One of the numbers is 22.
    (b) Is there more than one set of three numbers which satisfies all three conditions?

11. Is there a unique set of three numbers which satisfy all of the following three conditions? If so, what is it? If not, list three such sets.
        The sum of the three numbers is 72.
        The sum of two of the numbers is twice the third number.
        One of the numbers is 24.

12. Find all three-digit numbers, if any exist, which satisfy all of the following three conditions.
        The sum of all three digits is 12.
        The tens' digit is twice the hundreds' digit.
        When the digits are reversed, the number is unchanged.

13. Find all three-digit numbers, if any exist, which satisfy all of the following three conditions.

> The sum of all three digits is 14.
> The tens' digit is twice the hundreds' digit.
> When the digits are reversed, the number is unchanged.

14. For what values of a, b, and c will the points $(1, 1)$, $(4, 4)$, and $(-1, 9)$ lie on the graph of the equation $y = ax^2 + bx + c$?

---

15. (a) Can you find a unique solution for the following system?

$$\begin{cases} 7a - 2b + c = 0 \\ 4a + b + 7c = 0 \\ a + b + 4c = 0 \end{cases}$$

(b) Can you find a "trivial" solution for the system in part (a)?

(c) Is the number triple $(k, 3k, -k)$ a solution of the system when $k = 1$? when $k = 2$? for any other values of k?

*2-12   MATRICES AND DETERMINANTS

Rectangular arrays of numbers, such as

$$\begin{pmatrix} 2 & -1 \\ 3 & 4 \end{pmatrix}, \quad \begin{pmatrix} 8 & 12 & 0 \\ 9 & -3 & -5 \end{pmatrix}, \quad \begin{pmatrix} 0 & 3 & 3 \\ -5 & 2 & 7 \\ 2 & 7 & -3 \end{pmatrix},$$

are called *matrices*. Matrices arise naturally in describing a system of linear equations. Thus, if S is the system

$$\begin{cases} a_1x + b_1y = d_1, \\ a_2x + b_2y = d_2 \end{cases}$$

of two linear equations in the variables x and y, then the matrix

$$\begin{pmatrix} a_1 & b_1 \\ a_2 & b_2 \end{pmatrix}$$

is called the *matrix of coefficients* of the variables and

$$\begin{pmatrix} a_1 & b_1 & d_1 \\ a_2 & b_2 & d_2 \end{pmatrix}$$

is called the *augmented matrix* of S. For example, the system

$$\begin{cases} 2x - y = 7, \\ 3x + 4y = -2 \end{cases}$$

has matrix of coefficients

$$\begin{pmatrix} 2 & -1 \\ 3 & 4 \end{pmatrix}$$

and augmented matrix

$$\begin{pmatrix} 2 & -1 & 7 \\ 3 & 4 & -2 \end{pmatrix}.$$

A matrix is made up of *rows* and *columns* of numbers. The matrix

$$\begin{pmatrix} 2 & -1 \\ 3 & 4 \end{pmatrix}$$

has $(2, -1)$ as its *first row*, $(3, 4)$ as its *second row*, and

$$\begin{pmatrix} 2 \\ 3 \end{pmatrix}, \quad \begin{pmatrix} -1 \\ 4 \end{pmatrix}$$

as its *first and second columns*, respectively.

If a matrix has the same number of rows and columns, then it is called a *square matrix*. For example,

$$\begin{pmatrix} 5 & -8 \\ 7 & 4 \end{pmatrix}$$

and

$$\begin{pmatrix} -7 & 3 & 12 \\ 4 & 0 & 2 \\ 0 & -9 & 6 \end{pmatrix}$$

are square matrices; the first is called a 2×2 *matrix,* and the second is called a 3×3 *matrix.*

Each square matrix has associated with it a number called the *determinant* of the matrix. The 2×2 matrix

$$A = \begin{pmatrix} a_1 & b_1 \\ a_2 & b_2 \end{pmatrix}$$

has a determinant denoted by $|A|$ and defined by

$$|A| = \begin{vmatrix} a_1 & b_1 \\ a_2 & b_2 \end{vmatrix} = a_1 b_2 - b_1 a_2.$$

For example,

$$\begin{vmatrix} 8 & 5 \\ 2 & 3 \end{vmatrix} = (8 \cdot 3) - (5 \cdot 2), \quad \text{or } 14,$$

$$\begin{vmatrix} 2 & -1 \\ 3 & 4 \end{vmatrix} = (2 \cdot 4) - (-1 \cdot 3), \quad \text{or } 11.$$

Determinants afford a simple notation which we can use to write solutions of systems of linear equations in which there are the same number of equations as unknowns. For example, consider the following system of two linear equations in the variables x and y:

$$\begin{cases} a_1 x + b_1 y = d_1, \\ a_2 x + b_2 y = d_2. \end{cases} \tag{1}$$

The matrix

$$A = \begin{pmatrix} a_1 & b_1 \\ a_2 & b_2 \end{pmatrix}$$

of coefficients of the variables in system (1) has determinant

$$|A| = a_1 b_2 - b_1 a_2.$$

If either $b_1 = 0$ or $b_2 = 0$, then we can easily solve system (1). Thus, we shall assume that $b_1 \neq 0$ and $b_2 \neq 0$. To solve this system, we can multiply the first equation of (1) by b_2 and the second by $-b_1$. Thus, the system

$$\begin{cases} b_2 a_1 x + b_2 b_1 y = b_2 d_1, \\ -b_1 a_2 x - b_1 b_2 y = -b_1 d_2 \end{cases} \tag{2}$$

is equivalent to system (1) since each equation of (2) is equivalent to the corresponding equation of (1). The second equation in (3) is the sum of the equations in (2). Thus, the system

$$\begin{cases} b_2 a_1 x + b_2 b_1 y = b_2 d_1, \\ (b_2 a_1 - b_1 a_2) x = b_2 d_1 - b_1 d_2 \end{cases} \tag{3}$$

is equivalent to system (2). If $b_2a_1 - b_1a_2 \neq 0$ (that is, if $|A| \neq 0$) then from the second equation of (3), we obtain

$$x = \frac{b_2d_1 - b_1d_2}{b_2a_1 - b_1a_2}.$$

Substituting this value in the first equation of (3), we obtain

$$b_2a_1(b_2d_1 - b_1d_2) + b_2b_1(b_2a_1 - b_1a_2)y = b_2d_1(b_2a_1 - b_1a_2).$$

We solve this equation for y and obtain

$$y = \frac{a_1d_2 - d_1a_2}{b_2a_1 - b_1a_2}.$$

Thus,

$$\left\{ \left(\frac{b_2d_1 - b_1d_2}{b_2a_1 - b_1a_2}, \frac{a_1d_2 - d_1a_2}{b_2a_1 - b_1a_2} \right) \right\} \tag{4}$$

is the solution set of system (1) if $b_2a_1 - b_1a_2 \neq 0$.

The solution of system (1) can be expressed in terms of determinants. Thus, if we let

$$A = \begin{pmatrix} a_1 & b_1 \\ a_2 & b_2 \end{pmatrix}, \quad A_1 = \begin{pmatrix} d_1 & b_1 \\ d_2 & b_2 \end{pmatrix}, \quad A_2 = \begin{pmatrix} a_1 & d_1 \\ a_2 & d_2 \end{pmatrix},$$

then $|A| = a_1b_2 - b_1a_2$, $|A_1| = d_1b_2 - b_1d_2$, $|A_2| = a_1d_2 - d_1a_2$, and (4) has the form

$$\left\{ \left(\frac{|A_1|}{|A|}, \frac{|A_2|}{|A|} \right) \right\}, \quad \text{if } |A| \neq 0.$$

Although we assumed that $b_1 \neq 0$ and $b_2 \neq 0$ in solving system (1), it can be shown that the solution is valid even if $b_1 = 0$ or $b_2 = 0$, as long as $|A| \neq 0$. If $|A| = 0$, then system (1) has no solution when $|A_1|$ or $|A_2|$ is nonzero and many solutions when $|A_1|$ and $|A_2|$ are zero. Geometrically, these correspond to the cases in which the graphs of the two equations are parallel lines or the same straight line.

Problem 1. Use determinants to solve the following system.

$$\begin{cases} 2x - y = 7 \\ 3x + 4y = -2 \end{cases}$$

Solution. The matrices A, A_1, and A_2 are given by

$$A = \begin{pmatrix} 2 & -1 \\ 3 & 4 \end{pmatrix}, \quad A_1 = \begin{pmatrix} 7 & -1 \\ -2 & 4 \end{pmatrix}, \quad A_2 = \begin{pmatrix} 2 & 7 \\ 3 & -2 \end{pmatrix}.$$

Hence,

$$|A| = 11, \quad |A_1| = 26, \quad |A_2| = -25.$$

Since $|A| \neq 0$, the solutions of the system above are given by

$$x = \frac{|A_1|}{|A|}, \quad \text{or} \quad \frac{26}{11},$$

$$y = \frac{|A_2|}{|A|}, \quad \text{or} \quad \frac{-25}{11}.$$

In other words, $\left(\frac{26}{11}, -\frac{25}{11}\right)$ is the unique solution of the system.

The determinant of a 3×3 matrix is defined as follows:

$$\begin{vmatrix} a_1 & b_1 & c_1 \\ a_2 & b_2 & c_2 \\ a_3 & b_3 & c_3 \end{vmatrix} = \begin{aligned} & a_1 b_2 c_3 + b_1 c_2 a_3 + c_1 a_2 b_3 - c_1 b_2 a_3 \\ & - a_1 c_2 b_3 - b_1 a_2 c_3. \end{aligned}$$

Note that each of the six terms on the right side contains three different subscripts and three different letters. In other words, each term is a product of three numbers, one from each row and one from each column of the matrix. One way to remember this is to repeat the first two columns to the right of the third column. Then the six terms are obtained in the way shown below.

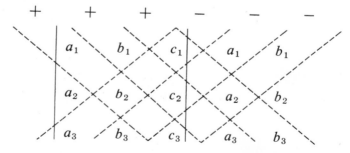

Thus, there are three terms having plus signs in front of them and three terms having minus signs. For example,

$$\begin{vmatrix} 8 & 2 & -1 \\ 4 & 7 & 6 \\ 2 & -3 & 5 \end{vmatrix} = \begin{vmatrix} 8 & 2 & -1 \\ 4 & 7 & 6 \\ 2 & -3 & 5 \end{vmatrix} \begin{matrix} 8 & 2 \\ 4 & 7 \\ 2 & -3 \end{matrix}$$

$$= (8 \cdot 7 \cdot 5) + (2 \cdot 6 \cdot 2) + [-1 \cdot 4 \cdot (-3)] - (-1 \cdot 7 \cdot 2)$$
$$- [8 \cdot 6 \cdot (-3)] - (2 \cdot 4 \cdot 5), \quad \text{or } 434.$$

A system of three linear equations in the variables x, y, and z,

$$\begin{cases} a_1x + b_1y + c_1z = d_1, \\ a_2x + b_2y + c_2z = d_2, \\ a_3x + b_3y + c_3z = d_3, \end{cases} \quad (5)$$

can be shown to have a unique solution if the determinant, $|A|$, of its matrix of coefficients is nonzero.

$$A = \begin{pmatrix} a_1 & b_1 & c_1 \\ a_2 & b_2 & c_2 \\ a_3 & b_3 & c_3 \end{pmatrix}$$

If we let

$$A_1 = \begin{pmatrix} d_1 & b_1 & c_1 \\ d_2 & b_2 & c_2 \\ d_3 & b_3 & c_3 \end{pmatrix}, \quad A_2 = \begin{pmatrix} a_1 & d_1 & c_1 \\ a_2 & d_2 & c_2 \\ a_3 & d_3 & c_3 \end{pmatrix}, \quad A_3 = \begin{pmatrix} a_1 & b_1 & d_1 \\ a_2 & b_2 & d_2 \\ a_3 & b_3 & d_3 \end{pmatrix},$$

then the unique solution of system (5) is given by

$$x = \frac{|A_1|}{|A|}, \quad y = \frac{|A_2|}{|A|}, \quad z = \frac{|A_3|}{|A|}.$$

This proof is similar to the proof of the corresponding result for system (1), and hence, is omitted.

Problem 2. Use determinants to solve the following system.

$$\begin{cases} 2x + y - z = -5 \\ -5x - 3y + 2z = 7 \\ x + 4y - 3z = 0 \end{cases} \quad (6)$$

Solution. The matrix of coefficients is given by

$$A = \begin{pmatrix} 2 & 1 & -1 \\ -5 & -3 & 2 \\ 1 & 4 & -3 \end{pmatrix},$$

and the augmented matrix is given by

$$\begin{pmatrix} 2 & 1 & -1 & -5 \\ -5 & -3 & 2 & 7 \\ 1 & 4 & -3 & 0 \end{pmatrix}.$$

The other three matrices are obtained from A by replacing each of the columns of A, in turn, by the last column of the augmented matrix.

$$A_1 = \begin{pmatrix} -5 & 1 & -1 \\ 7 & -3 & 2 \\ 0 & 4 & -3 \end{pmatrix} \qquad A_2 = \begin{pmatrix} 2 & -5 & -1 \\ -5 & 7 & 2 \\ 1 & 0 & -3 \end{pmatrix}$$

$$A_3 = \begin{pmatrix} 2 & 1 & -5 \\ -5 & -3 & 7 \\ 1 & 4 & 0 \end{pmatrix}$$

We see that

$$|A| = (2)(-3)(-3) + (1 \cdot 2 \cdot 1) + (-1)(-5)(4) - (-1)(-3)(1) \\ - (1)(-5)(-3) - (2 \cdot 2 \cdot 4), \quad \text{or } 6.$$

In a similar way, we can show that

$$|A_1| = -12, \quad |A_2| = 30, \quad |A_3| = 36.$$

Therefore, the solution of system (5) is given by

$$x = \frac{-12}{6}, \quad \text{or } -2; \qquad y = \frac{30}{6}, \quad \text{or } 5; \qquad z = \frac{36}{6}, \quad \text{or } 6.$$

The following is an interesting geometrical interpretation of a determinant. If the vertices of triangle ABC have coordinates (x_1, y_1), (x_2, y_2), and (x_3, y_3) in a cartesian coordinate system, as shown in Fig. 2–25, and if matrix H is defined by

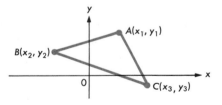

FIGURE 2-25

$$H = \begin{pmatrix} x_1 & y_1 & 1 \\ x_2 & y_2 & 1 \\ x_3 & y_3 & 1 \end{pmatrix},$$

then the *area* of triangle ABC is given by $\left|\frac{1}{2}|H|\right|$. (Here, the outer bars in the expression denote absolute value.) For example, if the vertices of a triangle are $(1, 1)$, $(-2, -3)$, and $(4, -2)$, then

$$H = \begin{pmatrix} 1 & 1 & 1 \\ -2 & -3 & 1 \\ 4 & -2 & 1 \end{pmatrix}, \quad |H| = 21,$$

and the area of the triangle is $\frac{21}{2}$.

We can apply the formula for the area of a triangle to determine whether three points in a plane are collinear. If points A, B, and C have respective coordinates (x_1, y_1), (x_2, y_2), and (x_3, y_3), then these points are collinear if, and only if, triangle ABC has area 0. Thus, A, B, and C are collinear if, and only if,

$$\begin{vmatrix} x_1 & y_1 & 1 \\ x_2 & y_2 & 1 \\ x_3 & y_3 & 1 \end{vmatrix} = 0.$$

From this result, it follows that

$$\begin{vmatrix} x_1 & y_1 & 1 \\ x_2 & y_2 & 1 \\ x & y & 1 \end{vmatrix} = 0$$

is an equation of the line passing through the two distinct points (x_1, y_1) and (x_2, y_2). For example, the line passing through the points $(2, 3)$ and $(-1, 1)$ has equation

$$\begin{vmatrix} 2 & 3 & 1 \\ -1 & 1 & 1 \\ x & y & 1 \end{vmatrix} = 0,$$

or

$$2x - 3y + 5 = 0.$$

The computation of determinants of square matrices is made easier if the following theorems are used.

Theorem 1. If matrix B is obtained from a matrix A by interchanging two rows or two columns of A, then $|B| = -|A|$.

Theorem 2. If matrix B is obtained from a matrix A by multiplying one row or one column of A by k and leaving the other rows or columns of A unchanged, then $|B| = k|A|$.

Theorem 3. If matrix B is obtained from a matrix A by multiplying each element of some row or column by k and adding the resulting number to the corresponding element of another row or column, then $|B| = |A|$.

Theorem 4. If an $n \times n$ matrix A has the form

$$\begin{pmatrix} a_1 & a_2 & a_3 \dots a_n \\ 0 & & \\ 0 & & B \\ \vdots & & \\ 0 & & \end{pmatrix} \text{ or } \begin{pmatrix} a_1 & 0 & 0 \dots 0 \\ a_2 & & \\ a_3 & & B \\ \vdots & & \\ a_n & & \end{pmatrix}$$

where B is an $(n-1) \times (n-1)$ matrix, then

$$|A| = a_1 |B|.$$

In Theorem 4, the notation $0\,0\dots 0$ indicates a row or column of zeros. The following problems illustrate the ways in which these theorems can be used.

Problem 3. Find $|A|$, given that

$$A = \begin{pmatrix} 2 & 3 & -5 \\ 4 & -1 & 3 \\ 1 & 6 & -2 \end{pmatrix}.$$

Solution. By Theorem 1, we interchange first and third rows and obtain $|A| = -|A_1|$ where

$$A_1 = \begin{pmatrix} 1 & 6 & -2 \\ 4 & -1 & 3 \\ 2 & 3 & -5 \end{pmatrix}.$$

By Theorem 3, we multiply the first row of A_1 by -4 and add the result to the second row to obtain $|A_1| = |A_2|$ where

$$A_2 = \begin{pmatrix} 1 & 6 & -2 \\ 0 & -25 & 11 \\ 2 & 3 & -5 \end{pmatrix}.$$

Again by Theorem 3, multiplying the first row of A_2 by -2 and adding the results to the third row, we obtain $|A_2| = |A_3|$ where

$$A_3 = \begin{pmatrix} 1 & 6 & -2 \\ 0 & -25 & 11 \\ 0 & -9 & -1 \end{pmatrix}.$$

Finally, by Theorem 4,

$$|A_3| = 1 \cdot \begin{vmatrix} -25 & 11 \\ -9 & -1 \end{vmatrix} = 25 + 99, \quad \text{or } 124.$$

Therefore, $|A| = -124$.

Problem 4. Find $|B|$, given that

$$B = \begin{pmatrix} -1 & 3 & 0 & 4 \\ 2 & 5 & -3 & 1 \\ 4 & -1 & 0 & 2 \\ 3 & 13 & -2 & 6 \end{pmatrix}.$$

Solution. This is our first 4×4 matrix. Make two applications of Theorem 3 to the first column of B. In other words, multiply the first column of B by 3 and add the result to the second column. Then multiply the first column of B by 4 and add the result to the fourth column. Thus, $|B| = |B_1|$ where

$$B_1 = \begin{pmatrix} -1 & 0 & 0 & 0 \\ 2 & 11 & -3 & 9 \\ 4 & 11 & 0 & 18 \\ 3 & 22 & -2 & 18 \end{pmatrix}.$$

By Theorem 4, we obtain $|B_1| = -1 \cdot |B_2|$ where

$$B_2 = \begin{pmatrix} 11 & -3 & 9 \\ 11 & 0 & 18 \\ 22 & -2 & 18 \end{pmatrix}.$$

By Theorem 2, we factor 11 out of the first column of B_2 and 9 out of the third column: $|B_2| = 11 \cdot 9 \cdot |B_3|$ where

$$B_3 = \begin{pmatrix} 1 & -3 & 1 \\ 1 & 0 & 2 \\ 2 & -2 & 2 \end{pmatrix}.$$

In two applications of Theorem 3, we multiply the first row of B_3 by -1 and add the result to the second row, and then multiply the first row by -2 and add the result to the third row to obtain $|B_3| = |B_4|$ where

$$B_4 = \begin{pmatrix} 1 & -3 & 1 \\ 0 & 3 & 1 \\ 0 & 4 & 0 \end{pmatrix}.$$

Finally, by Theorem 4, we have

$$|B_4| = 1 \cdot \begin{vmatrix} 3 & 1 \\ 4 & 0 \end{vmatrix} = -4.$$

Retracing our steps, we find

$$|B| = -1 \cdot 11 \cdot 9 \cdot (-4), \quad \text{or } 396.$$

Exercises

Use determinants to solve each of the following systems of linear equations.

1. $\begin{cases} 3x + 6y = 3 \\ 5x + 7y = -1 \end{cases}$

2. $\begin{cases} 7x - 9y = 8 \\ -8x + 15y = 5 \end{cases}$

3. $\begin{cases} 2x + 3y = 1 \\ 3x + 5y = -2 \end{cases}$

4. $\begin{cases} 5x + 11y = -10 \\ 9x - 2y = -127 \end{cases}$

5. $\begin{cases} 4x - 3y = 2 \\ 5x + 4y = 3 \end{cases}$

6. $\begin{cases} 3x + 7y = 4 \\ 4x - 9y = 3 \end{cases}$

7. $\begin{cases} 2x + 3y + 6z = 3 \\ -x + 2y + 2z = -1 \\ 3x - 4y - 5z = -6 \end{cases}$

8. $\begin{cases} 5x - 4y + 7z = -4 \\ 9x - 5y + 5z = 8 \\ 4x + 3y + 3z = 2 \end{cases}$

9. $\begin{cases} -3y + z = -5 \\ 5x + 3z = 1 \\ 3x - 5y = -6 \end{cases}$

10. $\begin{cases} 2x + 3y + 4z = 2 \\ -5x + 5y + 2z = 4 \\ 3x - 4y - 6z = 2 \end{cases}$

11. $\begin{cases} x - y + z = 2 \\ 2x + 3y - z = -1 \\ x + 2y - 3z = 3 \end{cases}$

12. $\begin{cases} 2x + y - z = 3 \\ x - 3y + 2z = -2 \\ 3x + y - 3z = -1 \end{cases}$

13. $\begin{cases} 2x + 3y + 4z + 5w = 4 \\ 4y + 3z - w = 1 \\ x - 2y + 3w = 2 \\ 3x + y - 2z + 7w = -7 \end{cases}$

14. $\begin{cases} 3x - 2z + 5w = 2 \\ -2x - y + 4z = 0 \\ x + 2y - 3z - 5w = 1 \\ 3y + 5z + 2w = -3 \end{cases}$

*2–13   LINEAR PROGRAMMING

The mathematical form of certain practical problems involves a system of linear inequalities. Such a system seldom has a unique solution, but rather has many solutions, as we saw in Section 2–10. However, of all possible solutions of a system of inequalities, some one solution will prove to be the best solution of the practical problem with which we started. The branch of mathematics which solves such problems is called *linear programming*. The following example illustrates the type of problem studied in linear programming.

Consider the problem faced by a manufacturer who has two warehouses, warehouse I containing 40 units of his product and warehouse II containing 50 units. He has two orders to fill, one from town A for 30 units and the other from town B for 40 units. Should he fill the order for town A from one warehouse and that for town B from the other, or is there a more economical distribution?

If we let x designate the number of units shipped from warehouse I to town A, then $30 - x$ units must be shipped from warehouse II to town A. Similarly, if we let y denote the number of units shipped from warehouse I to town B, then $40 - y$ units must be shipped from warehouse II to town B. Each of these four numbers must be greater than or equal to zero:

$$x \geqq 0,$$
$$30 - x \geqq 0, \quad \text{or } 30 \geqq x,$$
$$y \geqq 0,$$
$$40 - y \geqq 0, \quad \text{or } 40 \geqq y.$$

In addition, the number of units the manufacturer ships from each warehouse cannot exceed the number of units stored there:

$$x + y \leqq 40,$$
$$(30 - x) + (40 - y) \leqq 50, \quad \text{or } 20 \leqq x + y.$$

Thus, any ordered pair of *integers* that is a solution of the following system of inequalities is a solution of the manufacturer's problem.

$$\begin{cases} x \geqq 0 \\ x \leqq 30 \\ y \geqq 0 \\ y \leqq 40 \\ x + y \leqq 40 \\ x + y \geqq 20 \end{cases}$$

The graph of this system is the shaded pentagonal region of Fig. 2–26. (This is the intersection of the graphs of the inequalities.) Of course, the boundary of this pentagon is also included in the graph.

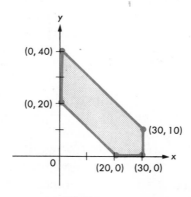

FIGURE 2–26

With what is given, there are many possible solutions of the manu-facturer's problem. However, we have not yet taken into account the shipping costs from each warehouse to each town. Suppose that the shipping costs are as follows.

From warehouse	To town	Cost per unit, in dollars	Number of units shipped
I	A	10	x
I	B	14	y
II	A	12	$30 - x$
II	B	15	$40 - y$

Thus, the total shipping costs are

$$10x + 14y + 12(30 - x) + 15(40 - y)$$

dollars. This linear form in x and y reduces to

$$10x + 14y + 360 - 12x + 600 - 15y,$$

or

$$960 - 2x - y.$$

Now, our problem is to find the solution of the original problem for which the total shipping costs are smallest. Mathematically speaking, we must find the point with integral coordinates in the pentagonal region of the figure at which the linear form

$$960 - 2x - y$$

has its smallest value.

The linear form has a value for every point in the region, and it would be impossible to compute all these values to find the smallest. Even the task of computing the values at the points with integral co-ordinates would be tedious. However, according to a result proved in the theory of linear programming, the maximum value of the linear form occurs at a vertex of the pentagon, and the minimum value occurs at another vertex.

To find the minimum value, let us compute the value of $960 - 2x - y$ (see the following table) at each of the vertices of the pentagon. According to the theory of linear programming, the maximum value of the linear form is 940, occurring at $(0, 20)$, and the minimum value is 890, occurring at $(30, 10)$. To see that the values are between 890 and 940, let us find the value at some points other than the vertices. At the interior point $(20, 10)$, the value is $960 - (2 \cdot 20) - 10$, or 910; at the boundary point (15, 25), the value is $960 - (2 \cdot 15) - 25$, or 905; at the interior point (29, 9), the value is $960 - (2 \cdot 29) - 9$, or 893.

Vertex	Value of $960 - 2x - y$
(20, 0)	$960 - (2 \cdot 20) - 0$, or 920
(30, 0)	$960 - (2 \cdot 30) - 0$, or 900
(30, 10)	$960 - (2 \cdot 30) - 10$, or 890
(0, 40)	$960 - (2 \cdot 0) \ - 40$, or 920
(0, 20)	$960 - (2 \cdot 0) \ - 20$, or 940

Clearly, the lowest shipping cost is \$890, occurring when $x = 30$ and $y = 10$. Thus, the manufacturer is advised to ship all 30 units to town A from warehouse I, and to ship 10 units from warehouse I and 30 units from warehouse II to town B. By doing this, he will make the greatest profit on his two orders.

We have used a theorem from linear programming which states that a linear form defined over a convex polygonal region of the plane assumes its maximum and minimum values at vertices of the region.

Exercises

1. (a) If, in the problem of this section, the shipping costs are \$15 per unit from warehouse I to town A, \$12 per unit from warehouse I to town B, \$14 per unit from warehouse II to town A, and \$10 per unit from warehouse II to town B, express the shipping costs as a linear form in x and y.
   (b) Find the value of this linear form at each corner point of the pentagon.
   (c) What shipping advice should be given to the manufacturer if he is to spend as little as possible on shipping?

2. An appliance wholesaler has 8 television sets in his warehouse in Lakeville and 8 sets in his warehouse in Alexandria. He receives orders to ship 6 sets to Central City and 4 sets to Stratford.
   (a) Let x be the number of sets to be shipped from Lakeville to Central City. What represents the number to be shipped from Alexandria to Central City? What is the lower limit of x? What is the upper limit of x?
   (b) Let y be the number of sets to be shipped from Lakeville to Stratford. What will represent the number to be shipped from Alexandria to Stratford? What is the lower limit of y? What is the upper limit of y?
   (c) Write the system of six inequalities describing the problem.
   (d) Graph the system of part (c).
   (e) If shipping costs per television set are \$6 from Lakeville to Central City, \$5 from Lakeville to Stratford, \$7 from Alexandria to Central

City, and $8.50 from Alexandria to Stratford, write and simplify a linear form for the total shipping cost.

(f) Find the value of the linear form of part (e) at each of the six corner points of your graph.

(g) For maximum profit, what advice should be given to the wholesaler?

3. Two machines A and B produce items at the rate of 50 per hour and 40 per hour, respectively. Under a certain production plan the total number of items needed is at least 1000 items, and the total number of man-hours available for running the machines is at most 24 hours.

(a) Let x be the number of hours machine A is used and y the number of hours machine B is used, and express the two conditions above as inequalities.

(b) Add to the system of inequalities in part (a) the two obvious inequalities resulting from the fact that x and y are non-negative numbers, and graph the system of these four inequalities. Find the corner points of the resulting polygon.

(c) If the hourly cost is $10 for running machine A and $7 for machine B, find the values of x and y which would yield the most economical production program.

(d) In part (c), if the hourly costs for A and B were $10 and $9, respectively, what would be the best plan?

(e) Assuming, in part (c), that the hourly costs for A and B are $10 and $8, respectively, show that two of the corner points give paired values of x and y which minimize the cost. (Actually any point (x, y) on the line segment between these corner points will lead to the same minimal cost.)

4. In the table below, the vitamin and mineral content of two brands of cereals, Soggies ("they sink") and Lumpies ("they clump"), is given in milligrams per ounce. The third column gives the daily minimum requirements of these vitamins and minerals. At the bottom of the first two columns, the cost per ounce of each cereal is listed. Find the number of ounces for each cereal which taken together will satisfy the daily minimum requirements of thiamine, niacin, and iron at lowest cost.

	Soggies	Lumpies	Daily min. requirement
Thiamine	.5	.25	2.00
Niacin	50	150	450
Iron	1.5	2.0	11.0
	$2\frac{1}{2}$¢	2¢	

5. A truck gardener has a plot of 50 acres and decides to plant two different vegetables, B and C. He has a maximum of 185 man-hours of labor to

devote to this garden and $205 which he may spend for seed. Let your variables be the number of acres to be planted in B and the number of acres to be planted in C.

(a) Write an inequality which states that he has 50 acres of land available.

(b) If an acre of B requires 4 man-hours for cultivation and an acre of C requires only 1 man-hour, write an inequality stating that he has 185 man-hours of labor at his disposal.

(c) If seed costs $2 an acre for B and $5 an acre for C, write an inequality stating that he has at most $205 to spend for seed.

(d) Write inequalities indicating the minimum number of acres which may be planted in each vegetable.

(e) Graph your system of inequalities.

(f) If labor costs $2.50 a man-hour, an acre's yield of vegetable B sells for $27, and an acre's yield of vegetable C sells for $14, find a linear form which expresses the profit of the gardener.

(g) How many acres should the gardener plant in each vegetable if he wishes to maximize his profit?

6. A couple decides to start a record collection. They can purchase records of musical shows for $5 apiece and records of a vocalist for $2 apiece. There are only 4 records of musical shows in which they are currently interested, and 6 of their favorite vocalist. They have $25 to invest and decide that 8 records should be their limit.

(a) Write two inequalities which express the number of records of musical shows which they can buy.

(b) Write two inequalities which express the number of vocalist records which they can buy.

(c) Write an inequality which shows that they have $25 to invest.

(d) Write an inequality which shows that 8 records should be their limit.

(e) Graph the system of inequalities which you have just written.

(f) They give a popularity rating of 3 to each record of a musical show and of 2 to each record of the vocalist. How many records of each type should they buy to give their collection the highest rating?

KEY IDEAS AND KEY WORDS

The **union** of sets A and B, $A \cup B$, consists of all elements in either A or B.

The **intersection** of A and B, $A \cap B$, consists of all elements common to A and B.

The **empty set** is denoted by $\emptyset$.

Algebraic expressions of the form

$$\text{(a number)}x + \text{(a number)}y + \text{(a number)}$$

are called **linear forms** in the variables x and y.

A linear equation in x and y is an algebraic expression made up of two linear forms in x and y connected by an equals sign.

A solution of an equation in x and y is an ordered pair (a, b) such that the equation is true when $x = a$ and $y = b$.

The **solution set of an equation in x and y** is the set of all solutions of the equation.

The **graph of an equation in x and y** is the graph of its solution set.

Two equations are called **equivalent equations** if they have the same solution set.

The **graph of a linear equation** in a cartesian coordinate system is a straight line.

A line divides a plane into two pieces, each of which is called a **half-plane.**

A linear inequality in x and y is made up of two linear forms in x and y connected by one of the symbols $>$, $<$, $\geq$, or $\leq$.

The **graph of a linear inequality** in a cartesian coordinate system is a **half-plane.**

A solution of an inequality in one variable is a value of the variable for which the inequality is true.

The **solution set of an inequality** is the set of all its solutions.

Two **inequalities** are called **equivalent inequalities** if they have the same solution set.

The abscissa of the point at which a line crosses the x-axis is called the **x-intercept;** the ordinate of the point at which it crosses the y-axis is called the **y-intercept.**

The quotient of the **rise** by the **run** of a nonvertical line in a cartesian coordinate system is called the **slope** of the line.

A matrix is a rectangular array of numbers.

The horizontal lines of numbers in a matrix are called its **rows** and the vertical lines are called its **columns.**

A determinant is a real number associated with each square matrix. The 2×2 matrix

$$\begin{pmatrix} a_1 & b_2 \\ a_2 & b_2 \end{pmatrix}$$

has determinant

$$\begin{vmatrix} a_1 & b_1 \\ a_2 & b_2 \end{vmatrix} = a_1 b_2 - b_1 a_2.$$

Linear programming is that branch of mathematics which is used to maximize or minimize a linear form when the variables are in the solution set of a system of linear equations or inequalities.

CHAPTER REVIEW

1. Solve each of the following equations and check each answer.

   (a) $8x - 15 = 3x + 5$
   (b) $4 - \dfrac{2x + 5}{4} = \dfrac{1}{2} - \dfrac{9(x + 3)}{8}$

2. Give the intersection of the solution sets of each pair of inequalities and, if possible, graph the intersection on a number line.
   (a) $3x - \frac{5}{9} < 2x - 1$ and $1 + \frac{2}{3}x \leq x + \frac{1}{4}$
   (b) $2(1 + 2x) < 3(3 + x)$ and $\frac{1}{3}(x + 2) > \frac{1}{2}x + \frac{2}{3}$
   (c) $4 + 3x < 5 + 4x$ and $3(2 - x) > 5 - 2x$

3. Graph the solution set of each of the following equations. For each graph, give the slope and both intercepts. Is there a solution in positive integers for either equation?
   (a) $y = 1 - 3x$
   (b) $x + \frac{1}{5}y = 2$

4. Find the solution set and draw the graph of each of the following inequalities.
   (a) $x \leq y$
   (b) $x + y > 2$
   (c) $2x - 3y \geq 6$

5. Find the solution set of each of the following systems of equations.
   (a) $\begin{cases} x + 2y = 9 \\ 4x - y = 0 \end{cases}$
   (b) $\begin{cases} 2x - 5y = 6 \\ 3x + 4y = 32 \end{cases}$

6. Given that

$$A = \{(x, y) \mid y + 3x + 6 = 0\}, \quad B = \{(x, y) \mid y = 4 - 3x\},$$

   (a) graph $A \cup B$.
   (b) describe $A \cap B$.

7. Tell whether the following system of equations is dependent, independent, or inconsistent.

$$\begin{cases} y + 3x + 6 = 0 \\ y = 4 - 3x \end{cases}$$

8. Prove that the points $(-1, 2)$, $(3, -4)$, and $(-5, 8)$ are collinear.

9. Write an inequality whose solution set has for its graph the half-plane above the line with slope $\frac{2}{3}$ and y-intercept -4.

10. Describe each solution set. In (a) and (b), draw the graph of each system of inequalities, and give the coordinates of the vertices of the regions.

   (a) $\begin{cases} x > -2 \\ x < 2 \\ 3y \leq x + 6 \\ x + 3y + 6 \geq 0 \end{cases}$
   (b) $\begin{cases} 9x + y - 14 \leq 0 \\ 2x + 5y + 16 \geq 0 \\ 7x - 4y + 13 \geq 0 \end{cases}$

   (c) $\begin{cases} 2r + 3s + 4t = 3 \\ r - 2t = 0 \\ 6r + 6s = 5 \end{cases}$

11. A newsboy has three times as many dimes as quarters. If the dimes and quarters total $7.15, how many of each does he have?

12. Mr. Smith spent 4 hours driving from his home to his cabin on the lake, while he spent only 3 hours and 20 minutes returning. If his speed on the return trip was 10 miles per hour faster than his speed going, what is the distance, in miles, from his home to his cabin?

13. Joe earns $30 a week less than twice what Jane earns. What is the minimum amount each can earn if they want to meet their combined weekly budget of $150? What is the least each could earn to meet a budget of $210 a week?

14. The sum of the digits of a three-digit number is 14. The tens' digit is 4 less than the sum of the hundreds' digit and the units' digit. If the tens' digit and the units' digit are interchanged, the number is increased by 18. Find the number.

15. John has a collection of nickels and dimes, with the dimes numbering three more than twice the nickels. If he has at least $2 and at most $3, what possible combinations of dimes and nickels could he have?

CHAPTER TEST

1. Solve the following equation.

$$\frac{3x + 10}{8} + \frac{x - 5}{2} = \frac{1}{2}$$

2. Find the solution set of the following inequality.

$$3(x + 2) - 1 > 2 - 3(x + 1)$$

3. On a number line, graph the solution set of the following inequality.

$$x + 5 > 2x + 1$$

4. Write an inequality whose solution set has for its graph the half-plane below the line which passes through the two points $(-1, 6)$ and $(3, -4)$.

5. Solve the following systems of equations.

(a) $\begin{cases} 2x - 4 = y \\ x + 3y = 5 \end{cases}$

(b) $\begin{cases} x - y + z = 2 \\ x + 2z = 7 \\ y - z = 1 \end{cases}$

6. Graph the solution set of the following system of inequalities.

$$\begin{cases} y \geq 8 - 4x \\ x \leq 8 \end{cases}$$

7. The units' digit of a two-digit number is 5 less than twice the tens' digit. If the digits are reversed, the number is decreased by 9. What is the number?

8. Suppose that 600 tickets for the ballet were sold, some for $1.60 each and some for $2.25 each. If the total receipts were $1122.50, how many tickets were sold at each price?

CHAPTER **3**

Second-degree Equations and Inequalities

Objectives...

- To show the relationship between quadratic equations and quadratic polynomials.
- To apply the "factors of zero" rule to the solution of quadratic equations.
- To solve quadratic equations by completing the square.
- To construct and analyze graphs of quadratic equations and inequalities.

3–1 QUADRATIC POLYNOMIALS

A first-degree equation in one variable generally has one solution, and a second-degree equation usually has two. An easy way to solve a second-degree equation such as

$$8x^2 - 5 = 9$$

is to observe that it is equivalent to the equation

$$x^2 = \tfrac{7}{4}.$$

Hence, its solutions are $x = \sqrt{7}/2$ and $x = -\sqrt{7}/2$.

The method above fails if there is a first-degree term in the equation. For example, the second-degree equation

$$8x^2 - 5x = 9$$

cannot be solved in the same simple way. However, there are systematic ways of solving such equations, as we shall see in this chapter.

An expression of the form

$$ax^2 + bx + c,$$

where a, b, and c are real numbers, with $a \neq 0$, is called a *quadratic polynomial* in the variable x. The number a is called the *coefficient* of x^2. We assume that $a \neq 0$, for if $a = 0$, the expression is a linear form. The number b is the *coefficient* of x, and the number c is called the *constant term*. For example, $x^2 - 6x + 8$ and $4x^2 - 49$ are quadratic polynomials in x.

Some quadratic polynomials can be factored, that is, expressed as a product of two linear polynomials. For example, we can verify that

$$x^2 - 6x + 8 = (x - 4)(x - 2).$$

The square of a linear polynomial $Ax + B$ has the form

$$(Ax + B)^2 = A^2x^2 + 2ABx + B^2.$$

Consequently, any quadratic polynomial of the form

$$A^2x^2 + 2ABx + B^2$$

can be factored into $(Ax + B)^2$. We call such a quadratic polynomial a *perfect square.* The polynomial $x^2 + 10x + 25$ has the form shown above, with $A = 1$ and $B = 5$. Hence,

$$x^2 + 10x + 25 = (x + 5)^2.$$

As another example, $4x^2 - 44x + 121$ has the above form, with $A = 2$ and $B = -11$: $4x^2 - 44x + 121 = (2x - 11)^2$.

Another type of quadratic polynomial which can be easily factored is one of the form $A^2x^2 - B^2$:

$$A^2x^2 - B^2 = (Ax + B)(Ax - B).$$

We call a polynomial of the form $A^2x^2 - B^2$ a *difference of two squares.* For example, $4x^2 - 49$ is a difference of two squares, with $A = 2$ and $B = 7$. Hence, $4x^2 - 49 = (2x + 7)(2x - 7)$.

If a quadratic polynomial has integral coefficients, then we can determine by trial and error whether or not it can be factored into two linear polynomials with integral coefficients. This is illustrated in the following problem.

Problem. If possible, factor each of the following polynomials into linear polynomials with integral coefficients.
(a) $x^2 - 3x - 10$ (b) $2x^2 - 7x + 6$ (c) $3x^2 - 8x - 12$

Solution.

(a) If $x^2 - 3x - 10$ can be factored, then

$$x^2 - 3x - 10 = (x + M)(x + N)$$

for some integers M and N. Since

$$(x + M)(x + N) = x^2 + (M + N)x + MN,$$

we must have

$$M + N = -3, \quad MN = -10.$$

In order for $MN = -10$, M and N must be in the set

$$\{\pm 1,\ \pm 2,\ \pm 5,\ \pm 10\}.$$

Thus, our problem is to select M and N from this set so that their sum is -3 and their product is -10. By trial and error, we find that $M = -5$ and $N = 2$ (or $M = 2$ and $N = -5$). Hence,

$$x^2 - 3x - 10 = (x - 5)(x + 2).$$

(b) This is somewhat more difficult than (a) because the coefficient of x^2 is not 1. However, the coefficient of x^2 is 2, a prime, so that if (b) can be factored, then it has the form

$$2x^2 - 7x + 6 = (2x + M)(x + N)$$

for some integers M and N. By multiplying out the right side of the above equation, $(2x + M)(x + N) = 2x^2 + (M + 2N)x + MN$, we see that

$$M + 2N = -7, \quad MN = 6.$$

Thus, our problem is to select M and N from the set $\{\pm 1, \pm 2, \pm 3, \pm 6\}$ so that $MN = 6$ and $M + 2N = -7$. By trial and error, we find that $M = -3$ and $N = -2$. Hence,

$$2x^2 - 7x + 6 = (2x - 3)(x - 2).$$

(c) We can factor this polynomial if, and only if, we can find integers M and N such that

$$3x^2 - 8x - 12 = (3x + M)(x + N)$$
$$= 3x^2 + (M + 3N)x + MN.$$

Thus, we must select M and N from the set

$$\{\pm 1, \pm 2, \pm 3, \pm 4, \pm 6, \pm 12\}$$

so that

$$M + 3N = -8, \quad MN = -12.$$

Since $M + 3N$ is an even integer, M and N must both be even or both be odd. However, M and N cannot both be odd and have a product of -12, so M and N must both be even. Therefore, one must be ± 2 and the other ± 6. We find that none of these values make

$$M + 3N = -8.$$

Hence, we conclude that the polynomial in (c) cannot be factored into linear polynomials with integral coefficients.

Exercises

If possible, factor each of the following polynomials.

1. (a) $x^2 + 15x + 54$ (b) $a^2 + 12a + 35$
2. (a) $x^2 + 31x + 30$ (b) $y^2 + 62y + 61$
3. (a) $a^2 - 8a + 12$ (b) $x^2 - 11x + 10$
4. (a) $y^2 - 26y + 48$ (b) $x^2 - 7x + 10$
5. (a) $x^2 + 18x + 81$ (b) $16x^2 - 8x + 1$
6. (a) $b^2 - b - 20$ (b) $x^2 - x - 72$
7. (a) $x^2 - 13x + 12$ (b) $y^2 - 17y + 72$
8. (a) $a^2 - 6a + 12$ (b) $2x^2 + 5x - 1$
9. (a) $25 - x^2$ (b) $196x^2 - 9$
10. (a) $x^2 - \frac{1}{4}$ (b) $y^2 - \frac{4}{9}$

---

11. (a) $y^2 + y - 42$ (b) $y^2 - y - 56$
12. (a) $y^2 + 3y - 54$ (b) $a^2 - 6a - 40$
13. (a) $y^2 + 8y - 15$ (b) $x^2 + 12x + 10$
14. (a) $b^2 + 9b + 14$ (b) $b^2 - 15b + 14$
15. (a) $y^2 + 7y + 49$ (b) $y^2 + 9y + 5$
16. (a) $(19x)^2 - 17^2$ (b) $15^2 - (4x)^2$
17. (a) $3x^2 - 16x + 16$ (b) $2y^2 + 5y - 12$
18. (a) $3y^2 + 19y - 40$ (b) $2y^2 - y - 6$
19. (a) $2x^2 + 5x + 2$ (b) $25y^2 - 10y + 1$
20. (a) $3x^2 - 10x + 3$ (b) $10x^2 - 29x + 10$

Express each of the following as a product of three or more factors.

21. $y^3 - 16y$ 22. $6x^2 - 216$
23. $30x^2 - 38x + 12$ 24. $-8x^2 + 56x - 98$
25. $6x^2 - 54x + 84$ 26. $6x^3 + 15x^2 + 6x$
27. $x^8 - 16$ 28. $16x^4 - 81$
29. $x^5 - x$ 30. $48y^3 - 147y$

3-2 EQUATIONS IN ONE VARIABLE

An equation of the form

$$ax^2 + bx + c = 0, \quad a \neq 0,$$

where a, b, and c are real numbers is called a *second-degree equation*, or *quadratic equation*, in the variable x. A number is called a *solution of a quadratic equation* if a true equation results when the variable is given the number as a value. The set of all solutions of the equation is called the *solution set of the quadratic equation*. If a quadratic equation has no solution, the solution set is the empty set.

The quadratic equation

$$2x^2 - 3x - 2 = 0$$

has 2 as a solution since

$$(2 \cdot 2^2) - (3 \cdot 2) - 2 = 0$$

is a true equation. The numbers 1 and $\frac{1}{2}$ are not solutions since

$$(2 \cdot 1^2) - (3 \cdot 1) - 2 = 0$$

and

$$[2 \cdot (\tfrac{1}{2})^2] - (3 \cdot \tfrac{1}{2}) - 2 = 0$$

are both false equations. However, $-\frac{1}{2}$ is a solution since the equation

$$[2 \cdot (-\tfrac{1}{2})^2] - 3 \cdot (-\tfrac{1}{2}) - 2 = 0$$

is true. In fact, we shall show that $\{2, -\frac{1}{2}\}$ is the solution set of the given equation later in the section.

If we can factor a quadratic polynomial as a product of two linear forms, we can easily solve the quadratic equation that results when the polynomial is set equal to zero. This is true because of the following property of the real number system.

FACTORS OF ZERO

$$r \cdot s = 0 \quad \textit{if, and only if,} \quad r = 0 \textit{ or } s = 0 \qquad \textit{(F-0)}$$

In other words, a product of two real numbers is zero if, and only if, at least one of the numbers is zero.

This property can be proved as follows. If $r \cdot s = 0$ and $r \neq 0$, then r has a reciprocal, and we may multiply both sides of the equation $r \cdot s = 0$ by $1/r$, obtaining

$$\frac{1}{r} \cdot (r \cdot s) = \frac{1}{r} \cdot 0, \qquad \text{(Mult-A)}$$

$$\left(\frac{1}{r} \cdot r\right) \cdot s = 0, \qquad \text{(A-M), (Zero-M)}$$

$$1 \cdot s = 0, \quad \text{or} \quad s = 0. \qquad \text{(Inv-M), (Id-M)}$$

Similarly, we may prove that if $r \cdot s = 0$ and $s \neq 0$, then $r = 0$. This proves that if $r \cdot s = 0$, then $r = 0$ or $s = 0$. On the other hand, we proved in Chapter 1 that if $r = 0$ or $s = 0$, then $r \cdot s = 0$.

By multiplication, we can show that

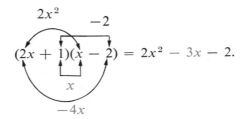

$$(2x + 1)(x - 2) = 2x^2 - 3x - 2.$$

Therefore, the equation

$$2x^2 - 3x - 2 = 0$$

is equivalent to the equation

$$(2x + 1)(x - 2) = 0$$

by the substitution principle. However, by the *factors of zero* theorem,

$$(2x + 1)(x - 2) = 0$$

if, and only if,

$$2x + 1 = 0 \quad \text{or} \quad x - 2 = 0.$$

When we solve each linear equation in the statement above, we find that

$$(2x + 1)(x - 2) = 0$$

if, and only if,

$$x = -\tfrac{1}{2} \quad \text{or} \quad x = 2.$$

If we let x denote any number other than $-\frac{1}{2}$ or 2, then both factors, $2x + 1$ and $x - 2$, will be nonzero. Therefore, their product will also be nonzero. Hence, no number except $-\frac{1}{2}$ or 2 is a solution of the given equation, and we conclude that the set $\{-\frac{1}{2}, 2\}$ contains all the solutions and is therefore *the* solution set of this quadratic equation.

Problem. Solve the equation $3x^2 - 5x = 2x^2 - 7x + 35$.

Solution. Adding $-2x^2 + 7x - 35$ to each side of the given equation yields the equivalent equation

$$x^2 + 2x - 35 = 0$$

with zero on the right side. If we can factor the quadratic polynomial $x^2 + 2x - 35$ as a product of two linear forms, then we can solve the equation using the factors of zero theorem. By inspection,

$$x^2 + 2x - 35 = (x + 7)(x - 5).$$

Therefore, the equation

$$(x + 7)(x - 5) = 0$$

is equivalent to the given one. Since

$$(x + 7)(x - 5) = 0$$

if, and only if,

$$x + 7 = 0 \quad \text{or} \quad x - 5 = 0,$$

the solution set of the given equation is

$$\{x \mid x + 7 = 0\} \cup \{x \mid x - 5 = 0\}, \quad \text{or} \quad \{-7, 5\}.$$

Check.

$$x = -7$$
$$3 \cdot (-7)^2 - 5 \cdot (-7) \overset{?}{=} 2 \cdot (-7)^2 - 7 \cdot (-7) + 35$$
$$(3 \cdot 49) + 35 \overset{?}{=} (2 \cdot 49) + 49 + 35$$
$$(3 \cdot 49) + 35 \overset{\checkmark}{=} [(2 + 1) \cdot 49] + 35$$

$$x = 5$$
$$(3 \cdot 5^2) - (5 \cdot 5) \overset{?}{=} (2 \cdot 5^2) - (7 \cdot 5) + 35$$
$$75 - 25 \overset{\checkmark}{=} 50 - 35 + 35$$

Exercises

For each of the given quadratic equations, select from the given set those numbers which are solutions of the equation.

1. (a) $6x^2 - x - 2 = 0$, $\{-1, -\frac{1}{2}, 1, \frac{2}{3}, 3, 0\}$
   (b) $x^2 - 5x = 2x - 6$, $\{1, 0, 5, 3, -2, 6\}$

2. (a) $(x - 1)(x + 2) = 40$, $\{1, -2, 8, 5, 6, 10, -7\}$
   (b) $3x^2 - 6x = 0$, $\{-3, -2, 0, 6, 1, 2, 3\}$

3. (a) $(x + 5)(x - 9) = 0$, $\{0, 1, 4, 9, -45, -5\}$
   (b) $(x - 7)(x + 7) = 0$ $\{0, 1, 6, 7, -6, -7\}$

Solve each of the following equations. Then substitute into the original equation to check each solution.

4. (a) $(x + 3)(x - 5) = 0$ (b) $(2x - 1)(x + 4) = 0$

5. (a) $(3x - 7)(3x + 7) = 0$ (b) $(x + 8)(x - 8) = 0$

6. (a) $3x(2x - 10) = 0$ (b) $2x(5x + 15) = 0$

7. (a) $(4x + 5)^2 = 0$ (b) $(3x - 10)^2 = 0$

8. (a) $x^2 - 7x + 10 = 0$ (b) $x^2 - 14x - 15 = 0$

9. (a) $2x^2 + 5x - 12 = 0$ (b) $x^2 - 3x - 40 = 0$

10. (a) $7x^2 + 21x = 0$ (b) $3x^2 = 5x$

11. (a) $x^2 + 4x + 4 = 0$ (b) $9x^2 + 12x + 4 = 0$

12. (a) $x^2 + 2x + 1 = 0$ (b) $y^2 + 49 = -14y$

Solve each of the following equations and check each solution.

13. $x^2 - 169 = 0$

14. $\dfrac{x^2}{9} - \dfrac{1}{4} = 0$

15. $5x^2 - 14x - 3 = 0$

16. $6t^2 - t - 1 = 0$

17. $51y^2 + y - 92 = 0$

18. $x^2 + x = 6$

19. $10 - 2t - 15t^2 = 2$

20. $z^2 = 3(8z + 27)$

21. $4x^2 + x = 0$

22. $3t^2 - \frac{7}{4}t - 3 = 0$

---

23. We can find the solution set of $(x + 3)^2 - 4(x + 3) - 77 = 0$ in two different ways. Complete each solution below.

First solution.
$$(x + 3)^2 - 4(x + 3) - 77 = 0$$
$$x^2 + 6x + 9 - 4x - 12 - 77 = 0$$
$$x^2 + \underline{}x - \underline{} = 0$$
$$(x + \underline{})(x - \underline{}) = 0$$
$$x + \underline{} = 0 \quad \text{or} \quad x - \underline{} = 0$$
$$\{x \mid (x + 3)^2 - 4(x + 3) - 77 = 0\} = \{\underline{}, \underline{}\}$$

Second solution. $(x + 3)^2 - 4(x + 3) - 77 = 0$
$$[(x + 3) - 11][(x + 3) + 7] = 0$$
$$(x + 3) - 11 = 0 \quad \text{or} \quad (x + 3) + 7 = 0$$
$$x - \underline{\quad?\quad} = 0 \quad \text{or} \quad x + \underline{\quad?\quad} = 0$$
$$\{x \mid (x + 3)^2 - 4(x + 3) - 77 = 0\} = \{\underline{\quad?\quad}, \underline{\quad?\quad}\}$$

24. The following equations can be solved in the two ways illustrated in Exercise 23. Use whichever method you prefer and check your solutions.
(a) $(x + 5)^2 - 9(x + 5) - 10 = 0$
(b) $(x + 2)^2 + 4(x + 2) - 5 = 0$
(c) $(x + 9)^2 - 225 = 0$
(d) $2(y - 1)^2 = 9(y - 1) + 161$

Solve each of the following equations and check each solution.

25. $4(2x + 1)^2 - 20(2x + 1) + 25 = 0$

26. $2(3x + 1)^2 + 5(3x + 1) - 12 = 0$

27. $(x - 1)^2 - 81 = 0$ **28.** $(x + 4)^2 = 19(x + 4)$

29. $25(t + 3)^2 - 256 = 0$ **30.** $(x - 1)(x + 2) = 10$

31. $(x + 6)(x - 4) = 24$ **32.** $y(3y - 5) - 12 = 0$

33. $t(2t + 1) = 28$

34. $(3y + 2)^2 - (2y - 3)^2 = 4(y^2 + 5y + 18)$

35. $2(t - 1)(t - 3) = (t - 3)(t - 2)$

3-3   MORE QUADRATIC EQUATIONS

An example of the use of quadratic equations is given in the following problem.

Problem. The flower garden shown in Fig. 3–1 is surrounded by a walk of uniform width. If the area of the walk is 1264 square feet, what is the width of the walk?

Solution. Let x designate the width of the walk in feet. Therefore, x must be a positive number. We may consider the walk to be composed of four rectangular pieces along the edge of the flower garden and four squares at the corners, as shown in

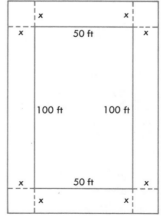

FIGURE 3–1

the figure. The areas of the four rectangles along the edge are $100x$, $100x$, $50x$, and $50x$; each corner square has area x^2. Thus,

$$300x + 4x^2$$

must be the area of the walk. By what is given,

$$300x + 4x^2 = 1264.$$

We have now reduced the problem to that of finding the positive solutions of the quadratic equation above. Each of the following quadratic equations is equivalent to the preceding one.

$$75x + x^2 = 316$$
$$x^2 + 75x - 316 = 0$$
$$(x + 79)(x - 4) = 0$$

Hence, $\{-79, 4\}$ is the solution set of the quadratic equation, and $\{4\}$ is the solution set of the problem, that is, the walk is 4 feet wide.

We may check this answer by noting that if the walk is 4 feet wide, then the flower garden, together with the walk, has dimensions 58 feet by 108 feet and area

$$58 \times 108, \quad \text{or } 6264 \text{ square feet.}$$

The area of the flower garden is 5000 square feet. Therefore, the area of the walk is

$$6264 - 5000, \quad \text{or } 1264 \text{ square feet,}$$

as given.

Exercises

1. An apartment building 200 feet by 300 feet is built on a lot containing 81,600 square feet. If a parking strip of uniform width surrounds the building, how wide is this strip?

2. A fringed rug covering three-fifths of a floor that measures 24 feet by 30 feet is placed so that a border of uniform width surrounds the rug. What are the dimensions of the rug?

3. Find the dimensions of a rectangle which has an area that is 216 square inches and a length that is 6 inches more than its width.

4. Find the dimensions of a rectangle if its area is 112 square inches and its length is 6 inches more than its width.

5. What are the dimensions of a rectangle which has a perimeter of 30 inches and an area of 54 square inches?

6. Find two numbers which differ by 4 and whose product is 96. Can you find a second set of two numbers which satisfy these conditions?

7. Find a pair of numbers such that their sum is 23 and the sum of their squares is 289. Is there more than one such pair?

8. The sum of two positive numbers is 10. Given that one number is 2 less then the square of the other, find both numbers.

9. Find three positive consecutive integers which have 509 as the sum of their squares.

10. The sum of the squares of two consecutive odd integers is 650. Find all such pairs of numbers.

11. Find two consecutive even integers whose product is 224. Find another such pair.

12. Find three consecutive positive integers which have 110 as the sum of their squares.

---

13. Find the lengths of the three sides of a right triangle if the hypotenuse is 1 foot longer than the longer leg and 3 feet less than 4 times as long as the shorter leg.

14. Find the set of numbers each of which is 30 less than its own square.

15. What two consecutive integers have cubes that differ by 217? How many such pairs are there?

Preparation for Section 3–4

Express each of the following in the form $A^2x^2 + 2ABx + B^2$.

1. $(x + 1)^2$ 2. $(x - 5)^2$

3. $(2x + 3)^2$ 4. $(5x - 1)^2$

5. $(x + \frac{1}{2})^2$ 6. $(x - \frac{2}{3})^2$

Factor each of the following.

7. $x^2 + 12x + 36$

8. $x^2 + 14x + 49$

9. $4x^2 - 20x + 25$

10. $9x^2 + 12x + 4$

11. $x^2 - \frac{1}{2}x + \frac{1}{16}$

12. $x^2 + \frac{2}{5}x + \frac{1}{25}$

3–4   COMPLETING THE SQUARE

Some quadratic polynomials are squares of linear forms.   For example,

$$x^2 = (x)^2,$$
$$x^2 + 100x + 2500 = (x + 50)^2,$$
$$49x^2 - 70x + 25 = (7x - 5)^2,$$

are squares of linear forms. As you learned in Section 3–1, a quadratic polynomial which is the square of a linear form is called a *perfect square.* Some quadratic equations are easily solved because they involve perfect squares. Consider the following example.

Problem 1. Solve the quadratic equation $4x^2 - 7 = 0$.

Solution. The given equation is equivalent to the equations

$$4x^2 = 7$$

and

$$x^2 = \tfrac{7}{4}.$$

The quadratic polynomial on the left side of this equation is a perfect square; the right side is a positive number. Evidently the only values of x that make this equation true are the square roots of $\tfrac{7}{4}$. Since each positive number has exactly two square roots, we have

$$x^2 = \tfrac{7}{4} \quad \text{if, and only if,} \quad x = \sqrt{\tfrac{7}{4}} \quad \text{or} \quad x = -\sqrt{\tfrac{7}{4}}.$$

Hence, the solution set of the given equation is

$$\{\tfrac{1}{2}\sqrt{7}, \ -\tfrac{1}{2}\sqrt{7}\}.$$

A given quadratic polynomial is a perfect square if, and only if, it has the pattern

$$x^2 + 2mx + m^2, \quad \text{or} \quad (x + m)^2.$$

Thus,

$$x^2 + 14x + 49$$

is a perfect square because $49 = (\tfrac{1}{2} \cdot 14)^2$, where $49 = m^2$ and $14 = 2m$. However,

$$x^2 + 10x + 20$$

is not a perfect square since $(\tfrac{1}{2} \cdot 10)^2$ is equal to 25, not 20.

If a quadratic polynomial has 1 as the coefficient of the square of the variable and zero as the constant term, then it is always possible to add a constant term to make the resulting quadratic polynomial a perfect square. For example, given the quadratic polynomial

$$x^2 + 18x,$$

we can add the square of half of the coefficient of x to it to make a perfect square:

$$x^2 + 18x + 9^2 = (x + 9)^2.$$

A second example is

$$y^2 - 11y$$

which can be made into a perfect square by adding $(-\frac{11}{2})^2$, or $\frac{121}{4}$, to it:

$$y^2 - 11y + \tfrac{121}{4} = (y - \tfrac{11}{2})^2.$$

The process of adding a constant term to a quadratic polynomial to make it a perfect square is called *completing the square*. This procedure enables us to solve quadratic equations with irrational solutions, as we shall now show.

Problem 2. Solve the quadratic equation $3x^2 + 4x - 8 = 0$.

Solution. The following two equations are equivalent to the given one.

$$3x^2 + 4x = 8$$
$$x^2 + \tfrac{4}{3}x = \tfrac{8}{3}$$

The quadratic polynomial $x^2 + \tfrac{4}{3}x$ may be made into a perfect square by adding the constant term $(\tfrac{1}{2} \cdot \tfrac{4}{3})^2$, or $(\tfrac{2}{3})^2$. If we add this number to each side of the last equation above, we get the equivalent equation

$$x^2 + \tfrac{4}{3}x + \tfrac{4}{9} = \tfrac{8}{3} + \tfrac{4}{9},$$

or

$$(x + \tfrac{2}{3})^2 = \tfrac{28}{9}.$$

Again,

$$(x + \tfrac{2}{3})^2 = \tfrac{28}{9}$$

if, and only if,

$$x + \tfrac{2}{3} = \sqrt{\tfrac{28}{9}} \quad \text{or} \quad x + \tfrac{2}{3} = -\sqrt{\tfrac{28}{9}},$$
$$x = -\tfrac{2}{3} + \tfrac{2}{3}\sqrt{7} \quad \text{or} \quad x = -\tfrac{2}{3} - \tfrac{2}{3}\sqrt{7}.$$

Thus,

$$\{-\tfrac{2}{3} + \tfrac{2}{3}\sqrt{7}, \ -\tfrac{2}{3} - \tfrac{2}{3}\sqrt{7}\}$$

is the solution set of the given equation. Using 2.646 as an approximation of $\sqrt{7}$, we find that the solutions are approximately 1.097 and -2.431.

The method illustrated in Problem 2 is called *solving a quadratic equation by completing the square.* Every quadratic equation can be solved by this method.

Exercises

Fill in the blanks to make each statement true.

1. (a) $x^2 + 2 \cdot 5x +$ __?__ $= (x +$ __?__$)^2$
   (b) $x^2 - 30x +$ __?__ $= (x -$ __?__$)^2$

2. (a) $x^2 - 2 \cdot 7x +$ __?__ $= (x -$ __?__$)^2$
   (b) $x^2 - 3x +$ __?__ $= (x -$ __?__$)^2$

3. (a) $x^2 + 16x +$ __?__ $= (x +$ __?__$)^2$
   (b) $x^2 + 7x +$ __?__ $= (x +$ __?__$)^2$

Give the value or values of k that will make each quadratic polynomial a perfect square.

4. (a) $x^2 + 18x + k$ (b) $x^2 + 9x + k$

5. (a) $x^2 - 18x + k$ (b) $x^2 + kx + \tfrac{25}{81}$

6. (a) $x^2 + kx + 400$ (b) $x^2 - 13x + k$

7. (a) $x^2 - kx + 196$ (b) $x^2 - kx + \tfrac{49}{36}$

Solve each of the following quadratic equations.

8. $4x^2 = 9$ **9.** $16x^2 = 49$

10. $(2x + 1)^2 = 4$ **11.** $(3x - 1)^2 = 9$

12. $(x - 2)^2 = 12$ **13.** $(x - 3)^2 = 18$

Use the method of completing the square to solve each of the following quadratic equations.

14. $y^2 + 4y - 2 = 0$ **15.** $z^2 - 6z - 16 = 0$

16. $t^2 + 5t + 1 = 0$ **17.** $v^2 - 15v - 15 = 1$

18. $10x - 19 = x^2$ **19.** $x^2 - 4x = 3$

20. $2y^2 + 2y - 1 = 0$ **21.** $6t - 1 = 2t^2$

22. $3x^2 + 5x - 1 = 0$ **23.** $5x^2 - 3x - 4 = 3$

24. $9x^2 + 42x + 5 = 1$ 25. $2x^2 - 7x + 4 = 0$
26. $4x^2 + 3x = 5$ 27. $4x^2 + 12x + 5 = 0$

28. (a) Use the method of completing the square to solve the quadratic equation $x^2 + 7x + 5 = 0$.
    (b) Check the larger of the two solutions in part (a).
    (c) Use the Table of Square Roots in the Appendix to find a three-decimal-place approximation of each irrational solution.

Use the method of completing the square to solve each of the following equations for x.

29. $x^2 + 2px + q = 0$ when $p^2 - q > 0$
30. $x^2 - rx - s = 0$ when $r^2 + 4s > 0$

3-5   MORE ON COMPLETING THE SQUARE

In the following problems, we shall give some more examples of quadratic equations which are solved by completing the square.

Problem 1. Solve the quadratic equation $x^2 - 2\sqrt{3}x + 1 = 0$.

Solution. We proceed in the following manner.

$$x^2 - 2\sqrt{3}x + 1 = 0$$
$$x^2 - 2\sqrt{3}x = -1$$
$$x^2 - 2\sqrt{3}x + \left(\frac{-2\sqrt{3}}{2}\right)^2 = -1 + \left(\frac{-2\sqrt{3}}{2}\right)^2$$
$$(x - \sqrt{3})^2 = -1 + 3$$
$$(x - \sqrt{3})^2 = (\sqrt{2})^2$$
$$x - \sqrt{3} = \sqrt{2} \quad \text{or} \quad x - \sqrt{3} = -\sqrt{2}$$
$$x = \sqrt{3} + \sqrt{2} \quad \text{or} \quad x = \sqrt{3} - \sqrt{2}$$

Hence, the solution set is

$$\{\sqrt{3} + \sqrt{2}, \ \sqrt{3} - \sqrt{2}\}.$$

Check. We shall check one answer and let you check the other.

$$(\sqrt{3} + \sqrt{2})^2 - 2\sqrt{3}(\sqrt{3} + \sqrt{2}) + 1 \overset{?}{=} 0$$
$$3 + (2\sqrt{3} \cdot \sqrt{2}) + 2 - [(2 \cdot 3) + (2\sqrt{3} \cdot \sqrt{2})] + 1 \overset{?}{=} 0$$
$$5 + 2\sqrt{6} - 6 - 2\sqrt{6} + 1 \overset{\vee}{=} 0$$

Although every quadratic equation can be solved by completing the square, not every quadratic equation has a real solution. The following equation is an example.

Problem 2. Solve the quadratic equation $x^2 - 4x + 5 = 0$.

Solution. We proceed to solve this equation by completing the square:

$$x^2 - 4x = -5,$$
$$x^2 - 4x + 4 = -5 + 4,$$
$$(x - 2)^2 = -1.$$

Because the square of a real number is nonnegative, we know that there is no real-number value of x which will make the equation $(x - 2)^2 = -1$ true. Thus, the equation has no real solution. Since the given equation is equivalent to $(x - 2)^2 = -1$, it also has no real solution. In other words, the solution set of the given equation is the empty set, $\emptyset$.

In the next chapter, we shall see that it is possible to enlarge our number system so that every quadratic equation has a solution in the larger system. However, as long as we restrict ourselves to the real number system, we shall find that some quadratic equations have empty solution sets.

Problem 3. Is it possible to construct a rectangle with a perimeter of 36 inches and an area of 36 square inches? If so, what are its dimensions?

Solution. Some possible rectangles having areas of 36 square inches are

6 inches $\times$ 6 inches,   9 inches $\times$ 4 inches,   12 inches $\times$ 3 inches,
18 inches $\times$ 2 inches,   36 inches $\times$ 1 inch.

Their respective perimeters are 24, 26, 30, 40, and 74 inches. It seems plausible that there is some rectangle with a length between 12 inches and 18 inches and a perimeter of 36 inches.

If the desired rectangle is x inches wide, then its length is $18 - x$ inches, as shown in Fig. 3–2. We are told that the area is 36 square inches, so that

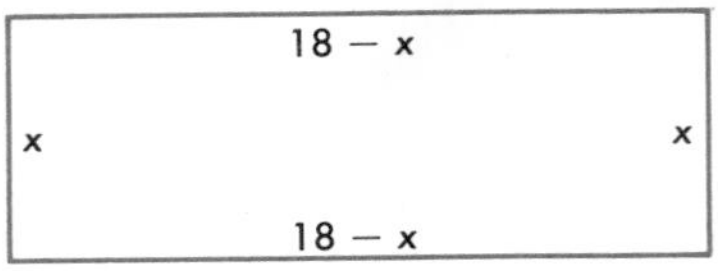

$$x(18 - x) = 36.$$

FIGURE 3–2

There does exist a rectangle with a perimeter of 36 inches and an area of 36 square inches if the equation above has a solution.

This equation is equivalent to each of the following equations:

$$18x - x^2 = 36,$$
$$x^2 - 18x = -36,$$
$$x^2 - 18x + (-9)^2 = -36 + (-9)^2,$$
$$(x - 9)^2 = -36 + 81,$$
$$(x - 9)^2 = 45.$$

Thus,

$$x - 9 = \sqrt{45} \quad \text{or} \quad x - 9 = -\sqrt{45},$$

or, equivalently,

$$x = 9 + 3\sqrt{5} \quad \text{or} \quad x = 9 - 3\sqrt{5}.$$

Which of these two numbers is a solution of the given problem? If $x = 9 + 3\sqrt{5}$, then

$$18 - x = 18 - (9 + 3\sqrt{5}) = 9 - 3\sqrt{5}.$$

Hence, the two solutions of the quadratic equation are the two dimensions of the desired rectangle. Since $\sqrt{5} \doteq 2.236$ ($\doteq$ means *is approximately equal to*), $9 + 3\sqrt{5} \doteq 15.71$ and $9 - 3\sqrt{5} \doteq 2.29$. Thus, the desired rectangle is approximately 15.71 by 2.29 inches.

Exercises

Solve each of the following quadratic equations. Check each solution by substitution. Compare the sum of the solutions with the coefficient of x. Compare the product of the solutions with the constant term.

1. (a) $x^2 - 2\sqrt{6}x + 2 = 0$ (b) $x^2 - 2\sqrt{6}x - 2 = 0$
2. (a) $x^2 - \sqrt{5}x + 1 = 0$ (b) $x^2 - \sqrt{5}x - 1 = 0$
3. (a) $x^2 + \sqrt{2}x - 4 = 0$ (b) $x^2 - 2\sqrt{7}x + 4 = 0$

In Exercises 4–7, some of the quadratic equations have real solutions and some do not. Find solutions for the equations that have them. Use the method of completing the square to show that there are no real solutions for the remaining equations.

4. (a) $3x^2 + 9x + 3 = 0$ (b) $3x^2 - 7x + 3 = 0$
5. (a) $x^2 - 4x + 8 = 0$ (b) $2t - 4 = t^2$
6. (a) $u^2 + 10u - 39 = 0$ (b) $2t^2 - 5t + 2 = 0$
7. (a) $3x^2 + 12 = 0$ (b) $2z^2 + 7 = 0$

Find the solution set of each of the following quadratic equations

8. $(x - 3)^2 = -4$ **9.** $x^2 - 20x = -200$

10. $x^2 + x + 1 = 0$ **11.** $4y^2 + 4y + 5 = 0$

12. $x^2 - 6x + 7 = 0$ **13.** $x^2 - 6x + 10 = 0$

14. (a) Use the method of completing the square to solve the given equation. Then check your answer.

$$x^2 - 2\sqrt{5}\,x + 3 = 0$$

     (b) Find the sum of the solutions found in part (a). Compare this sum with the coefficient of x in the quadratic equation.

     (c) Find the product of the solutions found in part (a). Compare this product with the constant term in the quadratic equation.

15. The length of a rectangle is 3 times its width. If the width is diminished by 1 foot and the length increased by 3 feet, the area will be 72 square feet. Find the dimensions of the original rectangle.

16. When a border of uniform width is added to a rectangular lot having dimensions 30 yards by 20 yards, the total area is double that of the original lot. Find the width of the border.

17. A piece of wire 40 centimeters long was cut into two pieces. Each piece was then bent to form a square frame. If the sum of the areas enclosed by the two wire frames is 58 square centimeters, how was the wire cut?

18. A rectangular field adjacent to a river is to be fenced in on only three sides, because the side on the river requires no fencing. A total of 100 rods of fencing are available.

     (a) Use x to denote the length of fence on each of the two sides at right angles to the river, and obtain a formula which gives the enclosed area A in terms of x.

     (b) If the enclosed area is to be 1200 square rods, what are the possible dimensions of the fence?

19. With a total of 300 rods of fencing, a rectangular field is to be completely surrounded with a fence and the enclosed area then divided in half by a fence parallel to one of the sides.

     (a) Obtain a formula for the total enclosed area A in terms of one variable.

     (b) Describe how the fencing can be used to make the total enclosed area 2400 square rods. Is there more than one way of doing this?

20. What is the largest value of k for each of the following that will give each quadratic equation real-number solutions?
(a) $x^2 - 6x + k = 0$ (b) $x^2 - 5x + k = 0$

21. What is the smallest positive value of k that will give the quadratic equation real-number solutions?
(a) $x^2 + kx + 64 = 0$ (b) $x^2 + kx + 10 = 0$

22. The sum of two numbers is 4 and the sum of their squares is 18. Find all possible pairs of numbers which satisfy this condition.

23. The length of a side of a square is 4 inches shorter than its diagonal. Find all squares having this property.

24. If a ball is thrown from the ground upward at a speed of 100 feet per second, the height it reaches t seconds after it is thrown is given by the formula

$$h = -16t^2 + 100t.$$

(a) How long does the ball take to rise to a height of 100 feet?
(b) Do both solutions of the quadratic equation in part (a) make sense?
(c) When does the ball return to the ground?

Review for Sections 3–1 through 3–5

If possible, factor each of the following polynomials.

1. $x^2 - x - 6$ **2.** $a^2 + 8a + 16$

3. $m^2 - 1$ **4.** $k^2 + 2k + 3$

5. $y^2 - 4x^2$ **6.** $2m^2 + 7m + 3$

Solve each of the following equations (using any of the methods presented) and check each solution in the original equation. Identify which equations have no real solutions.

7. $x^2 + x - 12 = 0$ **8.** $y^2 + 4y = 0$

9. $m^2 + 4 = 0$ **10.** $6t^2 + 7t + 4 = 2$

11. $12a^2 - 5a - 3 = 0$ **12.** $x^2 + 6x + 3 = 0$

13. $t^2 - 5t = 14$ **14.** $a^2 - 6a + 7 = 0$

15. $3k^2 - 16k + 5 = 0$ **16.** $m^2 + 9 = 0$

17. $y^2 - 4y - 32 = 0$ **18.** $3k^2 + 6k = 0$

19. $x^2 + 6x + 13 = 0$ **20.** $2t^2 - 11t - 21 = 0$

Answers to Review for Sections 3–1 through 3–5

1. $(x + 2)(x - 3)$ **2.** $(a + 4)^2$

3. $(m - 1)(m + 1)$ **4.** Not possible

5. $(y + 2x)(y - 2x)$ **6.** $(2m + 1)(m + 3)$

7. $\{3, -4\}$ **8.** $\{0, -4\}$

9. $\emptyset$, no real solution   **10.** $\{-\frac{1}{2}, -\frac{2}{3}\}$

11. $\{\frac{3}{4}, -\frac{1}{3}\}$ **12.** $\{-3 + \sqrt{6}, -3 - \sqrt{6}\}$

13. $\{7, -2\}$ **14.** $\{3 + \sqrt{2}, 3 - \sqrt{2}\}$

15. $\{\frac{1}{3}, 5\}$ **16.** $\emptyset$, no real solution

17. $\{-4, 8\}$ **18.** $\{0, -2\}$

19. $\emptyset$, no real solution   **20.** $\{7, -\frac{3}{2}\}$

3–6   QUADRATIC EQUATIONS OF THE FORM $y = ax^2 + c$

If a ball is dropped from a helicopter 400 feet above the ground, then the height h, in feet, of the ball above the ground t seconds after it is released is given by the equation

$$h = -16t^2 + 400.$$

This equation is correct in theory only, since it neglects the factor of friction involved. According to this formula,

$$h = 384 \text{ when } t = 1;$$
$$h = -64 + 400, \text{ or } 336, \text{ when } t = 2;$$
$$h = -144 + 400, \text{ or } 256, \text{ when } t = 3;$$
$$h = (-16 \cdot 25) + 400, \text{ or } 0, \text{ when } t = 5.$$

Thus, it takes 5 seconds for the ball to reach the ground.

The equation $h = -16t^2 + 400$ is an example of a quadratic equation in two variables, h and t. In this section, we shall study quadratic equations in two variables of the form

$$y = ax^2 + c, \qquad a \neq 0.$$

In particular, we shall study the graphs of equations of this form.

The simplest equation of this form is the one with $a = 1$ and $c = 0$:

$$y = x^2.$$

The graph of this equation is the graph of its solution set

$$S = \{(x, y) \mid y = x^2\},$$

or, equivalently,

$$S = \{(x, x^2) \mid x \text{ a real number}\}.$$

Several points on the graph of S are plotted in Fig. 3–3. The graph of S is a smooth curve, partially sketched in the figure. This curve is called a *parabola*. Some of the characteristics of this parabola are listed below.

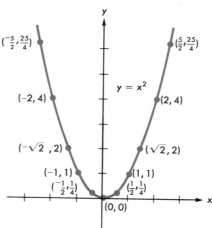

FIGURE 3-3

Symmetry. The points on the graph come in pairs:

$(1, 1)$ and $(-1, 1)$,
$(2, 4)$ and $(-2, 4)$,
$(\sqrt{2}, 2)$ and $(-\sqrt{2}, 2)$,
$(10^3, 10^6)$ and $(-10^3, 10^6)$,

and so on. In other words, if (x, y) is on the graph, then $(-x, y)$ is also on it. This means that the two parts of the graph on opposite sides of the y-axis are *mirror images* of each other. If we were to fold our paper along the y-axis, these two parts would coincide. We say that the y-axis is an *axis of symmetry* of the parabola, or, that the parabola is *symmetric about the y-axis*.

Vertex. The point at which the axis of symmetry cuts the parabola is called the vertex of the parabola. For the parabola above, the origin $(0, 0)$ is the vertex. In other words, the vertex is the *lowest point* on this particular parabola.

Infinite extent. The parabola extends far from its vertex. For example, the points $(10^{10}, 10^{20})$, $(10^{100}, 10^{200})$, and $(10^{1000}, 10^{2000})$ are on the parabola. Unlike a circle, a parabola is not a closed curve. The parabola above *opens upward.*

Next, let us consider the graph of the quadratic equation

$$y = -x^2.$$

Several points on the graph are plotted in Fig. 3–4, and a smooth

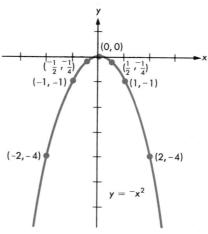

FIGURE 3-4

curve is drawn through them. This curve is also a parabola. Actually, it is the mirror image relative to the x-axis of the previous parabola. The y-axis continues to be the *axis of symmetry* of this parabola. Also, the origin $(0, 0)$ is the *vertex*. However, the vertex of this parabola is the *highest point* on the curve. This parabola *opens downward,* extending indefinitely far from its vertex.

Exercises

1. (a) On the same set of axes, graph the following equations.

$$y = 2x^2, \qquad y = -2x^2$$

Discuss the graphs by giving the symmetry, extent, and location of the vertex for each parabola.

(b) On the same set of axes, draw the parabolas which are the graphs of the given equations. Tell the axis of symmetry and location of the vertex for each parabola.

$$y = \tfrac{3}{2}x^2, \qquad y = -\tfrac{3}{2}x^2$$

2. (a) On the same set of axes draw the graphs of the equations below.

$$y = x^2, \qquad y = x^2 + 3$$

Write an equation of the axis of symmetry of each parabola.
Write the coordinates of the vertex of each parabola. What do the two points have in common?
In which direction does each parabola open?
Is the vertex the highest or the lowest point on each parabola?

(b) On the same set of axes, draw the graphs of the given equations.

$$y = 2x^2, \qquad y = 2x^2 - 5,$$

Give an equation of the axis of symmetry for each parabola.
Give the coordinates of the vertex for each parabola.
Could these parabolas be made to coincide with each other?

3. (a) On the same set of axes, draw the graphs of the given equations.

$$y = -\tfrac{1}{2}x^2, \qquad y = -\tfrac{1}{2}x^2 + 2$$

Do the curves have a common axis of symmetry? If so, give its equation.
Locate the vertices. What do they have in common?
Do the parabolas have a highest point or a lowest point?
Do these two graphs represent the same parabola located differently in the coordinate plane? What difference in their equations accounts for this difference in location?

(b) On the same set of axes, draw the graphs of the given equations.

$$y = \tfrac{1}{2}x^2, \qquad y = x^2, \qquad y = 2x^2$$

In what respect are the parabolas alike?
How do they differ?

4. (a) On the same set of axes, draw the graphs of the given equations.

$$y = -\tfrac{1}{3}x^2, \qquad y = -x^2, \qquad y = -3x^2$$

What do these parabolas have in common?

(b) For a given value of a, how do the graphs of $y = ax^2$ and $y = -ax^2$ differ? For each graph, discuss the symmetry, extent, and location of the vertex.

5. (a) In what quadrants does the graph of $y = ax^2$ lie when $a > 0$? $a < 0$?

(b) As $|a|$ increases, what happens to the graph of $y = ax^2$?

---

6. Consider the graphs of

$$y = ax^2 \quad \text{and} \quad y = ax^2 + c,$$

with a and c nonzero real numbers.
(a) What is the axis of symmetry for each parabola?
(b) Give the coordinates of the vertices.
(c) How do the directions of opening compare?
(d) What is a necessary condition for the parabolas to open upward?

7. Write an equation of the parabola with vertex at $(0, 4)$ and axis of symmetry on the y-axis when, in addition,
(a) it opens upward and has the same shape as the parabola with equation $y = 3x^2 + 8$.
(b) it opens downward and has the same shape as the parabola with equation $y = 2x^2 - 12$.

8. Write equations for the two parabolas which have a common vertex at the origin and the y-axis as the axis of symmetry of each, given that one parabola passes through the point $(1, 2)$ and the other passes through the point $(1, -2)$.

9. The equation

$$h = -16t^2 + 400,$$

which was discussed at the beginning of this section, may be graphed on a set of axes labeled t instead of x, and h instead of y. Draw the graph, using different scales on the two axes. Describe the graph. Why are we concerned only with those t-values which lie in the closed interval from 0 to 5?

10. The graph of a parabola described by an equation of the type

$$y = ax^2 + c$$

passes through the two points $(0, 3)$ and $(1, 5)$. What is an equation for this particular parabola? Show that the condition that the two points be on the parabola completely determines the values of a and c as the solution set of a system of two linear equations.

11. A parabola described by an equation of the type

$$y = ax^2 + c$$

is known to pass through points $(1, 4)$ and $(-1, 4)$.
    (a) Show that this condition is *not* sufficient to determine the particular parabola.
    (b) Give equations of three specific parabolas of this type which satisfy the condition given.

12. Why do the two points in Exercise 10 determine a unique parabola, although the two points in Exercise 11 do not?

13. Draw the graph of $y = -4x^2$ and the graph of $y - 3 = -4x^2$ on separate axes. Compare and contrast the graphs.

14. Draw the graph of $y = 4x^2$ and the graph of $y^2 = \frac{1}{4}x$ on the same set of axes. Compare and contrast the graphs.

3-7 QUADRATIC EQUATIONS OF THE FORM $y = ax^2 + bx + c$

In the preceding section, we considered dropping a ball from a helicopter. Now let us consider throwing a ball toward the ground with an initial speed of 80 feet per second. According to a law of physics, the height h of the ball above the ground t seconds after it is thrown is given by the equation $h = -16t^2 - 80t + 400$. Thus,

$$h = -16 - 80 + 400, \text{ or } 304, \text{ when } t = 1;$$
$$h = -64 - 160 + 400, \text{ or } 176, \text{ when } t = 2;$$
$$h = -144 - 240 + 400, \text{ or } 16, \text{ when } t = 3.$$

It is evident that the ball reaches the ground (that is, $h = 0$) slightly more than 3 seconds after it is thrown.

In this section, we shall study quadratic equations in two variables which have the form

$$y = ax^2 + bx + c, \qquad a \neq 0.$$

Problem 1. Discuss the graphs of the following equations.

(a) $y = (x - 3)^2$ (b) $y = (x - 3)^2 + 2$

Solution.

(a) Since $(x - 3)^2$ is nonnegative for every real number x, we must have $y \geq 0$ in each solution (x, y) of this equation. It follows that zero is the least value of y and therefore, $(3, 0)$ is the lowest, or minimum, point on the graph. Several points are plotted in Fig. 3–5. The points appear in pairs and are equally spaced on each side of the line $x = 3$. For example, if we let $y = 4$ in this equation, then $(x - 3)^2 = 4$, and either $x - 3 = 2$ or $x - 3 = -2$; that is, if $y = 4$, then either $x = 5$ or $x = 1$. Hence, the points $(1, 4)$ and $(5, 4)$ are on the graph. If we let $y = k$, then, by the same argument, we may show that the two points $(3 - \sqrt{k}, k)$ and $(3 + \sqrt{k}, k)$ are on the graph and are equally spaced on each side of the line $x = 3$.

The graph of $y = (x - 3)^2$ has the same shape as that of $y = x^2$, which is sketched in Fig. 3–3. Of course, the two graphs are located differently in relation to the coordinate axes. We conclude that the graph of $y = (x - 3)^2$ is a parabola with vertex $(3, 0)$ and the line $x = 3$ as its axis of symmetry. It opens upward, extending indefinitely far above the x-axis.

(b) If (r, s) is a point on the graph of $y = (x - 3)^2$, then $(r, s + 2)$ is a point on the graph of $y = (x - 3)^2 + 2$. For example, $(2, 1)$

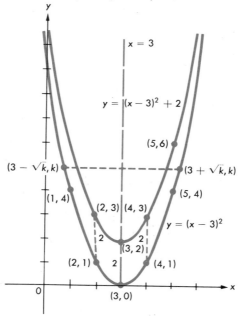

FIGURE 3–5

is on the graph of $y = (x - 3)^2$ and $(2, 3)$ is on the graph of $y = (x - 3)^2 + 2$; also, $(5, 4)$ is on the graph of $y = (x - 3)^2$ and $(5, 6)$ is on the graph of $y = (x - 3)^2 + 2$. Consequently, the graph of $y = (x - 3)^2 + 2$ is the graph of the preceding equation shifted vertically upward two units (the upper curve in Fig. 3–5). The vertex of this parabola is at $(3, 2)$ and the axis of symmetry is the line $x = 3$.

Problem 2. Discuss the graphs of the following equations.

(a) $y = \frac{1}{2}(x + 1)^2$ (b) $y = \frac{1}{2}(x + 1)^2 - 3$

Solution.
(a) Since $\frac{1}{2}(x + 1)^2$ is nonnegative for each real number x, and $\frac{1}{2}(x + 1)^2$ is zero if, and only if, $x = -1$, it follows that $(-1, 0)$ is the minimum point on the graph. Thus, the line $x = -1$ is an axis of symmetry of this graph. Several symmetrically placed pairs of points are sketched in Fig. 3–6. This graph is a parabola; its vertex is the point $(-1, 0)$. When we multiplied $(x + 1)^2$ by $\frac{1}{2}$, we caused this parabola to open wider than the corresponding parabola $y = (x + 1)^2$.

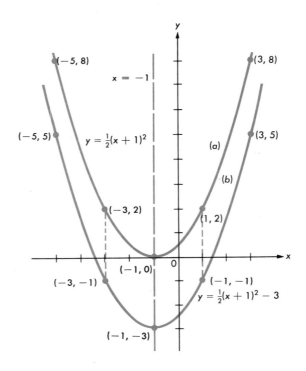

FIGURE 3–6

(b) For each real number r, $(r, \frac{1}{2}(r + 1)^2)$ is a point on graph (a) in Fig. 3–6, and $(r, \frac{1}{2}(r + 1)^2 - 3)$ is a point on graph (b). For example, $(3, 8)$ is on graph (a) and $(3, 5)$ is on graph (b). Thus, we conclude that the graph of this equation is the graph of the preceding equation shifted vertically downward three units (the lower curve in Fig. 3–6). The vertex of this parabola is at $(-1, -3)$.

Problem 3. Discuss the graph of the equation $y = -2x^2 - 4x + 3$.

Solution. We may complete the square as follows:

$$y = -2(x^2 + 2x) + 3,$$
$$y = -2(x^2 + 2x + 1) + 2 + 3, \quad \text{(because } -2 + 2 = 0, \text{ Inv-A)}$$
$$y = -2(x + 1)^2 + 5.$$

Since the last equation is equivalent to the given one, the graph of the given equation is the same as the graph of

$$y = -2(x + 1)^2 + 5.$$

Notice that the graph of this equation is symmetric about the line $x = -1$. Thus, for example, the pairs of points

$$(-2, 3) \quad \text{and} \quad (0, 3),$$
$$(-3, -3) \quad \text{and} \quad (1, -3)$$
$$(-11, -195) \quad \text{and} \quad (9, -195),$$

are symmetrically located about the line $x = -1$.

Since $-2(x + 1)^2 \leq 0$ for every real number x, the maximum value of y occurs when $-2(x + 1)^2 = 0$. Hence, the point $(-1, 5)$ is the highest point on the graph. We conclude that the graph is a parabola with vertex $(-1, 5)$ and the line $x = -1$ as its axis of symmetry. It opens downward and extends indefinitely far in that direction, as indicated in Fig. 3–7. By looking at the graph, we see that the parabola crosses the x-axis at approximately $(-2.6, 0)$ and $(.6, 0)$. Hence, -2.6 and $.6$ are approximations of the solutions of the equation

$$-2x^2 - 4x + 3 = 0.$$

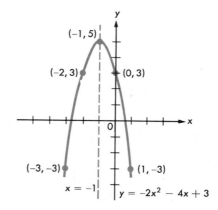

FIGURE 3-7

The exact solutions are

$$-1 - \tfrac{1}{2}\sqrt{10} \quad \text{and} \quad -1 + \tfrac{1}{2}\sqrt{10}.$$

Problem 3 is an example of the fact that every equation of the form

$$y = ax^2 + bx + c, \qquad a \neq 0 \tag{1}$$

can be changed into one of the form

$$y = a(x - h)^2 + k \tag{2}$$

where equations (1) and (2) are equivalent. The graph is a parabola with

axis of symmetry the line $x - h = 0$,
vertex the point (h, k).

The graph opens upward if $a > 0$, downward if $a < 0$. Letting $x = h \pm 1$, $h \pm 2$, and so on, we can quickly find ordered pairs in the solution set and sketch the graph.

Problem 4. (a) Discuss the graph of the equation $y = 2x^2 + 12x + 17$.
(b) From the graph approximate the solutions of the equation $2x^2 + 12x + 17 = 0$.

Solution.
(a) $y = 2x^2 + 12x + 17$ is equivalent to the equation $y = 2(x^2 + 6x) + 17$, which in turn is equivalent to each of the following equations.

$$y = 2(x^2 + 6x + 9) - 2 \cdot 9 + 17 \qquad \text{(Inv-A; Id-A)}$$
$$y = 2(x + 3)^2 - 1$$

From the equation

$$y = 2(x + 3)^2 - 1$$

we know the axis of symmetry of the parabola is the line $x + 3 = 0$ or $x = -3$ and the vertex is at $(-3, -1)$. The parabola opens upward because the coefficient of x^2 is positive. We let $x = -3 \pm 1$, -3 ± 2 and sketch the graph from these four points and the vertex.

x	$-3 - 2$	$-3 - 1$		$-3 + 1$	$-3 + 2$
	-5	-4	-3	-2	-1
$y = 2(x + 3)^2 - 1$	7	1	-1	1	7

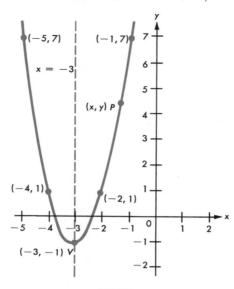

FIGURE 3-8

(b) Any point $P(x, y)$ on the parabola has coordinates that make the equation $y = 2x^2 + 12x + 17$ true. Points A and B on the x-axis each have $y = 0$. Hence the abscissa of A (also of B) makes the statement $2x^2 + 12x + 17 = 0$ true. Therefore, from the graph the solutions of the quadratic $2x^2 + 12x + 17 = 0$ are approximately -3.8 and -2.3.

We can find the exact solutions by completing the square as shown below.

$$2x^2 + 12x + 17 = 0$$

$$x^2 + 6x + 9 = \frac{-17}{2} + 9$$

$$(x + 3)^2 = \frac{1}{2}$$

$$x + 3 = \sqrt{\tfrac{1}{2}} \qquad \text{or} \qquad x + 3 = -\sqrt{\tfrac{1}{2}}$$

$$x = -3 + \tfrac{1}{2}\sqrt{2} \quad \text{or} \qquad x = -3 - \tfrac{1}{2}\sqrt{2}$$

$$-3 + \tfrac{1}{2}\sqrt{2} \doteq -3 + .7 \quad \text{or} \quad -2.3;$$

$$-3 - \tfrac{1}{2}\sqrt{2} \doteq -3 - .7 \quad \text{or} \quad -3.7$$

This agrees satisfactorily with our graphical estimates.

We have just seen that the solutions of a quadratic equation in x, $ax^2 + bx + c = 0$, are the abscissas of the crossing-points on the x-axis of the parabola which is the graph of the equation $y = ax^2 + bx + c$.

Exercises

1. (a) If $y = (x - 2)^2$, find y when $x = 2, 2 \pm 1, 2 \pm 3$. Record the results in a table.

x	$2 - 3$	$2 - 1$	2	$2 + 1$	$2 + 3$
y	?				

(b) If $y = (x + 2)^2$, find y when $x = -2, -2 \pm 1, -2 \pm 2$. Record the results in a table.

x	$-2 - 2$	$-2 - 1$	-2	$-2 + 1$	$-2 + 2$
y	?				

2. (a) If $y = (x - 1)^2$, for what two values of x does $y = 1$? 25? 36?
   (b) If $y = (x - 1)^2$, for what other value of x will y have the same value as it does when $x = \frac{3}{2}$? $\frac{5}{2}$? $\frac{7}{2}$?

3. (a) Graph the equation

$$y = (x - 1)^2.$$

Give an equation of the axis of symmetry and the coordinates of the vertex of the parabola. Does y have a minimum value? If so, what is it?

   (b) Graph the equation

$$y = (x - 1)^2 - 4.$$

Give an equation of the axis of symmetry and the coordinates of the vertex of the parabola. What is the minimum value of y? Where is the vertex of the parabola with equation $y = (x - 1)^2 + 5$?

4. (a) Discuss the graph of

$$y = -(x - 1)^2.$$

Give an equation of the axis of symmetry and the coordinates of the vertex. Does y have a minimum value? If so, what is it? Does y have a maximum value? If so, what is it?

   (b) Discuss the graph of

$$y = -(x - 1)^2 + 3,$$

and tell how it is related to the graph of $y = -(x - 1)^2$ in 6(a).

5. Sketch and discuss the graphs of each of the following equations.
   (a) $y = \frac{1}{4}(x - 2)^2$ \qquad\qquad (b) $y = \frac{1}{4}(x - 2)^2 + 4$

6. (a) On the same set of axes, draw the graphs of the equations $y = 2x^2$, $y = 2x^2 + 4$, and $y = 2(x - 5)^2$.

In what direction do the parabolas open?

Write an equation of the axis of symmetry of each parabola.

What change in the equation $y = 2x^2$ shifts the axis of symmetry?

What are the coordinates of the vertex of each parabola?

What change in the equation $y = 2x^2$ shifts the vertex horizontally?

What change in the equation $y = 2x^2$ shifts the vertex vertically?

Write an equation of a parabola which has its vertex at $(5, 4)$ and opens in the same direction as the graph of $y = 2x^2$.

(b) On the same set of axes, draw the graphs of the equations $y = -x^2$, $y = -x^2 + 2$, and $y = -(x + 2)^2$.

In what direction do the parabolas open?

Write an equation of the axis of symmetry of each parabola.

What change in the equation $y = -x^2$ shifts the axis of symmetry?

What are the coordinates of the vertex of each parabola?

What change in the equation $y = -x^2$ shifts the vertex horizontally?

What change in the equation $y = -x^2$ shifts the vertex vertically?

Sketch the graph of $y = -(x + 2)^2 + 2$. Locate the vertex and give an equation of the axis of symmetry.

Write each of the following equations in the form $y = a(x - h)^2$. Then locate the axis of symmetry and the vertex of the parabola which is the graph of each equation.

7. (a) $y = 3x^2 - 30x + 75$ (b) $y = -2x^2 + 20x - 50$

8. (a) $y = x^2 + 12x + 36$ (b) $y = 3x^2 - 6x + 3$

---

9. (a) Find an equation of the type $y = a(x - h)^2 + k$ which is equivalent to the equation $y = x^2 + 4x + 1$.

(b) Give an equation of the axis of symmetry of the graph

$$y = x^2 + 4x + 1.$$

(c) Give the coordinates of the vertex of the graph of $y = x^2 + 4x + 1$.

(d) Draw the graph of $y = x^2 + 4x + 1$.

(e) Give an approximation of the abscissas of the points at which the graph of $y = x^2 + 4x + 1$ crosses the x-axis.

(f) Find the exact solutions of the equation $x^2 + 4x + 1 = 0$, and compare them with the approximations in part (e).

Transform each equation into the form $y = a(x - h)^2 + k$, and draw its graph. In each case, give the coordinates of the vertex and an equation of the axis of symmetry.

10. $y = 3x^2 - 6x + 2$ **11.** $y = -9x^2 + 6x - 1$

12. $y + x^2 + 2x + 2 = 0$ **13.** $y + 2x^2 + 12x + 15 = 0$

14. Graph the equation

$$y = -2x^2 - 12x - 15.$$

Then compare the abscissas of the crossing points on the x-axis with the exact solutions of the equation

$$2x^2 + 12x + 15 = 0.$$

15. (a) Graph the equation $y = -x^2 - 2x - 2$.
(b) Does the graph cross the x-axis?
(c) By looking at the graph in part (a), what can you say about the solution set of $-x^2 - 2x - 2 = 0$?

16. A parabola described by an equation of the type

$$y = ax^2 + bx + c$$

is known to pass through points

$$(1, 3), \quad (-1, 5), \quad (2, 11).$$

What is the equation for this particular parabola?

17. Find the system of linear equations in a, b, and c which would have to be solvable for a parabola with an equation of the type

$$y = ax^2 + bx + c$$

to pass through points

$$(1, 1), \quad (2, 3), \quad (4, 7).$$

Does the system determine values for a, b, and c? Do these values for a, b, and c determine a parabola? Plot the three points to see what the difficulty is.

18. A projectile is thrown straight up from a height of 6 feet with an initial velocity of 192 feet per second. If air resistance is neglected, h, the projectile's height in feet after t seconds, is given by the equation

$$h = 6 + 192t - 16t^2.$$

Using h for the vertical axis and t for the horizontal axis, graph the equation. From the graph, determine at what time after the projectile is thrown it reaches its maximum height. What is this maximum height?

19. (a) Write a formula for the sum y of the squares of two numbers if one number is denoted by x and if it is given that the sum of the numbers is 30.
(b) Use the graph of the formula to determine the two numbers for which the sum of their squares is a minimum.
(c) Are there two numbers with a sum of 30 such that the sum of their squares is a maximum?

20. A piece of wire 40 inches long is cut into two pieces, and each piece is bent to form a square frame.
   (a) Write a formula for A, the sum of the areas of the two squares, in terms of x, the length of one piece of the wire.
   (b) Graph the formula for a meaningful x.
   (c) From the graph, determine how the wire should be cut to make two squares of minimum total area.
   (d) What is the minimum total area of the two squares?
   (e) Is there a maximum total area of the two squares? How could you use the wire to enclose this maximum area?
   (f) How does this exercise differ from Exercise 19?

21. (a) Write an equation expressing the area, y square feet, of a rectangle x feet long if the perimeter is 70 feet.
   (b) What values of x are meaningful in this problem? Sketch the graph for this set of x's. What are the coordinates of its vertex?
   (c) In this set of rectangles with perimeter 70 feet, what are the dimensions of the rectangle that encloses the maximum area?
   (d) What is the maximum area that can be enclosed by a rectangle with a perimeter of 70 feet?

22. Questionnaires were distributed at a Shakespearean festival in Stratford, Ontario. From them, it was learned that if tickets were sold at $1.50, then 200 people would come. Further sampling revealed that for each 10¢ reduction in the price of admission, 25 more people would attend. For what admission price would the gross income be a maximum?

3-8   QUADRATIC INEQUALITIES IN TWO VARIABLES

Just as a line divides the plane in which it lies into two parts, a parabola divides the plane in which it lies into two parts. For example, the parabola with equation

$$y = x^2$$

divides the plane. The shaded part of Fig. 3-9 is called the *inside* of the parabola, while the rest of the plane, excluding the parabola itself, is called the *outside* of the parabola.

For each real number x, the point (x, x^2) is on the parabola $y = x^2$. The point (x, y) is inside this parabola provided it is directly above

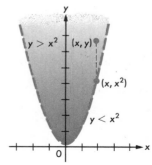

FIGURE 3-9

the point (x, x^2). In other words, the point (x, y) is inside the parabola if, and only if, $y > x^2$. Similarly, the point (x, y) is outside the parabola if, and only if, $y < x^2$. In the language of algebra, the inside of this parabola is the graph of the set

$$\{(x, y) \mid y > x^2\},$$

and the outside of this parabola is the graph of the set

$$\{(x, y) \mid y < x^2\}.$$

Problem 1. The parabola with equation

$$y = x^2 - 6x + 11$$

is drawn in Fig. 3–10. Describe the inside and the outside of this parabola.

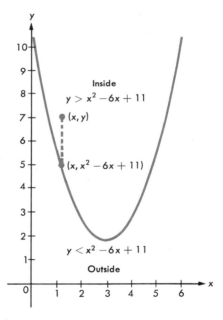

FIGURE 3–10

Solution. For each real number x, the point $(x, x^2 - 6x + 11)$ is on the parabola. Looking at the figure, we see that a point (x, y) is inside the parabola if, and only if it is directly above the point with coordinates $(x, x^2 - 6x + 11)$. Hence, the graph of the set

$$\{(x, y) \mid y > x^2 - 6x + 11\}$$

is the inside of the parabola, and the graph of the set

$$\{(x, y) \mid y < x^2 - 6x + 11\}$$

is the outside of the parabola.

Problem 2. The parabola with equation

$$y = -2x^2 - 4x + 3$$

is drawn in Fig. 3–11. Describe the inside and the outside of this parabola.

Solution. For each real number x, the point $(x, -2x^2 - 4x + 3)$ is on this parabola. Since this parabola opens downward, the inside is below the parabola. Thus, the graph of the set

$$\{(x, y) \mid y < -2x^2 - 4x + 3\}$$

is the inside, and the graph of the set

$$\{(x, y) \mid y > -2x^2 - 4x + 3\}$$

is the outside of this parabola.

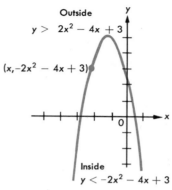

FIGURE 3-11

Problem 3. Describe the graph of the inequality $y + 3x^2 < 12x$.

Solution. By adding the quadratic polynomial $-3x^2$ to each side of this inequality, we derive the equivalent inequality

$$y < -3x^2 + 12x.$$

We complete the square for the quadratic polynomial $-3x^2 + 12x$ as follows:

$$-3x^2 + 12x = -3(x^2 - 4x),$$
$$-3x^2 + 12x = -3(x^2 - 4x + 4) + 12,$$
$$-3x^2 + 12x = -3(x - 2)^2 + 12.$$

Thus, the given inequality is equivalent to the inequality

$$y < -3(x - 2)^2 + 12.$$

The graph of the equation

$$y = -3(x - 2)^2 + 12$$

is a parabola with vertex $(2, 12)$. The line $x = 2$ is the axis of symmetry, and the parabola opens downward, as shown in Fig. 3-11. A point (x, y) for which

$$y < -3(x - 2)^2 + 12$$

is located inside the parabola. Thus, the graph of the given inequality is

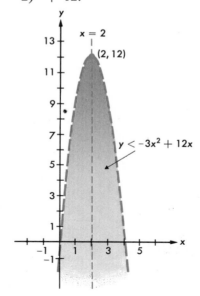

FIGURE 3-12

the inside of the parabola with equation

$$y = -3(x - 2)^2 + 12.$$

It is the shaded region shown in Fig. 3–12.

Problem 4. Find the solution set of the quadratic inequality in x, $x^2 - x - 6 \leq 0$, using algebraic methods.

Solution. The given inequality $x^2 - x - 6 \leq 0$ is equivalent to the inequality

$$(x - 3)(x + 2) \leq 0$$

with the trinomial $x^2 - x - 6$ in factored form. Thus, if

$$S = \{x \mid x^2 - x - 6 \leq 0\},$$

then

$$S = \{x \mid (x - 3)(x + 2) \leq 0\}.$$

Obviously $(x - 3)(x + 2) = 0$ if $x = 3$ or if $x = -2$. Hence the set $T = \{3, -2\}$ is a subset of S.

Other members of S are those values of x for which

$$(x - 3)(x + 2) < 0.$$

A product of two factors is negative if the factors have opposite signs. Therefore we require either of the following simultaneous conditions.

(1) $\begin{cases} x - 3 < 0 \\ x + 2 > 0 \end{cases}$ (2) $\begin{cases} x - 3 > 0 \\ x + 2 < 0 \end{cases}$

System (1) has solution set

$$R = \{x \mid x < 3\} \cap \{x \mid x > -2\} = \{x \mid -2 < x < 3\},$$

which is graphed in Fig. 3–13.

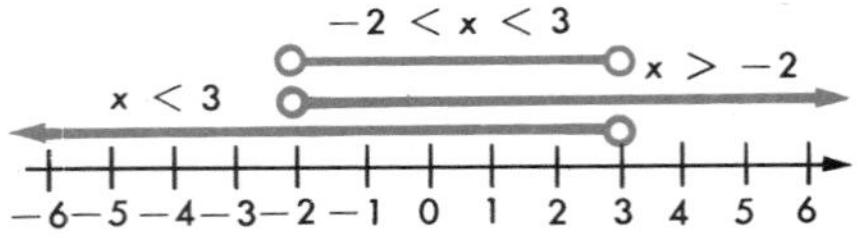

FIGURE 3–13

On the *open interval* $-2 < x < 3$ it is true that $x^2 - x - 6 < 0$. Thus $R = \{x \mid -2 < x < 3\}$ is a subset of S.

System (2) has solution set

$$\{x \mid x > 3\} \cap \{x \mid x < -2\},$$

which is graphed in Fig. 3–14.

FIGURE 3–14

Since the graphs do not intersect, the solution set of (2) is the empty set. We see now that S is the union of sets T and R; that is

$$\{x \mid x^2 - x - 6 \leq 0\} = \{-2, 3\} \cup \{-2 < x < 3\}.$$

Thus S is the *closed interval*

$$\{x \mid -2 \leq x \leq 3\}.$$

Problem 5. Using graphical methods, find the solution set of the quadratic inequality $x^2 - x - 6 \leq 0$.

Solution. Let $y = x^2 - x - 6$ and draw the graph of this equation. Whenever $y \leq 0$, $x^2 - x - 6 \leq 0$. Hence we want to know where the parabola crosses the x-axis and dips below the x-axis into quadrants III or IV. The equation

$$y = x^2 - x - 6$$

is equivalent to

$$y = (x^2 - x + \tfrac{1}{4}) - \tfrac{1}{4} - 6,$$

or

$$y = (x - \tfrac{1}{2})^2 - \tfrac{25}{4}.$$

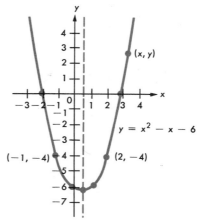

The graph of this last equation is the parabola with axis of symmetry $x = \tfrac{1}{2}$ and vertex $(\tfrac{1}{2}, -\tfrac{25}{4})$ sketched in Fig. 3–15. Obviously, $y \leq 0$ when $-2 \leq x \leq 3$. Therefore

FIGURE 3–15

$$\{x \mid x^2 - x - 6 \leq 0\} = \{x \mid -2 \leq x \leq 3\}.$$

Exercises

1. (a) Tell whether each of the following points is inside, outside, or on the graph of the parabola whose equation is $y = 4x^2 + 4$.

$$(-1, 8), \quad (0, 7), \quad (\tfrac{1}{2}, 5), \quad (2, 21), \quad (1, 1), \quad (-5, -10)$$

(b) Tell whether each of the following points is inside, outside, or on the graph of the parabola whose equation is $y = 6 - 5x^2$.

$$(0, -1), \quad (5, 2), \quad (0, 8), \quad (-3, 3), \quad (1, 1), \quad (2, -14), \quad (2, -1)$$

2. Graph the parabola for each of the following equations. Write an inequality that describes the inside and the outside of each parabola.
   (a) $y = x^2 - 6x - 1$ (b) $y = -3x^2 + 12x + 2$

3. Graph each of the following equations, and describe algebraically the inside and the outside of each parabola.
   (a) $2y = -x^2 + 8x - 12$ (b) $y = 2x^2 + 8x + 10$

4. Describe the graph of each of the following inequalities by graphing a related parabola.
   (a) $y + x^2 + 4x + 4 < 0$ (b) $y > 2x^2 - 4x - 1$

Graph each of the inequalities and describe the graph.

5. (a) $x^2 + y \leq 6y + 3$ (b) $4x^2 + 4x + 1 > 8y$
6. (a) $y + 3x^2 > 6x - 1$ (b) $y + 1 \leq -5x^2$

---

7. What value of x gives the quadratic form $10 - x^2$ its maximum value? Does it have a minimum value? (Hint: Graph $y = 10 - x^2$.)

8. What is the maximum value of each of the following quadratic polynomials for real values of x?
   (a) $-x^2 + 10x + 2$ (b) $3 - x^2 + 7x$

9. What is the minimum value of each of the following quadratic polynomials for real values of x?
   (a) $x^2 - 6x + 8$ (b) $x^2 - 5x - 2$

10. The height s, in feet, of an object above the ground at time t seconds is given by the equation $s = 64t - 16t^2$.
   (a) For what values of t is $s > 28$?
   (b) For what values of t is $s < 48$?
   (c) For what values of t is $s = 0$?

11. The volume V, in cubic inches, of water remaining in a leaking pail after t seconds is given by the equation $V = \tfrac{1}{5}(t - 100)^2$.
   (a) For what values of t is $V > 1000$?
   (b) For what values of t is $V < 500$?
   (c) When does the leaking stop?

12. (a) From Fig. 3–15, for what values of x is $x^2 - x - 6 > 0$?
(b) What is the minimum value of $x^2 - x - 6$?

13. (a) From Fig. 3–12, for what values of x is $12x - 3x^2 > 0$?
(b) Use Fig. 3–12 to solve the inequality $12x - 3x^2 < 0$.
(c) What is the maximum value of $12x - 3x^2$?

14. Use algebraic methods to answer the following questions.
(a) For what values of x is the quadratic form $10 - 3x - x^2$ negative?
(b) For what values of x is $10 - 3x - x^2$ positive?

Find the solution set of each quadratic inequality in x. Use either algebraic or graphical methods.

15. $x^2 - 4x + 4 > 0$ **16.** $x^2 - 2x + 1 < 0$

17. $x^2 - 5x - 6 \geq 0$ **18.** $x^2 - 4x - 5 < 0$

*19. (a) From Fig. 3–11, what is the maximum value of $-2x^2 - 4x + 3$?
(b) From Fig. 3–11, for what values of x is $-2x^2 - 4x + 3 > 0$?
(c) Find the exact solutions of the equation $-2x^2 - 4x + 3 = 0$ by the method of completing the square. Did you answer the question in (b) correctly?

*3–9 MODULAR ARITHMETIC

The real number system contains infinitely many elements, but this is not true of all number systems. In fact, there is a number system, called *integers modulo n,* where for every positive integer n, the system contains exactly n elements. Operations of addition and multiplication are defined in the system of integers modulo n, and most of the properties that apply to these operations are true for the modular system.

An example of such a modular system is the system of *integers modulo 6,* denoted by Z_6. The six elements of Z_6 are denoted by 0, 1, 2, 3, 4, and 5:

$$Z_6 = \{0, 1, 2, 3, 4, 5\}.$$

In Z_6 we add numbers by first adding them as we do in the system of integers and then "casting out," or subtracting, 6's until we obtain a number in Z_6. We perform multiplication in a similar way. For example, in each of the sums and products

$$1 + 2 = 3, \quad 0 + 4 = 4, \quad 2 + 3 = 5,$$
$$1 \times 2 = 2, \quad 2 \times 2 = 4, \quad 3 \times 0 = 0,$$

there is no need to "cast out" 6's because each sum and product is less than 6. However, $3 + 4 = 7$ in the system of integers and 7 is not in Z_6. In Z_6 we "cast out," or subtract, one 6 from 7 and obtain

$$3 + 4 = 1.$$

Also, $3 \times 5 = 15$, and 15 is not in Z_6. Therefore, we "cast out" two 6's from 15 and obtain

$$3 \times 5 = 3.$$

Similarly,

$$4 + 2 = 0, \quad 2 + 5 = 1, \quad 4 + 4 = 2,$$
$$4 \times 2 = 2, \quad 2 \times 5 = 4, \quad 4 \times 4 = 4.$$

It may be shown that in Z_6 the operations of addition and multiplication are commutative and associative and that the distributive law holds. Also, 0 is the additive identity element and 1 is the multiplicative identity element. Each number in Z_6 has an additive inverse, or opposite. Thus, $1 + 5 = 0$ and hence, 5 and 1 are opposites of each other:

$$5 = -1 \quad \text{and} \quad 1 = -5.$$

Also, $2 + 4 = 0$ and hence, 2 and 4 are opposites of each other:

$$4 = -2 \quad \text{and} \quad 2 = -4.$$

Also, $3 + 3 = 0$ and hence, 3 is its own opposite:

$$3 = -3.$$

Not every nonzero element of Z_6 has a multiplicative inverse, or reciprocal. For example, $5 \times 5 = 1$, and therefore, 5 is its own reciprocal:

$$5 = \tfrac{1}{5}.$$

This is not too surprising, since $-1 = 5$ in Z_6 and $(-1)^2 = 1$. On the other hand, 2, 3, and 4 do not have reciprocals. For example,

$$2 \times 0 = 0, \quad 2 \times 1 = 2, \quad 2 \times 2 = 4,$$
$$2 \times 3 = 0, \quad 2 \times 4 = 2, \quad 2 \times 5 = 4,$$

so that $2x$ is never equal to 1 for any x in Z_6.

We can solve equations in Z_6 as well as we can in the system of real numbers. For example, we can solve the linear equation

$$x + 4 = 2$$

in the usual way:

$$(x + 4) + 2 = 2 + 2,$$
$$x + 0 = 4,$$
$$x = 4.$$

Some linear equations have no solution. We saw above that the equation

$$2x = 1$$

has no solution. Some linear equations have more than one solution. For example, the equation $2x = 2$ has solutions

$$x = 1 \quad \text{and} \quad x = 4.$$

Every quadratic equation can be solved, that is, its solution set can be found. We can solve an equation in x by giving x the values 0, 1, 2, 3, 4, and 5, in turn, and then determining whether the resulting equation is true. For example, to solve the quadratic equation

$$x^2 + x + 4 = 0,$$

let x equal each of the following values and then determine whether the resulting equation is true.

If $x = 0$, then $0^2 + 0 + 4 = 0$, and $4 = 0$ is a false equation.
If $x = 1$, then $1^2 + 1 + 4 = 0$, and $0 = 0$ is a true equation.
If $x = 2$, then $2^2 + 2 + 4 = 0$, and $4 = 0$ is a false equation.
If $x = 3$, then $3^2 + 3 + 4 = 0$, and $4 = 0$ is a false equation.
If $x = 4$, then $4^2 + 4 + 4 = 0$, and $0 = 0$ is a true equation.
If $x = 5$, then $5^2 + 5 + 4 = 0$, and $4 = 0$ is a false equation.

Therefore, $\{1, 4\}$ is the solution set of the equation $x^2 + x + 4 = 0$ in Z_6.

As another example, we shall solve the equation $x^2 + x = 0$ in the same way that we solved the equation above.

If $x = 0$, then $0^2 + 0 = 0$, and $0 = 0$ is a true equation.
If $x = 1$, then $1^2 + 1 = 0$, and $2 = 0$ is a false equation.
If $x = 2$, then $2^2 + 2 = 0$, and $0 = 0$ is a true equation.

If $x = 3$, then $3^2 + 3 = 0$, and $0 = 0$ is a true equation.
If $x = 4$, then $4^2 + 4 = 0$, and $2 = 0$ is a false equation.
If $x = 5$, then $5^2 + 5 = 0$, and $0 = 0$ is a true equation.

Therefore, in Z_6, $\{0, 2, 3, 5\}$ is the solution set of the equation $x^2 + x = 0$. Thus, in Z_6 we have a quadratic equation which has *four* solutions, whereas every quadratic equation in the real number system has at most two solutions.

Exercises

Solve each of the following linear equations in Z_6.

1. (a) $x + 3 = 2$ (b) $5x + 1 = 4$

2. (a) $3x = 0$ (b) $3x = 1$

3. (a) $4x + 5 = 1$ (b) $4x + 2 = 0$

4. (a) $3x = 3$ (b) $2x + 1 = 0$

Solve each of the following quadratic equations in Z_6.

5. (a) $x^2 + 3x + 2 = 0$ (b) $x^2 + 2 = 0$

6. (a) $x^2 + 4x + 1 = 0$ (b) $2x^2 + 1 = 0$

7. (a) $x^2 + x + 1 = 0$ (b) $3x^2 + x = 0$

8. (a) $2x^2 + 4x = 0$ (b) $3x^2 + 3x = 0$

---

9. Discuss the system of integers modulo 7:

$$Z_7 = \{0, 1, 2, 3, 4, 5, 6\}.$$

Give examples of addition and multiplication in this system. Show that each nonzero number in Z_7 has a multiplicative inverse.

10. Prove that (Can-A) is valid for Z_6. Show by example that (Can-M) is not valid for Z_6.

11. Prove that both (Can-A) and (Can-M) are valid for Z_7.

12. What numbers have square roots in Z_6? in Z_7?

13. Mr. Ex, a superstitious scientist, plans to direct a 7-month expedition to Timbuctoo from May through November of some year. However, he insists that the group wait for a year in which no one of these months has a Friday the thirteenth. Explain why Mr. Ex's expedition will never take place. (Hint: Denote the days of the week by numbers from Z_7. Use 0 for Sunday, 1 for Monday, and so on. If the number x denotes May 13, what is the number for June 13? for July 13? for the thirteenth of each of the other months?)

EXTRA!

The square array of integers in Fig. 3–16 is called a *magic square*. It is made up of the first sixteen positive integers, arranged in such a way that the sum of the integers in each *row* is 34:

$$16 + 5 + 10 + 3 = 34,$$
$$9 + 4 + 15 + 6 = 34,$$
$$7 + 14 + 1 + 12 = 34,$$
$$2 + 11 + 8 + 13 = 34.$$

The sum in each *column* is 34:

$$16 + 9 + 7 + 2 = 34,$$
$$5 + 4 + 14 + 11 = 34,$$
$$10 + 15 + 1 + 8 = 34,$$
$$3 + 6 + 12 + 13 = 34.$$

16	5	10	3
9	4	15	6
7	14	1	12
2	11	8	13

FIGURE 3–16

The sum in each *diagonal* is 34:

$$16 + 4 + 1 + 13 = 34, \quad 3 + 15 + 14 + 2 = 34.$$

This is an example of a magic square of *order 4*.

Any square array of the integers 1, 2, 3, and so on up to n^2 for some positive integer n is called a *magic square of order n* if the sum of the integers in every row is equal to the sum in every column and in each of the two diagonals. The sum of all the integers from 1 through n^2 is given by

$$1 + 2 + 3 + \cdots + n^2 = \tfrac{1}{2}n^2(n^2 + 1).$$

Hence, the sum of each row, column, and diagonal of a magic square of order n must be the preceding sum divided by n, which is the number of rows.

$$\tfrac{1}{2}n(n^2 + 1)$$

For example, if $n = 4$, $2(16 + 1)$, or 34, is the sum of each row, column, and diagonal.

You can show without much trouble that there is no magic square of order 2.

We can now see how to begin to construct a magic square of order 3. We know that it is made up of the numbers 1, 2, 3, 4, 5, 6, 7, 8, 9 and that the sum of each row, column, and diagonal is

$$\tfrac{3}{2}(9 + 1), \quad \text{or } 15.$$

First, we can prove that the number x in the center of a magic square of order 3 must be 5. The sum of the numbers in the row, column, and two diagonals (indicated by arrowheads in Fig. 3–17) is 4 · 15, or 60. However, this sum includes all the numbers 1, 2, ..., 9 plus $3x$ (i.e., x is counted four times). Since $1 + 2 + \cdots + 9 = 45$, we have the equation

$$60 = 3x + 45.$$

On solving, we obtain $x = 5$.

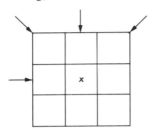

FIGURE 3–17

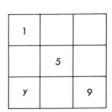

FIGURE 3–18

Next, we observe that the number 1 cannot appear at a corner of a magic square of order 3. For if 1 is at one corner, then 9 is at the opposite corner. (See Fig. 3–18.) What number can y be in the figure? Clearly, y is less than 5; if it were not, the bottom row would add up to more than 15. But if y is less than 5, the first column cannot add up to 15. Therefore, 1 and 9 cannot appear at corners. You prove that 3 and 7 also cannot appear at corners.

We conclude that in a magic square of order 3, the number 5 must appear in the middle, and the even numbers must appear in the four corners. With this information, you should easily be able to construct a magic square of order 3.

There are simple ways of constructing magic squares of any odd order. We will illustrate one way to construct a magic square of order 5. As shown in Fig. 3–19, there is a main diagonal 1 and parallel broken diagonals 2, 3, 4, and 5 in the square. Each diagonal, broken or not, contains 5 little squares. We imagine that each broken diagonal to the right of 1 is connected to the bottom of its other part below 1.

Now we will actually construct the square. Put 1 in the middle of

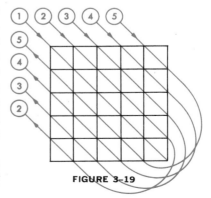

FIGURE 3–19

			2	
				3
4				
	5			
		1		

FIGURE 3-20

11	18	25	2	9
10	12	19	21	3
4	6	13	20	22
23	5	7	14	16
17	24	1	8	15

FIGURE 3-21

the bottom row. Then, put 2, 3, 4, and 5 in order *down* the broken diagonal from 1 and then *down* the rest of this broken diagonal above 1. This fills up the broken diagonal containing 1. (See Fig. 3-20.)

Next, put 6 directly above 5, and put 7, 8, 9, and 10 in the broken diagonal containing 6. We insert these numbers as we inserted the others. Then, put 11 directly above 10, and fill in the rest of its diagonal with 12, 13, 14, and 15. Then, put 16 directly above 15, and fill in the rest of its diagonal with 17, 18, 19, and 20. Finally, put 21 directly above 20, and fill in the rest of its diagonal with 22, 23, 24, and 25. The resulting array is a magic square of order 5, as shown in Fig. 3-21.

This method works for magic squares of any odd order, such as 7, 9, 11.

1. (a) Construct a magic square of order 7.
   (b) What is the sum of the elements in each row, column, and diagonal?
2. (a) Construct a magic square of order 9.
   (b) What is the sum of the elements in each row, column, and diagonal?

KEY IDEAS AND KEY WORDS

An expression of the form

$$ax^2 + bx + c, \quad a \neq 0,$$

where a, b, and c are real numbers, is called a **quadratic polynomial,** or **quadratic form.** The number a is called the **coefficient** of x^2, and c is called the **constant term.**

An equation of the form

$$ax^2 + bx + c = 0, \quad a \neq 0,$$

is called a **second-degree equation,** or **quadratic equation.** A number is called a **solution** of a quadratic equation if a true statement results when the variable is given the number as a value. The set of all solutions of the equation is called the **solution set** of the equation.

If a quadratic polynomial is the square of a linear form, then it is called a **perfect square.**

The process of adding a constant term to a quadratic polynomial to make it a perfect square is called **completing the square.**

The graph of the equation

$$y = ax^2 + bx + c, \quad a \neq 0,$$

is called a **parabola.** The **vertex** of a parabola is its highest or lowest point.

A line is the **axis of symmetry** of a parabola if the two parts of the graph on opposite sides of the line are **mirror images** of each other.

The system of **integers modulo 6** is made up of a set of six numbers:

$$0, \quad 1, \quad 2, \quad 3, \quad 4, \quad 5.$$

Addition and multiplication are defined in the following manner. We take the sum or product and then "cast out" sixes from the answer. For example,

$$4 + 5 = 3, \quad 4 \cdot 5 = 2, \quad 3 + 5 = 2, \quad 3 \cdot 5 = 3.$$

There is a similar system of **integers modulo n** for every positive integer n.

CHAPTER REVIEW

Find the solution set of each of the equations in Exercises 1–10.

1. $2x^2 + 5x - 3 = 0$ **2.** $7x^2 = 9x$

3. $20x^2 - 5 = 0$ **4.** $(3x^2 - 12)(9x^2 + 3x - 2) = 0$

5. $4x^2 - 20x + 25 = 0$

6. $3x^2 + 6x + 1 = 0$

7. $(2x - 1)^2 - 7(2x - 1) + 12 = 0$

8. $(x - 3)^2 - 8(x - 3) + 7 = 0$

9. $(x^2 - 8)(x^2 - 15) = x^2 - 8$

10. $x^2(x^2 - 225) = 0$

11. A grassy plot 25 feet by 30 feet is surrounded by a walk of uniform width. If the area of the walk is 300 square feet, how wide is it?

12. One side of a right triangle is 3 inches shorter than the hypotenuse and 3 inches longer than the other side. Find the dimensions of the triangle.

13. An engineer can decrease by 2 hours the time it takes to travel 200 miles if he increases the speed of the freight train by 5 miles per hour. What is the original speed of the train?

14. Two numbers whose sum is 57 have squares that differ by 627. Find the numbers.

15. Show that each of the following quadratic equations has no real solutions.
    (a) $3x^2 - 2x + 4 = 0$ (b) $x^2 + x + 1 = 0$

16. For what values of k will each of the following quadratic equations have real solutions?
    (a) $x^2 - kx + 6 = 0$ (b) $x^2 - 6x - k = 0$

17. Graph each of the following equations or inequalities. Give an equation of the axis of symmetry and the coordinates of the vertex of each parabola.
    (a) $y = -2(x + 3)^2 + 1$ (b) $y = 2x^2 - 4x + 1$
    (c) $y \leq 3x^2 + 6x + 1$ (d) $y + x^2 \leq 6x - 9$

18. Find the maximum or minimum value of each of the following quadratic polynomials.
    (a) $5x^2 - 2x - 2$ (b) $2 - 4x - 5x^2$

19. Solve each quadratic inequality in x.
    (a) $x^2 - 2x - 3 \geq 0$ (b) $9 + 8x - x^2 \geq 0$

20. Approximate the solutions of the equation $x^2 - 2x - 4 = 0$ from the graph of $y = x^2 - 2x - 4$.

21. Find an equation of a parabola if the graph of the parabola contains the points $(1, 1)$, $(-1, -5)$, and $(-3, 5)$.

CHAPTER TEST

Solve each of the equations in Exercises 1–4.

1. $(x^2 - 1)(7x^2 + 4x - 3) = 0$

2. $2(x - 3)^2 - 5(x - 3) - 12 = 0$

3. $(x - 2)^2(x^2 - 4) = 0$

4. $3x^2 - 6x - 2 = 0$

5. (a) Draw the graph of the equation $y = 2x^2 - 10x - 8$.
   (b) Find the axis of symmetry and the vertex of the parabola in part (a).

6. (a) Graph the solution set of $y \geq 10 + 12x - 3x^2$.
   (b) Find the maximum value of the quadratic form $10 + 12x - 3x^2$.

7. (a) Graph the solution set of $x^2 + x - 6 \leq y$.
   (b) Find the minimum value of the quadratic form $x^2 + x - 6$.

CHAPTER **4**

The Complex Number System

Objectives . . .

- To perform complex number arithmetic.
- To derive the quadratic formula.
- To compute the discriminant of a quadratic equation and use it to characterize the roots.
- To plot complex numbers in the complex number plane.

4–1 PURE IMAGINARY NUMBERS

Although the quadratic equation

$$x^2 + 4 = 0$$

has no real solution, it is possible to enlarge our number system so that this equation has a solution in our new system. In this section, we shall describe how to extend the real number system to a larger system in which every quadratic equation has a solution.

We shall choose a new number, which will be designated by i, and we shall assume that it is a solution of the quadratic equation

$$x^2 + 1 = 0.†$$

In other words, we shall assume that i is a new number with the property

$$i^2 = -1.$$

Clearly, i is not a real number, since no real number has a negative number for its square.

Along with the new number i, we wish to consider other new numbers such as $3i$, $-2i$, $7i$, $\sqrt{2}i$, and πi. Such numbers will be called *pure imaginary numbers,* or *i-numbers.* Thus, an i-number is a number of the form bi, where b is a real number.

The sum of two i-numbers is defined in a way consistent with the rules of arithmetic. If we think of bi as $b \cdot i$, and if we assume that the distributive axiom is valid for i-numbers, then

$$3i + 4i = (3 + 4)i, \quad \text{or } 7i;$$
$$-8i + 5i = (-8 + 5)i, \quad \text{or } -3i.$$

---

† The symbol i was introduced into mathematics by the famous eighteenth-century Swiss mathematician Euler (pronounced "Oiler"). It is possible that he chose i because it is the first letter of the Latin word *imaginarius* (imaginary).

These examples suggest that we define the addition of i-numbers in the following way.

Definition of Addition of i-Numbers

$bi + di = (b + d)i$ *for all real numbers b and d*   *(Def-Ai)*

According to this definition, the sum of two i-numbers is another i-number, that is, the set of all i-numbers is closed under addition.

Is addition of i-numbers commutative? In other words, is

$$3i + 4i = 4i + 3i,$$
$$-8i + 5i = 5i + (-8i),$$

and so on? By definition,

$$3i + 4i = (3 + 4)i,$$

whereas

$$4i + 3i = (4 + 3)i.$$

Since $3 + 4 = 4 + 3$ by the commutative axiom for addition of real numbers, it follows that $3i + 4i = 4i + 3i$. Similarly, it can be shown that

$$bi + di = di + bi$$

for any real numbers b and d. Therefore, addition of i-numbers is *commutative*.

The addition of i-numbers is also *associative*, that is,

$$bi + (di + fi) = (bi + di) + fi$$

for any real numbers b, d, and f. To prove this, observe that

$$bi + (di + fi) = bi + (d + f)i$$
$$= [b + (d + f)]i,$$

whereas

$$(bi + di) + fi = (b + d)i + fi$$
$$= [(b + d) + f]i.$$

Since the associative axiom of addition is valid for the real number system, we have

$$b + (d + f) = (b + d) + f.$$

This proves that the addition of i-numbers is an associative operation. Let us *define*

$$0i = 0.$$

Then it follows that

$$
\begin{aligned}
bi + 0 &= bi + 0i \\
&= (b + 0)i \\
&= bi.
\end{aligned}
$$

Therefore, 0 is the *additive identity element* for i-numbers as well as for real numbers.

Each i-number has an additive inverse. For example,

$$
\begin{aligned}
3i + (-3i) &= [3 + (-3)]i \\
&= 0i, \quad \text{or } 0,
\end{aligned}
$$

and $-3i$ is the additive inverse, or opposite, of $3i$. Similarly, it can be shown that $-bi$ is the opposite of bi for each real number b.

The product of a real number and an i-number is also defined in a way consistent with the rules of arithmetic. For example,

$$3 \cdot 4i = 12i, \quad -5(-7i) = 35i.$$

In other words, we define the multiplication of an i-number and a real number in the following way.

Definition of Multiplication of an i-Number and a Real Number

$$a \cdot bi = (a \cdot b)i \quad \text{*for any real numbers a and b*} \qquad (Def\text{-}Mi)$$
$$bi \cdot a = (b \cdot a)i$$

Note that the product of a real number and an i-number is an i-number. It is easily verified that the following properties are valid for this kind of multiplication.

Distributive properties

$$
\begin{aligned}
(a + c)bi &= abi + cbi \\
a(bi + di) &= abi + adi
\end{aligned}
\qquad (D)
$$

Associative property for multiplication

$$(a \cdot c)bi = a(c \cdot bi) \qquad \text{(A-M)}$$

Multiplicative identity

$$1 \cdot (bi) = bi \qquad \text{(Id-M)}$$

For example, let us prove one of the distributive properties, that $a \cdot (bi + di) = abi + adi$.

$$
\begin{aligned}
a \cdot (bi + di) &= a \cdot [(b + d)i] & \text{(Def-Ai)} \\
&= [a \cdot (b + d)]i & \text{(Def-Mi)} \\
&= (ab + ad)i & \text{(D)} \\
&= (ab)i + (ad)i & \text{(Def-Ai)} \\
&= abi + adi & \text{(Def-Mi)}
\end{aligned}
$$

Hence, $a \cdot (bi + di) = abi + adi$.

We have defined the sum of two i-numbers and the product of a real number and an i-number. Next, let us define the product of two i-numbers. If we think of $7i$ as $7 \cdot i$ and of $3i$ as $3 \cdot i$, then it is natural to define the product of $7i$ and $3i$ as follows:

$$
\begin{aligned}
7i \cdot 3i &= (7 \cdot 3) \cdot (i \cdot i) \\
&= 21i^2 \\
&= 21(-1), \quad \text{or} \quad -21.
\end{aligned}
$$

Thus, we define the multiplication of i-numbers in the following way.

Definition of Multiplication of i-Numbers

$bi \cdot di = -bd$ *for all real numbers b and d*   *(Def-i $\times$ i)*

Since $i \cdot (-i) = -i^2$, or 1, $-i$ is the *multiplicative inverse*, or reciprocal, of i. Interestingly enough, $-i$ also is the *additive inverse* of i since $i + (-i) = 0$. Every nonzero i-number has a reciprocal. For example, since

$$3i \cdot (-\tfrac{1}{3}i) = 3 \cdot (-\tfrac{1}{3}) \cdot i^2, \quad \text{or } 1,$$

$-\tfrac{1}{3}i$ is the reciprocal of $3i$. More generally,

$$-\frac{1}{b}i$$

is the *reciprocal* of bi for every nonzero i-number bi.

Exercises

Using the properties discussed in this section, perform the indicated operations with i-numbers.

1. (a) $(\frac{1}{2}\sqrt{3}i)^2$ (b) $(-\sqrt{2}i)^4$

2. (a) $3i(2i + \sqrt{2}i)$ (b) $-\frac{13}{2}(11i - 5i)$

3. (a) $(8i)(-\frac{1}{8}i)$ (b) $(\sqrt{3}i)[(2i)(-7i)]$

4. (a) $(3 \cdot 5i) - (8 \cdot 7i)$ (b) $(-7i)^2 + 49$

5. (a) $(4i)^2 - 16$ (b) $(-3i)^4 - 81$

6. (a) $i + i^3$ (b) $i^2 + i^4$

7. (a) $i^5 + i^7$ (b) $i^9 + i^{10} + i^{11} + i^{12}$

---

8. Find the value of i^n when n is 4, 8, 12, 16, 20, and 100. Write a statement about the value of i^n when n is a positive integral multiple of 4.

9. Find the value of i^n when n is 2, 6, 10, 14, 18, and 98. Make a statement about the value of i^n when n is 2, or 2 more than a positive integral multiple of 4.

10. Find the value of i^n when n is 1, 5, 9, 13, 17, and 97. Make a statement about the value of i^n when n is 1, or 1 more than a positive integral multiple of 4.

11. Find the value of i^n when n is 3, 7, 11, 15, 19, and 99. Make a statement about the value of i^n when n is 3, or 3 more than a positive integral multiple of 4.

12. Describe the pattern for i^n when n is a non-negative integer.

If we write i^{-3} as $1/i^3$ and multiply by i/i, we obtain

$$i^{-3} = \frac{1}{i^3} = \frac{1}{i^3} \cdot \frac{i}{i}, \quad \text{or } i.$$

We may simplify negative integral powers of i in a similar manner. Simplify each of the following expressions.

13. i^{-2} 14. i^{-7} 15. i^{-12} 16. i^{-17} 17. i^{-38} 18. i^{-19}

19. Verify that each of the following equations is true.
(a) $i^{4k} = 1$, k any integer   (b) $i^{4k+1} = i$, k any integer
(c) $i^{4k+2} = -1$, k any integer   (d) $i^{4k+3} = -i$, k any integer

Write each of the following quotients as a real number or as an i-number.

20. $\dfrac{1}{i^2}$ 21. $-\dfrac{1}{i^3}$ 22. $\dfrac{4}{i^4}$ 23. $-\dfrac{1}{2i}$ 24. $\dfrac{1}{7i^5}$ 25. $-\dfrac{3}{2i^{10}}$

We can use i-numbers to write the quadratic polynomial $x^2 + 9$ as a product of factors in the following way.

$$x^2 + 9 = x^2 - (9)(-1)$$
$$= x^2 - 9i^2$$
$$= (x + 3i)(x - 3i)$$

Using both i-numbers and real numbers, factor each of the following polynomials into as many linear factors as you can.

26. $x^2 + 16$ **27.** $x^4 - 16$ (four linear factors)

28. $9x^2 + 25$ **29.** $x^2 - 7$

30. $x^2 + 7$ **31.** $81x^4 - 1$ (four linear factors)

Find the solution set for each equation by factoring the left side into as many linear factors as you can. Use i-numbers, if necessary.

32. $x^2 + 36 = 0$ **33.** $x^2 - 36 = 0$

34. $9x^2 + 25 = 0$ **35.** $x^2 + 5 = 0$

36. $x^4 - 81 = 0$ (four solutions)   **37.** $\frac{1}{16}x^4 - 1 = 0$

38. Find two square roots of -49. (Hint: Let $\sqrt{-49} = \sqrt{-1} \cdot \sqrt{49}$.)

39. Find two square roots of 18.   **40.** Find two square roots of -12.

41. Find four fourth roots of 16 by finding the solution set of the equation $x^4 = 16$.

4–2   COMPLEX NUMBERS

We have worked with two number systems, the system of real numbers and the system of i-numbers. Both systems are closed with respect to addition. They have only one number in common: the additive identity 0.

Although we have defined the product of a real number and an i-number, we have not yet considered the sum of a real number and an i-number, such as $-3 + 7i$ or $\sqrt{2} + 5i$. Every number of the form

$$a + bi,$$

where a and b are real numbers, is called a *complex number*. Since

$$a = a + 0i,$$

it follows that every real number is also a complex number. Furthermore,

$$bi = 0 + bi.$$

Therefore, every *i*-number is a complex number. Consequently, both the set of all real numbers and the set of all *i*-numbers are contained in the set of all complex numbers. For a given complex number $a + bi$, it is customary to call a the *real part* and bi the *pure imaginary part* of $a + bi$. Two complex numbers are defined to be equal if, and only if, their real parts are equal and their pure imaginary parts are equal. Since $bi = di$ if, and only if, $b = d$,

$$a + bi = c + di \quad \textit{if, and only if,} \quad a = c \text{ and } b = d.$$

In particular,

$$a + bi = 0 \quad \text{if, and only if,} \quad a = 0 \text{ and } b = 0.$$

The adjectives *imaginary* and *complex* indicate the struggle that took place in the minds of the sixteenth-century mathematicians who first dared to use such numbers. As late as 1770, Euler apologized for the frequent use of complex numbers in his algebra book. He wrote,

All such expressions as $\sqrt{-1}$ (the number *i*), $\sqrt{-2}$, and so on, are impossible or imaginary numbers, since they represent roots of negative quantities, and of such numbers we may truly assert that they are neither nothing, nor greater than nothing, nor less than nothing, which necessarily constitutes them imaginary or impossible.

In spite of the early suspicions toward complex numbers, they have been as useful in mathematics as negative numbers, rational numbers, and irrational numbers, and have been an indispensable tool in many applications.

How shall we add and multiply complex numbers? If we assume that the basic axioms are valid, we can find the sum of two complex numbers as shown below.

$$(3 + 4i) + (-7 + 3i) = [3 + (-7)] + (4i + 3i)$$
$$= -4 + 7i$$

This example suggests that we define the sum of two complex numbers in the following way.

Definition of the Sum of Two Complex Numbers

$(a + bi) + (c + di) = (a + c) + (b + d)i$ (*Def-i + i*)
for all real numbers a, b, c, and d

Since $(c + di) + (a + bi) = (c + a) + (d + b)i$ according to this definition, it follows from the commutative axiom of addition for real numbers that

$$(a + bi) + (c + di) = (c + di) + (a + bi).$$

Thus, addition of complex numbers is commutative. In a similar way, we may show that addition of complex numbers is associative.

Since

$$0 + (a + bi) = (0 + a) + bi$$
$$= a + bi,$$

we conclude that *zero* is the *additive identity* element of the complex number system. The negative of the complex number $a + bi$ is $-a + (-bi)$. Thus,

$$(a + bi) + [-a + (-bi)] = [a + (-a)] + [b + (-b)]i$$
$$= 0 + 0i, \quad \text{or } 0.$$

Hence, we have $-(a + bi) = -a + (-bi)$.

If we recall how the operation of subtraction is defined in terms of addition, then we shall have no trouble in defining subtraction of complex numbers. Thus, by definition,

$$(a + bi) - (c + di) = (a + bi) + [-(c + di)]$$
$$= (a + bi) + [(-c) + (-di)]$$
$$= [a + (-c)] + [b + (-d)]i$$
$$= (a - c) + (b - d)i.$$

Just as we were able to define the sum of two complex numbers, we should be able to define their product. For example, if we assume that the distributive axiom and the rearrangement properties are valid for complex numbers, we can find the product of $3 + 4i$ and $-7 + 3i$ in the following way.

$$(3 + 4i) \cdot (-7 + 3i) = 3(-7 + 3i) + 4i(-7 + 3i)$$
$$= -21 + 9i + (-28i) + 12i^2$$
$$= -21 + 9i - 28i + 12 \cdot (-1)$$
$$= (-21 - 12) + (9i - 28i)$$
$$= -33 + (-19i)$$

Similarly,

$$(a + bi)(c + di) = a(c + di) + bi(c + di)$$
$$= ac + adi + bci - bd$$
$$= (ac - bd) + (ad + bc)i.$$

Thus, if we want multiplication of complex numbers to satisfy the usual rules of arithmetic, we must define it in the following way.

Definition of Multiplication of Complex Numbers

$(a + bi)(c + di) = (ac - bd) + (ad + bc)i$

for all real numbers a, b, c, and d

(*Def-MC*)

Although we shall not do so at this time, it can be proved that multiplication of complex numbers, as defined above, is both commutative and associative. It can also be proved that multiplication is distributive with respect to addition.

Since

$$(1 + 0i)(a + bi) = [(1 \cdot a) - (0 \cdot b)] + [(1 \cdot b) + (0 \cdot a)]i$$
$$= a + bi,$$

it is clear that the real number 1 is the multiplicative identity element of the complex number system. The search for multiplicative inverses of complex numbers will be discussed in the next section.

Exercises

Perform the indicated operations in the following exercises. In each exercise, state the real part and the pure imaginary part of the complex number.

1. (a) $(-7 + 2i) + (7 - 6i)$ (b) $(3 + i) - 7$

2. (a) $(2 + 3i) + (5 + i)$ (b) $(2 + 3i) + (2 - 3i)$

3. (a) $(2 + 7i) - (3 + 4i) + (7 - 6i)$
     (b) $(5 + 3i) - (6 + 2i) + (9 - 4i)$

4. (a) $(\sqrt{2} - i)^2$ (b) $(-1 + \sqrt{3}i)^2$

5. (a) $6(2 + i) - 3(3 + 2i)$ (b) $(5 - 12i)(\frac{5}{169} + \frac{12}{169}i)$

6. (a) $(2 - \sqrt{5}i)^2 - 4(2 - \sqrt{5}i) + 9$ (b) $\left(\frac{\sqrt{3}}{2} + \frac{1}{2}i\right)^3$

7. Find the value of the quadratic polynomial $x^2 - 4x + 7$ for each of the given values of x.

(a) $x = 2 + \sqrt{3}i$ (b) $x = -4 - 3i$

Perform the indicated operations in the following exercises. In each exercise, state the real part and the pure imaginary part of the complex number.

8. $\left(\dfrac{\sqrt{3}}{2} + \dfrac{1}{2}i\right)^6$ (Hint: $a^6 = (a^3)^2$.)

9. $(-\frac{24}{625} + \frac{7}{625}i)(-24 - 7i)$

10. $(a + bi)(a - bi)$

11. $(ap + bpi)(a - bi)$

Find the value of the quadratic polynomial $x^2 + x + 1$ for each of the given values of x.

12. $x = -1 + i$

13. $x = -\frac{1}{2} + \frac{1}{2}\sqrt{3}i$

14. $x = -\frac{1}{2} - \frac{1}{2}\sqrt{3}i$

15. $x = \frac{1}{2} - \frac{1}{2}\sqrt{3}i$

16. $x = \frac{1}{2} + \frac{1}{2}\sqrt{3}i$

17. $x = \frac{1}{3} + \frac{2}{3}i$

18. (a) Square and simplify

$$\left(\frac{\sqrt{2}}{2} + \frac{\sqrt{2}}{2}i\right)^2.$$

(b) Find the complex numbers that are solutions of the equation $x^2 = i$.

(c) Find two solutions of the equation $x^2 = -i$.

---

19. Show that $-1 + \sqrt{3}i$ is a solution of the equation $x^3 = 8$. Then find two other numbers that are solutions.

20. Prove the associative law of addition for complex numbers.

21. Supply a reason for each step in the following proof of the commutative law of multiplication for complex numbers.

$$
\begin{aligned}
(a + bi)(c + di) &= (ac - bd) + (ad + bc)i &&\underline{?\underline{} \\
&= (ac - bd) + (bc + ad)i &&\underline{?\underline{} \\
&= (ca - db) + (cb + da)i &&\underline{?\underline{} \\
&= (c + di)(a + bi) &&\underline{?\underline{}
\end{aligned}
$$

4–3   QUOTIENTS OF COMPLEX NUMBERS

The two complex numbers $3 + 4i$ and $3 - 4i$ are said to be *conjugates* of each other. We note that

$$(3 + 4i) + (3 - 4i) = 6$$
$$(3 + 4i) \cdot (3 - 4i) = (9 + 16) + (-12 + 12)i$$
$$= 25.$$

Every complex number $a + bi$ has a *conjugate:* $a - bi$. You can easily verify that

$$(a + bi) + (a - bi) = 2a,$$
$$(a + bi) \cdot (a - bi) = a^2 + b^2.$$

Thus, the sum of a complex number and its conjugate is a real number, and their product is also a real number.

We saw that 25 is the product of $3 + 4i$ and its conjugate $3 - 4i$. Therefore, it follows that 1 is the product of $3 + 4i$ and $\frac{1}{25}(3 - 4i)$, as shown below.

$$(3 + 4i)[\tfrac{1}{25}(3 - 4i)] = \tfrac{1}{25}[(3 + 4i)(3 - 4i)]$$
$$= \tfrac{1}{25}(25), \quad \text{or } 1$$

Thus,

$$\tfrac{1}{25}(3 - 4i), \quad \text{or } \tfrac{3}{25} - \tfrac{4}{25}i,$$

is the *reciprocal* of $3 + 4i$. We indicate this in the usual way:

$$\frac{1}{3 + 4i} = \frac{3}{25} - \frac{4}{25}\,i.$$

We can find the reciprocal of every nonzero complex number in the same way. If $a + bi \neq 0$, so that either a or b is nonzero, then $a^2 + b^2 > 0$, and

$$(a + bi)\left[\frac{1}{a^2 + b^2}(a - bi)\right] = 1,$$

according to the formula for the product of a complex number and its conjugate. Hence, the reciprocal of $a + bi$ is

$$\frac{1}{a + bi} = \frac{a}{a^2 + b^2} - \frac{b}{a^2 + b^2}\,i.$$

For example, we may obtain the reciprocal of $-\sqrt{2} + i$ by letting $a = -\sqrt{2}$ and $b = 1$ in the equation above:

$$\frac{1}{-\sqrt{2} + i} = -\frac{\sqrt{2}}{3} - \frac{1}{3}i.$$

We can now find the quotient of two complex numbers. For example, let us find $(-7 + 3i) \div (5 + 4i)$.

$$\begin{aligned}
(-7 + 3i) \div (5 + 4i) &= (-7 + 3i)\left(\frac{1}{5 + 4i}\right) \\
&= (-7 + 3i)(\tfrac{5}{41} - \tfrac{4}{41}i) \\
&= (-\tfrac{35}{41} + \tfrac{12}{41}) + (\tfrac{28}{41} + \tfrac{15}{41})i \\
&= -\tfrac{23}{41} + \tfrac{43}{41}i
\end{aligned}$$

There is a shorter method for finding the quotient of two complex numbers. For example, to find $(5 - 9i) \div (1 - i)$, we might proceed as follows:

$$\begin{aligned}
\frac{5 - 9i}{1 - i} &= \frac{5 - 9i}{1 - i} \cdot \frac{1 + i}{1 + i} \\
&= \frac{(5 - 9i)(1 + i)}{(1 - i)(1 + i)} \\
&= \frac{14 - 4i}{2} \\
&= 7 - 2i.
\end{aligned}$$

Notice that we simply multiplied the numerator and the denominator of the given quotient by the conjugate of the denominator, to eliminate the i-number from the denominator.

Exercises

Find the conjugate of each of the following complex numbers, and then find the sum and the product of each pair of conjugate complex numbers.

1. (a) $4 + 2i$ (b) $\sqrt{3} - \sqrt{5}i$

2. (a) -7 (b) $-\sqrt{2}i$

3. (a) $\dfrac{1}{2} - \dfrac{\sqrt{3}}{2}i$ (b) $\dfrac{2}{3} - \dfrac{\sqrt{2}}{4}i$

4. (a) What type of complex number is its own conjugate? Give some examples to support your answer.

(b) What type of complex number is the negative of its own conjugate? Give some examples to support your answer.

Express the reciprocal of each of the following complex numbers as a complex number.

5. (a) $1 + i$ (b) $5i$

6. (a) $2 + 3i$ (b) $6 - i$

7. (a) $-2 - 5i$ (b) $\sqrt{3} - 3i$

8. (a) $c - di$ (b) $a - bi$

Perform the indicated operations, and express each answer as a complex number of the form $a + bi$.

9. $\dfrac{1 + i}{1 - i}$ 10. $\dfrac{-3 + 2i}{7 + 4i}$ 11. $\left(\dfrac{1 - i}{1 + 3i}\right)\left(\dfrac{2 + 3i}{-1 + 4i}\right)$

12. $\dfrac{6 - 3i}{2 + i}$ 13. $\dfrac{4 + \sqrt{3}i}{2 - \sqrt{3}i}$ 14. $\dfrac{1}{2 + i}$

15. $\dfrac{i}{2 + i}$ 16. $\dfrac{6 + 3i}{2i}$ 17. $\dfrac{1 - i}{1 + 3i} + \dfrac{2 + 3i}{-1 + 4i}$

18. $\dfrac{3}{2 - 5i} - \dfrac{2i}{-2 - 5i}$ 19. $\left(\dfrac{2 + i}{3 - i}\right)\left(\dfrac{1 - 4i}{1 + 3i}\right)$

20. (a) Find the conjugates of $a + bi$ and $c + di$ and add them.
   (b) Add $a + bi$ and $c + di$ and find the conjugate of their sum.
   (c) How is the sum of the conjugates of two complex numbers related to the conjugate of their sum?

21. (a) Find the conjugates of $a + bi$ and $c + di$ and multiply them.
   (b) Multiply $a + bi$ by $c + di$ and find the conjugate of the product.
   (c) How is the product of the conjugates of two complex numbers related to the conjugate of their product?

22. (a) Find the conjugates of $a + bi$ and $c + di$ and subtract the latter conjugate from the former.
   (b) Subtract $c + di$ from $a + bi$ and find the conjugate of the difference.
   (c) Is there a relation between the difference of the conjugates of two complex numbers and the conjugate of their difference?

23. (a) Simplify $\dfrac{a - bi}{c - di}$.

   (b) Simplify $\dfrac{a + bi}{c + di}$ and find the conjugate of the quotient.

   (c) Is there a relation between the quotient of the conjugates of two complex numbers and the conjugate of their quotient?

24. Since two complex numbers are defined as equal if, and only if, their real parts are equal and their pure imaginary parts are equal, the real solutions of the equation $(2x - y) + (x + y)i = 5 + 4i$ are solutions of the system shown below. Solve the system for real values of x and y.

$$\begin{cases} 2x - y = 5, \\ x + y = 4. \end{cases}$$

Find the system defined by each of the following equations, and solve it for real values of x and y.

25. $x + yi = -5 + 4i$

26. $2x + 3yi - 6 + 9i = 0$

27. $-x + 4yi = (2 + 6i) - (7 - 2i)$ 28. $x + yi = (2 - i)(2 + i)$

29. The real number $a^2 + b^2$ which is the product of $a + bi$ and its complex conjugate is called the *norm* of $a + bi$ and is sometimes designated by $N(a + bi)$.
    (a) Find and compare the norms of $a + bi$ and $a - bi$.
    (b) Find the norms of $2 + 3i$ and $1 - i$, and find the product of the norms.
    (c) Find $N(a + bi)$ and $N(c + di)$ and find their product. Find the product of $a + bi$ and $c + di$, and find $N[(a + bi)(c + di)]$.
    (d) How is the product of the norms of two complex numbers related to the norm of the product of the numbers?

30. Use the results of Exercise 29 to prove that the product of two integers, each of which is the sum of the squares of two integers, is also the sum of the squares of two integers.

Review for Sections 4-1 through 4-3

Compute the following.

1. $(2\sqrt{3i})^2$

2. $(4i)(-5i)$

3. $(3 + 5i) + (8 - 4i)$

4. $(2 + \sqrt{3i})(2 - \sqrt{3i})$

5. $-\frac{2}{3}(4i + 17i)$

6. $(3 - i)^2$

7. $(6 - 2i) - (4 + 5i)$

8. $(4 + 2i)^3$

9. $4(7 - 3i) - \frac{1}{2}(6 + 8i)$

10. $(-6i)^2 + 16$

Find the solution set for each equation, including *i*-numbers.

11. $x^2 + 9 = 0$

12. $x^2 = -24$

13. $x^4 - 64 = 0$

14. $x^4 - 16 = 0$

Find the value of the quadratic polynomial $2x^2 - x + 1$ for each of the given values of x.

15. $x = 3 + i$

16. $x = \frac{1}{2} + 3i$

17. $x = 2\sqrt{3i}$

18. $x = -4 + 2i$

Find the conjugate of each of the following complex numbers. Then find the sum and the product of each pair of conjugate numbers.

19. $5 + 2i$

20. $\sqrt{3} + i$

21. $2 - \sqrt{5}i$

22. $\dfrac{1}{4} - \dfrac{\sqrt{2}}{4}i$

Express the reciprocal of each of the following complex numbers as a complex number.

23. $3 + i$

24. $4 - 2i$

25. $5 + 3i$

26. $7 - 6i$

Answers for Review for Section 4–1 through 4–3

1. -12 **2.** 20 **3.** $11 + i$

4. 7 **5.** $-14i$ **6.** $8 - 6i$

7. $2 - 7i$ **8.** $16 + 88i$ **9.** $25 - 16i$

10. -20 **11.** $\{3i, -3i\}$ **12.** $\{2\sqrt{6}i, -2\sqrt{6}i\}$

13. $\{2\sqrt{2}, -2\sqrt{2}, 2\sqrt{2}i, -2\sqrt{2}i\}$ **14.** $\{2, -2, 2i, -2i\}$

15. $14 + 11i$ **16.** $-17 + 3i$

17. $-23 - 2\sqrt{3}i$ **18.** $29 - 34i$

19. Conjugate $= 5 - 2i$, sum $= 10$, product $= 29$

20. Conjugate $= \sqrt{3} - i$, sum $= 2\sqrt{3}$, product $= 4$

21. Conjugate $= 2 + \sqrt{5}i$, sum $= 4$, product $= 9$

22. Conjugate $= \dfrac{1}{4} + \dfrac{\sqrt{2}}{4}i$, sum $= \dfrac{1}{2}$, product $= \dfrac{3}{16}$

23. $\frac{3}{10} - \frac{1}{10}i$ **24.** $\frac{1}{5} + \frac{1}{10}i$ **25.** $\frac{5}{34} - \frac{3}{34}i$ **26.** $\frac{7}{85} + \frac{6}{85}i$

4–4 QUADRATIC EQUATIONS

In this book, we first discussed the real number system. We have now found that it is a subsystem of a larger number system, the system of complex numbers. The five basic axioms of addition and multiplication stated in Chapter 1 are also valid for the complex number system. However, the order axioms of the real number system (page 11) are not valid for the system of complex numbers. In other words, it is not possible to define a set of positive complex numbers in such a way that the order axioms are valid.

An important property of any number system for which the five basic properties hold is the following:

$$r \cdot s = 0 \quad \text{if, and only if,} \quad r = 0 \text{ or } s = 0. \qquad \text{(F-0)}$$

The property of factors of zero was proved for real numbers r and s in Chapter 3. The same proof holds for complex numbers r and s. We shall use this property in the work below.

We saw previously that both $2i$ and $-2i$ are solutions of the quadratic equation

$$x^2 + 4 = 0.$$

Does this equation have any other solutions? To answer this question, we first observe that the quadratic polynomial $x^2 + 4$ can be factored as follows:

$$x^2 + 4 = (x + 2i)(x - 2i).$$

Hence, the given equation is equivalent to the equation

$$(x + 2i)(x - 2i) = 0.$$

Using factors of zero, we find that

$$(x + 2i)(x - 2i) = 0$$

if, and only if,

$$x + 2i = 0 \quad \text{or} \quad x - 2i = 0$$

or $(x + 2i)(x - 2i) = 0$ if, and only if,

$$x = -2i \quad \text{or} \quad x = 2i.$$

Hence, $\{-2i, 2i\}$ is the solution set of the equation $x^2 + 4 = 0$. Therefore, this equation has only two solutions: $2i$ and $-2i$.

In exactly the same way, we can show that for each positive real number a, the equation

$$x^2 + a = 0 \quad \text{has solution set} \quad \{\sqrt{a}i, -\sqrt{a}i\}.$$

A quadratic equation

$$ax^2 + bx + c = 0, \quad a \neq 0,$$

will be called *real* if the three numbers a, b, and c are real numbers. We recall from the preceding chapter that a real quadratic equation might or might not have real solutions. Does every real quadratic equation have complex solutions? Before answering this question, let us consider the following quadratic equation which, in Chapter 3, was shown to have no real solution.

Problem. Solve the real quadratic equation $x^2 - 4x + 5 = 0$.

Solution. The given equation is equivalent to each of the following equations:

$$x^2 - 4x = -5,$$
$$x^2 - 4x + 4 = -1.$$

The number -1 has two square roots, i and $-i$. Thus,

$$(x - 2)^2 = -1$$

if, and only if, $x - 2 = i$ or $x - 2 = -i$ or $(x - 2)^2 = -1$ if, and only if, $x = 2 + i$ or $x = 2 - i$. Thus,

$$\{2 + i,\ 2 - i\}$$

is the solution set of the given equation.

Check.

$$x = 2 + i$$
$$(2 + i)^2 - 4(2 + i) + 5 \overset{?}{=} 0$$
$$4 + 4i + i^2 - 8 - 4i + 5 \overset{?}{=} 0$$
$$4 - 1 - 8 + 5 \overset{\checkmark}{=} 0$$

$$x = 2 - i$$
$$(2 - i)^2 - 4(2 - i) + 5 \overset{?}{=} 0$$
$$4 - 4i + i^2 - 8 + 4i + 5 \overset{?}{=} 0$$
$$4 - 1 - 8 + 5 \overset{\checkmark}{=} 0$$

This problem suggests that every real quadratic equation has complex solutions.

Exercises

Solve each real quadratic equation by completing the square, and check each solution.

1. (a) $x^2 - 6x + 10 = 0$ (b) $x^2 + 4x + 13 = 0$
2. (a) $x^2 - 4x - 77 = 0$ (b) $x^2 + x + 1 = 0$
3. (a) $x^2 - 4x + 29 = 0$ (b) $x^2 + 8x + 25 = 0$
4. (a) $x^2 + 2x + 4 = 0$ (b) $x^2 + 2x - 4 = 0$
5. (a) $x^2 - 2\sqrt{3}x + 4 = 0$ (b) $x^2 - x + 1 = 0$

6. (a) If r and s are real numbers, we can find at least one real quadratic equation for which $\{r, s\}$ is the solution set:

$$(x - r)(x - s) = 0, \quad \text{or } x^2 - (r + s)x + rs = 0.$$

According to what property of real numbers is it true that r and s are solutions, and the only solutions, of this quadratic equation?

(b) If r and s are complex numbers, is it still true that

$$x^2 - (r + s)x + rs = 0$$

is a quadratic equation with solution set $\{r, s\}$? For what conditions on r and s is $x^2 - (r + s)x + rs = 0$ a real quadratic equation?

7. (a) Find the sum, $r + s$, and the product, rs, of each pair r, s of your solutions in Exercises 1(a) and 2(a). Then verify that each quadratic has the form given in Exercises 6(a) and (b). (This procedure is a second type of check on your solution.)

(b) Follow the directions of part (a), using your solutions in Exercises 1(b) and 2(b).

Each of the following is a solution set of a quadratic equation. In each case, write a quadratic equation that has the given solution set. (See Exercise 6.)

8. (a) $\{-3, 0\}$ (b) $\{8, -4\}$

9. (a) $\{-\frac{1}{3}, \frac{1}{2}\}$ (b) $\{-2, 4\}$

10. (a) $\{2 + \sqrt{3}, 2 - \sqrt{3}\}$ (b) $\{3 + \sqrt{2}, 3 - \sqrt{2}\}$

11. (a) $\{-3 + 4i, -3 - 4i\}$ (b) $\{0, i\sqrt{5}\}$

12. (a) $\{-1 + i, -1 - i\}$ (b) $\left\{\frac{\sqrt{2}}{2} + \frac{\sqrt{2}}{2}i, \frac{\sqrt{2}}{2} - \frac{\sqrt{2}}{2}i\right\}$

Let each of the following quadratic polynomials equal zero, and solve the resulting equation by completing the square. Then write each polynomial as a product of linear factors.

13. $x^2 + 4x + 20$ **14.** $x^2 + 4x + 1$ **15.** $x^2 - 2x + 4$

16. $6y^2 - 19y + 15$ **17.** $12x - 9x^2 - 5$

Let $a + bi$ and $c + di$ be two complex numbers, with $b \neq 0$ and $d \neq 0$. Verify that each of the following statements is true.

18. If the sum of these two complex numbers is a real number, then $b + d = 0$, or $d = -b$.

19. If the product of these two complex numbers is a real number, then $bc + ad = 0$.

20. If both the sum and product of these two complex numbers are real, then the numbers must be conjugate complex numbers.

21. If a real quadratic equation has one complex solution $a + bi$, with $b \neq 0$, then it must have $a - bi$ as its other solution.

4–5 THE QUADRATIC FORMULA

Let us try to solve the real quadratic equation

$$ax^2 + bx + c = 0, \quad a \neq 0,$$

by completing the square. Each of the following equations is equivalent to the preceding one.

$$ax^2 + bx + c = 0$$

$$x^2 + \frac{b}{a}x + \frac{c}{a} = 0$$

$$x^2 + \frac{b}{a}x = -\frac{c}{a}$$

$$x^2 + \frac{b}{a}x + \left(\frac{b}{2a}\right)^2 = \left(\frac{b}{2a}\right)^2 - \frac{c}{a}$$

$$\left(x + \frac{b}{2a}\right)^2 = \frac{b^2}{4a^2} - \frac{c}{a}$$

$$\left(x + \frac{b}{2a}\right)^2 = \frac{b^2 - 4ac}{4a^2}$$

The way in which we solve this last equation depends on whether or not the real number on the right side is negative. Since $4a^2$ is a positive number, the right side is negative if, and only if,

$$b^2 - 4ac$$

is negative. This number is called the *discriminant* of the given quadratic equation, and is designated by D:

$$D = b^2 - 4ac.$$

Case 1: $D > 0$. Since $\sqrt{D}/2a$ and $-(\sqrt{D}/2a)$ are the square roots of $D/4a^2$,

$$\left(x + \frac{b}{2a}\right)^2 = \frac{D}{4a^2}$$

if, and only if,

$$x + \frac{b}{2a} = \frac{\sqrt{D}}{2a} \quad \text{or} \quad x + \frac{b}{2a} = -\frac{\sqrt{D}}{2a}.$$

On solving these two linear equations, we see that

$$\left\{ \frac{-b + \sqrt{D}}{2a}, \frac{-b - \sqrt{D}}{2a} \right\}$$

is the solution set of the given equation; the solution set consists of two real numbers.

Case 2: $D = 0$. In this instance, the right side of the last equation above is zero. Hence,

$$x + \frac{b}{2a} = 0 \quad \text{and} \quad x = -\frac{b}{2a}.$$

Thus,

$$\left\{ -\frac{b}{2a} \right\}$$

is the solution set of the given quadratic equation; the solution set consists of one real number.

Case 3: $D < 0$. The negative number D has $\sqrt{-D}i$ and $-\sqrt{-D}i$ as its complex-number square roots. (*Remember that if $D < 0$, then $-D > 0$, and $\sqrt{-D}$ is a real number.*) Now

$$\left(x + \frac{b}{2a} \right)^2 = \frac{D}{4a^2}$$

if, and only if,

$$x + \frac{b}{2a} = \frac{\sqrt{-D}i}{2a} \quad \text{or} \quad x + \frac{b}{2a} = \frac{-\sqrt{-D}i}{2a}.$$

On solving these two linear equations, we obtain

$$\left\{ \frac{-b + \sqrt{-D}i}{2a}, \frac{-b - \sqrt{-D}i}{2a} \right\}$$

as the solution set of the given equation, and this solution set consists of two nonreal complex numbers which are conjugates of each other.

The three cases above can be combined into one statement. Let us use the notation $\sqrt{-2}$ for $\sqrt{2}i$, $\sqrt{-25}$ for $\sqrt{25}i$, or $5i$, and, in general,

$$\sqrt{D} \quad \text{for} \quad \sqrt{-D}i \quad \text{when } D \text{ is a negative real number.}$$

Using this notation, we can make the following statement which summarizes our discussion of the solutions of quadratic equations.

QUADRATIC FORMULA

The real quadratic equation

$$ax^2 + bx + c = 0, \quad a \neq 0,$$

has solutions

$$x = \frac{-b + \sqrt{D}}{2a} \quad \text{and} \quad x = \frac{-b - \sqrt{D}}{2a}$$

where the discriminant D is

$$b^2 - 4ac.$$

Problem 1. Solve the real quadratic equation $2x^2 - 4x - 7 = 0$.

Solution. For this equation, $a = 2$, $b = -4$, and $c = -7$. The discriminant D of this equation is $(-4)^2 - 4 \cdot 2 \cdot (-7)$, or 72. Hence, by the quadratic formula, the solutions of this equation are

$$x = \frac{4 + \sqrt{72}}{4} \quad \text{and} \quad x = \frac{4 - \sqrt{72}}{4}.$$

Since $72 = 36 \cdot 2$, we have $\sqrt{72} = 6\sqrt{2}$, and the two solutions are

$$x = 1 + \tfrac{3}{2}\sqrt{2} \quad \text{and} \quad x = 1 - \tfrac{3}{2}\sqrt{2}.$$

As expected, the solutions are real since $D > 0$. Using $\sqrt{2} \doteq 1.414$, we find that these two irrational solutions have rational approximations

$$3.121 \quad \text{and} \quad -1.121.$$

Problem 2. Solve the real quadratic equation $4x^2 - 12x + 9 = 0$.

Solution. For this equation, $a = 4$, $b = -12$, and $c = 9$. Hence,

$$D = (-12)^2 - (4 \cdot 4 \cdot 9), \quad \text{or } 0.$$

Since $D = 0$, the quadratic formula yields only one solution:

$$x = \frac{-(-12)}{2 \cdot 4}, \quad \text{or} \quad \frac{3}{2}.$$

Problem 3. Solve the real quadratic equation $3x^2 - 4x + 7 = 0$.

Solution. For this equation, $a = 3$, $b = -4$, and $c = 7$. Therefore, the discriminant D is $(-4)^2 - (4 \cdot 3 \cdot 7)$, or -68. Hence, by the quadratic formula, the solutions of this equation are

$$x = \frac{4 + \sqrt{-68}}{6} \quad \text{and} \quad x = \frac{4 - \sqrt{-68}}{6}.$$

Since $-68 = -4 \cdot 17$, we have $\sqrt{-68} = 2\sqrt{17}i$, and the solutions are

$$x = \tfrac{2}{3} + \tfrac{1}{3}\sqrt{17}i \quad \text{and} \quad x = \tfrac{2}{3} - \tfrac{1}{3}\sqrt{17}i.$$

Because $D < 0$, the two solutions are nonreal conjugate complex numbers.

Exercises

1. (a) Show that $(\sqrt{-2})(\sqrt{-8}) = -4$.
   (b) Show that $(\sqrt{-3})(\sqrt{-12}) = -6$.

Find the discriminant of each of the following quadratic equations, and from it, determine whether the equation has nonreal solutions, one real solution, real solutions which are rational, or real solutions which are irrational.

2. (a) $x^2 - 4x + 2 = 0$ (b) $y^2 + 6y + 9 = 0$
3. (a) $x^2 + x + 1 = 0$ (b) $x^2 + 3x + 2 = 0$
4. Using the solutions of the quadratic formula, show that if

$$ax^2 + bx + c = 0$$

   has two solutions, real or complex, then
   (a) the sum of the solutions is $-(b/a)$.
   (b) the product of the solutions is c/a.

Solve each of the following quadratic equations. Check your solutions by comparing the sum and product of the solutions with $-(b/a)$ and c/a, respectively.

5. (a) $x^2 + 9 = 0$ (b) $x^2 + 100 = 0$
6. (a) $2x^2 - 4x + 5 = 0$ (b) $x^2 - 4x + 4 = 0$

THE QUADRATIC FORMULA | 4-5

7. (a) $x = 1 - 3x^2$ (b) $x^2 + 2 = 4x$
8. (a) $3x^2 + 5x + 4 = 0$ (b) $5z^2 - 13z = 6$
9. (a) $\frac{1}{2}x^2 - \frac{2}{3}x + 1 = 0$ (b) $2 - \frac{1}{2}x - \frac{3}{5}x^2 = 0$
10. (a) $2x^2 + 9x = 0$ (b) $-16t^2 - 32t + 240 = 0$
11. (a) $(x - 2)^2 - 5(x - 2) + 6 = 0$
    (b) $(2x + 1)^2 - 3(2x + 1) - 4 = 0$
12. (a) $x^2 - (m + n)x + mn = 0, \; m \neq n$
    (b) $y^2 - 2\sqrt{5}y + 1 = 0$

If the formulas of Exercise 4 are applied to the solution set of a quadratic equation of the form $x^2 + bx + c = 0$, the sum of the solutions is $-b$ and the product of the solutions is c. This provides an alternative method for writing a quadratic equation when its solution set is given. For example, if the solution set is $\{3 + i, 3 - i\}$, then the sum, 6, equals $-b$ and the product, 10, equals c. Hence, $x^2 - 6x + 10 = 0$ is a quadratic equation with the given solution set. Use this method to write quadratic equations having the following solution sets.

13. $\{1 + \sqrt{3}, \; 1 - \sqrt{3}\}$ 14. $\{2 + i, \; 2 - i\}$
15. $\{2, -\frac{3}{2}\}$ 16. $\{2, -2\}$
17. $\{\frac{1}{2} - \frac{1}{2}\sqrt{5}, \; \frac{1}{2} + \frac{1}{2}\sqrt{5}\}$ 18. $\{9, -10\}$

19. $\left\{-\frac{1}{2} + \frac{\sqrt{3}}{2}i, \; -\frac{1}{2} - \frac{\sqrt{3}}{2}i\right\}$ 20. $\{i, -i\}$

---

21. The graph of the equation $y = ax^2 + bx + c$ can intersect the x-axis in two points, be tangent to the x-axis, or fail to intersect the x-axis. In each case, what type of solution or solutions does the quadratic equation $ax^2 + bx + c = 0$ have? In each case, what values does the discriminant have?

22. For what value or values of m does the graph of $y = x^2 - 3x + m$ cut the x-axis in two points?

23. For what value or values of m is the graph of $y = x^2 - 3x + m$ tangent to the x-axis?

24. For what value or values of m will the graph of $y = x^2 - 3x + m$ fail to cut the x-axis?

25. For what value or values of k is the graph of $y = x^2 - kx + k + 8$ tangent to the x-axis?

26. For what value or values of k does $x^2 - 4x - k = 0$ have one real solution?

Graph each of the following equations.

27. $y = x^2 + 6x + 9$ **28.** $y = x^2 - 5x + 6$

29. $y = 3x^2 + 5x + 4$ **30.** $y = 4 - 3x - x^2$

31. For what value or values of p does $px^2 - 6x + p = 0$ have nonreal solutions?

32. For what value or values of p is 2 in the solution set of the quadratic equation

$$px^2 - 4x + 3 = 0?$$

33. For what value or values of k is one solution of $x^2 - 6x + k = 0$ twice the other solution?

34. (a) Is $2 - 3i$ a solution of the complex quadratic equation

$$x^2 - (3 - 2i)x + (5 - i) = 0?$$

(b) Is $x = 1 + i$ a solution of the equation of part (a)?

(c) Factor

$$x^2 - (3 - 2i)x + (5 - i),$$

and check your factoring by multiplication.

35. Prove that if a and b are negative numbers, $\sqrt{a} \cdot \sqrt{b} = -\sqrt{ab}$.

4-6   THE COMPLEX NUMBER PLANE

We can assign complex numbers to points in a plane in the same way that we assign ordered pairs of real numbers. We start out with two perpendicular number lines; one line has real numbers for coordinates and the other line has i-numbers. These lines meet at their origins. Each complex number can be assigned as the coordinate of a unique point in the plane, as suggested in Fig. 4–1.

The horizontal number line in the figure is called the *real axis*. Every real number is the coordinate of a point on this axis. The vertical number line is called the *imaginary axis*. Each pure imaginary number, or i-number, is the coordinate of a point on this axis. Every point in the plane has a complex number $a + bi$ as its coordinate to describe the position of the point relative to the two axes. Thus, if lines are drawn through this point parallel to the axes, they will cross the axes at the point with coordinate a on the real axis and at the point with coordinate bi on the imaginary axis. (See Fig. 4–2.) This plane, which has a complex number assigned to each of its points, is called the *complex number plane*.

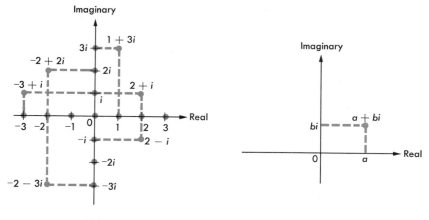

FIGURE 4-1   FIGURE 4-2

How does the complex number plane compare with a cartesian coordinate system in the plane? If we let the real axis be the usual x-axis and the imaginary axis be the y-axis, then the point with co-ordinate $a + bi$ in the complex number plane has coordinates (a, b) in the cartesian coordinate system.

The distance from the origin to the point with coordinate $a + bi$ is called the *absolute value* of the complex number $a + bi$. According to the pythagorean theorem, this distance is $\sqrt{a^2 + b^2}$. We shall use the notation $|a + bi|$ to designate the absolute value of $a + bi$. By definition,

$$|a + bi| = \sqrt{a^2 + b^2}.$$

For example, $|3 - 2i| = \sqrt{3^2 + (-2)^2}$, or $\sqrt{13}$.

The following problem from a prize examination shows an unusual way of using complex numbers and the complex number plane.

Problem. Two men left a certain place and walked, each in a straight line, to their destinations which were 4 miles apart. If the distance which one of them walked was one-half the square of the distance which the other man walked, how far did each man walk?

Solution 1. Let x be the distance one man walked and y be the distance the other man walked. We might be inclined to represent what is given by the following system of equations:

$$\begin{cases} y - x = 4, \\ y = \tfrac{1}{2}x^2. \end{cases}$$

When we solve the first equation for y and substitute it in the second, we obtain the equivalent system

$$\begin{cases} y = x + 4, \\ x + 4 = \tfrac{1}{2}x^2. \end{cases}$$

The second equation is equivalent to each of the following:

$$2x + 8 = x^2,$$
$$x^2 - 2x - 8 = 0,$$
$$(x - 4)(x + 2) = 0.$$

Thus, $x = 4$ or $x = -2$. Substituting these values in the first equation, we obtain the solutions $(4, 8)$ and $(-2, 2)$ for (x, y).

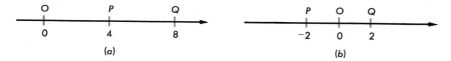

FIGURE 4–3

These two solutions for x and y may be pictured on a number line, as shown in Fig. 4–3; $d(OP) = x$ and $d(OQ) = y$. In Fig. 4–3(a) one man walks from O to P and the other from O to Q.

$$8 - 4 = 4 \quad \text{and} \quad 8 = \tfrac{1}{2} \cdot 4^2$$

In Fig. 4–3(b), $OP = -2$ and $OQ = 2$, and

$$2 - (-2) = 4, \quad 2 = \tfrac{1}{2}(-2)^2.$$

Solution 2. In the statement of the problem, it does not say which of the two distances is one-half the square of the other. Thus, our system of equations could just as well be

$$\begin{cases} y - x = 4, \\ x = \tfrac{1}{2}y^2. \end{cases}$$

If we solve the first equation for x and substitute it in the second, we obtain the equivalent system

$$\begin{cases} x = y - 4, \\ y - 4 = \tfrac{1}{2}y^2. \end{cases}$$

The second equation of this system may be solved as follows:

$$2y - 8 = y^2,$$
$$y^2 - 2y + 8 = 0,$$
$$y = \frac{2 + \sqrt{-28}}{2} \quad \text{or} \quad y = \frac{2 - \sqrt{-28}}{2}.$$

Since $\sqrt{-28} = 2\sqrt{7}i$, the two solutions of this quadratic equation are $1 + \sqrt{7}i$ and $1 - \sqrt{7}i$. Returning to the given system of equations, we have

$$x = (1 + \sqrt{7}i) - 4, \quad \text{or } x = -3 + \sqrt{7}i, \quad \text{when} \quad y = 1 + \sqrt{7}i.$$
$$x = (1 - \sqrt{7}i) - 4, \quad \text{or } x = -3 - \sqrt{7}i, \quad \text{when} \quad y = 1 - \sqrt{7}i.$$

Hence,

$$\{(-3 + \sqrt{7}i, \, 1 + \sqrt{7}i), \, (-3 - \sqrt{7}i, \, 1 - \sqrt{7}i)\}$$

is the solution set of the given system.

We can interpret complex numbers as solutions of the given problem if we think of each man as starting from the origin 0 of a complex plane. One man walks to point A with coordinate x and the other to point B with coordinate y. In Fig. 4–4, this possibility is sketched for the first element of the solution set, $x = -3 + \sqrt{7}i$ and $y = 1 + \sqrt{7}i$. Then $y - x = 4$, in this case, and 4 is the actual distance between points A and B. According to the definition of the absolute value of a complex number, the distances walked by the two men are $|x|$ and $|y|$.

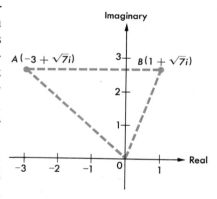

FIGURE 4–4

Since

$$|x| = \sqrt{(-3)^2 + (\sqrt{7})^2}, \quad \text{or } 4,$$

and

$$|y| = \sqrt{1^2 + (\sqrt{7})^2}, \quad \text{or } \sqrt{8},$$

it is true that

$$|x| = \tfrac{1}{2}|y|^2, \quad \text{or } 4 = \tfrac{1}{2} \cdot 8.$$

Hence, Fig. 4–4 represents another solution of this problem. The second elements of the solution set, $x = -3 - \sqrt{7}i$ and $y = 1 - \sqrt{7}i$, may be similarly interpreted.

Thus, we can assume that the men are walking in the same straight line, and we then find two solutions, one when they walk in the same direction and one when they walk in opposite directions. On the other hand, we can assume that they do not walk in the same straight line and we then find another solution in which the paths are oblique to each other.

Exercises

Plot each number on a complex number plane.

1. (a) $6 + 8i$ (b) $-8 + 6i$
2. (a) $1 - i$ (b) $2 - 3i$
3. (a) -10 (b) 5
4. (a) $5i$ (b) $-2i$
5. (a) Find the distance from the origin of each of the points plotted in Exercises 1(a), 2(a), 3(a), and 4(a). Which point is farthest from the origin? Which point is nearest the origin? Are any two or more points the same distance from the origin?
   (b) Follow the directions in part (a) for Exercises 1(b), 2(b), 3(b), and 4(b).

Find each of the absolute values.

6. (a) $|2 - 3i|$ (b) $|4 - 3i|$
7. (a) $\left| -\dfrac{\sqrt{3}}{2} + \dfrac{1}{2}i \right|$ (b) $|-6i|$
8. (a) $|3 + 4i|$ (b) $|-3 + 4i|$
9. (a) $|-3 - 4i|$ (b) $|3 - 4i|$
10. (a) $\left| -\dfrac{\sqrt{3}}{2} - \dfrac{1}{2}i \right|$ (b) $\left| \dfrac{1}{2} - \dfrac{\sqrt{3}}{2}i \right|$

---

11. (a) On a complex number plane, plot the following points: A with coordinate $2 + i$, B with coordinate $1 + 5i$, and C with coordinate 0.
    (b) Find point D such that $ADBC$ is a parallelogram, and give its coordinate.
    (c) Find the sum of $2 + i$ and $1 + 5i$. How does this number compare with the coordinate of D?

12. (a) On a complex number plane, plot the following points: P with coordinate $2 + 3i$, Q with coordinate $-4 + 2i$, and R with coordinate 0.
   (b) Find point S such that $PSQR$ is a parallelogram, and give its coordinate.
   (c) Find the sum of $2 + 3i$ and $-4 + 2i$, and plot the point T with this sum as the coordinate. How far is T from S?

13. In a plane with a cartesian coordinate system, consider points

$$E(0, 0), \quad F(a, b), \quad G(a + c, b + d), \quad H(c, d).$$

   (a) Find the slopes of $\overline{EF}$ and $\overline{GH}$.
   (b) Find the slopes of $\overline{FG}$ and $\overline{EH}$.
   (c) Show that $EFGH$ is a parallelogram.

14. In the complex number plane, consider points with coordinates $0 + 0i$, $a + bi$, $c + di$, and $(a + c) + (b + d)i$. Explain how complex numbers can be added graphically by constructing a parallelogram.

15. On a complex number plane, plot each pair of points P, Q with the coordinates given below. Find the coordinate of the point S such that $PSQR$ is a parallelogram with one vertex at R, the origin.
   (a) P: $-1 + 5i$, $\quad Q$: $3 + 2i$
   (b) P: $2 - 3i$, $\quad\ \ Q$: $-1 + 4i$
   (c) P: $4 + 6i$, $\quad\ \ Q$: $4 - 6i$

16. (a) On a complex number plane, plot the points C with coordinate $2 + 2i$ and D with coordinate $1 + 4i$.
   (b) Subtract $1 + 4i$ from $2 + 2i$ and plot the point F, with the difference as its coordinate.
   (c) Show that the line from the origin to F is parallel to CD.

---

17. In a plane with a cartesian coordinate system, consider points $E(0, 0)$, $F(a, b)$, $G(c, d)$, and $H(a - c, b - d)$.
   (a) Find the slopes of $\overline{FG}$ and $\overline{EH}$.
   (b) Find the slopes of $\overline{EG}$ and $\overline{HF}$.
   (c) Show that $EGFH$ is a parallelogram.

18. In the complex number plane, consider points with coordinates $a + bi$, $c + di$, and $(a - c) + (b - d)i$. Explain how complex numbers can be subtracted graphically by constructing a parallelogram.

Which, if any, of the following statements do you think is true for every pair of complex numbers x and y?

19. $|x| + |y| > |x + y|$ 20. $|x| + |y| \geqq |x + y|$

21. $|x| + |y| = |x + y|$ 22. $|x| + |y| \leqq |x + y|$

23. $|x| + |y| < |x + y|$

24. If a is real, the absolute value of a is defined by the equations

$$|a| = a \quad \text{if} \quad a \geqq 0,$$
$$|a| = -a \quad \text{if} \quad a < 0.$$

However, consider a to be the complex number $a + 0i$; then refer to the definition of absolute value of a complex number, and compare these two absolute values of a.

25. The graphical addition of complex numbers is given in Exercise 14. Remember that one side of a triangle can be no longer than the sum of the other two sides, and show geometrically that your answer to Exercises 19–23 is correct.

26. (a) Solve the system

$$\begin{cases} y^2 = 6x, \\ y - x = 4\frac{1}{6}. \end{cases}$$

(b) Graph your solutions on a complex number plane.

(c) Can you supply a physical interpretation of this system and its solution similar to that given for the problem of this section?

27. The notation $\bar{r}$ is frequently used for the conjugate of the complex number r.

(a) If $r = a + bi$, show that $r\bar{r} = a^2 + b^2$.

(b) Show that $\sqrt{r\bar{r}} = |r|$.

(c) Show that $|\bar{r}| = |r|$.

(d) Show that $|\overline{rs}| = |\bar{r}| \cdot |\bar{s}|$ for any two complex numbers r and s.

28. The complex number with a variable real part x and a variable pure imaginary part yi is called a *complex variable*, and z is the letter commonly used for $x + yi$. In the complex number plane, what is the graph

(a) of the equation $|z| = 4$?

(b) of the inequality $|z| < 2$?

(c) of the inequality $|z| \geqq 3$?

HISTORICAL NOTE

Simple quadratic equations were solved for countless centuries before a formal mathematical language was evolved. According to all the evidence we have, the completion of squares was one of the earliest methods used in solving quadratics. Therefore, it is not surprising that the quadratic formula appeared in print as soon as the appropriate symbolism was available.

Once the quadratic formula was commonly used, mathematicians tried to solve higher-degree polynomial equations by similar methods. In the sixteenth century, many mathematicians worked on solutions of cubic equations of the form

$$x^3 + ax^2 + bx + c = 0. \tag{1}$$

They soon discovered that the replacement of x by $y - a/3$ reduced Eq. (1) to the form

$$y^3 + py + q = 0. \tag{2}$$

Here p and q are simple combinations of a, b, and c. Once mathematicians found a solution r for Eq. (2), they then found that $r - a/3$ is a solution of Eq. (1).

One of the earliest solvers of Eq. (2) was the Italian mathematician Tartaglia. His solution was published in 1545 in Cardan's famous algebra book, *Ars Magna*. A somewhat more complicated solution was given by the Frenchman Vieta in 1591. The following is his solution.

First, let

$$y = z - \frac{p}{3z}$$

in Eq. (2). After simplifying the resulting equation, we obtain

$$z^6 + qz^3 - \frac{p^3}{27} = 0. \tag{3}$$

Since Eq. (3) is a quadratic equation in z^3, we can solve for z^3 by the quadratic formula:

$$z^3 = -\frac{q}{2} \pm \sqrt{D}, \text{ where } D = \frac{p^3}{27} + \frac{q^2}{4}.$$

Letting

$$A = \sqrt[3]{-\frac{q}{2} + \sqrt{D}} \text{ and } B = \sqrt[3]{-\frac{q}{2} - \sqrt{D}},$$

we can show that

$$y = A + B$$

is a solution of Eq. (2). For example, the equation

$$y^3 - 6y - 6 = 0$$

has solution

$$y = \sqrt[3]{4} + \sqrt[3]{2}.$$

Equation (2) usually has three solutions. The other two are

$$y = tA + t^2B \quad \text{and} \quad y = t^2A + tB,$$

where t is a complex cube root of 1, that is, $t = -\frac{1}{2} + \frac{1}{2}\sqrt{3}i$.

Quartic equations of the form

$$x^4 + ax^3 + bx^2 + cx + d = 0 \tag{4}$$

were also solved in *Ars Magna*. Supposedly, the first to solve the quartic equation was the Italian mathematician Ferrari in about 1540. He showed that the solution of Eq. (4) could be obtained from the solutions of associated cubic and quadratic equations.

KEY IDEAS AND KEY WORDS

Every number of the form $a + bi$ where a and b are real numbers, is called a **complex number**. For a given complex number $a + bi$, it is customary to call a the **real part** and bi the **pure imaginary part** of $a + bi$. **Pure imaginary numbers** are called *i*-numbers.

The **sum and product of two complex numbers** are defined as follows:

$$(a + bi) + (c + di) = (a + c) + (b + d)i,$$
$$(a + bi)(c + di) = (ac - bd) + (ad + bc)i.$$

The **additive inverse** of the complex number $a + bi$ is given by

$$-(a + bi) = -a + (-bi).$$

The **conjugate** of $a + bi$ is, by definition, $a - bi$. The sum and product of a complex number and its conjugate are real numbers:

$$(a + bi) + (a - bi) = 2a,$$
$$(a + bi)(a - bi) = a^2 + b^2.$$

With the exception of the order axioms, all the axioms of addition and multiplication in the real number system are valid in the complex number system.

If a, b, and c are real numbers, with $a \neq 0$, the equation

$$ax^2 + bx + c = 0$$

is called a **real quadratic equation** and the number $D = b^2 - 4ac$ is called its **discriminant**. By the **quadratic formula**, the solutions of this equation are

$$x = \frac{-b + \sqrt{D}}{2a} \quad \text{and} \quad x = \frac{-b - \sqrt{D}}{2a}.$$

If $D < 0$, then $\sqrt{D}$ is defined to be $\sqrt{-D}i$.

The plane having a complex number assigned to each of its points is called the **complex number plane.** The distance from the origin to the point with coordinate $a + bi$ is called the **absolute value** of the complex number $a + bi$. It is given by

$$|a + bi| = \sqrt{a^2 + b^2}.$$

CHAPTER REVIEW

In Exercises 1–7, perform the indicated operations.

1. $(\sqrt{2}i)^3$

2. $(-7 + \sqrt{2}i) - (6 - 3\sqrt{2}i)$

3. $(3 + 4i)(2 - 7i)$

4. $\left(\frac{1}{2} - \frac{\sqrt{3}}{2}i\right) + \left(\frac{1}{2} + \frac{\sqrt{3}}{2}i\right)$

5. $\left(\frac{1}{2} - \frac{\sqrt{2}}{2}i\right)\left(\frac{1}{2} + \frac{\sqrt{2}}{2}i\right)$

6. $\frac{2 + i}{3 - i}$

7. $\frac{3 - \sqrt{2}i}{3 + \sqrt{2}i}$

8. Evaluate each of the following.
(a) $|-3 - 4i|$
(b) $|(1 + \sqrt{2}i)(3 - \sqrt{3}i)|$

9. (a) Write the conjugate of the complex number $-\sqrt{2} + 7i$, and find the sum and product of this pair of conjugate numbers.
(b) Find the complex number which is the reciprocal of $-3 + 4i$.

10. Find the real numbers x and y for which

$$(x - y) + (2x + 3y)i = (5 + 4i) - (1 - 7i).$$

Solve the following quadratic equations and check your solutions.

11. $6x^2 - 13x + 6 = 0$

12. $x^2 + 4x + 7 = 0$

13. $9 + 4x^2 = 12x$

14. $3x^2 + 4x + 5 = 0$

Write a quadratic equation for each of the following solution sets.

15. $\{2i, -2i\}$

16. $\{3 - \sqrt{5}i, 3 + \sqrt{5}i\}$

17. $\{\frac{1}{2}, -3\}$

18. $\{-2 + 3i, -2 - 3i\}$

On a complex number plane, plot the points corresponding to each of the following numbers.

19. $-2 - 3i$

20. $-4 + 7i$

21. $5i$

22. -5

23. $-8i$

24. $3 - 2i$

CHAPTER TEST

1. Perform the following indicated operations in the system of complex numbers.
   (a) $(-3 + 5i) - (2 - 3i)$ (b) $(-3 + 5i)(2 - 3i)$
   (c) $\dfrac{2 + 7i}{4 - 6i}$ (d) $(-3i)^5$ (e) $\dfrac{1}{3 + 4i}$

2. Solve the following quadratic equations and check each solution.
   (a) $x^2 - 6x + 10 = 0$ (b) $7x^2 + 4x + 1 = 0$
   (c) $3x^2 + 5x - 2 = 0$

3. Write a quadratic equation for each of the following solution sets.
   (a) $\{-2, 5\}$ (b) $\{3 + \sqrt{3}i, 3 - \sqrt{3}i\}$

4. Plot the following numbers on a complex number plane. Give the absolute value of each number.
   (a) $2 + 5i$ (b) $-3 + 4i$ (c) $-7i$ (d) -7

5. Find real numbers x and y for which

$$(2x - y) + (x + 3y)i = 2(-4 + 5i).$$

CUMULATIVE REVIEW I

Perform the indicated operations and express each answer in simplest form.

1. $(\sqrt{28})(\sqrt{45})$ 2. $(\sqrt{3} - 1)(\sqrt{3} + 1)$
3. $\sqrt{\tfrac{8}{3}} + \sqrt{\tfrac{48}{8}} - \sqrt{\tfrac{25}{24}}$ 4. $(\sqrt[3]{14})(\sqrt[4]{686})$
5. $\sqrt{\tfrac{2}{3}} \div \sqrt{\tfrac{7}{15}}$ 6. $\dfrac{3}{\sqrt{5} + \sqrt{2}}$
7. $\dfrac{1 + \sqrt{2}}{1 - \sqrt{2}}$ 8. $\dfrac{\sqrt{2} + \sqrt{3}}{2\sqrt{2} + \sqrt{3}}$

Write each expression with positive exponents and then simplify.

9. $\dfrac{2^0 - 2^{-2}}{2 - 2(2)^{-2}}$ 10. $\dfrac{2a^{-1} + a^0}{a^{-2}}$
11. $\left(\dfrac{2^0}{8^{\frac{1}{3}}}\right)^{-1}$ 12. $\dfrac{(-3a)^3 \cdot 3a^{-\frac{2}{3}}}{(2a)^{-2} \cdot a^{\frac{1}{3}}}$

In Exercises 13–16, find all integral values of x for which each expression is true.

13. $|x + 2| = -3$ 14. $|x| - 3 = 5$
15. $|4 - x| \geq 8$ 16. $2 < |x + 1| < 5$
17. Solve the following inequalities.
    (a) $(2x + 5)(x - 6) > 36$ (b) $x^3 - x^2 < 6x$

18. If $a/b = c/d$ is a true equation and $a + b$ and $c + d$ are both different from zero, show that

$$\frac{a - b}{a + b} = \frac{c - d}{c + d}$$

is also a true equation.

19. Given the formula $s = \dfrac{a - rL}{1 - r}$, write a formula for r in terms of the other variables.

20. If the domain of x is the set of all real numbers, what is the minimum value of $4x^2 - 24x - 3$?

21. Show that $-\dfrac{2}{3} - \dfrac{\sqrt{5}}{3}i$ is a solution of the equation

$$6x^3 - x^2 - 6x - 9 = 0.$$

22. For what value or values of k does the entire graph of the equation $y = x^2 + kx - x + 9$ lie above the x-axis?

23. (a) Graph the equation $y = x^2 - 2x - 8$.
(b) From your graph, find the solution set of $x^2 - 2x - 8 > -5$.
(c) Solve the inequality $x^2 - 2x - 3 > 0$ by factoring.

In Exercises 24 and 25, solve each equation.

24. $x + 3 - \dfrac{10x^2 - 25}{x - 3} = 0$ **25.** $\dfrac{x}{4} + \dfrac{1}{x} = \dfrac{x}{3} + \dfrac{2}{3x}$

26. One numeral for a number is $\dfrac{2}{1 + \sqrt{2} - i}$. Find another numeral for the same number of the form $a + bi$, where a and b are real numbers.

27. A picture with dimensions 8 inches by 12 inches is surrounded by a frame of uniform width. If the area of the frame is one-half the area of the picture, find a one-decimal-place approximation for the width of the frame.

28. Graph each of the following equations on a cartesian plane.
(a) $|x| + |y| = 8$ (b) $|x + y| = 8$ (c) $|x| - |y| = 8$ (d) $|x - y| = 8$

29. Solve each of the following inequalities.
(a) $|2x - 3| < 1$ (b) $|2x + 3| < x$

30. A pet shop bought a litter of puppies for $80. All but 3 were sold, and the total receipt from the sale was also $80. If each puppy was sold for $6 more than was paid for it, how many puppies were there in the litter?

CHAPTER **5**

Conic Sections and Their Equations

Objectives . . .

- To recognize the analytic form of each of the conic sections.
- To apply the distance formula to the problem of finding equations of conic sections.
- To use algebraic methods in finding intersection points of conics with other conics and lines.

5-1 CIRCLES

The conic sections are plane curves, so named because each of them is the curve of intersection of a plane with a right circular cone. The conic section which is easiest to visualize is the circle, obtained by cutting a cone with a plane perpendicular to the axis of the cone. (See Fig. 5–1.) The circle may be defined equally well as the set of all points in a plane at a given distance from a fixed point in the plane. The given distance is called the *radius* and the fixed point the *center* of the circle.

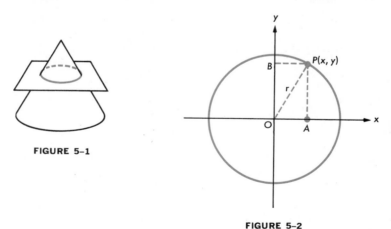

FIGURE 5–1

FIGURE 5–2

Consider a circle of radius r having its center at the origin of a cartesian coordinate system, as shown in Fig. 5–2. If P is a point in the plane with coordinates (x, y), then P is on this circle if, and only if, the distance from O to P is r. The distance from O to P is denoted by OP. Thus, P is on the circle if, and only if,

$$OP = r.$$

221

If we use the notation of Fig. 5–2, we have, by the pythagorean theorem,

$$(OP)^2 = (OA)^2 + (AP)^2.$$

Regardless of the quadrant in which P lies, $OA = |x|$ and $AP = OB$, or $|y|$. Hence,

$$(OP)^2 = |x|^2 + |y|^2$$
$$= x^2 + y^2.$$

We conclude that the point P with coordinates (x, y) is on the circle if, and only if,

$$x^2 + y^2 = r^2.$$

The graph of the second-degree equation

$$x^2 + y^2 = r^2,$$

in the two variables x and y, is a circle with its center at the origin and radius r.

For example, the graph of the equation

$$x^2 + y^2 = 16$$

is the circle of radius 4 sketched in Fig. 5–3.

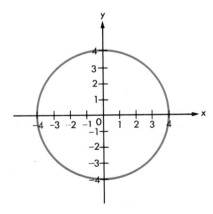

FIGURE 5-3

A circle divides the plane into three sets of points: the sets of points inside the circle, on the circle, and outside the circle. We have just described the set of points on the circle of Fig. 5–3 as the graph of

$$\{(x, y) \mid x^2 + y^2 = 16\}.$$

How do we describe the set of points inside this circle? A point $P(x, y)$ is inside this circle if, and only if, $OP < 4$, or $(OP)^2 < 16$. Since $(OP)^2 = x^2 + y^2$, the graph of

$$\{(x, y) \mid x^2 + y^2 < 16\}$$

is the set of all points inside this circle; similarly, the graph of

$$\{(x, y) \mid x^2 + y^2 > 16\}$$

is the set of all points outside this circle.

Exercises

1. (a) What is the radius of the circle with equation $x^2 + y^2 = 25$?
   (b) What is the radius of the circle with equation $x^2 + y^2 = 49$?

2. (a) Write an equation of a circle with its center at the origin and a radius of 6.
   (b) Write an equation of a circle with its center at the origin and a radius of 8.

3. (a) Write a mathematical statement describing the set of all points in the plane which are at least 4 units from the origin.
   (b) Write a mathematical statement describing the set of all points in the plane which are at least 9 units from the origin.

4. (a) A circle is drawn with its center at the origin of a cartesian coordinate system. The circle passes through the point $(2, 5)$. What is the radius of the circle? Write an equation of the circle.
   (b) A circle is drawn with its center at the origin of a cartesian coordinate system. The circle passes through the point $(-1, 3)$. What is the radius of the circle? Write an equation of the circle.

5. (a) Give three integral solutions of the system of inequalities

$$\begin{cases} x \leq 0, \\ x^2 + y^2 \leq 16. \end{cases}$$

   Graph the system.
   (b) Give three solutions, in ordered pairs of integers, of the system of inequalities

$$\begin{cases} x^2 + y^2 \leq 25, \\ y \geq 0. \end{cases}$$

   Graph the system.

---

6. Find a system of inequalities whose graph is the set of all points to the right of the y-axis that are inside the circle with equation

$$x^2 + y^2 = 49.$$

7. Classify the points

$$(2, 3), \quad (1, -1), \quad (1, \tfrac{4}{3}), \quad (-\sqrt{2}, -1), \quad (0, 2)$$

by indicating which are inside, which are outside, and which are on the circle with equation

$$9x^2 + 9y^2 = 25.$$

8. Describe algebraically the set of all points in the plane at a distance of 4 units or less from the origin.

---

9. The family of concentric circles, with center at the origin, may be characterized by the equation

$$x^2 + y^2 = k.$$

Describe the members of this family for which $k = 10^6$, 10^2, 5^2, 10, 5, 1, 0, and -1, respectively. For what real number values of k does $x^2 + y^2 = k$ represent a circle?

10. Find a system of inequalities whose graph is the set of all points in the region strictly between the circles with equations $x^2 + y^2 - 10 = 0$ and $9x^2 + 9y^2 - 25 = 0$. Graph the region so described.

Preparation for Section 5–2

1. Solve, by substitution, the system

$$\begin{cases} x - y = 4, \\ 3x - 5y = 8. \end{cases}$$

2. Define equivalent systems of equations.
3. Solve

$$x^2 + x - 12 = 0.$$

4. Where does the graph of $y = ax^2 + bx + c$ cross the x-axis if $ax^2 + bx + c = 0$ has no real solution?

5-2 THE INTERSECTION OF A CIRCLE AND A LINE

To find the point of intersection of two lines, we find the solution set of the system composed of the two equations of the lines. In the same way, we can find the points of intersection of a line and a circle by solving the system consisting of the equations of the line and the circle. A circle and a line intersect in two points at most. If the line is tangent to the circle, then they intersect in only one point. Of course, many lines and circles have no points of intersection.

Problem. Find the points of intersection, if any, of the circle with equation

$$x^2 + y^2 = 25$$

and the line with equation

$$x - y + 1 = 0.$$

Solution. One possible way of finding these points is to graph the circle and the line on the same set of axes. (See Fig. 5–4.) Then we can obtain rough approximations of the co-ordinates of the points of inter-section of the two graphs. Stated algebraically, the problem is to solve the following system of equations.

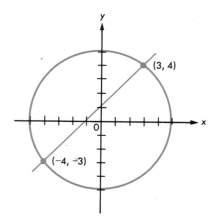

$$\begin{cases} x^2 + y^2 = 25 \\ x - y + 1 = 0 \end{cases}$$

In other words, we are seeking those, and only those, ordered pairs which are solutions of both equations. We can solve a system con-sisting of one linear and one quadratic equation by essentially the same methods employed with

FIGURE 5–4

systems of linear equations. For instance, the particular system above can be solved by using the substitution method. Thus, if we solve the linear equation for y and substitute its value in the quadratic equation, we obtain the equivalent system

$$\begin{cases} x^2 + (x + 1)^2 = 25, \\ \qquad\qquad y = x + 1. \end{cases}$$

The quadratic equation of this system is equivalent to each of the following equations.

$$x^2 + x^2 + 2x + 1 = 25$$
$$2x^2 + 2x - 24 = 0$$
$$x^2 + x - 12 = 0$$
$$(x + 4)(x - 3) = 0$$

Therefore, the given system is equivalent to the system

$$\begin{cases} (x + 4)(x - 3) = 0, \\ \qquad\qquad y = x + 1. \end{cases}$$

The only values of x that make the first equation true are $x = -4$ and $x = 3$. If $x = -4$, then $y = -4 + 1$, or -3; if $x = 3$, $y = 3 + 1$, or 4, from the second equation. Hence,

$$\{(-4, -3), (3, 4)\}$$

is the solution set of the given system.

Check.
$$\qquad\qquad\qquad (-4, -3)$$
$$(-4)^2 + (-3)^2 \overset{?}{=} 25 \qquad -4 - (-3) + 1 \overset{?}{=} 0$$
$$16 + 9 \overset{?}{=} 25$$

You can verify that the other solution also checks.

Exercises

Use a single set of axes on which to graph the circle and the line in each of the systems. From the graph, find the points of intersection of the circle and the line, if any.

1. (a) $\begin{cases} x^2 + y^2 = 9 \\ x + y = 3 \end{cases}$ (b) $\begin{cases} x^2 + y^2 = 16 \\ x - y = 4 \end{cases}$

2. (a) $\begin{cases} x^2 + y^2 = 36 \\ y - x = 9 \end{cases}$ (b) $\begin{cases} x^2 + y^2 = 25 \\ 3x = 4y + 25 \end{cases}$

3. (a) $\begin{cases} x^2 + y^2 = 20 \\ x - 2y = 10 \end{cases}$ (b) $\begin{cases} x^2 + y^2 - 1 = 0 \\ x + y - 2 = 0 \end{cases}$

4. (a)–6 (a). Solve algebraically each of the systems of equations in Exercises 1(a)–3(a). What does the solution of Exercise 2(a) tell you about the graph of these equations? What do you surmise about the graphs of the equations in Exercise 3(a)?

4. (b)–6 (b). Solve algebraically each of the systems in Exercises 1(b)–3(b). What do you surmise about the graphs of the equations in Exercise 2(b)? What does the solution of Exercise 3(b) tell you about the graphs of these equations?

---

7. In this section, we solved the following system.

$$\begin{cases} x^2 + y^2 = 25 \\ x - y + 1 = 0 \end{cases}$$

We discovered that where the line intersects the circle, x is -4 or 3. Then we found the ordinates of the points of intersection by using the linear equation

$$y = x + 1.$$

What error would occur if we were to find the ordinates of the points of intersection by using the quadratic equation

$$x^2 + y^2 = 25?$$

8. Find a system of inequalities whose graph is the set of all points above the line $x + y = 2$, but inside the circle $x^2 + y^2 = 4$. Graph this set of points.

9. A circle of radius $2\sqrt{5}$ is drawn with its center at the origin. Find the points of intersection of this circle with the line passing through the points $(-1, 7)$ and $(3, 3)$.

Draw the graph of each of the following systems of inequalities.

10. $\begin{cases} x^2 + y^2 \leq 10 \\ 2y \leq x + 5 \end{cases}$

11. $\begin{cases} x^2 + y^2 < 8 \\ y < x \\ y > 0 \end{cases}$

12. $\begin{cases} x^2 + y^2 > 4 \\ |x| < 2 \\ |y| < 2 \end{cases}$

13. $\begin{cases} x^2 + y^2 < 4 \\ |x| + |y| > 2 \end{cases}$

---

14. Consider the system of equations

$$\begin{cases} x^2 + y^2 = 9, \\ y = k, \end{cases}$$

which consists of a specific circle and a line which varies with k.
(a) For what values of k will the line $y = k$ fail to intersect the circle $x^2 + y^2 = 9$? Give an example.

(b) For what values of k will the line $y = k$ be tangent to the circle? How many such lines are there?

(c) For what values of k will the line $y = k$ intersect the circle in exactly two points? Give an example and check it by finding the points of intersection.

15. For what values of k will the graph of the equation $2x + y = k$ be tangent to the circle with equation $x^2 + y^2 = 4$?

16. What is the largest possible value of the linear form $2x + y$ if (x, y) is restricted so that it is in the set $\{(x, y) \mid x^2 + y^2 \leq 4\}$?

Preparation for Section 5–3

1. How do x and $|x|$ compare
   (a) for x negative?
   (b) for x zero?
   (c) for x positive?

2. How do x^2 and $|x|^2$ compare
   (a) for x negative?
   (b) for x nonnegative?

3. How far apart are $(-1, 0)$ and $(3, 0)$?

4. How far apart are $(0, 0)$ and $(3, 4)$?

5. How far apart are $(-1, -2)$ and $(2, 2)$?

5–3 THE DISTANCE FORMULA

Before discussing other conic sections, let us derive a formula for the distance between any two points in a plane. Such a formula will be useful in finding equations of conic sections.

Let us assume that a cartesian coordinate system has been drawn on the plane. We now wish to derive a formula for the distance PQ between points P and Q in terms of the coordinates (x_1, y_1) of P and (x_2, y_2) of Q. If point R is chosen as indicated in Fig. 5–5, then $\triangle PRQ$ is a right triangle, and

$$(PQ)^2 = (PR)^2 + (RQ)^2,$$

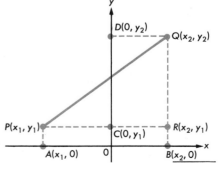

FIGURE 5-5

according to the pythagorean theorem. When we look at Fig. 5–5, we see that

$$PR = AB, \quad \text{or } |x_2 - x_1|,$$
$$RQ = CD, \quad \text{or } |y_2 - y_1|.$$

Hence,

$$(PQ)^2 = |x_2 - x_1|^2 + |y_2 - y_1|^2$$
$$= (x_2 - x_1)^2 + (y_2 - y_1)^2.$$

This proves the following important formula.

DISTANCE FORMULA

The distance between the points $P(x_1, y_1)$ and $Q(x_2, y_2)$ is given by

$$PQ = \sqrt{(x_2 - x_1)^2 + (y_2 - y_1)^2}.$$

The proof of the distance formula must be modified slightly if segment $\overline{PQ}$ is parallel to a coordinate axis, but the formula continues to apply.

Problem 1. Let $\triangle ABC$ be a triangle with vertices $A(9, 6)$, $B(1, -3)$, and $C(-1, 2)$. Find the length of each side of triangle ABC. Is $\triangle ABC$ a right triangle?

Solution. By the distance formula,

$$AB = \sqrt{(1 - 9)^2 + (-3 - 6)^2}$$
$$= \sqrt{8^2 + 9^2}, \quad \text{or } \sqrt{145}.$$
$$BC = \sqrt{(-1 - 1)^2 + [2 - (-3)]^2}$$
$$= \sqrt{2^2 + 5^2}, \quad \text{or } \sqrt{29}.$$
$$AC = \sqrt{(-1 - 9)^2 + (2 - 6)^2}$$
$$= \sqrt{10^2 + 4^2}, \quad \text{or } \sqrt{116}.$$

Thus, $\overline{AB}$ is the longest side. Hence, $\triangle ABC$ is a right triangle if, and only if,

$$(AB)^2 = (AC)^2 + (BC)^2,$$

according to the pythagorean theorem and its converse. The equation

$$(\sqrt{145})^2 = (\sqrt{116})^2 + (\sqrt{29})^2$$

or, equivalently,

$$145 = 116 + 29,$$

is true; therefore, $\triangle ABC$ is a right triangle.

Problem 2. Find an equation of the circle with its center, C, at $(-3, 4)$ and with a radius of 7.

Solution. Point P with coordinates (x, y) is on the circle if, and only if,

$$PC = 7,$$

that is,

$$\sqrt{(x + 3)^2 + (y - 4)^2} = 7.$$

Thus,

$$(x + 3)^2 + (y - 4)^2 = 49,$$

or

$$x^2 + y^2 + 6x - 8y - 24 = 0,$$

is an equation of the circle in Fig. 5-6.

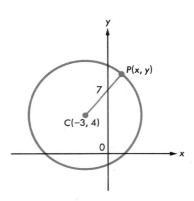

FIGURE 5-6

By the same argument as that used in Problem 2, we see that

$$(x - h)^2 + (y - k)^2 = r^2$$

is an equation of the circle having its center at (h, k) and a radius of r. An equivalent equation is

$$x^2 + y^2 - 2hx - 2ky + (h^2 + k^2 - r^2) = 0.$$

Conversely, if the graph of an equation of the form

$$Ax^2 + Ay^2 + Cx + Dy + E = 0, \quad A \neq 0,$$

consists of more than one point, then the graph is a circle. The following problem illustrates how the circle can be located in the coordinate plane.

Problem 3. Describe the graph of the equation

$$4x^2 + 4y^2 - 16x + 8y + 11 = 0.$$

Solution. We divide each side of this equation by 4, obtaining the equivalent equation

$$x^2 + y^2 - 4x + 2y + \tfrac{11}{4} = 0.$$

Then we proceed by completing the squares separately with the x-terms and the y-terms to get the equivalent equation

$$(x^2 - 4x + 4) + (y^2 + 2y + 1) = -\tfrac{11}{4} + 4 + 1,$$

or

$$(x - 2)^2 + (y + 1)^2 = \tfrac{9}{4}.$$

We recognize this as an equation of the circle with center at $(2, -1)$ and radius $\tfrac{3}{2}$.

We recall from Chapter 1 that the midpoint of a segment of a number line has as its coordinate the arithmetic average of the coordinates of the endpoints. In a similar way, it may be shown that the midpoint of the segment having endpoints $P(x_1, y_1)$ and $Q(x_2, y_2)$ has coordinates

$$\left(\frac{x_1 + x_2}{2}, \frac{y_1 + y_2}{2} \right).$$

Exercises

1. (a) How far is the point $(-9, 3)$ from the origin?
   (b) How far is the point $(-3, -4)$ from the point $(3, 4)$?
2. (a) Find an equation of the circle with center at $(2, -5)$ and radius 6. Simplify the equation.
   (b) Find an equation of the circle with center at $(-3, 4)$ and radius 5. Simplify the equation.
3. (a) Find the perimeter of triangle ABC with the following vertices.

$$A(-1, 3), \quad B(2, 5), \quad C(\tfrac{3}{2}, \tfrac{5}{2})$$

What type of triangle is ABC? Which angles have the same measure?
   (b) Prove that triangle ABC with the following vertices is a right triangle.

$$A(-7, 8), \quad B(-1, -4), \quad C(15, 4)$$

4. (a) Prove that triangle CDE with the following vertices is isosceles.

$$C(2, 3), \quad D(-\tfrac{13}{2}, 3), \quad E(1, 7)$$

Find the length of the altitude drawn from vertex D to base $\overline{CE}$.

(b) Prove that the angles at R and T are equal in the triangle with the following vertices.

$$R(-1, 5), \quad S(-1, -2), \quad T(6, -2)$$

5. (a) Use the distance formula to verify that the midpoint of the segment having endpoints $A(-1, 6)$ and $B(7, -10)$ has coordinates

$$\left(\frac{-1 + 7}{2}, \frac{6 + (-10)}{2}\right), \quad \text{or } (3, -2).$$

(b) Use the figure to prove that if P has coordinates (x_1, y_1), Q has coordinates (x_2, y_2), and $PM = MQ$, then M has coordinates

$$\left(\frac{x_1 + x_2}{2}, \frac{y_1 + y_2}{2}\right).$$

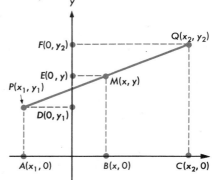

6. (a) A median of a triangle is a line joining a vertex to the midpoint of the opposite side. In triangle CDE with the following vertices, how long is the median drawn from C to the midpoint of DE?

$$C(-8, -5), \quad D(6, 2), \quad E(5, -4)$$

(b) Find the midpoints of the three sides of a triangle with the following vertices.

$$A(4, 4), \quad B(-2, 8), \quad C(2, -6)$$

Find the lengths of the three medians of the triangle. See part (a).

7. (a) Use the distance formula to find RS, ST, and RT, given that R has coordinates $(-1, 2)$, S has coordinates $(2, 3)$, and T has coordinates $(11, 6)$. Compare $RS + ST$ with RT to see whether points R, S, and T are collinear.

(b) Use the distance formula to find PQ, PR, and QR, given that P has coordinates $(-3, 2)$, Q has coordinates $(1, 1)$, and R has coordinates $(5, -2)$. Is $PQ + QR = PR$? Are points P, Q, and R collinear?

---

8. Is $|x_2 - x_1|^2$ always equal to $(x_2 - x_1)^2$? Why?

9. Find the center and radius of the circle having equation

$$x^2 + y^2 + 10x - 4y + 20 = 0.$$

10. If the line segment joining the points $(-3, -7)$ and $(9, 2)$ is a diameter of a circle, find an equation of the circle.

11. Triangle ABC has vertices at $A(7, 8)$, $B(-3, 4)$, and $C(-6, -2)$.
    (a) Find the length of $\overline{BC}$.
    (b) Find the midpoints of $\overline{AB}$ and $\overline{AC}$.
    (c) Find the distance between the midpoints of $\overline{AB}$ and $\overline{AC}$.
    (d) Compare the results of parts (a) and (c). What theorem in geometry does this comparison illustrate?

12. Find an equation of each of the following circles. Simplify each equation.
    (a) A circle of radius 5 with center at $(3, -4)$
    (b) A circle of radius 3 with center at $(-2, 1)$
    (c) A circle tangent to the coordinate axes and having radius 2. (How many such circles are there?)

13. Write the equation of each of the following circles in the form

$$(x - h)^2 + (y - k)^2 = r^2.$$

In each case, locate the center and give the radius.
    (a) $x^2 + y^2 - 2x - 6y + 6 = 0$
    (b) $x^2 + y^2 + 4x + 2y + 4 = 0$
    (c) $x^2 + y^2 - 6x + 1 = 0$
    (d) $36x^2 + 36y^2 - 36y = 7$

14. Two of the vertices of an equilateral triangle are located at $P(1, 2)$ and $Q(4, 5)$. Find the third vertex. Is there more than one possibility?

15. Find the fourth vertex, D, of the parallelogram $ABCD$ if three vertices are located as follows:

$$A(-1, 5), \quad B(-2, 3), \quad C(5, 4).$$

16. A set of points in a coordinate plane is found to have the following property: Every point of the set is twice as far from the point $A(-5, 1)$ as it is from the point $B(3, 8)$. Find an equation for which this set is the graph.

17. A point $P(x, y)$ is on the perpendicular bisector of the line segment joining $A(-3, 5)$ to $B(2, -6)$ if, and only if,

$$PB = PA.$$

Find an equation of the perpendicular bisector of $\overline{AB}$.

Review for Sections 5–1 through 5–3

Write an equation of each of the following.

1. A circle with its center at the origin and a radius of 7.

2. A circle with its center at the origin and passing through $(-2, -3)$.

3. The set of all points in the plane at a distance of more than 10 units from the origin.

4. The set of all points in the plane at a distance of 9 units or less from the origin.

Solve algebraically and graph each of the following systems of equations.

5. $\begin{cases} x^2 + y^2 = 49 \\ x + y = 7 \end{cases}$

6. $\begin{cases} x^2 + y^2 = 29 \\ y - x = 3 \end{cases}$

7. $\begin{cases} x^2 + y^2 = 50 \\ 2y + x = 9 \end{cases}$

8. $\begin{cases} x^2 + y^2 = 169 \\ y - x = 7 \end{cases}$

Draw the graph of each of the following systems of inequalities.

9. $\begin{cases} x^2 + y^2 \leq 25 \\ 3y - x \leq 3 \end{cases}$

10. $\begin{cases} x^2 + y^2 < 16 \\ x + y < 3 \end{cases}$

In each of the following find the perimeter of the triangle with the given vertices, and tell what type of triangle it is (right, isosceles).

11. $(7, -1)$, $(2, 2)$, $(4, 4)$ **12.** $(-5, 5)$, $(5, 3)$, $(1, -1)$

13. $(6, -5)$, $(2, -2)$, $(5, 2)$ **14.** $(-6, 0)$, $(3, -8)$, $(6, -1)$

Find the center and radius of the circles having the following equations.

15. $x^2 + y^2 - 6x + 10y + 28 = 0$

16. $x^2 + y^2 + 14x - 2y + 48 = 0$

17. $16x^2 + 16y^2 - 16x + 24y - 131 = 0$

18. $9x^2 + 9y^2 - 12x + 36y + 13 = 0$

Answers to Review for Sections 5–1 through 5–3

1. $x^2 + y^2 = 49$ **2.** $x^2 + y^2 = 13$

3. $x^2 + y^2 > 100$ **4.** $x^2 + y^2 \leq 81$

5. $\{(0, 7), \ (7, 0)\}$

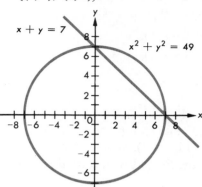

6. $\{(2, 5), \ (-5, -2)\}$

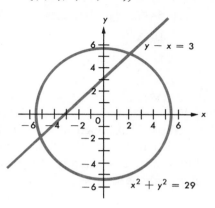

7. $\{(7, 1), \ (-\frac{17}{5}, \frac{31}{5})\}$

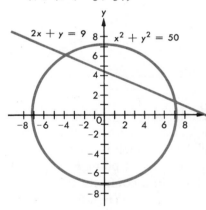

8. $\{(5, 12), \ (-12, -5)\}$

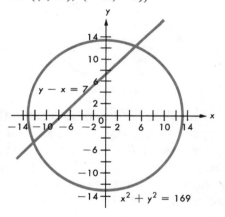

9.

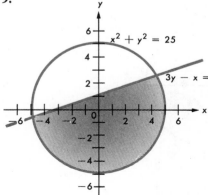

10.

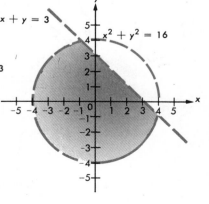

11. $2\sqrt{34} + 2\sqrt{2}$; isosceles   **12.** $2\sqrt{26} + 10\sqrt{2}$; right
13. $10 + 5\sqrt{2}$; right isosceles   **14.** $2\sqrt{145} + \sqrt{58}$; isosceles
15. $(3, -5)$, $\sqrt{6}$ **16.** $(-7, 1)$, $\sqrt{2}$
17. $(\frac{1}{2}, -\frac{3}{4})$, 3 **18.** $(\frac{2}{3}, -2)$, $\sqrt{3}$

5-4   ELLIPSES

An ellipse is obtained when we cut a cone by a plane which is almost perpendicular to the axis of the cone (Fig. 5–7). Thus, if we point our flashlight not quite directly at a wall, the lighted region on the wall has an elliptical shape.

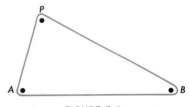

FIGURE 5-7   FIGURE 5-8

An ellipse can be constructed in the following way. Place a piece of paper on a drawing board, and put two thumb tacks into the paper at points A and B. Next, take a loop of thread which is long enough to fit over both tacks, and pull it taut with a pencil point P (Fig. 5–8). Keeping the thread taut, move the point P in a complete turn around points A and B. The figure drawn will be an ellipse (Fig. 5–9). As suggested by this construction, an ellipse consists of all points P such that

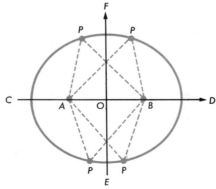

FIGURE 5-9

the sum $AP + BP + AB$ is a constant. Since the distance AB does not change, the ellipse really consists of all points P such that the sum $AP + BP$ is a constant.

Definition of an Ellipse

Given two points A and B in a plane and a positive number k greater than AB, the set consisting of all points P in the plane such that

$$AP + BP = k$$

is called an ellipse. Each of the points A and B is called a focus of the ellipse.

If line $\overleftrightarrow{CD}$ contains the foci A and B, and line $\overleftrightarrow{EF}$ is the perpendicular bisector of segment $\overline{AB}$, then it is reasonably clear from Fig. 5–9 that lines $\overleftrightarrow{CD}$ and $\overleftrightarrow{EF}$ are *axes of symmetry* of the ellipse. In other words, if we fold the paper along the line $\overleftrightarrow{CD}$, the upper half and the lower half of the ellipse will coincide. Similarly, if we fold the paper along the line $\overleftrightarrow{EF}$, the right half will coincide with the left half of the ellipse. The point O of intersection of the axes of symmetry is called the *center* of the ellipse.

Each ellipse has an equation which is quite similar to an equation of a circle, as we shall show. To illustrate how an equation of an ellipse can be found, let us place the foci A and B of an ellipse 2 inches apart, and let us choose the number $k = 4$ in the definition of an ellipse. Then point P in the plane is on the ellipse if, and only if,

$$AP + BP = 4. \tag{1}$$

In order to find an equation of this ellipse, we must choose a cartesian coordinate system in the plane. Although we may choose the axes as we see fit, the only choice that takes advantage of the symmetry of the ellipse is the pair of axes of symmetry. Thus, let us select the x-axis passing through the foci A and B, and the y-axis perpendicular to the x-axis at the center O of the ellipse (Fig. 5–10). Since the foci are 2 inches apart and equidistant from O, it follows that

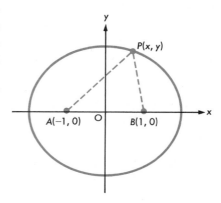

FIGURE 5–10

A has coordinates $(-1, 0)$ and B has coordinates $(1, 0)$. Therefore, if point P has coordinates (x, y),

$$AP = \sqrt{(x + 1)^2 + (y - 0)^2}, \quad \text{or} \quad \sqrt{x^2 + 2x + 1 + y^2},$$

and

$$BP = \sqrt{(x - 1)^2 + (y - 0)^2}, \quad \text{or} \quad \sqrt{x^2 - 2x + 1 + y^2}.$$

In view of Eq. (1), $P(x, y)$ is on the given ellipse if, and only if,

$$\sqrt{x^2 + 2x + 1 + y^2} + \sqrt{x^2 - 2x + 1 + y^2} = 4. \quad (2)$$

This is an *equation of the ellipse.* In other words, the graph of Eq. (2) is the ellipse drawn in Fig. 5–10.

Because Eq. (2) would be awkward to use, we shall simplify it. Equation (2) is equivalent to the equation

$$\sqrt{x^2 - 2x + 1 + y^2} = 4 - \sqrt{x^2 + 2x + 1 + y^2}. \quad (3)$$

This equation is, in turn, equivalent to the equation

$$(\sqrt{x^2 - 2x + 1 + y^2})^2 = (4 - \sqrt{x^2 + 2x + 1 + y^2})^2. \quad (4)$$

Although the equivalency between Eq. (3) and (4) is not as obvious as that between Eq. (1) and (2), it is clear that every solution of Eq. (3) is also a solution of this new equation. Carrying out the indicated operations in this new equation and simplifying, we obtain the following equivalent equations.

$$x^2 - 2x + 1 + y^2 = 16 - 8\sqrt{x^2 + 2x + 1 + y^2}$$
$$+ (x^2 + 2x + 1 + y^2)$$
$$8\sqrt{x^2 + 2x + 1 + y^2} = 16 + 4x$$
$$2\sqrt{x^2 + 2x + 1 + y^2} = 4 + x$$

Each solution of the equations above is also a solution of the equation

$$(2\sqrt{x^2 + 2x + 1 + y^2})^2 = (4 + x)^2.$$

This equation is, in turn, equivalent to each of the following equations.

$$4(x^2 + 2x + 1 + y^2) = 16 + 8x + x^2$$
$$4x^2 + 8x + 4 + 4y^2 = 16 + 8x + x^2$$
$$3x^2 + 4y^2 = 12$$
$$\frac{x^2}{4} + \frac{y^2}{3} = 1 \qquad\qquad (5)$$

Our work above shows only that every solution of Eq. (2) is also a solution of Eq. (5). To show that Eq. (5) is equivalent to Eq. (2), and hence, that Eq. (5) is an equation of the given ellipse, we must show that every solution of Eq. (5) is also a solution of Eq. (2).

If (x, y) is a solution of Eq. (5), (x, y) is a solution of $3x^2 + 4y^2 = 12$. Then $3x^2 \leq 12$, $x^2 \leq 4$, and therefore, $-2 \leq x \leq 2$. By adding 2 to each part of $-2 \leq x \leq 2$, we get $0 \leq 2 + x \leq 4$. However, if $0 \leq 2 + x$, then $0 \leq 4 + x$. Similarly, by adding $-x$ to each part of $-2 \leq x \leq 2$, we get $0 \leq 4 - x$. If $0 \leq 4 + x$ and $0 \leq 4 - x$,

$$\sqrt{(4 + x)^2} = 4 + x$$

and

$$\sqrt{(4 - x)^2} = 4 - x.$$

Consequently,

$$\sqrt{x^2 + 8x + 16} + \sqrt{x^2 - 8x + 16} = 8.$$

Recalling that $12 = 3x^2 + 4y^2$, we also have

$$\sqrt{x^2 + 8x + (4 + 3x^2 + 4y^2)}$$
$$+ \sqrt{x^2 - 8x + (4 + 3x^2 + 4y^2)} = 8,$$
$$\sqrt{4x^2 + 8x + 4 + 4y^2} + \sqrt{4x^2 - 8x + 4 + 4y^2} = 8,$$
$$2\sqrt{x^2 + 2x + 1 + y^2} + 2\sqrt{x^2 - 2x + 1 + y^2} = 8.$$

On dividing each side of this equation by 2, we obtain Eq. (2). Therefore, every solution of Eq. (5) is a solution of Eq. (2).

In the same way, it can be shown that every ellipse whose axes of symmetry are along the coordinate axes has an equation of the form

$$\frac{x^2}{a^2} + \frac{y^2}{b^2} = 1$$

for some positive numbers a and b. If we let $y = 0$ in this equation, we obtain

$$\frac{x^2}{a^2} = 1,$$
$$x^2 = a^2,$$
$$x = a \quad \text{or} \quad x = -a.$$

Thus, the ellipse crosses the x-axis at the points $(a, 0)$ and $(-a, 0)$. For this reason, we call a and $-a$ the x-*intercepts* of the ellipse. It may be shown in a similar way that the ellipse crosses the y-axis at the points $(0, b)$ and $(0, -b)$. We call b and $-b$ the y-*intercepts* of the ellipse. It is clear that the ellipse is a circle if, and only if, $a = b$.

Every ellipse has an equation of the form

$$\frac{x^2}{a^2} + \frac{y^2}{b^2} = 1,$$

and the graph of every equation of this form is an ellipse. We make use of this fact in working the following problems.

Problem 1. Describe the graph of the equation $16x^2 + 25y^2 = 400$.

Solution. If we divide each side of this equation by 400, we obtain the equivalent equation

$$\frac{x^2}{25} + \frac{y^2}{16} = 1, \quad \text{or} \quad \frac{x^2}{5^2} + \frac{y^2}{4^2} = 1.$$

Since the equation has the form

$$\frac{x^2}{a^2} + \frac{y^2}{b^2} = 1,$$

the graph is an ellipse with 5 and -5 as its x-intercepts, and 4 and -4 as its y-intercepts. The segments $\overline{CD}$ of the x-axis and $\overline{EF}$ of the y-axis, shown in Fig. 5–11, are called the *axes* of the ellipse. The longer one, $\overline{CD}$ in this case, is called the *major axis* and the shorter one, $\overline{EF}$ in our example, is called the *minor axis* of the ellipse.

The foci of this ellipse, say points A and B, are always on the major axis. If P is any point on the ellipse, then

$$AP + BP = AD + BD$$

since D is also a point on the ellipse. However, $BD = CA$ in Fig. 5–11 so that $AD + BD = AD + CA$, or CD. Hence, $AP + BP = 10$, the length of the major axis, for every point P on the ellipse. Since F is a point on the ellipse and $AF = BF$, it follows that $AF = 5$. Knowing the lengths of two sides of the right triangle, AOF, we find that the length of $\overline{AO}$ is 3 by the pythagorean theorem. Hence, the foci of this ellipse are the points $A(-3, 0)$ and $B(3, 0)$. We can now draw the ellipse by placing thumbtacks at points A and B and taking a loop of string 16 units long.

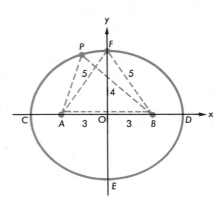

FIGURE 5–11

For the ellipse with equation

$$\frac{x^2}{a^2} + \frac{y^2}{b^2} = 1,$$

the distance, c, from the center of the ellipse to a focus may be found from either

$$c^2 = a^2 - b^2 \quad \text{if} \quad a > b$$

or

$$c^2 = b^2 - a^2 \quad \text{if} \quad b > a.$$

We can think of a circle as a special case of an ellipse when the two foci coincide at the center.

Problem 2. Describe the graph of the equation $9x^2 + 4y^2 = 36$.

Solution. Dividing each side of this equation by 36, we obtain the equivalent equation

$$\frac{x^2}{2^2} + \frac{y^2}{3^2} = 1.$$

Since the equation has the form

$$\frac{x^2}{a^2} + \frac{y^2}{b^2} = 1,$$

the graph is an ellipse with x-intercepts 2 and -2 and y-intercepts 3 and -3. The axis $\overline{CD}$ is shorter than the axis $\overline{EF}$ for this ellipse (Fig. 5–12). Therefore, $\overline{CD}$ is the minor axis and $\overline{EF}$ is the major axis. Since the major axis is on the y-axis, the foci A and B are on the y-axis also. The distance c from the origin to either A or B is given by

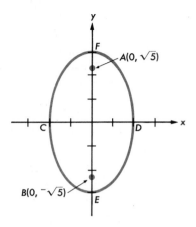

$$c^2 = 3^2 - 2^2, \quad \text{or} \quad c = \sqrt{5},$$

according to our statement in Problem 1. Hence, the foci have coordinates $(0, \sqrt{5})$ and $(0, -\sqrt{5})$, as shown in Fig. 5–12.

FIGURE 5–12

Given an equation of an ellipse, we can find points on the ellipse by solving the equation either for y in terms of x or for x in terms of y. Then by assigning values to one of the variables, we can easily compute the corresponding values of the other variable.

Exercises

1. (a) Consider the ellipse with equation

$$\frac{x^2}{4} + \frac{y^2}{3} = 1.$$

    (i) Find the x- and y-intercepts.
    (ii) Show that the points $(1, \frac{3}{2})$, $(-1, \frac{3}{2})$, $(1, -\frac{3}{2})$, and $(-1, -\frac{3}{2})$ are on the ellipse.
    (iii) If (x, y) is any point on the ellipse, where $x \neq 0$ and $y \neq 0$, find three other related points on the ellipse.

  (b) An ellipse has equation

$$\frac{x^2}{9} + \frac{y^2}{36} = 1.$$

    (i) Find the x- and y-intercepts and the foci.
    (ii) How long is the major axis? the minor axis?
    (iii) Find the values of x when $y = 3\sqrt{3}$ or when $y = -3\sqrt{3}$.
    (iv) Sketch the graph of the ellipse. Show the points mentioned in parts (i) and (iii). Where do these four points lie on the ellipse with reference to the foci?

2. (a) An ellipse has equation

$$\frac{x^2}{36} + \frac{y^2}{4} = 1.$$

    (i) Find the coordinates of the x- and y-intercepts and of the foci.

    (ii) Give the lengths of the major and minor axes.

    (iii) Find y if $x = 4\sqrt{2}$ or if $x = -4\sqrt{2}$. Where do these four points lie on the ellipse with reference to the foci?

    (iv) Sketch the graph of the ellipse. Show the points mentioned in parts (i) and (iii).

  (b) (i) Describe the graph of the equation $x^2 + 4y^2 = 36$, giving the coordinates of the intercepts and of the foci.

    (ii) A line through either focus perpendicular to the major axis cuts the ellipse in two points. Use the coordinates of the foci and the equation of the ellipse to find these four points.

    (iii) Graph the ellipse, showing all points mentioned in parts (i) and (ii).

Write an equation of the ellipses with foci at points A and B, given that P is on the ellipse. Simplify each equation.

3. (a) $A(2, 0)$, $B(-2, 0)$; $AP + BP = 6$

   (b) $A(0, 3)$, $B(0, -3)$; $AP + BP = 8$

4. (a) $A(4, 0)$, $B(-4, 0)$; $AP + BP = 11$

   (b) $A(0, 5)$, $B(0, -5)$; $AP + BP = 13$

5. (a) Draw the graph of the equation $x^2 + 2y^2 = 18$. List the coordinates of the intercepts and of the foci. Find the coordinates of the points on the ellipse that are vertically above or below the foci. Give the lengths of the major and minor axes.

   (b) Draw the graph of the equation $9x^2 + y^2 = 36$. List the coordinates of the intercepts and of the foci. Find the coordinates of the points on the ellipse that are horizontally to the right or to the left of the foci. Give the length of the major axis.

6. (a) Tell which of the following points are inside, which are outside, and which are on the ellipse with equation $4x^2 + 9y^2 = 36$.

$$(1, 1), \quad (1, 2), \quad (1, \tfrac{4}{3}\sqrt{2}), \quad (1, \sqrt{3}), \quad (1, -2), \quad (-2, \tfrac{5}{4}), \quad (-1, -2)$$

    Write an algebraic expression describing the points inside the ellipse. Write an algebraic expression describing the points outside the ellipse.

   (b) Draw and describe the graph of the equation $4x^2 + 18y^2 = 36$. Write a mathematical statement describing the points that are inside the ellipse. Write a mathematical statement describing the points that are on or outside the ellipse.

7. (a) Describe the graph of the inequality

$$\frac{x^2}{4} + \frac{y^2}{3} < 1.$$

   Find all integral solutions.

   (b) Draw the graph of the equation $64x^2 + 9y^2 = 16$. Give the coordinates and plot the intercepts, foci, and points on the ellipse that are horizontally to the right or to the left of the foci.

8. (a) The foci of an ellipse are at points $A(4, 0)$ and $B(-4, 0)$. A point is on the ellipse if, and only if, the sum of its distances from A and B is equal to 16. Find an equation of the ellipse and sketch it.

   (b) Find an equation of the ellipse with foci $A(0, -1)$, and $B(0, 1)$, given that point P is on the ellipse if, and only if, $AP + BP = 3$. What are the coordinates of the x- and y-intercepts?

---

9. Find the intersections of the ellipse $3x^2 + 4y^2 = 9$ with the straight line $x = k$ for each of the following values of k.

$$-4, \quad -\sqrt{3}, \quad 1, \quad \sqrt{3}, \quad 5$$

10. Consider the system of equations

$$\begin{cases} x^2 + 3y^2 = 12, \\ x + 3y = 6. \end{cases}$$

   (a) Find the solution set by graphing each member of the system and observing their points of intersection.

   (b) Use the substitution method to find the solution set.

11. Consider the system of equations

$$\begin{cases} x^2 + y^2 = 13, \\ 2x^2 + 3y^2 = 35. \end{cases}$$

   (a) Describe the graph of each equation of this system.

   (b) Solve the system.

   (Hint: The *method of addition* used on a system of linear equations in x and y is applicable here.)

12. Graph the solution set of the system of inequalities

$$\begin{cases} x^2 + 3y^2 \geq 3, \\ x^2 + y^2 \leq 5. \end{cases}$$

13. An equation of the family of ellipses with center at the origin and axes along the coordinate axes is

$$\frac{x^2}{a^2} + \frac{y^2}{b^2} = 1.$$

(a) Write an equation of the member of this family with y-intercepts 1 and -1, and x-intercepts 2 and -2.

(b) How many members of this family have x-intercepts 8 and -8? Write an equation of this set of ellipses. Write an equation of the ellipse which has these x-intercepts and also passes through the point $(4, 3)$.

(c) How many members of this family have y-intercepts 4 and -4? Write an equation of this set of ellipses. Write an equation of the ellipse which has these y-intercepts and also passes through the point with coordinates $(-3, 2)$. Through what other three points does this ellipse automatically pass because of its two axes of symmetry?

14. (a) Graph each of the following equations on a single set of axes.

$$\frac{x^2}{25} + \frac{y^2}{1} = 1, \quad \frac{x^2}{25} + \frac{y^2}{4} = 1, \quad \frac{x^2}{25} + \frac{y^2}{9} = 1,$$

$$\frac{x^2}{25} + \frac{y^2}{16} = 1, \quad \frac{x^2}{25} + \frac{y^2}{25} = 1$$

(b) Find c and c/a for each of the ellipses you just graphed, where c is half the distance between the foci and a is half the length of the major axis. Tell how the appearance of the ellipse changes as c/a changes. Is there a maximum value for c/a? What is the minimum value for c/a?

(c) The quotient c/a is called the *eccentricity* of the ellipse. Two ellipses are drawn, each with major axis 20 units long. How do their appearances compare if the eccentricity of one is $\frac{1}{20}$ and that of the other $\frac{19}{20}$?

Preparation for Section 5-5

1. Find the distance AP from $A(-5, 0)$ to $P(x, y)$.

2. Find the distance BP from $B(5, 0)$ to $P(x, y)$.

3. Find the difference, $AP - BP$.

4. Set the difference in Exercise 3 equal to 8.

5. Simplify the equation in Exercise 4 by squaring until you have no more radicals in the equation.

6. Find the difference, $BP - AP$.

7. Set the difference in Exercise 6 equal to 8.

8. Simplify the equation in Exercise 7 in the same way you did that in Exercise 4.

9. What relation, if any, exists between the equations in Exercises 4, 5, 7, and 8? Are any of them equivalent?

5-5 HYPERBOLAS

To visualize a hyperbola completely, we must start with a cone that has two *nappes* (see Fig. 5–13 at the bottom of the page). Then any plane which cuts both nappes without passing through the vertex intersects the cone in a hyperbola. Thus, the hyperbola has two separate parts, or branches, each extending indefinitely far. The following is a description of the hyperbola relative to its focal points.

Definition of a Hyperbola

Given two points A and B in a plane and a positive number k less than AB, the set consisting of every point P in the plane such that either

$$AP - BP = k \quad or \quad BP - AP = k$$

is called a hyperbola. Each of the points A and B is called a focus of the hyperbola.

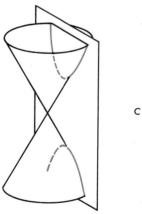

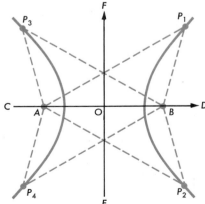

FIGURE 5–13   FIGURE 5–14

In Fig. 5–14, we have sketched the hyperbola for $AB = 6$ and $k = 4$. The figure shows four symmetrically placed points of the hyperbola: P_1, P_2, P_3, and P_4. Points P_1 and P_2 are closer to B, so that

$$AP_1 - BP_1 = 4, \quad AP_2 - BP_2 = 4.$$

Points P_3 and P_4 are closer to A, so that

$$BP_3 - AP_3 = 4, \quad BP_4 - AP_4 = 4.$$

The points closer to B form the right-hand branch of the hyperbola of Fig. 5–14, and the points closer to A form the left-hand branch.

The hyperbola, like the ellipse, has two axes of symmetry, the line $\overleftrightarrow{CD}$ through the foci and the line $\overleftrightarrow{EF}$ which is the perpendicular bisector of segment $\overline{AB}$, as shown in Fig. 5–14. The point O, in which these two axes intersect, is called the center of the hyperbola.

To find an equation of the hyperbola of Fig. 5–14, we naturally select our coordinate axes as the axes of symmetry described above. Since $AB = 6$ by assumption, A has coordinates $(-3, 0)$ and B has coordinates $(3, 0)$. Point P of the plane (Fig. 5–15) is on the right-hand branch if, and only if,

$$AP - BP = 4.$$

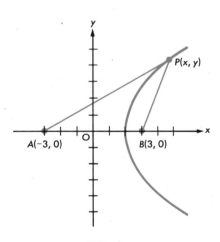

FIGURE 5-15

If P has coordinates (x, y) then

$$AP = \sqrt{(x + 3)^2 + (y - 0)^2}$$

and

$$BP = \sqrt{(x - 3)^2 + (y - 0)^2}$$

so that P is on the right-hand branch of the hyperbola if, and only if,

$$\sqrt{x^2 + 6x + 9 + y^2} - \sqrt{x^2 - 6x + 9 + y^2} = 4. \quad (1)$$

Thus, Eq. (1) is an *equation of the right-hand branch* and

$$\sqrt{x^2 - 6x + 9 + y^2} - \sqrt{x^2 + 6x + 9 + y^2} = 4 \quad (2)$$

is an *equation of the left-hand branch* of this hyperbola.

Let us simplify Eq. (1) as we did the equation of the ellipse. We proceed in the following manner.

$$\sqrt{x^2 + 6x + 9 + y^2} = 4 + \sqrt{x^2 - 6x + 9 + y^2}$$
$$x^2 + 6x + 9 + y^2 = 16 + 8\sqrt{x^2 - 6x + 9 + y^2}$$
$$+ (x^2 - 6x + 9 + y^2)$$
$$12x - 16 = 8\sqrt{x^2 - 6x + 9 + y^2}$$
$$3x - 4 = 2\sqrt{x^2 - 6x + 9 + y^2}$$
$$9x^2 - 24x + 16 = 4(x^2 - 6x + 9 + y^2)$$
$$5x^2 - 4y^2 = 20$$
$$\frac{x^2}{4} - \frac{y^2}{5} = 1 \quad (3)$$

We leave it to you to verify that Eq. (2) also simplifies to Eq. (3). Thus, the graph of Eq. (3) contains both branches of the hyperbola.

To show that the graph of Eq. (3) is the hyperbola of Fig. 5–14, we must show that every solution of Eq. (3) is also a solution of either Eq. (1) or Eq. (2). With this in mind, let (x, y) be a solution of Eq. (3). Then $5x^2 = 20 + 4y^2$, $5x^2 \geq 20$, and $x^2 \geq 4$. Hence, either

$$x \geq 2 \quad \text{or} \quad x \leq -2.$$

If (x, y) is a solution of (3) for which $x \geq 2$, then $3x + 4 \geq 0$ and $3x - 4 \geq 0$. Furthermore,

$$\sqrt{(3x + 4)^2} = 3x + 4, \quad \sqrt{(3x - 4)^2} = 3x - 4.$$

Hence,

$$\sqrt{9x^2 + 24x + 16} - \sqrt{9x^2 - 24x + 16} = 8.$$

Now $9x^2 = 4x^2 + 5x^2$ and $5x^2 = 20 + 4y^2$, or $9x^2 = 4x^2 + 20 + 4y^2$.

Therefore,

$$\sqrt{4x^2 + 20 + 4y^2 + 24x + 16}$$
$$- \sqrt{4x^2 + 20 + 4y^2 - 24x + 16} = 8,$$

or

$$\sqrt{4x^2 + 24x + 36 + 4y^2} - \sqrt{4x^2 - 24x + 36 + 4y^2} = 8,$$
$$2\sqrt{x^2 + 6x + 9 + y^2} - 2\sqrt{x^2 - 6x + 9 + y^2} = 8.$$

On dividing each side of this equation by 2, we obtain Eq. (1). Thus, every solution of Eq. (3) for which $x \geq 2$ is also a solution of Eq. (1).

It may be shown in exactly the same way that every solution (x, y) of Eq. (3) for which $x \leq -2$ is also a solution of Eq. (2). Consequently, the graph of Eq. (3) is the hyperbola of Fig. 5–14.

In Eq. (3), what significance do the numbers 4 and 5 have in relation to the hyperbola? If we let $y = 0$, we obtain the equation

$$\frac{x^2}{4} = 1, \quad x^2 = 4,$$

and finally,

$$x = 2 \quad \text{or} \quad x = -2.$$

Thus, the x-intercepts of this hyperbola are 2 and -2. If we let $x = 0$ in the equation above, we obtain the equation

$$\frac{-y^2}{5} = 1, \quad \text{or } y^2 = -5.$$

The solutions of this equation are the complex numbers $\sqrt{5}i$ and $-\sqrt{5}i$. Since the graph consists of only the real solutions of Eq. (3), we conclude that the hyperbola has no y-intercepts. We note that the sum of 4 and 5 is the square of the distance from the center of the hyperbola to each focus. Thus, 3, the positive square root of 9, is this distance.

It can be shown that every hyperbola with the coordinate axes as its axes of symmetry has an equation either of the form

$$\frac{x^2}{a^2} - \frac{y^2}{b^2} = 1$$

or of the form

$$\frac{y^2}{a^2} - \frac{x^2}{b^2} = 1.$$

Conversely, it may be shown that every equation of either form has a hyperbola as its graph. If we let

$$c^2 = a^2 + b^2,$$

then the hyperbola

$$\frac{x^2}{a^2} - \frac{y^2}{b^2} = 1 \quad \text{has foci at } (c, 0) \text{ and } (-c, 0).$$

$$\frac{y^2}{a^2} - \frac{x^2}{b^2} = 1 \quad \text{has foci at } (0, c) \text{ and } (0, -c).$$

Problem 1. Discuss the graph of the equation $16y^2 = 9x^2 + 144$.

Solution. This equation is equivalent to each of the following equations.

$$16y^2 - 9x^2 = 144$$

$$\frac{16y^2}{144} - \frac{9x^2}{144} = 1$$

$$\frac{y^2}{9} - \frac{x^2}{16} = 1$$

$$\frac{y^2}{3^2} - \frac{x^2}{4^2} = 1$$

Since this equation has form

$$\frac{y^2}{a^2} - \frac{x^2}{b^2} = 1,$$

its graph is a hyperbola. The y-intercepts are 3 and -3. There are no x-intercepts. Since

$$3^2 + 4^2 = 5^2,$$

the foci are 5 units below and above the center. Hence, $(0, 5)$ and $(0, -5)$ are the foci.

We may find points on this hyperbola if we solve its equation for y in terms of x or for x in terms of y. We solve for y in terms of x as follows:

$$\frac{y^2}{3^2} = \frac{x^2}{4^2} + 1,$$

$$y^2 = \frac{3^2}{4^2}(x^2 + 4^2),$$

$$y = \tfrac{3}{4}\sqrt{x^2 + 16} \quad \text{or} \quad y = -\tfrac{3}{4}\sqrt{x^2 + 16}.$$

Hence,

$$y = \tfrac{3}{4}\sqrt{x^2 + 16}$$

is an equation of the upper branch, and

$$y = -\tfrac{3}{4}\sqrt{x^2 + 16}$$

is an equation of the lower branch of the hyperbola. You can verify that the following points are on the upper branch by letting x equal 0, 2, 3, and 8 in the equation of the upper branch.

$$(0, 3), \quad \left(2, \frac{3\sqrt{5}}{2}\right), \quad \left(3, \frac{15}{4}\right), \quad (8, 3\sqrt{5})$$

We used the approximation $\sqrt{5} \doteq 2.2$ to plot points in Fig. 5-16. The other points plotted in the figure were obtained by considering the symmetry of the hyperbola about the coordinate axes.

The points $C(0, -3)$ and $D(0, 3)$ are called the *vertices* of the hyperbola, and the segment $\overline{CD}$, which joins them, is called the *transverse axis* of the hyperbola. The branches of a hyperbola extend indefinitely far from the axes. In other words, the curve is unbounded.

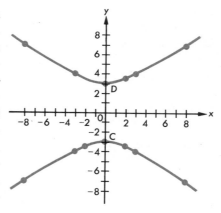

FIGURE 5-16

If two conic sections are drawn in the same plane, then they might have several points of intersection. It is intuitively clear that an ellipse and a hyperbola might have as many as four points of intersection. The following problem illustrates an algebraic method of finding the points of intersection of two conic sections.

Problem 2. Find the points of intersection of the circle with equation

$$x^2 + y^2 = 16$$

and the hyperbola with equation

$$4x^2 - y^2 = 4.$$

Solution. Algebraically, the problem is to find all solutions of the system of equations

$$\begin{cases} x^2 + y^2 = 16, \\ 4x^2 - y^2 = 4. \end{cases}$$

If we solve the system by the addition method, we obtain the equivalent system

$$\begin{cases} x^2 + y^2 = 16, \\ 5x^2 = 20. \end{cases}$$

The latter equation is easily solved, yielding $x = 2$ or $x = -2$. Letting $x = 2$ in the first equation, we get the equation

$$y^2 = 12,$$

which is solved to yield $y = 2\sqrt{3}$ or $y = -2\sqrt{3}$. Thus, $(2, 2\sqrt{3})$ and $(2, -2\sqrt{3})$ are solutions of the system. If we let $x = -2$ in the first equation, we again obtain $y = 2\sqrt{3}$ or $y = -2\sqrt{3}$. Thus, $(-2, 2\sqrt{3})$ and $(-2, -2\sqrt{3})$ are also solutions. Therefore, the four points of intersection of the circle and the hyperbola have coordinates

$$(2, 2\sqrt{3}), \quad (2, -2\sqrt{3}),$$
$$(-2, 2\sqrt{3}), \quad (-2, -2\sqrt{3}).$$

These four points are identified in Fig. 5–17.

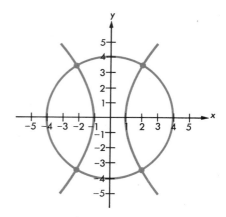

FIGURE 5–17

Exercises

1. (a) A hyperbola has equation $x^2/25 - y^2/16 = 1$.
   (i) Find the x-intercepts and show that there are no y-intercepts.
   (ii) Find the coordinates of the foci.
   (iii) Find the points of the hyperbola directly above and below the foci by substituting $x = \pm\sqrt{41}$ in the equation of the hyperbola and solving for y.
   (iv) Solve the equation for y in terms of x and find y when $x = \pm 6, \pm 7,$ and ± 10.
   (v) Graph the hyperbola showing all the points found in parts (i) through (iv).

(b) A hyperbola has equation $y^2/16 - x^2/9 = 1$.
   (i) Find the y-intercepts and show that there are no x-intercepts.
   (ii) Find the coordinates of the foci.
   (iii) Find the points horizontally directly to the right and left of the foci by substituting $y = \pm 5$ in the equation of the hyperbola and solving for x.
   (iv) Solve the equation for x in terms of y and find x when $y = \pm 6, \pm 7$, and ± 10.
   (v) Graph the hyperbola, showing all the points found in parts (i) through (iv).

2. (a) Sketch the graph of $16y^2 - 25x^2 = 400$.
   (b) Sketch the graph of $9x^2 - 16y^2 = 144$.

In Exercises 3 and 4 the foci of a hyperbola are at points A and B with coordinates $(-4, 0)$ and $(4, 0)$, respectively. A point is on the hyperbola if the difference of its distances from these two points is 6.

3. (a) Using the distance formula, write the equation which says that $PA - PB = 6$ where $P(x, y)$ is a point on the hyperbola.
   (b) Using the distance formula, write the equation which says that $PB - PA = 6$ where $P(x, y)$ is a point on the hyperbola.

4. (a) Find the x-intercepts of this hyperbola. Sketch the hyperbola.
   (b) Show that this hyperbola does not have y-intercepts.

5. Find an equation, in simplified form, of a hyperbola if the foci are at points A and B with coordinates as given, and if point P on the hyperbola has the given number as the difference of its distances from A and B.

   (a) $A(1, 0)$, $B(-1, 0)$; 1   (b) $A(0, 2)$, $B(0, -2)$; 3

For each of the following equations, find the intercepts of the hyperbola. Also, use the Table of Squares and Square Roots to approximate the coordinates of eight other points on the hyperbola. Sketch each graph.

6. (a) $\dfrac{x^2}{4} - \dfrac{y^2}{9} = 1$ (b) $\dfrac{x^2}{9} - \dfrac{y^2}{9} = 1$

7. (a) $\dfrac{y^2}{9} - \dfrac{x^2}{16} = 1$ (b) $25y^2 - 4x^2 = 100$

---

8. Use algebraic methods to find the points of intersection of the hyperbola $y^2 - 3x^2 = 6$ and each of the lines given below. In each case, sketch the graph of the hyperbola and the line.
   (a) $x + y - 4 = 0$
   (b) $x - y + 2 = 0$
   (c) $x - y - 1 = 0$

9. Solve the system of equations

$$\begin{cases} 4x^2 - 5y^2 = 20, \\ 16x^2 + 25y^2 = 400, \end{cases}$$

and sketch the graph of each conic section.

10. Use algebraic methods to find the solution set of the systems of equations

$$\begin{cases} x^2 - 3y^2 + 12 = 0, \\ 4x^2 + 3y^2 - 192 = 0. \end{cases}$$

Check your solutions by graphing.

11. Use algebraic methods to find the points of intersection of the two conic sections $x^2 + 4y^2 = 16$ and $x^2 - y^2 = 16$. Check your answer by sketching a graph.

---

12. (a) Solve the equation $x^2/4 - y^2/5 = 1$ for y in terms of x. What values of x lead to real values for y?

(b) Solve the equation $x^2/4 - y^2/5 = 1$ for x in terms of y. Are there any real values for y that lead to complex values for x?

13. A hyperbola is drawn with focus B at $(c, 0)$ and focus A at $(-c, 0)$. For every point $P(x, y)$ on the hyperbola, it is true that $PA - PB = 2a$, or $-2a$, depending on which branch of the hyperbola is being considered. Use the distance formula to find an equation of this hyperbola. Your equation contains the constants a and c. Show that $c^2 - a^2$ is positive and then replace it by b^2 to obtain an equation containing the constants a and b. You should see now why we said in this section that $c^2 = a^2 + b^2$.

Preparation for Section 5–6

1. Graph the equation $y = x^2 - 5x - 6$.

2. What is the lowest point on the graph in Exercise 1?

3. Use your graph in Exercise 1 to estimate the real solutions of each of the following quadratic equations.

(a) $x^2 - 5x - 6 = 0$
(b) $x^2 - 5x - 6 = 3$
(c) $x^2 - 5x - 6 = -7$

4. What is the distance AP from $A(3, 0)$ to $P(x, y)$?

5. What is the distance from $P(x, y)$ to the line $x = -3$?

6. Set the distances in Exercises 4 and 5 equal to each other and simplify the resulting equation.

5-6 PARABOLAS

The conic sections studied so far have been *central conics;* that is, each has had two axes of symmetry and a center. The final conic section to be studied, the parabola, is not a central conic. The parabola is the curve of intersection of a plane with a cone; the plane is parallel to an edge of the cone. (See Fig. 5–18.)

The parabola may be described relative to a point and a line in the following way.

Definition of a parabola

Given a point F and a line L not containing F, the set consisting of every point P in the plane such that

$$PF = PQ,$$

where Q is the foot of the perpendicular drawn from P to line L (Fig. 5–19), is called a parabola. The point F is called the focus and the line L the directrix of the parabola.

FIGURE 5–18

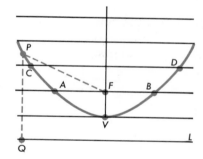

FIGURE 5–19

With a piece of graph paper and a compass, it is easy to find as many points on a parabola as you wish. Let the directrix L be along one of the lines of the paper and let F also be on a line. In Fig. 5–19, F is two units above L. Clearly one point of the parabola is the point V halfway between F and L, that is, one unit directly under F. Incidentally, V is called the *vertex* of the parabola. Now open the compass to a radius of two units, place the point of the compass at F, and mark off points A and B on the line two units above L. Next, open the compass to a radius of three units, place the point of the compass at F, and mark off points C and D on the line three units above L, and so on.

The line through the focus of a parabola and perpendicular to the directrix is called the *axis* of the parabola. From Fig. 5–19, it can be seen that the axis of the parabola is also the axis of symmetry of the parabola.

Let us find an equation of a parabola. The axis of the parabola is an obvious choice for one coordinate axis, say the *y*-axis. While it might seem plausible to select the directrix *L* as the *x*-axis, a still better choice for the *x*-axis is the line through the vertex *V*, as indicated in Fig. 5–20.

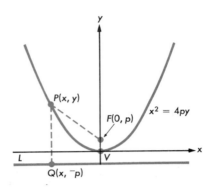

Let *p* be the distance from the vertex *V* to the focus *F*. Then *F* has coordinates $(0, p)$, and the directrix *L* has equation $y = -p$. A point *P* in the plane is on the parabola if, and only if,

FIGURE 5–20

$$PF = PQ,$$

where *Q* is the point at the foot of the perpendicular drawn from *P* to line *L*. If *P* has coordinates (x, y), it follows that *Q* then has coordinates $(x, -p)$. Since

$$PF = \sqrt{(x - 0)^2 + (y - p)^2}$$

and

$$PQ = \sqrt{(x - x)^2 + (y + p)^2},$$

$P(x, y)$ is on the parabola if, and only if,

$$\sqrt{x^2 + (y - p)^2} = \sqrt{(y + p)^2}.$$

The equation above is equivalent to the equation

$$x^2 + (y - p)^2 = (y + p)^2$$

for the reason that, if *b* and *c* are positive numbers, then $\sqrt{b} = \sqrt{c}$ if, and only if, $b = c$. In turn, this equation is equivalent to the equation

$$x^2 + y^2 - 2py + p^2 = y^2 + 2py + p^2,$$

which simplifies to

$$x^2 = 4py.$$

Thus, this simple quadratic equation is an equation of the given parabola.

Problem 1. Find an equation of the parabola with focus $(0, 3)$ and directrix $y = -3$.

Solution. We need only let $p = 3$ in $x^2 = 4py$ to find

$$x^2 = 12y$$

as an equation of the parabola.

If we choose the x-axis on the axis of the parabola and the y-axis through the vertex V, as shown in Fig. 5–21, then we shall obtain the same equation for the parabola except that x and y will be interchanged. Thus,

$$y^2 = 4px$$

is an equation of the parabola under consideration.

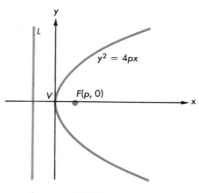

FIGURE 5–21

Problem 2. Find an equation of the parabola with focus $(\frac{1}{4}, 0)$ and directrix $x = -\frac{1}{4}$.

Solution. We let $p = \frac{1}{4}$ in $y^2 = 4px$ obtaining

$$y^2 = 4 \cdot \tfrac{1}{4}x, \quad \text{or } y^2 = x,$$

as an equation of this parabola.

Problem 3. Find the coordinates of the points of intersection, if any, of the parabola with equation

$$x^2 = 4y$$

and the line with equation

$$x + 2y - 4 = 0.$$

Solution. We are asked to solve the system of equations

$$\begin{cases} x^2 = 4y, \\ x + 2y - 4 = 0. \end{cases}$$

If we solve the second equation for $2y$ and substitute its value in the first equation, we obtain the equivalent system

$$\begin{cases} x^2 = 2(4 - x), \\ 2y = 4 - x. \end{cases}$$

The first equation of this system may be solved as follows:

$$x^2 = 8 - 2x,$$
$$x^2 + 2x - 8 = 0,$$
$$(x + 4)(x - 2) = 0,$$
$$x = -4 \quad \text{or} \quad x = 2.$$

If we let $x = -4$ in the second equation, we obtain

$$2y = 4 - (-4), \quad \text{or } y = 4.$$

If we let $x = 2$, we obtain

$$2y = 4 - 2, \text{ or } y = 1.$$

Thus,

$$\{(-4, 4), (2, 1)\}$$

is the solution set of the system that we were asked to solve.

Figure 5–22 shows the two points of intersection of the given parabola and the given line.

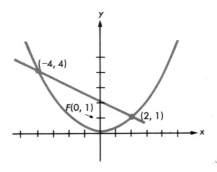

FIGURE 5-22

Exercises

1. Find an equation of the parabola with
   (a) focus $(0, -3)$ and directrix $y = 3$.
   (b) focus $(-\frac{1}{4}, 0)$ and directrix $x = \frac{1}{4}$.
2. (a) Find the points on the parabola $x^2 = 12y$ for which $y = 3$. How long is the line segment joining these points?
   (b) Find the points where the line $x = \frac{1}{4}$ intersects the parabola $y^2 = x$. How long is the line segment joining these points?

The line segment through the focus perpendicular to the axis, terminating in two points on the parabola, is called the *latus rectum* of the parabola. Find the length of this line and the coordinates of its endpoints for each of the following parabolas.

3. (a) $x^2 = 16y$ (b) $3x^2 = 20y$

4. (a) $y^2 = 12x$ (b) $5y^2 = 16x$

Draw the graph of each of the following parabolas, showing vertex, focus, directrix, and *latus rectum*. List the coordinates of vertex, focus, and of the endpoints of the *latus rectum*. Write the equation of the directrix and of the axis of symmetry.

5. (a) $x^2 = 8y$ (b) $x^2 = -8y$

6. (a) $y^2 = 10x$ (b) $y^2 = -10x$

Graph each of the following equations. List the coordinates of vertex, the focus, and the endpoints of *latus rectum* for each parabola. Also give the equations of the directrix and the axis of symmetry of each parabola.

7. (a) $x^2 = 20y$ (b) $y^2 = 24x$

8. (a) $x^2 + 6y = 0$ (b) $3y^2 + 4x = 0$

In each exercise, find an equation of the parabola with focus and directrix as given below.

9. (a) $(0, \frac{1}{2})$; $y = -\frac{1}{2}$ (b) $(5, 0)$; $x = -5$

10. (a) $(-3, 0)$; $x = 3$ (b) $(0, -\frac{5}{2})$; $y = \frac{5}{2}$

---

11. If the focus of a parabola is at $(0, 4)$ and the directrix is the x-axis, does the origin lie on the parabola? Is $(0, 0)$ a solution of the equation of the parabola? Could an equation of the parabola be of the form $x^2 = 4py$?

12. Graph the set $\{(x, y) \mid x = y^2 - 6y + 7\}$ by finding the points corresponding to $y = 0, 1, 2, 3, 4, 5,$ and 6 and drawing a smooth curve through them.

13. (a) Solve the system

$$\begin{cases} x^2 = 4y, \\ x + y = 1. \end{cases}$$

(b) Sketch the graph of each equation of the system.

Find the points of intersection of the parabola and the line. Draw the appropriate graph.

14. $\begin{cases} y^2 = 4x \\ x + 2y + 3 = 0 \end{cases}$ 15. $\begin{cases} x^2 + y = 0 \\ 2x - y - 3 = 0 \end{cases}$

16. $\begin{cases} 2x^2 - 3y = 0 \\ 4x - y - 6 = 0 \end{cases}$ **17.** $\begin{cases} y^2 + x = 0 \\ x - y = 4 \end{cases}$

Graph the solution set of each system of inequalities.

18. $\begin{cases} y^2 \leq 4x \\ y + 2x \leq 4 \end{cases}$

19. $\begin{cases} y^2 - x^2 \geq 8 \\ y^2 \leq 9x \end{cases}$

20. $\begin{cases} y^2 \geq 2x + 10 \\ x^2 + y^2 \leq 25 \end{cases}$

21. Using the definition of a parabola, find an equation of the parabola with
   (a) focus $(0, 0)$ and directrix $y = -4$.
   (b) focus $(0, 0)$ and directrix $y = 2$.
   (c) focus $(0, 3)$ and directrix $y = 1$.
   (d) focus $(0, -2)$ and directrix $y + 1 = 0$.

   Study these four equations to observe the effect when the vertex is not placed at the origin, the directrix is kept parallel to the x-axis, and the focus is on the y-axis. In each case, locate the vertex, and try to put the equation in a form which shows the coordinates of the vertex.

Graph each of the following parabolas, showing its vertex, focus, and directrix.

22. $x^2 = 4(y - 1)$

23. $x^2 = -4(y - 1)$

24. $x^2 = 6(y + 2)$

25. $x^2 = -6(y + 2)$.

KEY IDEAS AND KEY WORDS

The distance between the points $P(x_1, y_1)$ and $Q(x_2, y_2)$ is given by the **distance formula**:

$$PQ = \sqrt{(x_2 - x_1)^2 + (y_2 - y_1)^2}.$$

A **circle** is the set of all points in a plane at a given distance, called the **radius**, from a fixed point in the plane, called the **center**. If its radius is r and its center has coordinates (h, k), then

$$(x - h)^2 + (y - k)^2 = r^2$$

is an **equation of the circle**.

If A and B are points in a plane and k is a number greater than AB, then the set of all points P in the plane such that

$$AP + PB = k$$

is called an **ellipse.** Each of the points A and B is called a **focus** of the ellipse. The midpoint O of the segment $\overline{AB}$ is called the **center** of the ellipse. The line L which passes through A and B and the line K which passes through O and is perpendicular to L, are the **axes of symmetry** of the ellipse. If the coordinate axes are axes of symmetry of the ellipse, then it has an equation of the form

$$\frac{x^2}{a^2} + \frac{y^2}{b^2} = 1$$

for some positive numbers a and b.

If A and B are points in a plane and k is a positive number less than AB, then the set of all points P in the plane such that either

$$AP - BP = k \quad \text{or} \quad BP - AP = k$$

is called a **hyperbola.** Each of the points A and B is called a **focus** of the hyperbola. A hyperbola has two **perpendicular axes of symmetry** meeting at the **center** of the hyperbola. If the coordinate axes are axes of symmetry of the hyperbola, then it has an equation of the form

$$\frac{x^2}{a^2} - \frac{y^2}{b^2} = 1 \quad \text{or} \quad \frac{y^2}{b^2} - \frac{x^2}{a^2} = 1$$

for some positive numbers a and b.

If F is a point and L is a line not containing F, then the set of all points P in the plane containing F and L such that

$$PF = PQ,$$

where Q is at the foot of the perpendicular drawn from P to L, is called a **parabola.** Point F is called the **focus,** and line L is called the **directrix** of the parabola. The point halfway between the focus and the directrix is called the **vertex** of the parabola. The line through the focus and vertex is the **axis of symmetry** of the parabola. If one coordinate axis is the axis of symmetry and the vertex is at the origin of the coordinate system, then the parabola has an equation of the form

$$x^2 = 4py \quad \text{or} \quad y^2 = 4px$$

for some nonzero number p, and the directrix of the parabola is parallel to one of the coordinate axes.

CHAPTER REVIEW

1. (a) Show that the following points are the vertices of an equilateral triangle.
$$A(0,0), \quad B(6,0), \quad C(3, 3\sqrt{3})$$
   (b) Find the coordinates of the midpoints of $\overline{AC}$ and $\overline{BC}$.
   (c) Find the length of the segment joining the midpoints of part (b).

2. Write an equation of a circle having
   (a) its center at the origin and radius $5\sqrt{2}$.
   (b) its center at $(-4, 3)$ and radius 9.

Discuss and sketch the graph of each of the following.

3. (a) $4x^2 + 25y^2 = 100$ (b) $4x^2 + 25y^2 > 100$
4. (a) $25x^2 - 4y^2 = 100$ (b) $25x^2 - 4y^2 > 100$
5. (a) $y^2 - 4x^2 = 4$ (b) $y^2 - 4x^2 < 4$

6. Discuss the graph of each of the following equations. Give the coordinates of the vertex and the focus, an equation of the directrix, and an equation of the axis of symmetry.
   (a) $x^2 = 6y$ (b) $y^2 + 7x = 0$

7. Solve algebraically and graphically the system of equations
$$\begin{cases} y^2 - x^2 = 1, \\ x^2 + y^2 = 1. \end{cases}$$

8. Use algebraic methods to find the intersections of the following pairs of conic sections. Sketch graphs to check your answers.
   (a) $\begin{cases} y^2 - 3x - 19 = 0 \\ x^2 + y^2 - 29 = 0 \end{cases}$ (b) $\begin{cases} 4x^2 + 5y - 10 = 0 \\ 5y^2 - 4x^2 = 20 \end{cases}$

9. Using the definition of a parabola, find an equation of the parabola with
   (a) focus $(0, 2)$ and directrix $y = -2$.
   (b) focus $(-1, 0)$ and directrix $x = 1$.

10. A square with sides parallel to the coordinate axes is inscribed in the ellipse $4x^2 + y^2 = 20$. Find its area.

11. Graph each of the following systems of inequalities.
   (a) $\begin{cases} 3y^2 \leq 4x \\ 4x^2 + 9y^2 \leq 72 \end{cases}$ (b) $\begin{cases} x^2 > 4y \\ x + 2y < 4 \end{cases}$

12. Solve each of the following systems algebraically.
   (a) $\begin{cases} x + y = 1 \\ 4x^2 + 4y^2 = 1 \end{cases}$ (b) $\begin{cases} 3x^2 - y^2 = 7 \\ 2x^2 + 3y^2 = 23 \end{cases}$

13. Find the center and/or vertices of each of the following conic sections.
   (a) $x^2 + y^2 - 6x + 8y = 0$ (b) $y = x^2 - 2x - 3$
   (c) $x = 3y^2 - 6y - 2$ (d) $3x^2 + 2y^2 - 12x + 6y - 3 = 0$

CHAPTER TEST

1. Find an equation of the circle with diameter $\overline{AB}$, given that the coordinates of A and B are $(5, -1)$ and $(-1, 3)$, respectively.

2. Sketch the graph of $4y^2 - x^2 = 9$. Locate the center, intercepts, and foci.

3. Solve algebraically the system

$$\begin{cases} 3x - 4y + 5 = 0, \\ 3x^2 + 8y^2 = 1. \end{cases}$$

4. (a) Find an equation of an ellipse with foci at $A(-5, 0)$ and $B(5, 0)$, given that the sum of the distances from any point $P(x, y)$ of the ellipse to points A and B is 12.
   (b) Sketch the graph of the equation in part (a).

5. Find the vertex and focus and give an equation of the directrix of the parabola with equation $y = x^2 - 4x + 5$. Sketch the graph.

6. Name the graph of each of the following equations.
   (a) $x + y = 5$
   (b) $x^2 + 3x = y$
   (c) $5x^2 + 5y^2 = 125$
   (d) $x^2 - 3y^2 = 12$
   (e) $y^2 - x^2 = 4$
   (f) $2x^2 + y^2 = 15$

CHAPTER **6**

Functions

Objectives . . .

- To express numerical relationships in the language of *functions*.
- To write functional relationships using functional notation.
- To develop constant functions and linear functions and their graphs.
- To develop graphs of power functions and exponential functions.

6–1 DEFINITION OF A FUNCTION

Every person in North America has a surname. If we consider one set consisting of all people in North America and a second set consisting of all of their surnames, then there is a definite correspondence between these two sets that associates with each person his or her surname. Such a correspondence between two sets is an example of a *function.* The set of people in North America is called the *domain,* and the set of surnames is called the *range* of this function.

A map of Mexico contains numerous dots, each of which is accompanied by the name of a city. Thus, on the one hand, we have a set of dots on a piece of paper and, on the other hand, a set of cities in Mexico. There is a definite correspondence between these two sets that associates with each dot in the one set a city in the other set. Again, this correspondence is an example of a function whose domain is the set of dots on the map of Mexico and whose range is the set of cities in Mexico.

The formula $A = s^2$ gives the area A of a square in terms of the length s of a side. For example, if $s = 6$, then $A = 36$, and if $s = \sqrt{2}$, then $A = 2$. This formula associates a positive number A with each positive number s, and hence, defines a function whose domain and range are the set P of positive numbers.

These examples suggest the following definition.

Definition of function, domain, image, and range

A function is a correspondence between two sets that associates with each element of the first set a unique element of the second set. The first set is called the domain of the function. For each element x of the domain, the corresponding element y of the second set is called the image of x under the function. The set of all images of the elements of the domain is called the range of the function.

The examples already given illustrate different ways of defining functions. Some functions are defined by equations, others by verbal statements.

The area function defined by $A = s^2$ has domain $D = \{s \mid s > 0\}$ and range $R = \{s^2 \mid s > 0\}$. Obviously, $D = R$ in this example. The distance an automobile travels at a rate of 50 miles per hour is 50 times the number of hours spent traveling. This verbal statement defines a function in which the set of positive real numbers is both the range and the domain of the function. This distance function can also be defined by the following formula.

$$d = 50t \quad \text{if } t > 0$$

A precise statement of the range of a function is not important. As long as we know the domain and have directions for finding the image of each element of the domain, we have a complete definition of the function. Often the domain of a function defined by an equation or verbal statement is not given explicitly. In such a case, the domain is assumed to be the set of all numbers for which the equation or verbal statement makes sense.

We can also consider a function as a *set of ordered pairs* in which no two different pairs have the same first element. The set of all first elements is the *domain*, and the set of all second elements is the *range* of the function. Thus, there is associated with each element x in the domain a unique element y in the range.

An example of a set of ordered pairs is

$$S = \{(x, |x|) \mid x \text{ a real number}\}.$$

In this set, no two different pairs have the same first element. Set S is the *absolute-value function,* which associates with each real number x its absolute value, $|x|$.

Exercises

Each of the following formulas defines a function. State the domain of each function.

1. (a) $C = 10n$; n representing the number of articles, and C the total cost of n articles if each costs 10¢.

    (b) $d = 50t$; t representing the time, in hours, spent, and d the distance, in miles, covered by a car traveling at a constant speed of 50 miles per hour.

2. (a) $p = 4s$; s the side and p the perimeter of a square.

(b) $d = s\sqrt{2}$; s the side and d the diagonal of a square.

3. (a) $s = 64 - 16t^2$; t representing the time, in seconds, elapsed after an object is dropped from a height of 64 feet, and s the distance, in feet, of the object above the ground at time t.

(b) $C = 1.25 + .045(n - 15)$; n representing the number of words in a telegram having at least 15 words, and C the cost of the telegram.

Each of the following tables defines a function. Using set notation, describe the domain and range of each function.

4. (a)

x	2	3	4
y	4	9	16

(b)

x	7	8	9
y	9	10	11

5. (a)

x	7	8	9
y	-3	2	0

(b)

x	1	2	3	4
y	2	1	2	1

6. (a)

x	1	2	3	4
y	1	1	1	1

(b)

x	2	5	7	9
y	$\frac{1}{2}$	$\frac{1}{5}$	$\frac{1}{7}$	$\frac{1}{9}$

7. (a) (i) Solve the linear equation $5x + 2y = 10$ for y in terms of x.

(ii) Does the resulting equation in part (i) define y as a function of x?

(iii) Solve the linear equation in part (i) for x in terms of y.

(iv) Does the resulting equation in part (iii) define x as a function of y?

(b) (i) Solve the linear equation $4x + 3y = 12$ for y in terms of x.

(ii) Does the resulting equation in part (i) define a function of x?

(iii) Solve the linear equation in part (i) for x in terms of y.

(iv) Does the resulting equation in part (iii) define a function of y?

8. (a) Take any number between 0 and 10; multiply this number by 5, then add 11. Express the answer A as a function of the number x first chosen. What is the domain of this function?

(b) Take any number between 0 and 10; add 20 to this number, then divide by 5. Express the answer A as a function of the number x first chosen. What is the domain of this function?

9. (a) Why is the following set of ordered pairs *not* a function?

$$\{(1, 3,) \ (2, 3), \ (2, 4), \ (3, 1)\}$$

(b) Why is the following set of ordered pairs *not* a function?

$$\{(1, 1), \ (1, 2), \ (2, 3), \ (3, 4)\}.$$

10. The following table gives the distance a car travels for various car speeds before a driver's reactions cause him to apply his brakes. (This information is based on the assumption that the average driver takes three-fourths of a second to apply his brakes.)

Speed (in mph)	20	30	40	50	60
Distance (in ft)	22	33	44	55	66

   (a) Use set notation to give the domain and the range of the function defined by this set of ordered pairs.

   (b) Let d denote distance in feet and s the speed in miles per hour. Find a formula in which d is expressed as a function of s and for which the values in the table form a partial list of ordered pairs.

11. For parking a car, a garage charges 50¢ for the first half-hour or any part of the half-hour and 25¢ per half-hour or any part of a half-hour thereafter. The minimum charge is 50¢, and the maximum amount of time a car may park in one day is 16 hours.

   (a) Describe the domain of the function.

   (b) Describe the range of the function.

12. (a) Solve the equation $4y - 8x^2 = 12$ for y in terms of x.

   (b) Does the resulting equation in part (a) define a function of x?

   (c) Solve the equation in part (a) for x in terms of y.

   (d) Does the resulting equation in part (c) define a function of y?

13. Each rectangle in a set of rectangles has one side 3 units longer than the other. Write a formula which expresses the area function A of a rectangle in this set in terms of the shorter side x. Give the domain and range of A.

14. A square piece of tin is 10 inches on each side. A small square is cut from each corner and the tin folded to form an open box. (See the figure.) Find a formula which expresses the volume function V of the open box in terms of x, the side of a cut-out square. Give the domain and range of V.

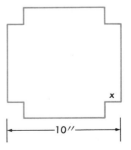

15. Each rectangle in a set of rectangles has an area of 100 square units. Write a formula expressing the base function B for a rectangle in this set in terms of the height h. Give the domain and range of B.

16. Exactly 50 yards of fencing is available for enclosing a rectangular garden. Write a formula for the area function A in terms of one of the sides of the rectangle. Give the domain and range of A.

17. A page with dimensions 12 inches by 14 inches has a border of uniform width x surrounding the printed part of the page. Write a formula for the area function A of the printed part in terms of the width of the border x. Give the domain and range of A.

18. A rectangle y inches long and x inches wide has a perimeter of 10 inches.
(a) Express y as a function of x.
(b) Express the area of the rectangle as a function of x.

6–2   FUNCTIONAL NOTATION

An important feature of algebra is its symbolic language. For example, we can use the symbols

$$x + y = 37$$

to express the following sentence:

The sum of two numbers is thirty-seven.

Just as we use letters to designate variables, we shall use letters such as f, g, and A to designate functions. When we use the letter f to designate a function, then for each x in the domain of f,

$$f(x)$$

denotes the *image of x* under f. The symbol $f(x)$ is read "f of x." Therefore, if $x = 2$, we denote the image of 2 as $f(2)$.

Let us consider the *squaring function* f having the set P of positive real numbers as its domain D. The image $f(x)$ of each x in P is the square of x, that is,

$$f(x) = x^2 \quad \text{for each } x \text{ in } P.$$

For example, the numbers 3, $\sqrt{2}$, and 10 are in the domain of f, and their images in the range of f are as follows:

$$f(3) = 3^2, \text{ or } 9; \quad f(\sqrt{2}) = (\sqrt{2})^2, \text{ or } 2; \quad f(10) = 10^2, \text{ or } 100.$$

This function f has geometric significance: It is the *area function* of a square. Thus, if the length of a side of a square is 3 inches, the area of the square is $f(3)$, or 9 square inches. We could just as well denote this function by A and define it by the formula

$$A(s) = s^2 \quad \text{for each positive real number } s.$$

These two functions f and A are equal; that is, they have the same domain P and $f(a) = A(a)$ for each number a in P. On the other hand, the function g, defined by

$$g(x) = x^2 \quad \text{for every real number } x,$$

is not equal to f, although the equation defining g is the same as the equation defining f. They are different because the domain of g is the set of all real numbers, but the domain of f is the set of all *positive* real numbers. For example,

$$g(-3) = (-3)^2, \quad \text{or } 9,$$

but $f(-3)$ is not defined since -3 is not in the domain of f.

As a second example, let us consider function s and its domain D, defined in the following manner.

$$s(t) = 64 - 16t^2, \quad D = \{t \mid 0 \leq t \leq 2\}.$$

Some images of elements of D under s are

$$s(0) = 64 - (16 \cdot 0^2), \quad \text{or } 64;$$
$$s(\tfrac{1}{2}) = 64 - [16 \cdot (\tfrac{1}{2})^2], \quad \text{or } 60;$$
$$s(1) = 64 - [16 \cdot 1^2], \quad \text{or } 48;$$
$$s(\tfrac{3}{2}) = 64 - [16 \cdot (\tfrac{3}{2})^2], \quad \text{or } 28;$$
$$s(2) = 64 - [16 \cdot 2^2], \quad \text{or } 0.$$

The function s has physical significance as a *distance function*. If an object is dropped from a point 64 feet above the ground, then the distance of the object from the ground t seconds after it is dropped is $s(t)$ feet. For example, 1 second after the object is dropped, it is 48 feet above the ground. Since $s(2) = 0$, it takes the object 2 seconds to reach the ground.

As a third example, consider the function C which has the set of positive integers as its domain and is defined in the following way.

$$C(n) = \begin{cases} 1.25 & \text{if } 0 < n \leq 15 \\ 1.25 + .045(n - 15) & \text{if } n > 15 \end{cases}$$

Note that two equations are used to define C. From the first equation, we know that each of the following is equal to 1.25.

$$C(1), \ C(2), \ \ldots, \ C(15)$$

From the second equation, we know that

$$C(25) = 1.25 + .045 \cdot (25 - 15)$$
$$= 1.25 + .45, \quad \text{or} \quad 1.70.$$

This function might describe the cost, in dollars, of sending a telegram having n words. Thus, a 25-word telegram would cost $1.70.

If we want a formula such as $f(x) = 7/(x - 3)$ to give the image of each real number x in the domain of the function f, then we must exclude the value $x = 3$. In this case, it is customary to write the complete description of f as

$$f(x) = \frac{7}{x - 3}, \quad x \text{ real and } x \neq 3.$$

Exercises

1. (a) Let the function f be defined as follows: The domain of f is the set of all real numbers and the image of each real number is given by the formula

    $$f(x) = 2x^2 + 5x - 3.$$

    Find $f(-3)$, $f(-\sqrt{2})$, $f(-\frac{5}{4})$, and $f(0)$.
   (b) Let the function f be defined as follows: The domain of f is the set of all real numbers and the image of each real number is given by the formula

    $$f(x) = 3x^2 - 4x + 1.$$

    Find $f(-1)$, $f(5)$, $f(0)$, $f(-\frac{1}{2})$.

2. (a) If $g(x) = 4/(x^2 - 1)$ gives the image of a real number x under the function g, what real numbers must be excluded from the domain of g? Write a complete description of the function g.
    Find $g(2)$, $g(-2)$, $g(3)$, $g(-3)$, $g(4)$, and $g(-4)$.
    For the real number k, $k \neq \pm 1$, how does $g(k)$ compare with $g(-k)$?
   (b) If $g(x) = \dfrac{3}{x + 2}$ gives the image of a real number x under the function g, what number must be excluded from the domain of g? Find $g(-1)$, $g(0)$, $g(\frac{1}{5})$, $g(-\frac{5}{2})$, $g(-\frac{3}{2})$.

Give the restrictions, if any, on the domain of each of the following functions.

3. (a) $f(x) = \dfrac{5}{x + 4}$ (b) $f(x) = 1 + \dfrac{1}{x}$

4. (a) $f(x) = \sqrt{x^2 - 1}$ (b) $f(x) = -5$

5. (a) $f(x) = \dfrac{3}{x - 2}$ (b) $f(x) = x + \dfrac{1}{x}$

6. (a) $f(x) = 4$ (b) $f(x) \doteq \sqrt{16 - x^2}$

7. (a) For each of the functions defined in Exercises 3(a), 4(a), 5(a), and 6(a), find $f(2)$, $f(-1)$, and $f(\frac{3}{2})$.

    (b) For each of the functions defined in Exercises 3(b), 4(b), 5(b), and 6(b), find $f(3)$, $f(-3)$, and $f(\frac{4}{3})$.

8. (a) A function g is defined by the equation $g(x) = 3$, and the domain of g is the set of all real numbers. This type of function is called a *constant function*.

       Find $g(-7)$, $g(-3)$, and $g(0)$.

       What is the range of g?

    (b) A function f is defined by the equation $f(x) = \sqrt{9 - x^2}$.

       Find $f(1)$, $f(-1)$, $f(9)$, $f(-9)$, and $f(0)$.

       Use set notation to describe the domain of f.

       Use set notation to describe the range of f.

9. (a) A function f whose domain is the set of real numbers is defined by the equation

$$f(x) = \sqrt{x^2 + 1}.$$

       Find $f(2\sqrt{2})$, $f(\sqrt{15})$, $f(0)$, and $f(-1)$.

       Use set notation to describe the range of f.

    (b) If $g(x) = -\sqrt{x^2 + 1}$ and the domain of g is the set of real numbers, use set notation to describe the range of the function g.

---

10. Given that $g(x) = x^2$, with the domain of g the set of all real numbers,

    (a) find $g(3)$, $g(4)$, $g(7)$, and compare $g(7)$ with $g(3) + g(4)$.

    (b) find $g(-2)$, $g(5)$, $g(3)$, and compare $g(3)$ with $g(-2) + g(5)$.

    (c) do you think that the equation $g(a) + g(b) = g(a + b)$ will be true for any pair a, b of real numbers? Explain your answer.

11. Given that $g(x) = x^2$, with the domain of g the set of all real numbers,

    (a) find $g(3)$, $g(5)$, $g(15)$, and compare the number $g(15)$ with the product $g(3) \cdot g(5)$.

    (b) find $g(-2)$, $g(6)$, $g(-12)$, and compare $g(-12)$ with $g(-2) \cdot g(6)$.

    (c) find $\dfrac{g(28)}{g(7) \cdot g(4)}$.

12. The weight W of an object varies directly with its volume V, that is, $W = kV$ for some constant of proportionality k.
    (a) An object weighs 14 grams and has a volume of 10 cubic centimeters. Find the constant of proportionality.
    (b) Use functional notation to write an expression for this weight function W. What is its domain?
    (c) Find $W(20)$ and $W(15)$.

13. The number N of articles purchased varies inversely with the price p per article, that is, $N = k/p$ for some constant k.
    (a) If 11 articles at 12¢ per article can be bought with available money, find the constant of proportionality.
    (b) Using functional notation, write an expression for the function N. What is the domain of N?
    (c) Find $N(11)$, $N(6)$, and $N(4)$.

---

14. The function N whose domain is the set of real numbers is defined in the following way.

$$N(x) = \begin{cases} x \text{ if } x \text{ is a nonnegative real number} \\ -x \text{ if } x \text{ is a negative real number} \end{cases}$$

    (a) Find $N(2)$, $N(\sqrt{3})$, $N(1 - \sqrt{2})$, $N(-2)$, $N(-\sqrt{3})$, $N(\sqrt{2} - 1)$, and $N(0)$.
    (b) Describe this function and write a single equation defining $N(x)$.

15. The operation of multiplying each real number by 7 defines a certain function. If we designate this function by O, then $O(x) = 7x$ for each real number x. Similarly, each of the following operations defines a function which you may designate by O. Assume that the domain of each function O is the largest possible set of real numbers, and define each function O by an equation.
    (a) Each number x is multiplied by 10.
    (b) Each number x is added to 7.
    (c) Each number x is divided by -3.
    (d) Each number x is multiplied by 1.
    (e) Each number x is replaced by 1.

16. (a) Show that the function f defined by the two equations

$$f(x) = \begin{cases} \dfrac{x - 9}{\sqrt{x} - 3}, & x \neq 9 \text{ and } x \geq 0, \\ 6 \text{ if } x = 9 \end{cases}$$

    can be defined by one equation whose domain x is the set of nonnegative numbers.
    (b) Find $f(4)$, $f(16)$, $f(25)$, and $f(100)$.

17. The function g is given by the following two equations. Find one equation which defines this function.

$$\begin{cases} g(x) = \dfrac{\sqrt{x} - 2}{x - 4}, & x \neq 4 \text{ and } x > 0, \\ g(4) = \tfrac{1}{4} \end{cases}$$

18. (a) The two functions g, h are defined below. Are they equal functions?

$$g(x) = \frac{\sqrt{x^2 + 16} - 5}{x^2 - 9}, \quad x \neq \pm 3,$$

$$h(x) = \frac{1}{\sqrt{x^2 + 16} + 5}$$

(b) For what values of x does $g(x) = h(x)$?

Preparation for Section 6–3

1. Graph the equation $y = 2x - 3$.
   (a) What is the slope of this line? What is the y-intercept?
   (b) Find the x-intercept of this line.
   (c) Which of the following points are on this line?

$$(1, -1), \ (2, 5), \ (-\tfrac{1}{2}, -4), \ (0, -3), \ (4, 4), \ (x, 2x - 3)$$

2. Graph the equation $y = x^2$.
3. Graph the equation $y = x^2 + x + 1$.

6–3 THE GRAPH OF A FUNCTION

If both the domain and the range of a function are sets of real numbers, then the function may be displayed by a graph in a cartesian coordinate system. The graph of a function is defined in the following way.

Definition of graph of a function

The graph of a function f having domain D is the graph of the set

$$\{(x, f(x)) \mid x \text{ in } D\}.$$

A function L of the form

$$L(x) = mx + b,$$

where m and b are given real numbers, is called a *linear function*. Its graph is a straight line. The following problem is an example of the linear function.

Problem 1. Graph the linear function L defined by

$$L(x) = 2x - 3, \quad D = \{x \mid x \text{ real}\}.$$

Solution. We are asked to graph the set

$$\{(x, 2x - 3) \mid x \text{ in } D\},$$

which is the same as the set

$$\{(x, y) \mid y = 2x - 3\}.$$

The graph of the latter set is the straight line of Fig. 6–1. This line has slope 2 and y-intercept -3. What is its x-intercept?

A function P defined by

$$P(x) = x^n,$$

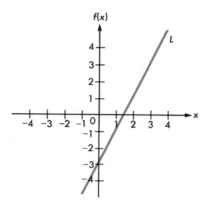

FIGURE 6–1

for some number n, is called the *power function with exponent n*. Its domain is the set of all real numbers having an nth power.

Problem 2. Graph the following power function with exponent 3.

$$P(x) = x^3, \quad D = \{x \mid x \text{ real}\}$$

Solution. The graph of P is the graph of the set

$$\{(x, y) \mid y = x^3\}.$$

The following table of values will help us to draw this graph (shown in Fig. 6–2).

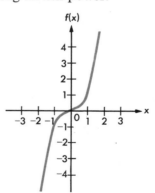

FIGURE 6–2

x	-3	-2	-1.5	-1	$-.5$	0	$.5$	1	1.5	2	3
$P(x)$	-27	-8	-3.375	-1	$-.125$	0	$.125$	1	3.375	8	27

The part of the graph close to the origin is very flat, but the part of the graph away from the origin is quite steep.

Problem 3. The *greatest-integer function* F is defined in the following way. For each real number x, $F(x)$ is the largest integer that is less than or equal to x. In the notation given in Section 1–6, $F(x) = [x]$. Graph the function F.

Solution. By definition,

$$\begin{aligned}
F(x) &= -2 \quad \text{if} \quad -2 \leq x < -1, \\
F(x) &= -1 \quad \text{if} \quad -1 \leq x < 0, \\
F(x) &= 0 \quad \text{if} \quad 0 \leq x < 1, \\
F(x) &= 1 \quad \text{if} \quad 1 \leq x < 2, \\
F(x) &= 2 \quad \text{if} \quad 2 \leq x < 3,
\end{aligned}$$

and so on. Thus, the graph consists of an infinite number of line segments, or steps, as shown in Fig. 6–3. Each step includes its left-hand endpoint, indicated by the solid dot, and does not include its right-hand endpoint, indicated by the hollow dot.

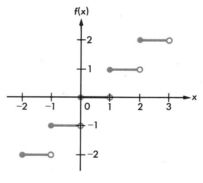

FIGURE 6–3

Exercises

1. (a) Graph the function defined by $f(x) = |x|$.
    (b) Graph the function defined by $f(x) = |x - 1|$.

2. (a) Graph on the same axes the functions defined below.

$$f(x) = x, \quad g(x) = x^2, \quad h(x) = x^3, \quad k(x) = x^4$$

    Compare and contrast the graphs.

    (b) Graph the functions defined below on the same axes.

$$f(x) = x^2, \quad g(x) = x^2 + 4, \quad h(x) = x^2 - 1, \quad k(x) = 3x^2$$

    Compare and contrast the graphs.

3. (a) Graph the quadratic function $f(x) = x^2 + 2x + 3$.

(b) Graph the quadratic function $f(x) = x^2 - 2x + 4$.

4. (a) What is the domain of the function f defined by the equation

$$f(x) = \sqrt{9 - x^2}?$$

Graph the function f.

How does your graph compare with the graph of the equation $x^2 + y^2 = 9$?

Write another function g whose graph is the remaining portion of the graph defined by the above equation. Graph g.

(b) What is the domain of the function f defined by the equation

$$f(x) = -\sqrt{4 - x^2}?$$

Graph the function f.

How does your graph compare with the graph of the equation $x^2 + y^2 = 4$?

Write another function g whose graph is the remaining portion of the graph defined by the above equation. Graph g.

5. (a) The shipping charges of a mail-order company are 25¢ for the first pound or fraction thereof, an additional 25¢ for orders weighing more than 1 pound but not more than 2 pounds, and so on, for each additional pound or fraction thereof.

Graph this shipping function, F. What is its domain? Describe the range of F.

(b) Given that $f(x) = 2^x$ for x a nonnegative *integer*, graph this function.

---

6. The figure shows the graph of a function f whose domain is the interval $\{x \mid -2 \leq x \leq 3\}$ and whose range is the interval $\{y \mid -1 \leq y \leq 1\}$. Sketch the graph of each of the following equations, carefully labeling your scale on each axis.

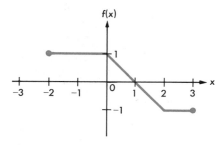

(a) $y = f(x) + 2$

(b) $y = 2f(x)$

(c) $y = -f(x)$

(d) $y = |f(x)|$

7. We can define four functions by solving each of the following equations first for y and then for x. In each case, give the definitions of the functions, and show how their graphs are related to the graph of the given equation.
   (a) $x^2 + y^2 = 4$
   (b) $x^2 - y^2 = 1$
   (c) $9x^2 + 25y^2 = 225$
   (d) $x^2 + 4y^2 = 4$

8. The function f, defined by the equation $f(x) = 3/(x - 2)$, has domain $D = \{x \mid x \neq 2\}$. The graph of this function is sketched below. Although we can find no points with abscissa 2, we can find points with abscissas as close to 2 as we wish. Complete the following table to see the behavior of the curve near $x = 2$ and then for $|x|$ very large.

x	1	1.5	1.75	1.9	3	2.5	2.25	2.1	12	102	1002	-8	-98	-998
$f(x)$	?	?	?	?	?	?	?	?	?	?	?	?	?	?

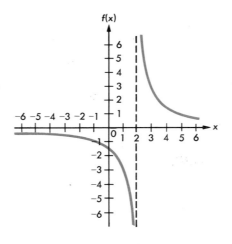

Graph the following functions, paying particular attention to points whose abscissas are close to numbers excluded from the domain of the function. Draw dashed vertical lines at the excluded numbers. (See Exercise 8.)

9. $f(x) = x + \dfrac{1}{x}$

10. $g(x) = \dfrac{3}{(x + 2)^2}$

11. $f(x) = \dfrac{x - 2}{x - 3}$

12. $f(x) = 1 + \dfrac{1}{x - 3}$

13. $g(x) = \dfrac{4}{x^2 - 4}$

14. $h(x) = \dfrac{4x}{x^2 - 4}$

Preparation for Section 6–4

1. Simplify.

$$2^{-3}, \ 2^{-1}, \ 25^{-\frac{1}{2}}, \ (\tfrac{1}{27})^{-\frac{1}{3}}, \ 36^{\frac{3}{2}}, \ 4^{-2.5}, \ 4^{1.5}$$

2. Using a table of square roots, give 2-decimal approximations for the following.

$$2^{-2.5}, \ 2^{-1.5}, \ 2^{-.5}, \ 2^{.5}, \ 2^{1.5}, \ 2^{2.5}$$

3. Simplify.

$$16^{\frac{1}{8}}, \ 9^{\frac{1}{4}}, \ 27^{-\frac{1}{9}}$$

6–4 EXPONENTIAL FUNCTIONS

So far, we have defined the rth power of each positive real number a for every rational number r. Thus, for each positive real number a and each rational number r, there is defined a unique positive real number a^r. You may wonder whether it is possible to define a^r in a sensible way for an irrational exponent r. For example, can one formulate a reasonable definition of $2^{\sqrt{3}}$? Actually, it is possible to do so in a way that we shall describe in this section.

Consider, for example, the equation

$$y = 2^x.$$

We know that for every rational value of x, there is a unique real value of y which makes this equation true. We can get some idea of the shape of the graph by plotting points from the values given in the table.

x	-3	-2.5	-2	-1.5	-1	$-.5$	0	$.5$	1	1.5	2	2.5	3	3.5	4
y	.125	.18	.25	.35	.5	.71	1	1.41	2	2.83	4	5.66	8	11.31	16

The points we have plotted seem to lie on a smooth curve. If we were to take many more rational values of x and plot the points corresponding to them, we would obtain a better picture of this curve. In fact, we could plot so many points, say between $x = 0$ and $x = 1$, that we would not be able to distinguish between our set of points and a curve showing no breaks for irrational values of x. It would then seem reasonable to define 2^x, for x irrational, as the y-coordinate of the curve through these points. Thus, let us make the reasonable assumption that to each real number x there corresponds a unique positive number y such that the point (x, y) is on the smooth curve

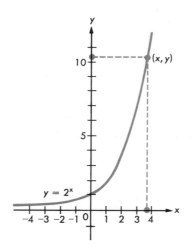

indicated in Fig. 6–4. Using this assumption, we can say that for each real number x, there is a unique positive number y such that the equation $y = 2^x$ is true.

A number such as $2^{\sqrt{3}}$ can be approximated in the following way. Since $1 < \sqrt{3} < 2$ and since the curve in Fig. 6–4 is rising, we must have $2^1 < 2^{\sqrt{3}} < 2^2$, that is, $2 < 2^{\sqrt{3}} < 4$. A better approximation of $2^{\sqrt{3}}$ can be obtained by taking a better approximation of $\sqrt{3}$. Thus, $1.7 < \sqrt{3} < 1.8$ and therefore,

$$2^{1.7} < 2^{\sqrt{3}} < 2^{1.8}.$$

Note that $2^{1.7}$ and $2^{1.8}$ are rational powers of 2 and hence, have been previously defined. Thus, $1.7 = \frac{17}{10}$ and $2^{1.7} = \sqrt[10]{2^{17}}$; similarly, $2^{1.8} = \sqrt[5]{2^9}$. It can be shown that $2^{1.7} \doteq 3.2$ and $2^{1.8} \doteq 3.5$ and therefore, that $3.2 < 2^{\sqrt{3}} < 3.5$.

We can now define the function E:

$$E(x) = 2^x.$$

From our discussion, we know that the domain of E is the set of all real numbers. We call E the *exponential function with base* 2. The graph of E is sketched in Fig. 6–4.

For each positive real number b not equal to 1, we may similarly define the exponential function E with base b.

Definition of the exponential function

$$E(x) = b^x, \quad \textit{domain of } E = \{x \mid x \textit{ real}\}$$

If $b > 1$, the graph of the exponential function with base b is similar to that in Fig. 6–4. If $b = 1$, the function E, defined by

$$E(x) = 1^x,$$

is simply the constant function

$$E(x) = 1,$$

and this case is usually excluded from consideration as an exponential function.

If $0 < b < 1$, then b^x gets smaller and smaller as x assumes larger and larger positive values, and b^x increases as x assumes smaller and smaller negative values. For example, if E is the exponential function with base $\frac{1}{2}$,

$$E(x) = (\tfrac{1}{2})^x.$$

Then

$$E(x) = 2^{-x},$$

and the graph of E (in Fig. 6–5) is the mirror image in the y-axis of Fig. 6–4.

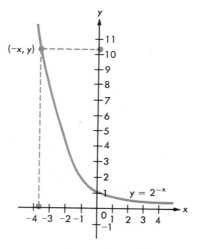

Exponential functions have many applications in the sciences. If ideal conditions for growth and reproduction prevail, then the growth curve of a population is exponential in nature. For example, the number of bacteria in a culture might be given by the exponential function

FIGURE 6–5

$$E(t) = 1000 \cdot 3^t.$$

Thus, initially, there are 1000 bacteria, that is, $E(0) = 1000$. Then

$$\begin{aligned}
\text{1 hour later, } \quad E(1) &= 3^1 \times 1000 = 3000; \\
\text{2 hours later, } \quad E(2) &= 3^2 \times 1000 = 9000; \\
\text{3 hours later, } \quad E(3) &= 3^3 \times 1000 = 27{,}000;
\end{aligned}$$

and so on.

Exercises

1. Graph each of the following groups of exponential functions on the same set of axes. Compare and contrast the graphs of each group.
   (a) $E(x) = 3^x$, $E(x) = 3^{-x}$, $E(x) = 3^x + 2$
   (b) $E(x) = 3^x + 1$, $E(x) = 3^{\frac{x}{2}}$, $E(x) = 3^{x+1}$

2. (a) Consider the following exponential function which describes the growth of bacteria. In this function, t is time measured in hours and $E(t)$ is the number, in thousands, of bacteria in a culture.

$$E(t) = 100 \times 16^t$$

   What is the initial number of bacteria?
   After $\frac{1}{4}$ hour, how many bacteria are there?
   After $\frac{1}{2}$ hour, how many bacteria are there?
   After 1 hour, how many bacteria are there?
   Verify that $E(t) = 100\sqrt{2}$ when $t = \frac{1}{8}$.

   (b) The following exponential function describes the growth of bacteria.

$$E(t) = 3 \times 16^t$$

   What is the initial number of bacteria?
   After $\frac{1}{4}$ hour, how many bacteria are there?
   After $\frac{1}{2}$ hour, how many bacteria are there?
   After 1 hour, how many bacteria are there?
   Verify that $E(t) = 3\sqrt{2}$ when $t = \frac{1}{8}$.

3. (a) The decay curve of a radioactive element is exponential. If the initial quantity of an element is a, then the quantity present after t units of time is given by the function

$$E(t) = a \times b^{-t}.$$

   The base b will depend on the element and also on the choice of units for time. Consider the specific law of decay

$$E(t) = 150 \times 2^{-.002t},$$

   where t is the time, in years, and $E(t)$ is the amount, in milligrams, of a radioactive substance present at time t.

   What is the initial quantity?
   How much is left after 1000 years?
   How long does it take for the initial quantity to decay to $\frac{1}{8}$ the original amount?
   Will the amount present ever vanish completely?

(b) A culture of bacteria, which contains 2000 bacteria, has a count of 18,000 bacteria after 2 hours. Assuming the exponential law of growth, show that the following function fits the above conditions:

$$E(t) = 2 \times 3^t.$$

Here $E(t)$ is the number of thousands of bacteria present after t hours. Find the number of bacteria present after 1 hour.

4. Graph each of the following exponential equations. You will find it convenient to choose different scales for the two axes.
   (a) $y = 10^x$ (b) $y = 10^{-x}$

---

5. A culture with an initial count of 1000 bacteria contains 8000 bacteria 3 hours later. Assuming exponential growth, find the growth formula. How long does it take this culture to double in size?

6. Sometimes the population growth of a town approximately follows an exponential law for the limited period of time. Assuming this type of growth, find the estimated population in 1970 for a hypothetical town, given the following data.

$$\text{1950 population} \quad 5000$$
$$\text{1960 population} \quad 7070$$

7. The half-life of radium is known to be approximately 1600 years, since it takes 1600 years for a given quantity of radium to decay to one-half its initial mass. Start with 300 milligrams of radium, and verify that the law of decay is given by

$$E(t) = 300 \times 2^{-\frac{t}{1600}}.$$

Find the quantity present at the end of the first 800 years.

8. A radioactive element has a law of decay given by

$$E(t) = 400 \times 4^{-\frac{t}{1000}}.$$

Determine its half-life by finding the time at which the amount present is one-half the original amount.

---

9. When $b > 1$, the graph of $E(x) = b^x$ rises steadily, that is

$$b^{x_1} > b^{x_2} \quad \text{if, and only if,} \quad x_1 > x_2.$$

We may use this property of the exponential function to solve such inequalities as $2^x > 32$, since $32 = 2^5$ and $2^x > 2^5$ if, and only if, $x > 5$. In other words, the solution set of this inequality is

$$\{x \mid x > 5\}.$$

Solve each of the following inequalities.
(a) $3^x \leq 81$ (b) $3^{2x} > 27$
(c) $4^x < 8$ (d) $2^x > 1$

10. Inequalities such as $(\frac{1}{3})^x > \frac{1}{81}$ involve the exponential function with a base less than 1. Such inequalities can be solved by the use of the property stated in Exercise 9 since $(\frac{1}{3})^x = 3^{-x}$ and $\frac{1}{81} = 3^{-4}$. Thus, $3^{-x} > 3^{-4}$ if, and only if, $-x > -4$ or $x < 4$. Solve each of the following inequalities.

(a) $(\frac{1}{32})^{2x} < \frac{1}{64}$ (b) $(\frac{4}{9})^{3x} < \frac{32}{243}$
(c) $128^{-x} \geq 16$ (d) $(\frac{1}{2})^x > 64$

*6–5 THE ALGEBRA OF FUNCTIONS

We shall consider only functions which have the set of real numbers as their domains and ranges. We shall show how the operations of the real number system lead to corresponding operations with functions.

If f and g are functions, then we define $f + g$, the sum of f and g, as

$$(f + g)(x) = f(x) + g(x),$$
$$\text{domain of } (f + g) = (\text{domain of } f) \cap (\text{domain of } g).$$

For example, if

$$f(x) = x^2 \quad \text{and} \quad g(x) = 5x,$$

then the function $f + g$ associates with each number x the sum of x^2 and $5x$:

$$(f + g)(x) = x^2 + 5x.$$

Here the domains of f and g are assumed to be the set R of all real numbers. Thus, the domain of $f + g$ is also the set of all real numbers.

Similarly, we define fg, the product of two functions f and g, as

$$(fg)(x) = f(x)g(x),$$
$$\text{domain of } (fg) = (\text{domain of } f) \cap (\text{domain of } g).$$

For example, let us consider the functions above. If

$$f(x) = x^2 \quad \text{and} \quad g(x) = 5x,$$

then the function fg associates with each number x the product of x^2 and $5x$:

$$fg(x) = x^2 \cdot 5x, \quad \text{or } 5x^3.$$

Since f and g have R as their domain, fg also has R as its domain.

As another example, let $f(x) = \sqrt{36 - 4x^2}$ and $g(x) = x + 1$. The domain S of function f is the set of all numbers for which $f(x)$ is a real number:

$$S = \{x \mid 36 - 4x^2 \geq 0\}.$$

Thus,

$$\begin{aligned}
S &= \{x \mid 4x^2 \leq 36\} \\
&= \{x \mid x^2 \leq 9\} \\
&= \{x \mid -3 \leq x \leq 3\}.
\end{aligned}$$

The domain R of function g is the set of all real numbers. The function $f + g$ is defined by

$$(f + g)(x) = \sqrt{36 - 4x^2} + (x + 1),$$
$$\text{domain of } (f + g) = S \cap R = S.$$

The function fg is defined by

$$(fg)(x) = (x + 1)\sqrt{36 - 4x^2},$$
$$\text{domain of } (fg) = S \cap R = S.$$

We can graph the function $f + g$ by graphing f and g in the same coordinate system and then *adding ordinates.* In other words, for each x, we add the y-coordinates of the points $((x, f(x))$ and $(x, g(x))$, and obtain the point $(x, f(x) + g(x))$ on the graph of $f + g$. This is illustrated in Fig. 6-6 for the functions considered previously:

$$f(x) = \sqrt{36 - 4x^2}$$

and

$$g(x) = x + 1.$$

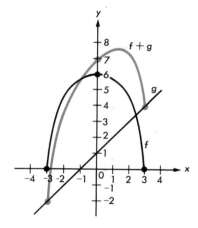

FIGURE 6-6

Exercises

For each of the following pairs of functions, give the sum and product functions and specify the domain of each.

1. (a) $f(x) = 3x + 2$, $g(x) = x - 3$
    (b) $f(x) = x$, $g(x) = 2^x$

2. (a) $f(x) = \sqrt{9 - x^2}$, $g(x) = x^2$
    (b) $f(x) = x$, $g(x) = \dfrac{1}{x^2}$

3. (a) $f(x) = x$, $g(x) = \dfrac{1}{x}$

   (b) $f(x) = x^2$, $g(x) = \sqrt{x^2 + 1}$

4. (a) $f(x) = \dfrac{1}{x}$, $g(x) = x^2 + x - 3$

   (b) $f(x) = 3^x$, $g(x) = 2^x$

5. (a) $f(x) = \sqrt{16 - x^2}$, $g(x) = 4 - x$

   (b) $f(x) = \sqrt{16 - x^2}$, $g(x) = -\sqrt{16 - x^2}$

Use the technique of adding ordinates to graph each function h below.

6. (a) $h(x) = x + 2^x$ (b) $h(x) = x + \dfrac{1}{x^2}$

7. (a) $h(x) = x + \dfrac{1}{x - 1}$ (b) $h(x) = x - 4x^3$

8. (a) $h(x) = x + |x|$ (b) $h(x) = 2^x + 2^{-x}$

In Exercises 9–17, tell whether the equation $f(a + b) = f(a) + f(b)$ is true for every pair a, b of numbers in the domain of f. For example, if $f(x) = 3x$, we have $f(a + b) = 3(a + b)$ and $f(a) = 3a$, $f(b) = 3b$. Then because $3(a + b) = 3a + 3b$, the equation $f(a + b) = f(a) + f(b)$ is true for this particular f.

9. $f(x) = 3x + 2$ 10. $f(x) = x^2$ 11. $f(x) = -6x$

12. $f(x) = 3^x$ 13. $f(x) = \sqrt{x}$ 14. $f(x) = 2^{-x}$

15. $f(x) = |x|$ 16. $f(x) = 5$ 17. $f(x) = x^3$

18. For which of the functions in Exercises 9–17 is the following equation true: $f(ab) = f(a) \cdot f(b)$?

19. For which of the functions in Exercises 9–17 is the following equation true: $f(a + b) = f(a) \cdot f(b)$?

20. For which of the functions in Exercises 9–17 is the following equation true: $f(ab) = f(a) + f(b)$?

KEY IDEAS AND KEY WORDS

If to each value of one variable there corresponds a unique value of a second variable, then the correspondence between these two variables is called a **function.** If to each value of a variable x there corresponds a unique value of a variable y, then we say **y is a function of x.**

The set of values of x is called the **domain of the function,** and the set of values of y is called the **range of the function.**

For each element x of the domain, the corresponding element y of the range is called the **image** of x under the function.

When we use the **functional notation** $f(x)$, the letter f designates a function and $f(x)$ denotes the image of x under the function f.

If f denotes a function, then the graph of the set of all ordered pairs $(x, f(x))$ is called the **graph of the function.**

The function f, defined by

$$f(x) = c$$

where c is a single real number, is called a **constant function.**

The **linear function** f is defined by the first-degree equation

$$f(x) = mx + b.$$

The function f, defined by

$$f(x) = x^n$$

for some number n, is called the **power function with exponent** n. Its domain is the set of all real numbers having an nth power.

The function f, defined by

$$f(x) = b^x$$

where b is a positive real number that is not equal to one and x is a real number, is called the **exponential function with the base** b.

The **sum function** of two functions f and g is defined as the function $f + g$, where

$$(f + g)(x) = f(x) + g(x).$$

The **domain of the sum function** $(f + g)$ is defined as

(domain of f) $\cap$ (domain of g).

The **product function** of two functions f and g is defined as the function fg, where

$$(fg)(x) = f(x)g(x).$$

The **domain of the product function** fg is defined as

(domain of f) $\cap$ (domain of g).

The sum function, $(f + g)$, may be graphed by **adding ordinates;** if for each x, we add the y-coordinates of the points $(x, f(x))$ and $(x, g(x))$, obtaining the point $(x, f(x) + g(x))$ on the graph of $f + g$.

CHAPTER REVIEW

1. The number of degrees centigrade, C, is related to the number of degrees Fahrenheit, F, by the formula $C = \frac{5}{9}(F - 32)$.
   (a) Solve this equation for F and express the resulting formula in functional notation.
   (b) Find F(0), F(100), and F(−40).
   (c) What type of function is F?

2. Boyle's law states that the volume V of a gas kept at constant temperature varies inversely with the pressure P. For a particular gas kept at a certain temperature, a volume of 300 cubic inches is formed under a pressure of 15 pounds per square inch. Write an expression for the volume function V and use it to find $V(20)$.

3. Graph each of the following functions and give the domain.
   (a) $f(x) = \dfrac{1}{3x + 6}$ (b) $f(x) = \sqrt{16 - x^2}$
   (c) $f(x) = 2^x$ (d) $f(x) = x^{\frac{1}{4}}$

4. (a) If a function f is defined by the equation
$$f(x) = \frac{3}{x^2} - 4,$$
   what real numbers must be excluded from the domain of f?
   (b) For the function f in part (a), find
$$f(0), \quad f(\tfrac{1}{2}), \quad f(-\tfrac{1}{2}), \quad f(1), \quad f(-1), \quad f(3), \quad f(-3), \quad f(\tfrac{3}{2}), \quad f(6).$$
   (c) Graph the function f.

5. If the domain of the function f is $\{x \mid -2 \le x \le 4\}$ and $f(x) = x - 1$, graph each of the following equations.
   (a) $y = f(x)$ (b) $y = f(-x)$
   (c) $y = f(|x|)$ (d) $y = f(x + 2)$

6. Graph the function defined by the equation
$$f(x) = \left[\frac{x}{2}\right].$$
   Remember that the notation for greatest integer in x is $[x]$.

7. The function g whose domain is the set of real numbers is defined as follows:
$$g(x) = \begin{cases} 0 & \text{if } x \text{ is a negative number,} \\ x & \text{if } x \text{ is a nonnegative number.} \end{cases}$$
   Find $g(-3)$, $g(-2)$, $g(0)$, $g(\tfrac{7}{4})$, $g(\sqrt{5})$, $g(6)$, and $g(\pi)$.

8. Graph each of the following functions on the same set of axes.
   (a) $f(x) = x - 3$ (b) $g(x) = (x - 3)^2$
   (c) $h(x) = (x - 3)^3$ (d) $k(x) = (x - 3)^4$

9. The law of decay of a radioactive element is given by

$$A = 700 \times 8^{-\frac{t}{1500}}.$$

Determine the half-life of the element by finding the time at which the amount present is one-half the original amount.

10. Find the sum and product of functions f and g, defined by the equations

$$f(x) = \sqrt{x^2 - 4}, \quad g(x) = x.$$

Give the domains of f, g, $f + g$, and fg.

CHAPTER TEST

1. The function f with a domain that is the set of real numbers is defined by the equation

$$f(x) = 3x^2.$$

Find each of the following.
(a) $f(0)$ (b) $f(-2)$ (c) $f(5)$
(d) $f(1 + \sqrt{2})$ (e) $f(1 - \sqrt{2})$

Give the domain (within the set of real numbers) of each of the functions defined in Exercises 2–5.

2. $h(x) = x - 2$ **3.** $f(x) = \dfrac{1}{2x - 1}$

4. $g(x) = \sqrt{9 - x^2}$ **5.** $k(x) = x^{\frac{1}{3}}$

6. Graph each of the following functions.
(a) $f(x) = x - 2$ (b) $f(x) = \sqrt{9 - x^2}$

7. A rectangular area is enclosed by 200 feet of fence.
(a) Express the area A as a function of the length x of one side of the rectangle.
(b) Use an appropriate domain, graph the function.

8. If $y = 3x + 7$, solve the equation for x in terms of y, and express x as a function of y.

9. Which of the following tables determine a function of x? of y? of neither?

(a)
x	y
1	0
2	0
3	0

(b)
x	y
0	1
0	2
0	3

(c)
x	y
1	1
2	2
3	3

(d)
x	y
1	1
1	2
2	2

10. Graph the following function, using the technique of *adding ordinates*.

$$h(x) = \sqrt{25 - x^2} + \tfrac{3}{4}x$$

CHAPTER **7**

Logarithms

Objectives . . .

- To solve simple exponential equations.
- To apply the basic properties of logarithms.
- To graph the logarithm function.
- To apply the laws of logarithms to exponential equations.
- To use common logarithms to approximate values of products, quotients, and roots.

7–1 COMPUTING WITH A TABLE OF POWERS

There are two general classes of functions, algebraic and transcendental. Included in the class of algebraic functions are polynomial functions, such as

$$f(x) = 3x^2 - 4x + 2,$$

rational functions, such as

$$g(x) = \frac{3x + 1}{3x - 1},$$

and functions involving roots, such as

$$h(x) = \sqrt{4 - x^2}.$$

Included in the class of transcendental functions are the exponential functions studied in Chapter 6, logarithmic functions to be studied in this chapter, and trigonometric functions to be studied in Chapters 9 and 10.

Logarithms and exponents are closely related to each other. Before defining the logarithm of a number, let us indicate how exponents can be used to work problems of arithmetic. Logarithmic computations are carried out in a very similar way, as we shall see in later sections.

The table below lists the first twenty positive integral powers of 2.

$2^1 = 2$	$2^6 = 64$	$2^{11} = 2048$	$2^{16} = 65{,}536$
$2^2 = 4$	$2^7 = 128$	$2^{12} = 4096$	$2^{17} = 131{,}072$
$2^3 = 8$	$2^8 = 256$	$2^{13} = 8192$	$2^{18} = 262{,}144$
$2^4 = 16$	$2^9 = 512$	$2^{14} = 16{,}384$	$2^{19} = 524{,}288$
$2^5 = 32$	$2^{10} = 1024$	$2^{15} = 32{,}768$	$2^{20} = 1{,}048{,}576$

We can use this table to solve the following arithmetic problems.

$$32 \times 512 = 2^5 \times 2^9$$
$$= 2^{5+9}, \quad \text{or } 2^{14}$$
$$= 16{,}384$$

$$131{,}072 \div 256 = 2^{17} \div 2^8$$
$$= 2^{17-8}, \quad \text{or } 2^9$$
$$= 512$$

$$\sqrt[3]{32{,}768} = \sqrt[3]{2^{15}}$$
$$= (2^{15})^{\frac{1}{3}}, \quad \text{or } 2^5$$
$$= 32$$

$$32^4 = (2^5)^4$$
$$= 2^{20}$$
$$= 1{,}048{,}576$$

These arithmetic problems are easily solved primarily because each number involved appears in the table. Secondly, each operation is carried out by adding, subtracting, multiplying, or dividing simple exponents according to the laws of exponents. The table would be of no use with problems not involving powers of 2. For example, it would not help us find 132×8046. However, more extensive tables can be constructed to work all such problems to yield at least approximate results.

Exercises

Continue the table in Section 7–1 through 2^{25}. Use the table to compute the following.

1. (a) 8192×128 (b) $2{,}097{,}152 \div 1024$

2. (a) $16 \cdot 512$ (b) $131{,}072 \div 32{,}768$

3. (a) $(512)^2$ (b) $(256)^3$

4. (a) $(8{,}388{,}608) \div (4096 \times 32)$ (b) $\dfrac{64 \times 128}{2048}$

5. (a) $\left(\dfrac{262{,}144}{512 \times 16{,}384}\right)^2$ (b) $\sqrt{65{,}536}$

6. (a) $\sqrt[3]{2{,}097{,}152}$ (b) $(1{,}048{,}576)^{-\frac{3}{4}}$

7. (a) 16^5 (b) $(16{,}777{,}216)^{\frac{2}{3}}$

8. (a) $\sqrt{\dfrac{524,288 \times 8192}{4,194,304}}$ (b) $\sqrt{\tfrac{1}{8} \times 2048}$

9. (a) $\dfrac{32,768 \times \sqrt[3]{4096}}{(256)^{\frac{3}{4}} \times \sqrt[3]{512}}$ (b) $\sqrt{2^3 + 2^3}$

10. (a) Find x if $2^x = 32,768$.   (b) Find x if $2^x = (32,768)^{\frac{1}{2}}$.

11. (a) Find x if $4^x = 8,388,608$.   (b) Find x if $4^x = (65,536)^{\frac{1}{4}}$.

12. (a) Is there an entry in the table representing $2^6 + 2^7$?
    (b) Is there an entry in the table representing $2^{10} + 2^5$?

Make a table of positive integral powers of 3 through 3^{15}. Use the table to do the following exercises.

13. 243×6561

14. $1,594,323 \div 2187$

15. $\sqrt[3]{14,348,907}$

16. $(2187)^2$

17. $(4,782,969)^{\frac{2}{7}}$

18. $(531,441)^{-\frac{5}{6}}$

19. Find x if $3^x = 6561$.

20. Find x if $3^x = \dfrac{1}{6561}$.

21. Find x if $9^x = 2187$.

22. Find x if $3^{2x+1} = 243$.

23. Find x if $9^{2x} = 19,683$.

---

24. Find x and y if $2^{x+y} = 16,384$ and $3^{x-y} = 729$.

25. Use the tables of powers of 2 and of 3 to find the following.
    (a) 6^5
    (b) 12^4
    (c) 18^4

Preparation for Section 7–2

1. If $f(x) = 2^x$, find $f(3)$ and $f(-3)$.

2. If $f(x) = 2^x$ and $f(a) = 32$, is a uniquely determined?

3. If $f(x) = 2^x$ and $f(a) = b$, what type number must b be?

7-2 LOGARITHMS

Let us consider an exponential function E, defined by

$$E(x) = b^x,$$
$$\text{where } b > 0 \text{ and } b \neq 1.$$

The domain of E is the set of all real numbers, and the range of E is the set of *positive* real numbers. Thus, for each real number r, there exists a unique positive real number s such that $s = b^r$.

If we draw the graph of E, as shown in Fig. 7-1, then another property of the function can be seen: For each positive number s, the line $y = s$ intersects the graph of E in one, and only one, point, (r, s). This means that the range of E is the set of all positive real numbers, and that for each positive real number s, there exists a *unique* real number r such that $b^r = s$.

The remarks above lead us to define the logarithm function to the base b, denoted by $\log_b$, in the following manner.

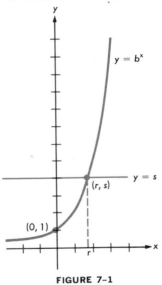

FIGURE 7-1

Definition of the Logarithm Function

For every positive number s,

$$\log_b s = r,$$

where r is the number such that $b^r = s$ (assuming $b > 0$ and $b \neq 1$).

According to this definition, the function $\log_b$ has the set of all positive real numbers as its domain. Also,

$\log_b s$ is the power to which b must be raised to give s.

To illustrate the definition, let us find each of the following logarithms.

log₂ 16.   If we let $r = \log_2 16$, then $2^r = 16$.   Since $16 = 2^4$, we conclude that $r = 4$. Thus,

$$\log_2 16 = 4.$$

log₂ $\sqrt[3]{2}$.   If we let $r = \log_2 \sqrt[3]{2}$, then $2^r = \sqrt[3]{2}$.   Since $\sqrt[3]{2} = 2^{\frac{1}{3}}$, we conclude that $2^r = 2^{\frac{1}{3}}$ and $r = \frac{1}{3}$. Thus,

$$\log_2 \sqrt[3]{2} = \tfrac{1}{3}.$$

log₂ $\frac{1}{4}$ If we let $r = \log_2 \frac{1}{4}$, then $2^r = \frac{1}{4}$.   Since $\frac{1}{4} = 2^{-2}$, we conclude that $r = -2$. Thus,

$$\log_2 \tfrac{1}{4} = -2.$$

log₅ 5.   If we let $r = \log_5 5$, then $5^r = 5$.   Since $5^1 = 5$, we conclude that $r = 1$ and

$$\log_5 5 = 1.$$

log₈ 16.   If we let $r = \log_8 16$, then $8^r = 16$.   To find the power of 8 that is equal to 16, we replace 8 by 2^3, obtaining the equation $(2^3)^r = 16$ or, equivalently, $2^{3r} = 16$.   Since $16 = 2^4$, we conclude that $2^{3r} = 2^4$ and $3r = 4$. Thus, $r = \frac{4}{3}$ and

$$\log_8 16 = \tfrac{4}{3}.$$

log$_{\frac{1}{10}}$ 1000.   If we let $r = \log_{\frac{1}{10}} 1000$, then $(\frac{1}{10})^r = 1000$.   Since $\frac{1}{10} = 10^{-1}$, we conclude that $(10^{-1})^r = 1000$, or

$$10^{-r} = 1000.$$

Now $1000 = 10^3$, and, therefore, $-r = 3$ or $r = -3$. Thus,

$$\log_{\frac{1}{10}} 1000 = -3.$$

Each problem above is solved by using the fact that the two equations

$$y = \log_b x \quad and \quad b^y = x$$

are equivalent, that is, that they have the same solution set.

Problem.   Solve each of the following equations.

(a) $4 = \log_5 x$ (b) $y = \log_4 32$ (c) $\frac{2}{3} = \log_b 9$

Solution.

(a) The equation $4 = \log_5 x$ is equivalent to the equation $5^4 = x$. Hence, $x = 625$ is the solution.

(b) The equation $y = \log_4 32$ is equivalent to the equation $4^y = 32$. Since $4 = 2^2$ and $32 = 2^5$, another equivalent equation is $(2^2)^y = 2^5$, or $2^{2y} = 2^5$. Hence, $2y = 5$ and $y = \frac{5}{2}$.

(c) The equation $\frac{2}{3} = \log_b 9$ is equivalent to the equation $b^{\frac{2}{3}} = 9$. In turn, this latter equation is equivalent to the equation $(b^{\frac{2}{3}})^{\frac{3}{2}} = 9^{\frac{3}{2}}$, or $b = 9^{\frac{3}{2}}$. Hence, $b = 27$ is the solution. Although it is true that $(-27)^{\frac{2}{3}} = (\sqrt[3]{-27})^2$, or 9, so that $b = -27$ is a solution of the equation $b^{\frac{2}{3}} = 9$, no negative number can be a base for logarithms. Thus, $b = 27$ is the only solution of the given equation.

The following properties of logarithms follow from the definition of a logarithm.

$$\log_b 1 = 0 \quad since \quad b^0 = 1$$
$$\log_b b = 1 \quad since \quad b^1 = b$$
$$\log_b b^r = r \quad since \quad b^r = b^r$$

$$\log_{\frac{1}{b}} x = -\log_b x \quad since \quad \left(\frac{1}{b}\right)^r = b^{-r}$$

In view of the last property, we might as well restrict the base b to be greater than 1, for if $0 < b < 1$, then $1/b > 1$, and each logarithm to the base b is easily expressed in terms of a logarithm to the base $1/b$. For example,

$$\log_{\frac{1}{2}} 4 = -\log_2 4, \quad \text{or} \quad -2,$$
$$\log_{\frac{1}{10}} .001 = -\log_{10} .001, \quad \text{or} \quad -(-3), \quad \text{or} \quad 3.$$

Exercises

Write the logarithmic equation that corresponds to each of the following exponential equations.

1. (a) $2^5 = 32$ (b) $3^{-2} = \frac{1}{9}$

2. (a) $7^0 = 1$ (b) $25^{\frac{3}{2}} = 125$

3. (a) $16^{-\frac{3}{2}} = \frac{1}{64}$ (b) $10^0 = 1$

4. (a) $16^{-\frac{3}{4}} = .125$ (b) $(\frac{1}{3})^{-2} = 9$

Write the exponential equation that corresponds to each of the following logarithmic equations.

5. (a) $\log_{10} 100 = 2$ (b) $\log_8 4 = \frac{2}{3}$

6. (a) $\log_{\frac{1}{3}} 81 = -4$ (b) $\log_{25} \frac{1}{125} = -\frac{3}{2}$

7. (a) $\log_8 1 = 0$ (b) $\log_a y = x$

8. (a) $\log_n 256 = 2$ (b) $\log_{16} 8 = \frac{3}{4}$

9. (a) $\log_n 9 = .4$ (b) $\log_{\frac{1}{8}} 4 = -\frac{2}{3}$

Find the value of each of the following logarithms.

10. (a) $\log_{10} 10^2$ (b) $\log_2 2^{10}$

11. (a) $\log_b b^4$ (b) $\log_b b$

12. (a) $\log_7 \sqrt[3]{7}$ (b) $\log_2 8\sqrt{32}$

13. (a) $\log_7 \frac{1}{49}$ (b) $\log_3 \sqrt[5]{81}$

14. (a) $\log_{10} \sqrt[3]{100}$ (b) $\log_{27} 81$

15. (a) $\log_{\frac{1}{10}} 100$ (b) $\log_{100} .001$

Solve each of the following equations for n.

16. $\log_{10} .0001 = n$ **17.** $\log_{36} n = -\frac{3}{2}$ **18.** $\log_n 125 = -\frac{3}{4}$

19. $\log_7 7^{-3} = n$ **20.** $\log_{49} n = \frac{3}{2}$ **21.** $\log_n 1000 = 1.5$

22. $\log_{16} 8 = n$ **23.** $\log_{64} n = \frac{7}{6}$ **24.** $\log_n \left(\frac{1}{81}\right) = -2$

In Exercises 25–30, solve each of the equations for x.

25. $\log_{10} 1 = x$ **26.** $\log_x 1 = 0$ **27.** $\log_4 x = -3$

28. $\log_x 3 = \frac{1}{4}$ **29.** $x = \log_{36} 216$ **30.** $x = \log_2 2$

7–3 LOGARITHMIC GRAPHS

The graph of the function $\log_b$ is simply the graph of the equation

$$y = \log_b x.$$

The particular graph of $\log_2$ is sketched in Fig. 7–2 from the following table of values.

x	$\frac{1}{8}$	$\frac{1}{4}$	$\frac{1}{2}$	1	2	4	8	16
y	-3	-2	-1	0	1	2	3	4

This graph is very similar to the exponential graph with base 2 sketched in Fig. 7–1. In fact, the two graphs can be made to coincide by turning over the piece of paper on which one is drawn and placing the positive x-axis of the logarithmic graph along the positive y-axis of the exponential graph. This is so because the two equations $y = \log_2 x$ and $2^y = x$ are equivalent.

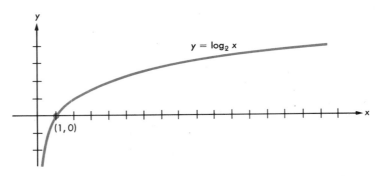

FIGURE 7-2

The logarithmic graph with base $b > 1$ has the following important properties, which are illustrated in Fig. 7–2.

1. *The entire graph is to the right of the y-axis.*
2. *The graph has x-intercept 1.*
3. *The graph is rising as we traverse it from left to right. In other words,*

$$\log_b x_1 > \log_b x_2 \quad \textit{if, and only if,} \quad x_1 > x_2.$$

The first property is true because $\log_b x$ is defined only if $x > 0$, and the second property is true because $\log_b x = 0$, if and only if, $x = 1$. The proof of the third property is too difficult to be included in this text.

Exercises

1. (a) Graph each of the following equations on the same set of axes.

$$y = \log_5 x, \quad y = 5^x$$

Is there a line of folding so that the two graphs would coincide? By what transformation could one equation be obtained from the other?

(b) Graph each of the following equations on the same set of axes.

$$y = \log_2 x, \quad y = \log_3 x, \quad y = \log_5 x, \quad y = \log_{10} x$$

What point does the following family of logarithmic curves have in common?

$$\{y = \log_b x \mid b \text{ a real number}, \ b > 1\}$$

Using Property 3 of the logarithmic curve with base $b > 1$, give two consecutive integers between which each of the following numbers lies.

  2. (a) $\log_2 6.45$
     (b) $\log_{10} 36.125$

  3. (a) $\log_{10} .375$
     (b) $\log_2 .3$

  4. (a) If $0 < N < 1$, what can be said about $\log_{10} N$?
     (b) If $N > 1$, what can be said about $\log_{10} N$?

---

  5. If M is a number greater than the positive number N, how do the num-
     bers $\log_{10} M$ and $\log_{10} N$ compare?

Graph each of the following equations.

  6. $y = \log_3 x$　　　　　7. $y = \log_3 2x$　　　　　8. $y = 2 + \log_3 x$
  9. $y = \log_3 (x + 2)$　　10. $y = 2 \log_3 x$　　　　11. $y = \log_3 x^2$
 12. $y = \frac{1}{2} \log_3 x$　　　　13 $y = \log_3 \sqrt{x}$
 14. Refer to Exercises 6–13 to answer the following questions.
     (a) Which of the graphs are identical?
     (b) Which of the graphs have the same x-intercept?
     (c) For what set of values of x is each equation defined?

 15. (a) Graph $y = \log_2 (-x)$.
     (b) For what set of values of x is $\log_2 (-x)$ defined?

---

 16. Graph $y = \log_3 (-x)$ and $y = -\log_3 x$ on the same set of axes.
 17. For what set of values of x is $\log_2 (x + 1)$ defined? Graph the equation
     $y = \log_2 (x + 1)$. Compare the graph with that of $y = \log_2 x$.
 18. (a) Sketch the graph of the equation $y = \log_5 1/x$.
     (b) Graph the equation $y = -\log_5 x$.

Preparation for Section 7–4

  1. What is the exponential equation equivalent to $\log_b x = r$?
  2. What is the exponential equation equivalent to $\log_b y = s$?
  3. Simplify $b^r \cdot b^s$.
  4. Try to combine your results in the three preceding exercises to write an
     equation relating $\log_b xy$ to $\log_b x$ and $\log_b y$.

7-4 THE LAWS OF LOGARITHMS

The laws of exponents, which we verified first for use with positive integers and later for use with rational numbers, will now be assumed to be valid for real numbers. Since $\log_b x = y$ if, and only if, $x = b^y$, we might expect that the laws of exponents could be translated into the language of logarithms. This is the case, as we shall show below. In our development, the base b is always assumed to be a real number greater than 1.

According to the first law of exponents, the equation

$$b^{r+s} = b^r \cdot b^s$$

is true for every pair r, s of real numbers. Let us try to convert this equation into one relating logarithms by letting

$$z = b^{r+s}, \quad x = b^r, \quad y = b^s.$$

By the first law of exponents, $z = xy$. Each of the above equations can be translated into the language of logarithms, yielding the three equivalent equations

$$r + s = \log_b z, \quad r = \log_b x, \quad s = \log_b y.$$

Since $r + s$ is the sum of r and s, it follows that

$$\log_b z = \log_b x + \log_b y.$$

If we recall that $z = xy$, then we have proved the following law.

FIRST LAW OF LOGARITHMS

$$\log_b xy = \log_b x + \log_b y \qquad (LL\text{-}1)$$

This equation is true for every pair x, y of positive real numbers. The first law of logarithms can be stated in words in the following way.

The logarithm of the product of two positive numbers is the sum of the logarithms of the two numbers.

If we start with the second law of exponents and reason as we did above, then we can derive the following law.

SECOND LAW OF LOGARITHMS

$$log_b \frac{x}{y} = log_b x - log_b y \qquad (LL\text{-}2)$$

This equation is also true for every pair x, y of positive real numbers. The second law of logarithms can be stated in words in the following way.

> *The logarithm of the quotient of two positive numbers is the logarithm of the dividend minus the logarithm of the divisor.*

According to the third law of exponents, the equation

$$b^{ar} = (b^a)^r$$

is true for every pair a, r of real numbers. To convert this equation to one relating logarithms, let

$$y = b^{ar} \quad \text{and} \quad x = b^a.$$

By the third law of exponents, $y = x^r$. The two equations above are equivalent to the two logarithmic equations

$$ar = log_b y, \quad a = log_b x.$$

Since ar equals r times a, we have

$$log_b y = r \cdot log_b x.$$

Replacing y by x^r, we obtain the following law.

THIRD LAW OF LOGARITHMS

$$log_b x^r = r \cdot log_b x \qquad (LL\text{-}3)$$

This equation is true for every real number r and every positive real number x. The third law of logarithms can be stated in words in the following way.

> *The logarithm of the rth power of a positive number is r times the logarithm of the number.*

Problem 1. Find each of the following.

(a) $\log_2 16\sqrt{8}$ (b) $\log_3 \dfrac{\sqrt[4]{27}}{9}$

Solution.

(a)

$$
\begin{aligned}
\log_2 16\sqrt{8} &= \log_2 16 + \log_2 \sqrt{8} && \text{(LL-1)}\\
&= \log_2 16 + \log_2 8^{\frac{1}{2}}\\
&= \log_2 16 + \tfrac{1}{2}\log_2 8 && \text{(LL-3)}\\
&= \log_2 2^4 + \tfrac{1}{2}\log_2 2^3\\
&= 4 + (\tfrac{1}{2}\cdot 3), \quad \text{or } \tfrac{11}{2}
\end{aligned}
$$

In other words, $\log_2 16\sqrt{8} = \tfrac{11}{2}$.

(b)

$$
\begin{aligned}
\log_3 \frac{\sqrt[4]{27}}{9} &= \log_3 \sqrt[4]{27} - \log_3 9 && \text{(LL-2)}\\
&= \log_3 27^{\frac{1}{4}} - \log_3 9\\
&= \tfrac{1}{4}\log_3 27 - \log_3 9 && \text{(LL-3)}\\
&= \tfrac{1}{4}\log_3 3^3 - \log_3 3^2\\
&= (\tfrac{1}{4}\cdot 3) - 2, \quad \text{or } -\tfrac{5}{4}
\end{aligned}
$$

In other words,

$$
\log_3 \frac{\sqrt[4]{27}}{9} = -\frac{5}{4}.
$$

Problem 2. Express the following number as the logarithm of a single number.

$$
3\log_5 4 - 2\log_5 6 + \tfrac{3}{2}\log_5 18
$$

Solution. We proceed as follows:

$$
\begin{aligned}
3\log_5 4 &- 2\log_5 6 + \tfrac{3}{2}\log_5 18\\
&= \log_5 4^3 - \log_5 6^2 + \log_5 18^{\frac{3}{2}} && \text{(LL-3)}\\
&= \log_5 64 - \log_5 36 + \log_5 (\sqrt{18})^3\\
&= \log_5 \tfrac{64}{36} + \log_5 (3\sqrt{2})^3 && \text{(LL-2)}\\
&= \log_5 \tfrac{16}{9} + \log_5 54\sqrt{2}\\
&= \log_5 (\tfrac{16}{9}\cdot 54\sqrt{2}) && \text{(LL-1)}\\
&= \log_5 (96\sqrt{2}).
\end{aligned}
$$

Problem 3. Solve the equation $\log_4 3 + \log_4 (x + 2) = 2$.

Solution. Using the first law of logarithms, we have

$$\log_4 3 + \log_4 (x + 2) = \log_4 3(x + 2).$$

Hence, the given equation is equivalent to the equation

$$\log_4 3(x + 2) = 2.$$

This logarithmic equation is equivalent to the exponential equation

$$3(x + 2) = 4^2.$$

Hence,

$$3x + 6 = 16 \quad \text{and} \quad x = \tfrac{10}{3}.$$

Exercises

Find the value of each of the following by using the laws of logarithms.

1. (a) $\log_2 \sqrt[3]{32}$ (b) $\log_3 \left(\dfrac{\sqrt[5]{9}}{3} \right)$

2. (a) $\log_5 \left(\dfrac{\sqrt[3]{25}}{\sqrt{5}} \right)$ (b) $\log_{10} (10 \sqrt[3]{100})$

3. (a) $\log_5 (25 \cdot 125)$ (b) $\log_6 \sqrt{216}$

4. (a) $\log_3 \sqrt[4]{9^5}$ (b) $\log_7 (49 \div 7^5)$

5. (a) $\log_3 81\sqrt{27}$ (b) $\log_2 \dfrac{\sqrt[4]{8}}{4}$

Express each of the following numbers as the logarithm of a single number.

6. (a) $\log_5 6 - \log_5 2$ (b) $\log_5 80 + \log_5 \tfrac{1}{4}$

7. (a) $4 \log_3 10 - 2 \log_3 5$ (b) $5 \log_7 9 - 4 \log_7 15 + \tfrac{3}{2} \log_7 12$

If $\log_{10} 2 = p$ and $\log_{10} 3 = q$, find an expression in terms of p and q for each logarithm in Exercises 8–13.

8. $\log_{10} 4$ **9.** $\log_{10} \left(\tfrac{2}{3}\right)$

10. $\log_{10} \sqrt{2}$ **11.** $\log_{10} .5$

12. $\log_{10} 30$ **13.** $\log_{10} \tfrac{1}{3}$

If $\log_{10} 5 = r$ and $\log_{10} 7 = s$, find an expression for each of the following in terms of r and s.

14. $\log_{10} 35$ **15.** $\log_{10} \tfrac{7}{5}$

16. $\log_{10} 49$ **17.** $\log_{10} \tfrac{343}{25}$

18. $\log_{10} \left(\sqrt{7} \cdot \sqrt[3]{5} \right)$

19. $\log_{10} \frac{7}{10} \cdot \log_{10} 125$

20. $\log_{10} 50 - \log_{10} 700$

21. $\log_{10} \sqrt{\frac{7}{5}}$

Solve each of the following equations.

22. $\log_4 72 - \log_4 9 = N$

23. $\log_5 6 = \log_5 x - \log_5 7$

24. $\log_7 98 + \log_7 3.5 = N$

25. $\log_3 63 - \log_3 7x = \log_3 2$

26. $\log_8 \sqrt{.125} = x$

27. $\log_5 4 + \log_5 (2x - 3) = 20$

28. Prove the second law of logarithms, (LL-2).

In Exercises 29–31, use the laws of logarithms to prove that each of the equations is true.

29. $\log_b 16 - \log_b 8 + \log_b 5 = \log_b 10$

30. $2 \log_x a - 2 \log_x b + 3 \log_x \sqrt{b} - \frac{1}{3} \log_x a = \frac{1}{6} \log_x \frac{a^{10}}{b^3}$

31. $\log_3 \frac{x^2 3^x}{3^{x^2}} = x - x^2 + 2 \log_3 x$

32. Solve the following equation for x.

$$\log_2 2 + \log_2 (x + 2) - \log_2 (3x - 5) = 3$$

33. Prove that

$$\log_{10} \frac{3x - \sqrt{9x^2 - 1}}{3x + \sqrt{9x^2 - 1}} = 2 \log_{10} (3x - \sqrt{9x^2 - 1}).$$

34. Solve each of the following equations.

(a) $y = 2 \log_2 8$

(b) $y = 3 \log_3 81$

(c) $y = 10 \log_2 4$

(d) $-y = b \log_b b^5$

Review for Sections 7–1 through 7–4

Write the logarithmic equation that corresponds to each of the following exponential equations.

1. $4^3 = 64$

2. $9^0 = 1$

3. $8^{\frac{2}{3}} = 4$

4. $49^{\frac{3}{2}} = 343$

5. $10^{-x} = y$

6. $a^{-\frac{3}{2}} = c$

Write the exponential equation that corresponds to each of the following logarithmic equations.

7. $\log_6 6 = 1$

8. $\log_3 243 = 5$

9. $\log_4 \frac{1}{2} = -\frac{1}{2}$

10. $\log_5 \frac{1}{25} = -2$

11. $\log_8 y = 2x$

12. $\log_7 3y = x$

Solve each of the following equations for x.

13. $\log_3 27 = x$ **14.** $\log_4 64 = x$

15. $\log_{16} x = \frac{1}{2}$ **16.** $\log_{25} x = \frac{3}{2}$

17. $\log_x \frac{1}{49} = -2$ **18.** $\log_x \frac{1}{81} = -4$

Graph each of the following and name the x-intercept.

19. $y = \log_5 x$ **20.** $y = \log_5 (x + 1)$

21. $y = \frac{1}{2} \log_5 x$ **22.** $y = 2 \log_5 x$

Solve each of the following equations.

23. $y = \frac{1}{2} \log_3 81$ **24.** $y = -\frac{1}{2} \log_2 \frac{1}{64}$

25. $y = \log_2 2\sqrt{2}$ **26.** $y = \log_3 9\sqrt{27}$

Answers to Review for Sections 7–1 through 7–4

1. $\log_4 64 = 3$ **2.** $\log_9 1 = 0$

3. $\log_8 4 = \frac{2}{3}$ **4.** $\log_{49} 343 = \frac{3}{2}$

5. $\log_{10} y = -x$ **6.** $\log_a c = -\frac{3}{2}$

7. $6^1 = 6$ **8.** $3^5 = 243$

9. $4^{-\frac{1}{2}} = \frac{1}{2}$ **10.** $5^{-2} = \frac{1}{25}$

11. $8^{2x} = y$ **12.** $7^x = 3y$

13. $x = 3$ **14.** $x = 3$

15. $x = 4$ **16.** $x = 125$

17. $x = 7$ **18.** $x = 3$

19.

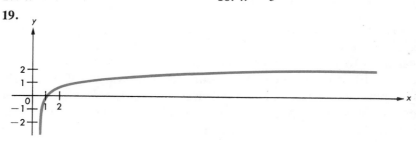

20.

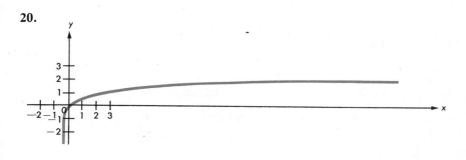

21.

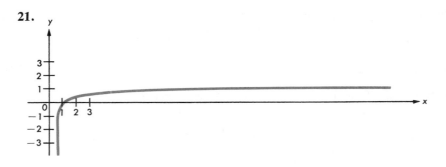

22.

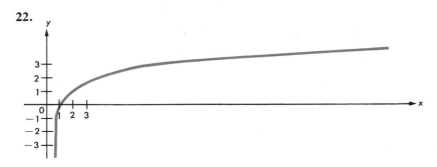

23. $y = 2$ **24.** $y = 3$

25. $y = \frac{3}{2}$ **26.** $y = \frac{7}{2}$

7–5   COMMON LOGARITHMS

There are two bases for logarithms that are extensively used today. One is the base e ($e \doteq 2.71828$) widely used in higher mathematics. Logarithms to the base e are called *natural logarithms.* The other is the base 10, chosen because of our decimal system of notation. Logarithms to the base 10 are called *common logarithms.* We shall discuss only common logarithms in this section. Whenever we write $\log N$ without indicating the base, it is always understood that the base is 10; that is,

$$\log N \quad \text{means} \quad \log_{10} N.$$

By the very definition of logarithms,

$$\log 10^n = n$$

for every real number n. Thus, for example,

$$\log .01 = -2 \quad \text{because} \quad .01 = 10^{-2},$$
$$\log .1 = -1 \quad \text{because} \quad .1 = 10^{-1},$$

$$\log\ \ 1 = 0 \quad \text{because} \quad 1 = 10^0,$$
$$\log\ 10 = 1 \quad \text{because} \quad 10 = 10^1,$$
$$\log 100 = 2 \quad \text{because} \quad 100 = 10^2,$$

and so on.

We do not know, offhand, the logarithm of any positive rational number other than an integral power of 10. For example, we do not know what $\log 7$ is. Since 7 is between 1 and 10, and since $\log 1 = 0$ and $\log 10 = 1$, we have by the third property in Section 7–3 that $\log 7$ is between 0 and 1:

$$0 < \log 7 < 1.$$

Actually, it is shown in more advanced mathematics that $\log 7$ is an irrational number, so that it cannot possibly be represented as a quotient of two integers. However, as is the case with any irrational number, we can *approximate* $\log 7$ by a rational number. It can be shown that

$$\log 7 \doteq .8451$$

to four-decimal-place accuracy.

If we know a four-decimal-place approximation of $\log 7$, we can easily find four-decimal-place approximations of $\log 70$, $\log 700$, $\log .7$, and so on. Thus, since $70 = 10 \times 7$,

$$\begin{aligned}
\log 70 &= \log (10 \times 7) \\
&= \log 10 + \log 7 \\
&= 1 + \log 7 \\
&= 1 + .8451 \\
&\doteq 1.8451.
\end{aligned}$$

Similarly,

$$\begin{aligned}
\log 700 &= \log (100 \times 7) \\
&= \log 100 + \log 7 \\
&= 2 + \log 7 \\
&\doteq 2 + .8451 \\
&\doteq 2.8451.
\end{aligned}$$

Also,

$$\begin{aligned}
\log .7 &= \log (7 \div 10) \\
&= \log 7 - \log 10 \\
&\doteq .8451 - 1 \\
&\doteq -.1549.
\end{aligned}$$

Furthermore, we can approximate $\log 49$, since $49 = 7^2$, and

$$
\begin{aligned}
\log 49 &= \log 7^2 \\
&= 2 \log 7 \\
&\doteq 2 \times .8451 \\
&\doteq 1.6902.
\end{aligned}
$$

In computing with logarithms, it is usually helpful to think of each positive real number as a number expressed in *scientific notation.* The positive number N is represented in scientific notation if it is expressed as the product of a number between 1 and 10 and an integral power of 10, that is, if

$$N = B \times 10^k, \quad \text{where } 1 \leq B < 10 \text{ and } k \text{ is an integer.}$$

For example, each of the following positive numbers is expressed in scientific notation.

Number	Scientific notation
123	1.23×10^2
.0123	1.23×10^{-2}
98,752	9.8752×10^4
.1961	1.961×10^{-1}
1,000,000	1×10^6

If the positive integer N is expressed in scientific notation,

$$N = B \times 10^k, \quad \text{where } 1 \leq B < 10 \text{ and } k \text{ is an integer,}$$

then

$$
\begin{aligned}
\log N &= \log (B \times 10^k) \\
&= \log B + \log 10^k.
\end{aligned}
\qquad \text{(LL-1)}
$$

Since $\log 10^k = k$, we have

$$\log N = \log B + k.$$

Note that

$$0 \leq \log B < 1 \quad \text{since} \quad 1 \leq B < 10.$$

Thus, $\log N$ is expressed as a sum of an integer and a nonnegative real number less than 1. Clearly,

$$k \leq \log N < k + 1$$

so that k is the *greatest integer* contained in log N and log B is the *fractional part* of log N. The nonnegative number log B is often called the *mantissa* of log N and the integer k the *characteristic* of log N.

To summarize, if we express N in scientific notation,

$$N = B \times 10^k, \quad \text{where } 1 \leq B < 10, \ k \text{ an integer,}$$

then

$$\log N = \underbrace{k}_{\text{characteristic}} + \underbrace{\log B,}_{\text{mantissa}} \quad 0 \leq \log B < 1.$$

with *greatest integer* over k and *fractional part* over log B.

The Table of Common Logarithms in the Appendix lists four-decimal-place approximations of the mantissas of the common logarithms of all integers from 100 to 999. The characteristic of log N if $100 \leq N < 1000$ is 2, since $10^2 \leq N < 10^3$ means that

$$2 \leq \log N < 3.$$

A portion of this table is reproduced below.

N	0	1	2	3	4	5	6	7	8	9
38	.5798	.5809	.5821	.5832	.5843	.5855	.5866	.5877	.5888	.5899
39	.5911	.5922	.5933	.5944	.5955	.5966	.5977	.5988	.5999	.6010

This part of the table lists the mantissa of the logarithm of each integer from 380 through 399. The characteristic of the logarithm of each of these integers is obviously 2. Thus, from the table,

$\log 380 \doteq 2 + .5798, \quad \log 381 \doteq 2 + .5809, \quad \log 387 \doteq 2 + .5877,$
$\log 390 \doteq 2 + .5911, \quad \log 394 \doteq 2 + .5955, \quad \log 399 \doteq 2 + .6010.$

We should keep in mind the definition of the logarithm. Thus, since

$$\log 381 \doteq 2.5809,$$

we have

$$10^{2.5809} \doteq 381,$$

and so on.

In using this table, we can think of it as a table of logarithms of numbers from 1.00 to 9.99. Hence, if we express a given number in scientific notation, the mantissa of the logarithm of the number may be read directly from the table. For example, $39,600 = 3.96 \times 10^4$ in scientific notation. Hence,

$$\log 39,600 = \log 3.96 + \log 10^4,$$
$$\doteq .5977 + 4, \quad \text{or} \quad 4.5977.$$

Also,

$$.0388 = 3.88 \times 10^{-2},$$
$$\log .0388 = \log 3.88 + \log 10^{-2}$$
$$\doteq .5888 - 2.$$

We could express the final answer in the form -1.4112, but to simplify the work of some operations with logarithms we usually want it in the first form, $.5888 - 2$.

Exercises

Express the numbers in each of the following statements in scientific notation.

1. (a) The distance that light travels in one year is called a *light-year*, which is approximately 5,870,000,000,000 miles.
   (b) The diameter of the Einstein universe, according to the theory of relativity, is 2,000,000,000 light-years, or

   11,740,000,000,000,000,000,000 miles.

2. (a) The thickness of an oil film is about .0000005 centimeters.
   (b) The diameter of the orbit of an electron of a hydrogen atom is about .000 000 000 53 millimeters.

If $\log 5 \doteq .6990$, find each of the following logarithms.

3. (a) $\log 500$ (b) $\log .005$
4. (a) $\log 25$ (b) $\log 125$
5. Complete each of the following statements.
   (a) $10^2 < 123 < $ __?__;   __?__ $< \log 123 < 3$
   (b) __?__ $< 1230 < 10^4$; $3 < \log 1230 < $ __?__

For each number given, first find the successive integral powers of 10 between which the number lies. Then find the successive integers between which the logarithm of the number lies.

6. (a) 15.6   (b) 15,600
7. (a) 1.56   (b) .156

Give the integral part, or characteristic, of the common logarithm of each of the following numbers.

8. (a) 1.23×10^2 (b) 1.23×10^{-1}
9. (a) 1.23×10^{-2} (b) 1.23×10^4

Write each number in scientific notation and give the integral part, or characteristic, of its logarithm to the base 10.

10. (a) 342.1   (b) .4762

11. (a) 20.51   (b) .003021

12. (a) 56,500   (b) .00006789

Use the Table of Common Logarithms to find the common logarithm of each of the following numbers. Then express each number as a power of 10.

13. (a) 1540   (b) .0764

14. (a) 7.08   (b) 650,000

15. (a) .000403   (b) .000008

16. (a) 923   (b) 32,500

Given that N equals each of the numbers in Exercises 17–31, find log N.

17. .256   **18.** 256

19. .0256   **20.** 2560

21. .000256   **22.** 256,000

23. 32.4   **24.** 32,400

25. 3,240,000   **26.** .00852

27. 8.52   **28.** .0000852

29. 2060   **30.** .0206

31. 20,600

32. (a) Consider the set of all numbers with a single digit to the left of the decimal, such as 1, 2.435, and 9.7468. Between which consecutive integral powers of 10 does N lie if $1 \leq N < 10$? What is the characteristic, or integral part, of log N?

    (b) Consider the set of all numbers with two digits to the left of the decimal, such as 10, 21.5, and 99.06. If $10 \leq N < 100$, between which consecutive integral powers of 10 does N lie? What is the characteristic of log N?

    (c) If $100 \leq N < 1000$, what is the integral part of log N?

    (d) If N is a positive number with k digits to the left of the decimal, between which consecutive integral powers of 10 does N lie? What is the characteristic of log N?

    (e) State a rule for finding the characteristic of log N when N is any positive number greater than or equal to 1.

33. (a) Consider the set of all numbers less than 1, but not less than .1, such as .1, .1012, .234, and .9999. If $.1 \leq N < 1$, between which consecutive integral powers of 10 does N lie? What is the characteristic of log N?

(b) If $.01 \leqq N < .1$, between which consecutive integral powers of 10 does N lie? What is the characteristic of log N?

(c) List six members of the set

$$\{N \mid .001 \leqq N < .01\}.$$

For each such N, what is the greatest integer contained in log N?

(d) If N is a positive number less than 1, having its first nonzero digit in the kth place to the right of the decimal, what is the characteristic of log N?

Preparation for Section 7–6

Express the following as sums and differences of logarithms.

1. $\log ab$ **2.** $\log \dfrac{a}{b}$ **3.** $\log \dfrac{ab}{cd}$

Express the following as fractions of sums and differences of logarithms.

4. $\log \sqrt{a}$ **5.** $\log \sqrt[3]{ab}$ **6.** $\log \sqrt[5]{\dfrac{a}{b}}$

7–6 LOGARITHMS OF PRODUCTS, QUOTIENTS, AND POWERS

With the aid of the Table of Common Logarithms in the Appendix and the laws of logarithms, we can find logarithms of products, quotients, and powers of numbers. The following problems illustrate how we might do this.

Problem 1. Find log $(56.4 \times .0709)$.

Solution. We approximate this logarithm as follows:
$$\log (56.4 \times .0709) = \log 56.4 + \log .0709. \qquad \text{(LL-1)}$$

Now

$$
\begin{aligned}
\quad \log 56.4 &= \log (5.64 \times 10^1) &\doteq& \quad .7513 + 1 \\
+ \quad \log .0709 &= \log (7.09 \times 10^{-2}) &\doteq& \quad \underline{.8506 - 2} \\
& & & \quad 1.6019 - 1
\end{aligned}
$$

Hence,
$$\log (56.4 \times .0709) \doteq .6019.$$

Our final answer is reasonable, since $56.4 \times .0709 \doteq 60 \times .07$, or 4.2, and log 4.2 is between 0 and 1.

Problem 2. Find log (56.4 ÷ .0709).

Solution. We use logarithms from Problem 1 in our work below.

$$\log (56.4 \div .0709) = \log 56.4 - \log .0709 \qquad \text{(LL-2)}$$

Now

$$\begin{array}{rl}
\log 56.4 &\doteq .7513 + 1 = 1.7513 \\
- \quad \log .0709 &\doteq .8506 - 2 = \underline{.8506 - 2} \\
& \qquad\qquad\qquad .9007 + 2
\end{array}$$

We rewrote .7513 + 1 in the form 1.7513 in order to keep the decimal part of the difference of the two logarithms positive. Thus,

$$\log (56.4 \div .0709) = 2.9007.$$

Our final answer is reasonable, since 56.4 ÷ .0709 $\doteq$ 56 ÷ .07, or 800, and log 800 is less than, but close to, 3.

Problem 3. Find log $\sqrt[3]{942}$.

Solution. We proceed as follows:

$$\begin{aligned}
\log \sqrt[3]{942} &= \log 942^{\frac{1}{3}} \\
&= \tfrac{1}{3} \log 942 \\
&= \tfrac{1}{3}(\log 9.42 \times 10^2) \\
&\doteq \tfrac{1}{3}(.9741 + 2), \\
&\doteq \tfrac{1}{3}(2.9741), \quad \text{or } .9914.
\end{aligned}$$

Our answer is reasonable, since $\sqrt[3]{942} < \sqrt[3]{1000}$, or 10, and, therefore, log $\sqrt[3]{942} < 1$.

Problem 4. Find log $\sqrt[3]{.942}$.

Solution. Since .942 = 9.42 × 10^{-1}, we have, as in Problem 3,

$$\log \sqrt[3]{.942} \doteq \tfrac{1}{3}(.9741 - 1).$$

Before dividing by 3, we change the form of .9741 − 1 so that the negative part of log .942 is exactly divisible by 3. Thus, we express

$$.9741 - 1 \quad \text{in the form} \quad 2.9741 - 3.$$

Then

$$\tfrac{1}{3}(2.9741 - 3) = .9914 - 1.$$

Hence,

$$\log \sqrt[3]{.942} \doteq .9914 - 1.$$

Problem 5. Find $\log \dfrac{3}{\sqrt[5]{.008}}$.

Solution. We proceed as follows:

$$\log \frac{3}{\sqrt[5]{.008}} = \log 3 - \log \sqrt[5]{.008} \qquad\qquad \text{(LL-2)}$$

$$= \log 3 - \tfrac{1}{5} \log .008. \qquad\qquad \text{(LL-3)}$$

Since $\log .008 = \log (8 \times 10^{-3}) \doteq .9031 - 3$, then

$$\begin{aligned} \tfrac{1}{5} \log .008 &\doteq \tfrac{1}{5}(.9031 - 3) \\ &\doteq \tfrac{1}{5}(2.9031 - 5) \\ &\doteq .5806 - 1. \end{aligned}$$

The $\log 3 \doteq .4771$, but before subtracting, we change the form of $\log 3$ and proceed as below.

$$\begin{array}{r l} \log 3 & \doteq 1.4771 - 1 \\ -\quad \log \sqrt[5]{.008} & \doteq \underline{\;\;.5806 - 1} \\ & \quad\;\; .8965 \end{array}$$

Thus,

$$\log \frac{3}{\sqrt[5]{.008}} \doteq .8965.$$

Exercises

1. (a) Find $\log (863 \times .145 \times 20.7)$ by completing the solution.

  Partial solution.

$$\log (863 \times .145 \times 20.7) = \log 863 + \log .145 + \log 20.7$$

$$\begin{aligned} \log 863 &= \log (8.63 \times 10^2) &\doteq \underline{\;\;?\;\;} + 2 \\ \log .145 &= \log (1.45 \times 10^{-1}) &\doteq \underline{\;\;?\;\;} - 1 \\ +\quad \log 20.7 &= \log (2.07 \times 10) &\doteq \underline{\;\;?\;\;} + 1 \\ & & \underline{\;\;?\;\;} \end{aligned}$$

(b) Find log (79,200 ÷ 345) by completing the solution.

Partial solution.

$$\log (79{,}200 \div 345) = \log 79{,}200 - \log 345$$

$$\log (7.92 \times 10^4) \doteq \underline{\quad ? \quad}$$
$$- \quad \log (3.45 \times 10^2) \doteq \underline{\quad ? \quad}$$
$$\overline{}$$
$$\underline{\quad ? \quad}$$

2. (a) Find log $\sqrt[4]{.163}$ by completing the solution.

Partial solution.

$$\log .163 = \log (1.63 \times 10^{-1}) \doteq .2122 - 1$$
$$\log \sqrt[4]{.163} \doteq \tfrac{1}{4}(.2122 - 1) = \tfrac{1}{4}(3.2122 - 4) = \underline{\quad ? \quad}$$

(b) Find log (3.16 ÷ 405) by completing the solution.

Partial solution.

$$\log 3.16 \doteq .4997 = \underline{\quad ? \quad}$$
$$\log (4.05 \times 10^2) \doteq .6075 + 2 = \underline{\quad ? \quad}$$

Given that x equals each of the following numbers, find log x.

3. 4.96 × .0175

4. 49.6 ÷ .175

5. $\sqrt{\dfrac{13.5}{.0472}}$

6. $\sqrt[4]{496}$

7. $(.00504)^3$

8. $\tfrac{563}{392}$

9. $\sqrt{.824}$

10. $\sqrt[3]{.0875}$

11. $\dfrac{1}{\sqrt[5]{.002}}$

12. $\dfrac{30.4}{726}$

13. 36.5 × 89,700 × .475

14. $\dfrac{89{,}700}{36.5 \times .475}$

15. $(37.8)^{\frac{3}{2}}$

*7-7 COMPUTING WITH LOGARITHMS

Before computing with logarithms, we must learn how to approximate
N if we know $\log N$. In the first place, if

$$0 \leq \log N < 1,$$

we can approximate N by looking in the body of the Table of Common
Logarithms for the closest entry to $\log N$. Then N is approximately
the number whose logarithm is this entry.

For example, given that

$$\log N = .8785,$$

we note that .8785 appears in the body of the table in the row marked
75 and in the column marked 6. Hence,

$$\log 7.56 \doteq .8785 \quad \text{and} \quad N \doteq 7.56.$$

If $\log N$ is not between 0 and 1, then we express $\log N$ as the sum
of its fractional part and the greatest integer contained in it, that is,

$$\log N = A + k, \quad \text{where } 0 \leq A < 1 \text{ and } k \text{ is an integer.}$$

Since A is between 0 and 1, we can find a positive number B whose
logarithm is A from the table. Thus, $\log N = \log B + \log 10^k$ and

$$N = B \times 10^k, \quad \text{where } 1 \leq B < 10 \text{ and } \log B = A.$$

For example, suppose that we are given

$$\log N = 1.8785.$$

Then the fractional part of $\log N$ is .8785, and the greatest integer
contained in $\log N$ is 1. We may write

$$\log N = .8785 + 1.$$

From the preceding example, $\log 7.56 \doteq .8785$. Hence,

$$N \doteq 7.56 \times 10^1, \quad \text{or } 75.6.$$

Let us consider a second example. If

$$\log N = -2.4522,$$

then

$$-3 < \log N < -2.$$

Hence, -3 is the greatest integer contained in log N, and

$$-2.4522 - (-3), \quad \text{or } .5478,$$

is the fractional part of log N. Thus,

$$\log N = .5478 - 3.$$

By the Table of Common Logarithms,

$$\log 3.53 \doteq .5478.$$

Therefore,

$$N \doteq 3.53 \times 10^{-3}, \quad \text{or } .00353.$$

When we represent log N in the form $A + k$, where $0 \leqq A < 1$ and k is an integer, we are expressing log N as the sum of its *mantissa A* and its *characteristic k*. The mantissa determines the digits in N, and the characteristic determines the placement of the decimal point.

If M and N are numbers such that $M = \log N$, then N is often called the *antilogarithm* of M, and we write

$$N = \text{antilog } M.$$

Thus, in the example above, $.00353 \doteq$ antilog (-2.4522). Of course, if $M = \log N$, then $N = 10^M$ according to the definition of logarithms. Hence, antilog M is just 10^M.

Problem 1. Compute each of the following.
(a) $87,500 \times 314$ (b) $.0147 \div .397$

Solution.
(a) If we let N designate the desired product, then

$$\log N = \log (87,500 \times 314)$$
$$= \log 87,500 + \log 314.$$

Thus,

$$\log 87,500 = \log (8.75 \times 10^4) \doteq .9420 + 4$$
$$\underline{+ \quad \log 314 \quad = \log (3.14 \times 10^2) \doteq .4969 + 2}$$
$$\log N \doteq 1.4389 + 6 = .4389 + 7.$$

Since log N has characteristic 7 and mantissa .4389,

$$N = B \times 10^7, \quad \text{where } \log B = .4389.$$

The mantissa .4389 is not in the body of the Table of Common Logarithms. The closest entry is .4393 $\doteq$ log 2.75. Using this value we have log $B \doteq$ log 2.75 and $B \doteq$ 2.75. Thus,

$$N \doteq 2.75 \times 10^7, \quad \text{or} \quad 27{,}500{,}000.$$

(b) If N designates the desired quotient, then

$$\log N = \log (.0147 \div .397)$$
$$= \log .0147 - \log .397.$$

Thus,

$$\log .0147 = \log (1.47 \times 10^{-2}) \doteq .1673 - 2$$
$$- \quad \log .397 \;= \log (3.97 \times 10^{-1}) \doteq .5988 - 1$$

In order to keep a positive mantissa when we subtract, we change .1673 $-$ 2 to 1.1673 $-$ 3, as shown below.

$$\log .0147 \doteq 1.1673 - 3$$
$$- \quad \log .397 \;\doteq \quad .5988 - 1$$
$$\overline{ .5685 - 2}$$

Hence,

$$\log N = .5685 - 2$$

and

$$N \doteq B \times 10^{-2}, \quad \text{where} \quad \log B = .5685.$$

Again, the mantissa .5685 is not in the Table of Common Logarithms. The closest entry is .5682 $\doteq$ log 3.70. Thus, $B \doteq$ 3.70 and

$$N \doteq 3.70 \times 10^{-2}, \quad \text{or} \quad .0370.$$

If we multiply 87,500 $\times$ 314 in Problem 1(a) we get 27,475,000, which is not the answer that we obtained by using logarithms. However, the answer we obtained by using logarithms is correct to three *significant digits;* that is, if we round off the numeral above, keeping the first three digits (reading from left to right), then we get 27,500,000 as an approximation to three significant digits. We replaced the block of digits 475 by 500 since 475 is closer to 500 than to 400.

Similarly, the answer we obtained for Problem 1(b) is an approximation of the correct answer to three significant digits. If we divide .0147 by .397, we get .03702 . . . Note that the three significant digits in this case are 3, 7, and 0, in that order. We wrote the answer in the form

$$.0370 \quad \text{rather than} \quad .037$$

to indicate that the last 0 was a significant digit.

When a physicist declares that the speed of light is 186,000 miles per second, he does not mean to imply that all six digits of this number are necessarily significant. Rather, he probably means that this is the approximate speed of light, accurate to three significant digits. In the early years of this century, the American physicist Michelson determined the speed of light, accurate to six significant digits, to be 186,234 miles per second.

Problem 2. Approximate $\sqrt[3]{.301}$ to three significant digits.

Solution. If we let

$$N = \sqrt[3]{.301},$$

then

$$\log N = \log (.301)^{\frac{1}{3}}$$
$$= \tfrac{1}{3} \log .301. \qquad\qquad \text{(LL-3)}$$

Now

$$\tfrac{1}{3} \log .301 = \tfrac{1}{3} \log (3.01 \times 10^{-1})$$
$$\doteq \tfrac{1}{3}(.4786 - 1)$$
$$\doteq \tfrac{1}{3}(2.4786 - 3)$$
$$\doteq .8262 - 1.$$

Hence, $N \doteq B \times 10^{-1}$, where $\log B = .8262$.
By the Table of Common Logarithms, $B \doteq 6.70$. Hence,

$$N \doteq 6.70 \times 10^{-1}, \quad \text{or} \quad .670,$$

accurate to three significant digits.

Problem 3. Approximate $873 \div \sqrt[5]{.079}$ to three significant digits.

Solution. If

$$N = 873 \div \sqrt[5]{.079},$$

then

$$\log N = \log 873 - \log \sqrt[5]{.079}$$
$$= \log 873 - \tfrac{1}{5} \log .079.$$

First, we find

$$\tfrac{1}{5} \log .079 = \tfrac{1}{5} \log (7.9 \times 10^{-2})$$
$$\doteq \tfrac{1}{5}(.8976 - 2)$$
$$\doteq \tfrac{1}{5}(3.8976 - 5)$$
$$\doteq .7795 - 1$$

and

$$\log 873 \doteq 2.9410.$$

Continuing the solution of Problem 3, we see that

$$\log 873 \doteq 2.9410$$
$$- \quad \tfrac{1}{5} \log .079 \doteq \quad .7795 - 1$$
$$\overline{\qquad\qquad\qquad 2.1615 + 1}$$

and

$$\log N \doteq .1615 + 3.$$

Therefore,

$$N = B \times 10^3,$$

where

$$\log B \doteq .1615.$$

From the Table of Common Logarithms, $B \doteq 1.45$. Hence,

$$N = 1.45 \times 10^3, \quad \text{or } 1450,$$

accurate to three significant digits.

Problem 4. Compute $\sqrt[3]{-.136}$.

Solution. We first observe that

$$\sqrt[3]{-.136} = \sqrt[3]{(-1)^3(.136)}$$
$$= - \sqrt[3]{.136}.$$

Since

$$\log \sqrt[3]{.136} = \tfrac{1}{3} \log .136$$
$$\doteq \tfrac{1}{3}(2.1335 - 3)$$
$$\doteq .7112 - 1,$$

we have

$$\sqrt[3]{.136} \doteq .514.$$

Therefore,

$$\sqrt[3]{-.136} \doteq -.514.$$

Exercises

Find an approximate value of N in each of the following exercises.

1. (a) $\log N = 2.5105$ (b) $\log N = .6513 + 1$
2. (a) $\log N = .8149 - 1$ (b) $\log N = .3617 - 2$
3. (a) $\log N = 3.0334$ (b) $\log N = 7.9538 - 10$
4. (a) $\log N = 14.8082 - 10$ (b) $\log N = 0.7042$
5. (a) $\log N = 3.8482 - 4$ (b) $\log N = 18.5752 - 20$
6. (a) $\log N = -.3698$ (b) $\log N = -2.6819$

Use logarithms to approximate each of the following numbers to three significant digits.

7. (a) $(.317)(94.2)$ (b) $\sqrt[5]{1960}$
8. (a) $\dfrac{821}{37,500}$ (b) $\dfrac{2.050}{.00045}$
9. (a) $(.0126)(.115)$ (b) $\sqrt[9]{764}$

Use logarithms to approximate each of the following numbers to three significant digits.

10. $\dfrac{(245)(7.53)}{(6.14)^2}$ 11. $\dfrac{16.8}{(0.871)^{\frac{1}{2}}}$ 12. $\left[\dfrac{\sqrt{647}\,(.0013)}{181}\right]^{\frac{1}{2}}$

13. $\sqrt[3]{\dfrac{3}{4}\left(\dfrac{275}{3.14}\right)}$ 14. $(4.71)^{-\frac{2}{3}}$ 15. $\sqrt[4]{7810}$

16. $\sqrt{(.0417)(.123)}$ 17. $\dfrac{5750}{9.32}$ 18. $(.00752)^{-\frac{3}{5}}$

19. $(186,000)(.445)$ 20. $\sqrt{\dfrac{(6.15)(37.7)}{255}}$ 21. $\sqrt[8]{\dfrac{705}{5.14}}$

===

22. The formula for the volume V of a sphere with radius r units is $V = \frac{4}{3}\pi r^3$. Assuming the earth to be a perfect sphere with a radius of 3960 miles, determine the volume of the earth to three significant digits. (Use $\pi \doteq 3.14$.)

23. The number of seconds required for a complete swing of a pendulum is called the period of the pendulum. The period t (in seconds) of a pendulum L feet long is given by the formula

$$t = 2\pi\sqrt{\frac{L}{g}},$$

where $g \doteq 32.2$. Find, to three significant digits, the period of a pendulum 3 feet long.

24. The weight of a man d miles above the surface of the earth is given by the formula

$$W = \frac{W_0(4000)^2}{(4000 + d)^2},$$

where W_0 is the man's weight at the surface of the earth. Determine the approximate weight of a 160-pound man in a space capsule 500 miles above the earth. Find your own weight if you were in the capsule.

25. When a principal P is invested at an annual interest rate of r per cent compounded k times a year, a formula for the amount A at the end of n years is

$$A = P\left(1 + \frac{r}{k}\right)^{nk}.$$

If the sum of $1000 is invested at an annual rate of 4%, compute the amount A
(a) after 20 years if interest is compounded semiannually.
(b) after 20 years if interest is compounded quarterly.
(c) after 5 years in a bank which compounds interest daily.

26. Use the formula of the preceding exercise to find how many years it will take a sum of money invested at 4% compounded semiannually to double itself.

27. A certain radioactive substance decays according to the formula

$$A = A_0 \times 2^{-\frac{t}{1500}}.$$

If the initial quantity A_0 is 425 milligrams, how much of the substance remains after 50 years?

28. In 1950 the population of a certain town was 25,000. If the population growth is exponential, the population P after t years have elapsed is given by the formula

$$P = 25{,}000 \times \left(\tfrac{6}{5}\right)^{\frac{1}{10}t}.$$

(a) Find the population in 1955.
(b) How long will it take for the population to double?

29. Heron's formula for the area of a triangle in terms of its three sides a, b, c, and semiperimeter s is

$$A = \sqrt{s(s - a)(s - b)(s - c)}.$$

Find, to three significant digits, the area of a triangle having sides of length 57 inches, 62 inches, and 43 inches. (The semiperimeter is one-half the sum of the lengths of the three sides.)

*7–8 LINEAR INTERPOLATION

Using the Table of Common Logarithms, we can find logarithms of numbers having three significant digits. If we are willing to interpolate, this table can be used to find products, quotients, and powers of numbers with four significant digits. How this interpolation is done will be shown below.

If you examine this table carefully, you will note that the *difference between consecutive numbers* in the table stays about the same in any particular row. For example, in the row

N	0	1	2	3	4	5	6	7	8	9
38	.5798	.5809	.5821	.5832	.5843	.5855	.5866	.5877	.5888	.5899

the differences between consecutive entries are as follows:

.0011, .0012, .0011, .0011, .0012, .0011, .0011, .0011, .0011.

Hence, if we graph the equation

$$y = \log x$$

every hundredth of a unit between $x = 3.80$ and $x = 3.89$, the graph will be, in essence, a straight line with slope

$$\frac{.0011}{.01}, \quad \text{or } .11.$$

Since, in this interval, the graph is essentially a straight line, we should be able to compute quite accurately the logarithms of numbers *between* entries of the table. For example, we may compute new entries between 383 and 384 as shown below.

N	0	1	2	3	4	5	6	7	8	9
383	.5832	.5833	.5834	.5835	.5836	.5838	.5839	.5840	.5841	.5842

We must realize, however, that these entries may be wrong by one unit in the last digit.

The process of approximating new entries in a table is called *linear interpolation*. It is apparent that we do not have to make up a whole new row, as we did above, to find some particular logarithm. For example, we can find log 3.836 as follows:

$$\log 3.836 \doteq \log 3.83 + \tfrac{6}{10}(.0011)$$
$$\doteq .5832 + .0007, \quad \text{or } .5839.$$

Given a number between 0 and 1 that does not appear in the Table of Common Logarithms, we can use linear interpolation to find a number having that logarithm and four-digit accuracy. For example, the number .6861 is not listed in the Table. Let us find N such that

$$\log N = .6861.$$

From the Table,

$$\log 4.85 \doteq .6857,$$
$$\log 4.86 \doteq .6866.$$

Since .6861 is between these two consecutive entries, N is between 4.85 and 4.86. Is N equal to 4.851, or to 4.852, and so on? Since

$$.6866 - .6857 = .0009$$

and

$$.6861 - .6857 = .0004,$$

the fourth digit of N should be the closest tenth of

$$\frac{.0004}{.0009}, \quad \text{or } \frac{4}{9}.$$

The closest tenth is 4, and therefore,

$$N \doteq 4.854$$

to four significant digits.

Problem. Compute the following to four significant digits.

$$\frac{4.913 \times \sqrt{88.15}}{.0003021}$$

Solution. If we let

$$N = \frac{4.913 \times \sqrt{88.15}}{.0003021},$$

then

$$\log N = \log (4.913 \times \sqrt{88.15}) - \log .0003021$$
$$= \log 4.913 + \log \sqrt{88.15} - \log .0003021.$$

Using the Table of Common Logarithms, we interpolate for each logarithm separately.

1. $\log 4.913 \doteq .6911 + \frac{3}{10}(.0009) \doteq .6911 + .0003 \doteq .6914$

2. $\log \sqrt{88.15} = \frac{1}{2}[(\log 8.815) + 1]$
   $\doteq \frac{1}{2}[.9450 + \frac{5}{10}(.0005) + 1]$
   $\doteq \frac{1}{2}[.9450 + .0002 + 1]$
   $\doteq \frac{1}{2}[1.9452] \doteq .9726$

3. $\log .0003021 = (\log 3.021) - 4$
   $\doteq .4800 + \frac{1}{10}(.0014) - 4$
   $\doteq .4800 + .0001 - 4 \doteq .4801 - 4$

Hence, we have

$$\begin{array}{rcl} \log 4.913 & \doteq & .6914 \\ + \quad \log \sqrt{88.15} & \doteq & .9726 \\ \hline & & 1.6640 \end{array}$$

Therefore,

$$\begin{array}{rcl} \log (4.913 \times \sqrt{88.15}) & \doteq & 1.6640 \\ - \quad \log .0003021 & \doteq & .4801 - 4 \\ \hline \log N & \doteq & 1.1839 + 4 \\ & \doteq & 5.1839 \end{array}$$

Thus,

$$N = B \times 10^5 \quad \text{where} \quad \log B \doteq .1839.$$

Since

$$\begin{array}{l} \log 1.52 \doteq .1818 \\ \log B \quad \doteq .1839 \\ \log 1.53 \doteq .1847 \end{array} \Bigg] .0021 \Bigg] .0029 \quad \text{and} \quad \frac{21}{29} \doteq \frac{7}{10},$$

it follows that

$$B \doteq 1.527.$$

Finally,

$$N \doteq 1.527 \times 10^5.$$

We remind ourselves that the logarithms computed above enable us to write each number exponentially. Thus,

$$4.913 \doteq 10^{.6914}, \quad 88.15 \doteq 10^{1.9452}, \quad .0003021 \doteq 10^{.4801-4}.$$

Therefore,

$$N \doteq \frac{10^{.6914} \times (10^{1.9452})^{\frac{1}{2}}}{10^{.4801-4}}$$

$$\doteq \frac{10^{.6914} \times 10^{.9726}}{10^{.4801-4}}$$

$$\doteq 10^{.6914+.9726-(.4801-4)}$$

$$\doteq 10^{5.1839}$$

$$\doteq 10^{.1839} \times 10^5.$$

By looking under .1839 in the Table of Common Logarithms, we find that $10^{.1839} \doteq 1.527$. Hence,

$$N \doteq 1.527 \times 10^5.$$

Exercises

Use linear interpolation to find the logarithm of each of the following numbers to the nearest ten-thousandth.

1. (a) 65.42   (b) .3527
2. (a) 1.543   (b) .04895
3. (a) 120.4   (b) .005066
4. (a) $(18.78) \times (2.609)$ (b) $(.4308) \div (.02031)$
5. (a) $\sqrt{.5612}$ (b) $\sqrt[3]{.3012}$

Use linear interpolation to find N to four significant digits in each of the following equations.

6. (a) $\log N = .4719$ (b) $\log N = 1.5343$
7. (a) $\log N = .6097 - 1$ (b) $\log N = 2.6742$
8. (a) $\log N = .8529 - 2$ (b) $\log N = 3.9158$

Find x, given each of the following conditions.

9. $\log x = 1.5643$

10. $10^x = .001234$

11. $x = \log 81.53$

12. $\log x = -.7654$

13. $x = 10^{\log .06789}$

14. $x = \log \dfrac{1}{2.564}$

15. $x = 10^{3.0472}$

16. $x = (\tfrac{1}{10})^{2.4601}$

17. $\log x = \tfrac{1}{2} \log 576.0$

18. $x = 10^{-3.0012}$

19. $\log x = \log .1432 - \log .4296$

20. $\log x = \tfrac{1}{3} \log .08432$

Use the method of linear interpolation to find answers correct to four significant digits for the expressions in Exercises 21–39.

21. $5.712 \times .09232$

22. $-173.2 \div 7.32$

23. $\sqrt{1984}$

24. $(1.025)^{14}$

25. $\sqrt[5]{163.7}$

26. $\sqrt{2.503 \times 16.24}$

27. $(.3567 \times 4.108)^3$

28. $\sqrt{(28.06)^2 - (20.39)^2}$
(Hint: Factor first.)

29. $\dfrac{\sqrt{.5723}}{\sqrt[3]{-4.218}}$

30. $(132.3)^{1.7}$

31. $\sqrt{518.4 \times .3142}$

32. $\sqrt[5]{4816}$

33. $\sqrt{(-19.8)^2 + (23.4)^2}$

34. $\dfrac{57.91 \times 80.24}{6.307}$

35. $\sqrt[3]{\dfrac{72.24}{275.8}}$

36. $(423.1)^{-\frac{2}{7}}$

37. $\dfrac{(-82.25) \times 47.17}{15.19 \times 49.93}$

38. $23.7 \times \dfrac{302}{325} \times \dfrac{14.7}{12.2}$

39. Find each of the following numbers.
(a) $\log (\log 2)$
(b) $\log (\log 6)$
(c) $(\log 2)\ (\log 6)$
(d) $(\log 2) \div (\log 6)$
(e) $\log 2 + \log 6$
(f) $(\log 2)^2$

40. Using logarithms to approximate the squares of the legs and to compute the square root of their sum, find an approximation for the length of the hypotenuse of a right triangle if one leg is 235.1 inches long and the other is 15.24 inches long.

41. Use logarithms to find an approximation to four significant digits of the area of the triangle in Exercise 41.

42. Find the approximate radius of a sphere whose volume is 137.7 cubic feet. (Use $\pi \doteq 3.142$ and $V = \tfrac{4}{3}\pi r^3$.)

43. Find the approximate surface area $(A = 4\pi r^2)$ of a sphere with a radius of 17.34 inches.

44. Find the approximate length of an edge of a cube whose volume is twice as big as the volume of a cube whose edge is 3 feet long.

45. Find the approximate radius of a circle with an area of 15 square inches.

46. Use Heron's formula (Exercise 29, page 323) to find a four-digit approximation of the area of a triangle with sides of length 14.32 inches, 16.36 inches, and 15.71 inches.

47. Find the approximate length of the side of an equilateral triangle which has an area of 136 square feet.

*7–9   LOGARITHMS TO A BASE OTHER THAN 10

When we have a table of logarithms to the base 10, such as the Table of Common Logarithms, we can readily construct a table of logarithms to another base. For example, if we wish to approximate

$$\log_5 7,$$

we first observe that the two equations

$$N = \log_5 7 \quad \text{and} \quad 5^N = 7$$

are equivalent, according to the definition of a logarithm.

The solution of the second equation may be obtained in the following way. Two positive numbers are equal if, and only if, their logarithms to the base 10 are equal. Hence, the equation

$$\log 5^N = \log 7$$

is equivalent to each equation above. In turn, by the third law of logarithms, the equation

$$N \log 5 = \log 7$$

is equivalent to each equation above. This last equation is linear and has the solution

$$N = \frac{\log 7}{\log 5}.$$

Hence,

$$\log_5 7 = \frac{\log 7}{\log 5}.$$

From the Table of Common Logarithms,

$$\log_5 7 \doteq \frac{.8451}{.6990}.$$

We can compute the above quotient either by use of logarithms or by long division. In either case,

$$\log_5 7 \doteq 1.209.$$

In general, it can be shown that

$$\log_b N = \frac{\log N}{\log b}.$$

This equation can be used to convert logarithms from base 10 to base b.

Problem 1. Find an answer correct to four significant digits for each of the following.
(a) $\log_4 17$
(b) $\log_{0.5} 25$

Solution.

(a) $\log_4 17 = \dfrac{\log 17}{\log 4}$

$\doteq \dfrac{1.2304}{0.6021}$

$\doteq 2.044$

(b) $\log_{0.5} 25 = \dfrac{\log 25}{\log 0.5}$

$\doteq \dfrac{1.3979}{(0.6990 - 1)}$

$\doteq \dfrac{1.3979}{-0.3010}$

$\doteq -4.644$

Problem 2. Find x if $3^x = 2^{\log_4 2}$.

Solution. We first determine $\log_4 2$.

$$\log_4 2 = \frac{\log 2}{\log 4}$$

$$\doteq \frac{0.3010}{.6021}, \quad \text{or } .5$$

Hence, the given equation is equivalent to the equation

$$3^x = 2^{.5}.$$

Using the third law of logarithms, we have

$$x \log 3 = .5 \log 2,$$

$$x = \frac{.5 \log 2}{\log 3}$$

$$\doteq \frac{.5 \times 0.3010}{0.4771}$$

$$\doteq \frac{.1505}{.4771}, \quad \text{or } .3154.$$

Exercises

For each of the following, find an answer correct to four significant digits.

1. (a) $\log_3 10$ (b) $\log_{\frac{1}{2}} 5$

2. (a) $\log_2 23$ (b) $\log_5 652$

3. (a) $\log_{2.718} 32$ (b) $3^{1.65}$

In Exercises 4–12, solve each equation for x.

4. $5^x = 30^{3 \log_2 4}$ **5.** $5^{\log_5 x} = 2$

6. $7^x = 27^{\log_3 3}$ **7.** $2^x \cdot 16^3 = 4^{5 \log_5 5}$

8. $100^{x \log_y y} = 35$ **9.** $2^{x^2} = 27 \log_4 16$

10. $\log_{10}(3x - 5) = 2$ **11.** $\log_{10} x^3 = 12$

12. $4^{\log_4 2} + 2^{\log_2 2} = 8^{\log_8 x}$

13. Prove that the equation $\log_a b \cdot \log_b a = 1$ is true for every pair a, b of positive numbers other than 1.

Solve each of the following inequalities.

14. $2^x > 5$ **15.** $3(2^x) \leqq 7$ **16.** $(\frac{1}{2})^x < .01$

EXTRA!

Logarithmic functions are often used in science. One example in chemistry is the formula for determining the acidity of a solution; this formula gives the pH of a solution, and the pH indicates the solution's acidity. The formula is

$$\text{pH} = \log \frac{1}{[\text{H}^+]}$$

where H^+ is the concentration of the hydrogen ion. Since

$$\log \frac{1}{[H^+]} = \log [H^+]^{-1},$$

the formula can be expressed

$$pH = -\log [H^+].$$

The pH of a neutral solution is 7; that of an acid solution is less than 7; and that of an alkaline solution is more than 7.

For example, the pH of a solution having a hydrogen ion concentration of 0.0036 moles per liter is $-\log (3.6 \times 10^{-3}) = -\log 3.6 - \log 10^{-3} = -\log 3.6 + 3(\log 10) = 3 - .5563 = 2.4437$. The solution is acid.

Logarithms are also useful in astronomy, for example in studying the magnitudes of stars. The magnitude of a star is a measure of the brightness of the star; this is measured in such a way that stars with greatest magnitudes are faintest. That is, a star with magnitude of 6 is much fainter than a star with magnitude of 0. The sun has a magnitude of -26.7. Stars of the sixth magnitude are visible to the naked eye. Fainter stars can be seen using telescopes. The magnitude of stars made visible through a telescope depends on the aperture of the telescope. This is given by

$$m = 9 + \log a$$

where m is the magnitude of the faintest star made visible and a is the aperture of the telescope in inches.

Calculate the pH for each of the hydrogen ion concentrations given. Tell whether the solution is acid, neutral, or alkaline.

1. 0.00053   2. 0.0153
3. 0.0277   4. 0.0009
5. 3.7×10^{-9} 6. 9.9×10^{-8}

Calculate the magnitude of the faintest star made visible by telescopes having the following apertures. Round to the nearest tenth.

7. 1 inch
8. 10 inches
9. 6 inches
10. 20 inches
11. 24 inches
12. 1000 inches

HISTORICAL NOTE

At the beginning of the seventeenth century, logarithms were invented for the specific purpose of aiding in astronomical computations. The Scotch-man Napier (1550–1617) is usually given credit for their invention because they appeared in his *Descriptio*, published in 1614. However, the Swiss watchmaker Bürgi (1552–1632) discovered them independently at about the same time. The first table of logarithms is believed to have been published by Bürgi in 1620.

In 1624, the Englishman Briggs published a table of common logarithms of all integers from 1 to 20,000 and from 90,000 to 100,000. In this table, each logarithm was approximated to fourteen-decimal-place accuracy. In view of the limited mathematical knowledge of his period, this was quite an achievement. A portion of a page from this table is reproduced below.

Chilias vicesima.

Num. absolut.	Logarithmi.	Num. absolut.	Logarithmi.	Num. absolut.	Logarithmi.
19901	4,29887,48997,0470 / 2,18221,9843	19919	4,29926,75316,0861 / 2,18024,7908	19937	4,29965,98088,6701 / 2,17827,9533
19902	4,29889,67219,0313 / 2,18211,0197	19920	4,29928,93340,8769 / 2,18013,8460	19938	4,29968,15916,6234 / 2,17817,0284
19903	4,29891,85430,0510 / 2,18200,0563	19921	4,29931,11354,7229 / 2,18002,9024	19939	4,29970,33733,6518 / 2,17806,1045
19904	4,29894,03630,1073 / 2,18189,0939	19922	4,29933,29357,6253 / 2,17991,9598	19940	4,29972,51509,7563 / 2,17795,1817
19905	4,29896,21819,2012 / 2,18178,1327	19923	4,29935,47349,5851 / 2,17981,0184	19941	4,29974,69304,9380 / 2,17784,2600
19906	4,29898,39997,3339 / 2,18167,1725	19924	4,29937,65330,6035 / 2,17970,0781	19942	4,29976,87089,1980 / 2,17773,3394
19907	4,29900,58164,5064 / 2,18156,2135	19925	4,29939,83300,6816 / 2,17959,1388	19943	4,29979,04862,5374 / 2,17762,4198
19908	4,29902,76320,7199 / 2,18145,2555	19926	4,29942,01259,8204 / 2,17948,2006	19944	4,29981,22614,9572 / 2,17751,5014
19909	4,29904,94465,9754 / 2,18134,2987	19927	4,29944,19208,0210 / 2,17937,2636	19945	4,29983,40406,4586 / 2,17740,5841
19910	4,29907,12600,2741 / 2,18123,3430	19928	4,29946,37145,2846 / 2,17926,3276	19946	4,29985,58147,0427 / 2,17729,6679
19911	4,29909,30723,6171 / 2,18112,3883	19929	4,29948,55071,6122 / 2,17915,3927	19947	4,29987,75876,7106 / 2,17718,7527
19912	4,29911,48836,0054 / 2,18101,4348	19930	4,29950,72987,0049 / 2,17904,4590	19948	4,29989,93595,4633 / 2,17707,8387
19913	4,29913,66937,4402 / 2,18090,4823	19931	4,29952,90891,4639 / 2,17892,5263	19949	4,29992,11303,3020 / 2,17696,9257
19914	4,29915,85027,9225 / 2,18079,5310	19932	4,29955,08784,9902 / 2,17882,5947	19950	4,29994,29000,2277 / 2,17686,0139
19915	4,29918,03107,4535 / 2,18068,5808	19933	4,29957,26667,5849 / 2,17871,6643	19951	4,29996,46686,2416 / 2,17675,1031
19916	4,29920,21176,0343 / 2,18057,6316	19934	4,29959,44539,2492 / 2,17860,7349	19952	4,29998,64361,3447 / 2,17664,1934
19917	4,29922,39233,6659 / 2,18046,6835	19935	4,29961,62399,9841 / 2,17849,8066	19953	4,30000,82025,5381 / 2,17653,2849
19918	4,29924,57280,3494 / 2,18035,7367	19936	4,29963,80249,7907 / 2,17838,8794	19954	4,30002,99678,8230 / 2,17642,3774

KEY IDEAS AND KEY WORDS

The definition of the **logarithm function** to the base b, $\log_b$, is given by

$$\log_b s = r, \quad \text{where } b^r = s \quad \text{(assuming } b > 0, \ b \neq 1\text{).}$$

The domain of $\log_b s$ is the set of all positive real numbers.
The **laws of logarithms** are as follows:

$$\log_b xy = \log_b x + \log_b y, \qquad \text{(LL-1)}$$
$$\log_b \frac{x}{y} = \log_b x - \log_b y, \qquad \text{(LL-2)}$$
$$\log_b x^r = r \log_b x. \qquad \text{(LL-3)}$$

Logarithms to the base 10 are called **common logarithms.** We understand

$$\log N \quad \text{to mean} \quad \log_{10} N.$$

The greatest integer contained in $\log N$ is called the **characteristic** of $\log N$, and the fractional part is called the **mantissa.** If N is expressed in scientific notation,

$$N = B \cdot 10^k, \quad \text{where } 1 \leq B < 10.$$

Then

$$k = \text{characteristic} \quad \text{and} \quad \log B = \text{mantissa}$$

of $\log N$.
If we know $\log N$, we can find $\log_b N$ with the aid of the following equation.

$$\log_b N = \frac{\log N}{\log b}$$

If M and N are numbers such that $M = \log N$, then N is called the **antilogarithm** of M.

CHAPTER REVIEW

Tell which of the following statements are true and which are false. Correct the ones that you marked false.

1. If $r > s$, then $(-2)^r > (-2)^s$.   2. $\dfrac{\log 5}{\log 3} = \log 2$

3. $\log (r + s) = \log r + \log s$ 4. $\log 3x = 3 \log x$

5. If $f(x) = \log (1 - x)$, the domain of f is $\{x \mid x < 1\}$.

6. If $g(x) = \log (x^2 + 1)$, the domain of g is the set of real numbers.

7. $\log x^n = (\log x)^n$

8. $\log_9 3 = \dfrac{1}{\log_3 9}$

9. $\log \sqrt{\dfrac{a}{b^2}} = \frac{1}{2}(\log a - 2 \log b)$

10. $\log_4 16 = \dfrac{\log_2 16}{\log_2 4}$

Solve each of the following equations for x without referring to logarithm tables.

11. $\log 5 + \log 4 = \log x$

12. $\log_7 x^5 - 3 \log_7 x = 2$

13. $\log (4x - 1) - 2 \log x = \log 3$

14. $\log_3 42 - \log_3 8 = \log_3 x$

15. $2^{3x-2} = 64$

16. $\log_x \frac{1}{49} = -2$

17. $\log_8 x = \frac{4}{3}$

18. $\log_{\frac{3}{2}} \frac{8}{27} = x$

Use logarithms to find approximations to four significant digits for each of the following numbers.

19. $45.23 \div 861.7$

20. $45,320 \times .008617$

21. $\sqrt[3]{4532}$

22. $(.4532)^2$

In Exercises 23–26, graph each of the equations. For what values of x is each equation defined?

23. $y = \log_{12} x$

24. $y = \log_{12} |x|$

25. $y = \log_3 (x + 2)$

26. $y = \log_3 (2 - x)$

27. Solve each of the following equations for x.

(a) $\log_{10} (x + 1) - \log_{10} x = .3247$
(b) $3^{1+2x} = 5^{1-2x}$

28. The star Betelgeuse is approximately 1.59×10^{15} miles from the earth. How many years does it take light from Betelgeuse to reach us?

29. The speed of sound in water is 1.46×10^5 centimeters per second. If it takes a sound 2.00×10^{-2} seconds to travel from the surface of a body of water to the bottom and back, how deep is the water?

CHAPTER TEST

1. Solve each of the following equations for N.
   (a) $\log_2 \frac{1}{8} = N$ (b) $\log_5 N = -3$ (c) $\log_N 16 = \frac{1}{2}$

2. Sketch the graph of each of the following equations. For what values of x is each equation defined?
   (a) $y = \log_3 x$ (b) $y = \log_5 (x + 3)$

In Exercises 3–8, solve each equation for x.

3. $10^x = 235.4$

4. $\log x = 2.4561$

5. $x = (43.85)^3$

6. $x = \sqrt{.4385}$

7. $7^{x+1} = 49$

8. $x = \log_3 7$

9. Solve for n if $\log (15n + 1) + \log n = \log 2$.

CUMULATIVE REVIEW II

1. For what real values of x and y, if any, do the following pairs of algebraic expressions have the same value?

   (a) xy^{-2} and $\dfrac{1}{xy^2}$ (b) $x^{-1} + y^{-1}$ and $\dfrac{1}{x + y}$

2. A point P moves in a coordinate plane in such a way that its distance from the point $(-1, 3)$ is always twice its distance from the point $(2, -4)$. Prove that the path traced by P is a circle. Find the center and radius of the circle.

3. On the same set of axes, sketch the graph of each of the following equations.
   (a) $y = x$ (b) $y = x^2$ (c) $y = x^3$ (d) $y = x^4$

4. Describe the graph of $y = x^n$, given that n is a positive integer. (Hint: Consider the cases n even and n odd separately.)

5. On the same set of axes, sketch the graph of each of the following equations.
   (a) $y = x^{-1}$ (b) $y = x^{-2}$ (c) $y = x^{-3}$ (d) $y = x^{-4}$

6. Describe the graph of $y = x^n$, given that n is a negative integer.

7. Find all points on the line $x = -1$ that are at a distance of $\sqrt{17}$ units from the point $(-2, 1)$.

8. Let the functions f, g, and h be defined by the equations

$$f(x) = x^2, \quad g(x) = \frac{1}{x}, \quad h(x) = x^2 + \frac{1}{x}.$$

(a) Graph f and g on the same set of axes.
(b) Noting that $h(x) = f(x) + g(x)$, graph h on the same set of axes.

9. Let the function f be defined by

$$f(x) = \left(1 + \frac{1}{x}\right)^x, \quad x > 0.$$

(a) Find $f(1)$, $f(2)$, $f(3)$, $f(4)$, $f(5)$, and $f(6)$.
(b) What do you observe about the behavior of $f(x)$ as x takes on larger and larger values?

10. Sketch the graph of each of the following equations.

(a) $y = \dfrac{2^x + 2^{-x}}{2}$ $\qquad$ (b) $y = \dfrac{2^x - 2^{-x}}{2}$

11. Let the functions f, g, and h be defined by the following equations.

$$f(x) = x^2 + 1, \quad g(x) = x^3 - 5x, \quad h(x) = \sqrt{4 - x^2}$$

(a) For each point (a, b) of the first quadrant on the graph of f, which of the points $(-a, b)$, $(a, -b)$, $(-a, -b)$, and (b, a) are also on the graph of f?
(b) Answer the same question for the graph of g.
(c) Answer the same question for the graph of h.

12. Solve each of the following equations.
(a) $(\log x)^2 - \log x^2 + 1 = 0$
(b) $\log (\log x) = 2$
(c) $(\log x)(\log x^2) + \log x^3 - 9 = 0$

13. Find the solution set of each of the following expressions.
(a) $3^x = 5^x$ $\qquad$ (b) $3^x < 5^x$ $\qquad$ (c) $3^x > 5^x$

Simplify each of the following by rationalizing the denominator.

14. $\dfrac{1}{\sqrt{2} - \sqrt{5}}$ $\qquad\qquad$ **15.** $\dfrac{1}{\sqrt{x + 1} - 1}$

16. For what real number or numbers k is the line $3x + ky = 15$ tangent to the circle $x^2 + y^2 = 9$?

17. (a) How many digits are there in the numeral of 2^{50}?
(b) How many zeros precede the first significant digit in the decimal numeral of 2^{-50}?

18. The lengths of the sides of a triangle are 6, 8, and 12 inches. Find the length of the altitude drawn to the longest side.

19. Sketch the graph of the function f defined by $f(x) = \sqrt{x^2}$. Describe the domain and range of f. Define f in terms of linear functions.

20. If the birth rate of a nation is 12% and the death rate 2% per year, how many years (to the closest integer) will it take for the population to double?

CHAPTER 8

Polynomials

Objectives . . .

- To apply the basic arithmetic operations to polynomials.
- To compare the algebra of polynomials with that of the integers.
- To find quotients of polynomials by synthetic division.
- To compute values of a polynomial function by using the remainder theorem.
- To use synthetic division to find zeros of polynomials.
- To use graphs to find irrational zeros of polynomials.

8–1 THE ALGEBRA OF POLYNOMIALS IN ONE VARIABLE

Algebraic expressions of the form

$$4x^3 - 3x^2 + 2, \quad \tfrac{1}{5}x^5 - x - 4, \quad 17x^{17} - 3x$$

are called polynomials in the variable x. Such expressions are not new to us, since we studied both linear and quadratic polynomials in one variable in previous chapters. In the present chapter, we wish to consider the algebraic system of all polynomials in one variable whose coefficients are real numbers.

After looking at the examples of polynomials above, you might have anticipated the following definition.

Definition of a polynomial

A polynomial is an algebraic expression of the form

$$a_n x^n + a_{n-1} x^{n-1} + \cdots + a_1 x + a_0$$

where n is a nonnegative integer, x is a variable, and the coefficients $a_n, a_{n-1}, \ldots, a_1, a_0$ are real numbers.

The numbers $a_n, a_{n-1}, \ldots, a_1, a_0$ occurring in a polynomial are called its *coefficients*. Thus, a_n is called the coefficient of x^n, a_{n-1} the coefficient of x^{n-1}, and so on. The number a_n is called the *leading coefficient;* it is the coefficient of the highest power of x occurring in the polynomial. The number a_0 is called the *constant term* of the polynomial. If $a_n \neq 0$, then n is called the *degree* of the polynomial.

If $n = 0$ in the polynomial above, then the polynomial consists of just one term, a_0. Such a polynomial is called a *constant polynomial.*

If $a_0 \neq 0$, the constant polynomial a_0 has degree 0. For a reason to be explained later, the *constant polynomial* 0 *is not given a degree.*

If $n = 1$, the resulting polynomial

$$a_1 x + a_0$$

is called a *linear polynomial.* Its degree is 1 if $a_1 \neq 0$. Of course, if $a_1 = 0$, this polynomial is equivalent to the constant polynomial a_0.

Each polynomial of degree 2 has the form

$$a_2 x^2 + a_1 x + a_0, \quad a_2 \neq 0.$$

We have called such algebraic expressions *quadratic polynomials.* A polynomial of degree 3 is called a *cubic polynomial* and has the form

$$a_3 x^3 + a_2 x^2 + a_1 x + a_0, \quad a_3 \neq 0.$$

A polynomial of degree 4 is often called a *quartic polynomial.*

Let us consider the set of all polynomials in the variable x. Two polynomials in this set are considered equal if, and only if, they have the same degree and their corresponding coefficients are equal; that is,

$$a_n x^n + a_{n-1} x^{n-1} + \cdots + a_1 x + a_0$$
$$= b_n x^n + b_{n-1} x^{n-1} + \cdots + b_1 x + b_0$$

if, and only if,

$$a_n = b_n, \quad a_{n-1} = b_{n-1}, \quad \ldots, \quad a_1 = b_1, \quad \text{and} \quad a_0 = b_0.$$

We would like to define the sum of two polynomials so that the rearrangement properties and the distributive axiom will hold. For example, we define

$$(2x^3 - 4x^2 + 5x + 1) + (-x^3 + 11x^2 - 3x + 7)$$
$$= (2x^3 - x^3) + (-4x^2 + 11x^2) + (5x - 3x) + (1 + 7)$$
$$= (2 - 1)x^3 + (-4 + 11)x^2 + (5 - 3)x + (1 + 7)$$
$$= x^3 + 7x^2 + 2x + 8.$$

Definition of the sum of two polynomials

The sum of two polynomials is the polynomial which has as each of its coefficients the sum of the corresponding coefficients of the two polynomials.

To add two polynomials of different degrees, we shall assume that the missing terms have zero coefficients. For example,

$$(-3x^2 + 1) + (5x^3 - x + 4)$$
$$= (0x^3 - 3x^2 + 0x + 1) + (5x^3 + 0x^2 - x + 4)$$
$$= (0 + 5)x^3 + (-3 + 0)x^2 + (0 - 1)x + (1 + 4)$$
$$= 5x^3 - 3x^2 - x + 5.$$

According to this definition of addition, the set of all polynomials in the variable x is *closed* with respect to addition.

The constant polynomial 0 is the *additive identity element* since the sum of 0 and any given polynomial is the given polynomial. We shall call 0 the *zero polynomial* since it plays the same role in the set of all polynomials as the number 0 does in the real number system.

Each polynomial has an *additive inverse*. For example, the additive inverse of $5x^3 - x + 4$ is $-5x^3 + x - 4$, since their sum is 0. As usual, we shall call the additive inverse of a polynomial its negative.

Definition of additive inverse

The negative, or additive inverse, of a polynomial is the polynomial which has as each of its coefficients the negative of the corresponding coefficient of the given polynomial.

It can be verified that the same axioms that are valid for addition in the real number system are valid for addition in the set of all polynomials: Addition of polynomials is *commutative* and *associative;* there is an *additive identity*, or *zero polynomial;* and each polynomial has an *additive inverse*. These axioms are valid because addition of polynomials is defined in terms of addition of coefficients, which are real numbers. For example, if

$$P = 3x^3 + 4x^2 + 10,$$
$$Q = 2x^2 + x + 5,$$

then

$$P + Q = (3x^3 + 4x^2 + 10) + (2x^2 + x + 5)$$
$$= 3x^3 + 6x^2 + x + 15,$$

and

$$Q + P = (2x^2 + x + 5) + (3x^3 + 4x^2 + 10)$$
$$= 3x^3 + 6x^2 + x + 15.$$

In general, if $a_i x^i$ is a term of a polynomial P and $b_i x^i$ is the corresponding term of a second polynomial Q, then $(a_i + b_i)x^i$ is the corresponding term in $P + Q$ and $(b_i + a_i)x^i$ is the corresponding term in $Q + P$. Since $a_i + b_i = b_i + a_i$ because of the commutative axiom of addition of real numbers, corresponding terms of $P + Q$ and $Q + P$ have equal coefficients. Hence, $P + Q = Q + P$. Thus, addition is commutative in the set of all polynomials. It is possible to prove the other axioms of addition in a similar way.

We can define the multiplication of monomials (polynomials with one term) by means of the first law of exponents. For example, we define

$$(7x^2) \cdot (4x^3) = (7 \cdot 4)x^{2+3}, \quad \text{or } 28x^5.$$

In general,

$$(ax^i) \cdot (bx^j) = (ab)x^{i+j}.$$

We define the product of two polynomials as if the distributive axiom were valid. For example, we define

$$
\begin{aligned}
(4x^3 - 2x - 3) \cdot (3x^2 + 5) \\
&= (4x^3 - 2x - 3)3x^2 + (4x^3 - 2x - 3)5 \\
&= (4x^3 \cdot 3x^2) + (-2x \cdot 3x^2) + (-3 \cdot 3x^2) + (4x^3 \cdot 5) \\
&\quad + (-2x \cdot 5) + (-3 \cdot 5) \\
&= 12x^5 - 6x^3 - 9x^2 + 20x^3 - 10x - 15 \\
&= 12x^5 + 14x^3 - 9x^2 - 10x - 15.
\end{aligned}
$$

Thus, the product consists of all terms obtained by multiplying each term of one polynomial by every term of the other polynomial.

Definition of the product of two polynomials

If

$$a_n x^n + a_{n-1}x^{n-1} + \cdots + a_1 x + a_0$$

and

$$b_k x^k + b_{k-1}x^{k-1} + \cdots + b_1 x + b_0$$

are any two polynomials, then their product is the polynomial whose terms are all monomials of the form

$$a_i b_j x^{i+j}, \quad \text{where } i = 0, 1, 2, \ldots, n \text{ and } j = 0, 1, 2, \ldots, k.$$

The product of two polynomials may be found by a method very similar to that used in finding the product of two integers. This method is illustrated below.

$$
\begin{array}{l}
x^2 - 3x + 4 \\
2x^2 + 2x - 1 \\
\hline
2x^4 - 6x^3 + 8x^2 \qquad\qquad = 2x^2(x^2 - 3x + 4) \\
 2x^3 - 6x^2 + 8x \qquad = 2x(x^2 - 3x + 4) \\
 -x^2 + 3x - 4 \qquad = -1(x^2 - 3x + 4) \\
\hline
2x^4 - 4x^3 + x^2 + 11x - 4
\end{array}
$$

According to this definition of multiplication, the set of all polynomials in x is *closed* with respect to multiplication. Although we shall not do so, we could prove that multiplication of polynomials is both *commutative* and *associative*. There is a *multiplicative identity element*, which is the constant polynomial 1, and the *distributive axiom* is valid. Does each nonzero polynomial have a multiplicative inverse, or reciprocal, which is also a polynomial? Although

$$\frac{1}{x}, \quad \text{or} \quad x^{-1},$$

is the reciprocal of x, the algebraic expression x^{-1} is not a polynomial. Remember that a polynomial in x is made up of terms of the form ax^n, where a is a real number and n is a *nonnegative* integer. Actually, no polynomial of degree 1 or higher has a reciprocal which is a polynomial.

When we speak of the *algebra of polynomials*, we mean the set of polynomials together with the operations of addition and multiplication as described above.

The five basic axioms of addition and multiplication given in Chapter 1, with the exception of the multiplicative inverse axiom, (Inv-M), are valid for the algebra of polynomials.

We might recall that, with the same exception, the system of integers also satisfies these five basic axioms. Further similarities between the algebras of polynomials and integers will be described in this chapter.

The operation of *subtraction* is defined in the algebra of polynomials in the following way. If P and Q are polynomials, then

$$P - Q = P + (-Q),$$

where $-Q$ designates the negative, or additive inverse, of Q. For example,

$$(3x^2 - 7x + 2) - (2x^3 - 5x^2 + x - 8)$$
$$= (3x^2 - 7x + 2) + [-(2x^3 - 5x^2 + x - 8)]$$
$$= (3x^2 - 7x + 2) + (-2x^3 + 5x^2 - x + 8)$$
$$= -2x^3 + 8x^2 - 8x + 10.$$

If the nonzero polynomials

$$P = a_n x^n + a_{n-1} x^{n-1} + \cdots + a_1 x + a_0, \quad a_n \neq 0,$$

and

$$Q = b_k x^k + b_{k-1} x^{k-1} + \cdots + b_1 x + b_0, \quad b_k \neq 0,$$

are multiplied together, what is the degree of their product PQ? Since $a_n \neq 0$ and $b_k \neq 0$, their product $a_n b_k \neq 0$, and

$$(a_n x^n) \cdot (b_k x^k), \quad \text{or} \quad a_n b_k x^{n+k},$$

is the term of highest degree in PQ. Thus, PQ has degree $n + k$. This result can be stated in the following manner.

The degree of the product of two nonzero polynomials is the sum of the degrees of the two polynomials.

The result above is true even if one of the polynomials is a nonzero constant. For example, if

$$P = 3 \quad \text{and} \quad Q = x^2 + 3x - 2,$$

then

$$PQ = 3x^2 + 9x - 6.$$

Since $0 + 2 = 2$, we see that the sum of the degrees of P and Q is the degree of PQ.

If we multiply a polynomial by the zero polynomial, the product is zero. For example,

$$0(x^2 + 3x - 2) = (0 \cdot x^2) + (0 \cdot 3x) + [0 \cdot (-2)], \quad \text{or} \quad 0.$$

This is the reason we did not assign a degree to the polynomial 0. If we had assigned a degree, say k, then the theorem above would demand that $k + 2 = k$. Since this equation is false for every number k, we conclude that there is no degree that can be assigned to the zero polynomial.

The following property is a consequence of the one stated above. It is also a property of the system of integers.

ZERO MULTIPLICATION

If P and Q are polynomials, then

$$PQ = 0 \quad \text{if, and only if,} \quad P = 0 \text{ or } Q = 0. \quad (Zero\text{-}M)$$

Proof. If either $P = 0$ or $Q = 0$, then $PQ = 0$. Conversely, if both $P \neq 0$ and $Q \neq 0$, then PQ cannot be the polynomial 0 since the polynomial PQ has a degree, whereas the polynomial 0 has no degree. Hence, if $PQ = 0$, then $P = 0$ or $Q = 0$.

Exercises

1. (a) Illustrate the associative law of addition in the set of polynomials, using the three polynomials

$$4x^2 - 3, \quad 7x^2 - 2x + 4, \quad 4x + 5.$$

   (b) Illustrate the associative law of multiplication in the set of polynomials, using the three polynomials

$$x - 3, \quad x + 3, \quad 2x + 5.$$

2. Illustrate the distributive law in the set of polynomials, using the following polynomials
   (a) $x - 3$, $x^2 + 3x + 9$
   (b) $2x + 3$, $4x^2 - 6x + 9$

Perform the indicated operations with polynomials.

3. (a) $(x^2 + 3x + 5) + (2x - 2)$ (b) $(2x^2 - 3x + 5) + (x^3 - x + 7)$
4. (a) $(3x^3 - 5x + 7) - (7 + 3x^3 - 5x)$
   (b) $(x^5 - 5x + 7) + (-x^5 + 5x - 7)$
5. (a) $(4x^2 - 3x + 5) - (x^3 - 3x + 7)$
   (b) $(7x^3 - 4x^2 + 2x - 4) - (7x^3 - 4x^2 - 4)$
6. (a) $(4x^3 - x^2 + 3x - 2) + (-3x^3 + 7x)$
   (b) $(x^4 + 3x) + (12x^3 - 2x^2 + 5)$
7. (a) $0 \cdot (x + 5)$
   (b) $0 \cdot (-4x^5 + 7x^2 + 2)$

8. (a) $(x^3 + 2x + 3)(x^4 + 7)$ (b) $(x^2 + 2x - 5)(2x^2 - 4x + 3)$

9. (a) $(-5x^3 + x^2 - 1)(x^3 - 2x + 4)$
   (b) $(x^7 - 3x^5 + x^3 - x)(x^6 - x^4 + 3x^2 - 2)$

10. (a) $(x^2 - \frac{1}{2})(x^4 + \frac{1}{2}x^2 + \frac{1}{4})$ (b) $(x^3 + \frac{1}{2}x - \frac{1}{3})(x^3 + \frac{1}{2}x + \frac{1}{3})$

---

11. Given two polynomials of unequal degree, what is the degree of their sum? Illustrate your answer with two examples.

12. Given two polynomials of equal degree, what can be said about the degree of their sum? Give examples to show the possible alternatives.

13. Make a statement about the degree of the product of three polynomials, and prove it.

14. Consider the set of all fourth-degree polynomials in x:

$$a_4x^4 + a_3x^3 + a_2x^2 + a_1x + a_0, \quad a_4 \neq 0.$$

(a) If a_4, a_3, a_2, a_1, and a_0 are real numbers, is the set closed with respect to any of the operations of arithmetic? If so, which?

(b) If a_4, a_3, a_2, a_1, and a_0 are positive real numbers, under which, if any, of the operations of arithmetic is the set closed?

8-2   THE DIVISION PROCESS

A quotient of two polynomials is not necessarily a polynomial, just as a quotient of two integers is not necessarily an integer. However, it is possible to divide one integer by another, obtaining both an integral quotient and an integral remainder. For example, 354 divided by 13 gives a quotient of 27 and a remainder of 3: $354 = (27 \times 13) + 3$.

In the same way, it is possible to divide one polynomial by another, obtaining a quotient and a remainder, each of which is a polynomial. For example, we can divide $6x^3 - 8x^2 + 5x - 1$ by $3x^2 - x + 2$.

$$
\begin{array}{r}
2x - 2 \\
3x^2 - x + 2\overline{)6x^3 - 8x^2 + 5x - 1} \\
\underline{6x^3 - 2x^2 + 4x} \\
-6x^2 + x - 1 \\
\underline{-6x^2 + 2x - 4} \\
-x + 3
\end{array}
$$

In other words,

$$6x^3 - 8x^2 + 5x - 1 = (2x - 2)(3x^2 - x + 2) + (-x + 3).$$

The justification of this division process is essentially the same as the justification of the division process for integers. In this example, $2x - 2$ is the *quotient* and $-x + 3$ is the *remainder*.

The quotient and remainder obtained when one integer is divided by another are unique. Symbolically, this means that if a and b are integers, with $b > 0$, then there is one, and only one, integer q and one, and only one, integer r such that

$$a = qb + r$$

and

$$0 \leqq r < b.$$

The integer q is the quotient and r is the remainder when a is divided by b.

Similarly, the quotient and remainder obtained by dividing one polynomial by another are unique. Thus, if A and B are polynomials in x, with $B \neq 0$, then there exist unique polynomials Q and R such that

$$A = (Q \cdot B) + R$$

with $R = 0$ or the degree of R less than the degree of B.

If the remainder $R = 0$, then $A = (Q \cdot B)$ and B is called a *divisor*, or *factor*, of A. We also say that A is a *multiple* of B. Of course, if the remainder $R \neq 0$, then B is not a divisor of A and A is not a multiple of B. In practice, on dividing one polynomial by another, we find the quotient and remainder by division, as illustrated in the following problems. (Note that both divisor and dividend are arranged so that the exponents of x are in decreasing order.)

Problem 1. Find the quotient and remainder on dividing the polynomial $3x^4 - 7x^2 + 2x$ by $x^2 + x - 3$.

Solution.

$$
\begin{array}{r}
3x^2 - 3x + 5 \\
x^2 + x - 3 \overline{)3x^4 \qquad\quad - 7x^2 + 2x} \\
\underline{3x^4 + 3x^3 - 9x^2} \\
-3x^3 + 2x^2 + 2x \\
\underline{-3x^3 - 3x^2 + 9x} \\
5x^2 - 7x \\
\underline{5x^2 + 5x - 15} \\
-12x + 15
\end{array}
$$

In the division above, $3x^2 - 3x + 5$ is the quotient and $-12x + 15$ is the remainder when $3x^4 - 7x^2 + 2x$ is divided by $x^2 + x - 3$. Note that we left space for the missing term of degree 3 and also for the missing constant term. We may express the results of this division process as follows:

$$3x^4 - 7x^2 + 2x = (3x^2 - 3x + 5)(x^2 + x - 3) + (-12x + 15).$$

Note that the degree of the remainder is 1, which is less than 2, the degree of the divisor.

Problem 2. Find the quotient and remainder on dividing the polynomial $x^4 + x^3 + x^2 + 3x - 2$ by $2x^3 - 4x^2 + 3x - 2$.

Solution.

$$
\require{enclose}
\begin{array}{r}
\frac{1}{2}x + \frac{3}{2} \\
2x^3 - 4x^2 + 3x - 2 \enclose{longdiv}{x^4 + x^3 + x^2 + 3x - 2} \\
\end{array}
$$

$$
\begin{array}{r}
x^4 - 2x^3 + \frac{3}{2}x^2 - x \\
\hline
3x^3 - \frac{1}{2}x^2 + 4x - 2 \\
3x^3 - 6x^2 + \frac{9}{2}x - 3 \\
\hline
\frac{11}{2}x^2 - \frac{1}{2}x + 1
\end{array}
$$

Therefore, $\frac{1}{2}x + \frac{3}{2}$ is the quotient and $\frac{11}{2}x^2 - \frac{1}{2}x + 1$ is the remainder. We may express the results of this division process in the following way.

$$
\begin{aligned}
x^4 + x^3 + x^2 &+ 3x - 2 \\
&= (\tfrac{1}{2}x + \tfrac{3}{2})(2x^3 - 4x^2 + 3x - 2) + (\tfrac{11}{2}x^2 - \tfrac{1}{2}x + 1)
\end{aligned}
$$

Problem 3. Find the quotient and remainder on dividing the polynomial $2x^3 - 5x^2 + x - 1$ by $x - 3$.

Solution.

$$
\begin{array}{r}
2x^2 + x + 4 \\
x - 3 \enclose{longdiv}{2x^3 - 5x^2 + x - 1} \\
2x^3 - 6x^2 \\
\hline
x^2 + x - 1 \\
x^2 - 3x \\
\hline
4x - 1 \\
4x - 12 \\
\hline
11
\end{array}
$$

Thus, $2x^3 - 5x^2 + x - 1 = (2x^2 + x + 4)(x - 3) + 11$.

Exercises

In each of the following exercises, find the quotient and remainder on dividing the first polynomial A by the second polynomial B. Then express the first polynomial A in the form $A = (Q \cdot B) + R$, with $R = 0$ or the degree of R less than the degree of B.

1. (a) $4x^3 - 5x^2 + 3x - 2$ by $x + 1$
   (b) $4x^3 - 5x^2 + 3x - 2$ by $x + 2$
2. (a) $3x^3 - 5x^2 + 2x - 1$ by $x^2 - 3x + 1$
   (b) x^3 by $x^2 + 7x - 11$
3. (a) $x^2 - 2x + 3$ by $x^2 + x - 2$
   (b) $4x^2 - 9$ by $2x^2 - 7$
4. (a) $3x + 5$ by $6x - 1$
   (b) $3x + 1$ by $2x - 5$
5. (a) $5x^4 - 3x + 8$ by $x^3 - 5x^2 + 2x - 1$
   (b) $5x^4 - 3x + 8$ by $x^3 - x - 1$
6. (a) $2x^3 - 8x^2 + 9x - 2$ by $2x^2 - 4x + 1$
   (b) $x^4 + 4$ by $x^2 - 2x + 2$
7. (a) $1 - x^2 + x^4$ by $1 - x$
   (b) $1 - x^2 + x^4$ by $1 + x$

---

8. Write $x^3 + x^2 - 4x - 4$ as a product of three linear factors by first dividing by $x - 2$ and then factoring the quotient.

9. Use the fact that

$$x^4 + 2x^3 + 5x^2 + 8x + 4$$

is divisible by $x^2 + 4$ to write the fourth-degree polynomial as a product of three polynomials.

10. Factor $x^4 - 6x^2 + 5$ by first dividing by $x^2 - 5$.

11. Factor $x^3 + 5x^2 + 8x + 4$ by first dividing by $x + 1$.

12. Factor $x^4 - 2x^3 - 3x^2 + 4x + 4$ by first dividing by $(x + 1)^2$.

13. Use the fact that

$$x^5 + 6x^4 + 9x^3 + 8x^2 + 48x + 72$$

is divisible by $x^3 + 8$ to write the fifth-degree polynomial as a product of four polynomials.

14. Factor $x^5 + 2x^4 - 4x^3 - 8x^2$ by first dividing by $x^2(x - 2)$.

15. (a) Divide $4x^3 - 5x^2 + 3x - 2$ by $x - 1$ and record the remainder R.
    (b) Evaluate $4x^3 - 5x^2 + 3x - 2$ for $x = 1$, and compare this value with R found in 15(a).

16. (a) Divide $2x^3 - 3x^2 + 5x - 7$ by $x - 2$ and record the remainder R.
    (b) Evaluate $2x^3 - 3x^2 + 5x - 7$ for $x = 2$ and compare this value with R found in 16(a).

17. (a) Evaluate $2x^3 - 5x^2 + x - 1$ for $x = 3$.
    (b) Compare the value in 17(a) with the remainder R in Problem 3, page 348.

8–3 SYNTHETIC DIVISION

The division process can be considerably shortened if the divisor is a linear polynomial of the form $x - a$. For example, the solution of Problem 3 on page 348 can be shortened in the following way.

$$
\begin{array}{r}
2x^2 + x + 4 \\
x - 3\overline{\smash{\big)}\,2x^3 - 5x^2 + x - 1} \\
-6x^2 \\
\hline
x^2 \\
-3x \\
\hline
4x \\
-12 \\
\hline
11
\end{array}
$$

We can shorten the division process by moving terms up under the dividend. The resulting array is shown below.

$$
\begin{array}{r}
2x^2 + x + 4 \\
x - 3\overline{\smash{\big)}\,2x^3 - 5x^2 + x - 1} \\
-6x^2 - 3x - 12 \\
\hline
2x^3 x^2 4x 11
\end{array}
$$

Note that in this latter array we have also put the leading term of the divisor, $2x^3$, on the bottom line. Next, we observe that the quotient $2x^2 + x + 4$ is repeated on the lower line, except that each term has been multiplied by x. Thus, we can omit the top line if we remember how it is obtained from the bottom line. We may also omit all powers of x, leaving the following array of coefficients.

$$\begin{array}{r|rrrr} -3 & 2 & -5 & 1 & -1 \\ & & -6 & -3 & -12 \\ \hline & 2 & 1 & 4 & 11 \end{array}$$ (subtract)

The top row of the array consists of -3, which comes from the polynomial $x - 3$, and the numbers 2, -5, 1, and -1, which are the coefficients (arranged in descending order) of the given polynomial, $2x^3 - 5x^2 + x - 1$.

Each number in the last row is obtained by subtracting the number in the middle row from the number in the top row. Each number in the middle row is obtained by multiplying the number preceding it in the bottom row by -3. The bottom row of the array contains both the quotient and the remainder. Thus, 2, 1, and 4 are the coefficients (in descending order) of the quotient $2x^2 + x + 4$, and the last number, 11, is the remainder.

One final simplification can be made when we realize that if we multiply by 3, and add, instead of multiplying by -3, and subtracting, we obtain the same result. This new array is shown below.

$$\begin{array}{r|rrrr} 3 & 2 & -5 & 1 & -1 \\ & & 6 & 3 & 12 \\ \hline & 2 & 1 & 4 & 11 \end{array}$$ (add)

The process described above for dividing a polynomial by $x - a$ is called *synthetic division.* Some further illustrations of its use are given below.

Problem 1. Find the quotient and remainder on dividing the polynomial $3x^4 - 11x^3 - 21x^2 + 3x + 17$ by $x - 5$.

Solution. We first write the coefficients of the dividend in order of decreasing powers of x. Then we write the number 5, from $x - 5$, as shown below.

$$\begin{array}{r|rrrrr} 5 & 3 & -11 & -21 & 3 & 17 \end{array}$$

Next, the leading coefficient, 3, is brought down to the bottom line, and the product of 3 and 5 is placed under the second term, -11.

$$\begin{array}{r|rrrrr} 5 & 3 & -11 & -21 & 3 & 17 \\ & & 15 \\ \hline & 3 \end{array}$$

We now *add* 15 to -11 and place the sum on the bottom line. Continuing, we have the following.

$$
\begin{array}{r|rrrrr}
5 & 3 & -11 & -21 & 3 & 17 \\
  &   & 15 & 20 & -5 & -10 \\
\hline
  & 3 & 4   & -1 & -2 & 7
\end{array}
$$

The numbers 3, 4, -1, and -2 in the bottom line are the coefficients of the powers of x (given in descending order) in the quotient; the last number, 7, is the remainder. Since the dividend is a polynomial of degree 4 and the divisor of degree 1, the quotient is a polynomial of degree 3. Thus,

$$3x^3 + 4x^2 - x - 2$$

is the quotient and 7 is the remainder. We can express this result by the equation

$$3x^4 - 11x^3 - 21x^2 + 3x + 17 = (3x^3 + 4x^2 - x - 2)(x - 5) + 7.$$

Problem 2. Find the quotient and remainder on dividing the polynomial $-5x^3 + 14x - 7$ by $x + 2$.

Solution. We note that the coefficient of x^2 in the dividend is zero, and that $x + 2 = x - (-2)$. The synthetic division for this problem is shown below.

$$
\begin{array}{r|rrrr}
-2 & -5 & 0 & 14 & -7 \\
   &   & 10 & -20 & 12 \\
\hline
   & -5 & 10 & -6 & 5
\end{array}
$$

Therefore, $-5x^2 + 10x - 6$ is the quotient and 5 is the remainder.

$$-5x^3 + 14x - 7 = (-5x^2 + 10x - 6)(x + 2) + 5.$$

Exercises

Use synthetic division to find the quotient and remainder on dividing the first polynomial A by the second polynomial B. Express the results in the form $A = (Q \cdot B) + R$, with $R = 0$ or the degree of R less than the degree of B.

1. (a) $(2x^3 - x^2 + 4x - 5) \div (x + 2)$
   (b) $(3x^4 - x^2 + 5) \div (x - 3)$
2. (a) $4x^2 - 3x + 7$ by $x - 2$
   (b) $2x^2 + 5x - 3$ by $x - 3$

3. (a) $x^3 - 3x^2 + 4x + 8$ by $x + 1$
   (b) $-2x^4 + 3x^3 - x^2 + 2x - 4$ by $x + 3$

4. (a) $x^4 + x^2 + 1$ by $x + 3$
   (b) $x^5 - 3x^3 + 4x - 7$ by $x - 1$

5. (a) $x^5 + 1$ by $x - 1$
   (b) $x^5 + 32$ by $x + 2$

6. (a) $3x^4 - 4x$ by $x + 2$
   (b) $-3x^5 + 2x^2 - 2$ by $x - 2$

7. (a) $3x^4 - 4x^3 + x^2 + 6x + 17$ by $x - \frac{1}{3}$
   (b) $-4x^3 + 3x + 5$ by $x + \frac{1}{2}$

---

8. Determine k so that when $2x^3 - x^2 + 3x + k$ is divided by $x - 1$, the remainder is zero.

9. Determine a and b so that when $x^4 + x^3 - 7x^2 + ax + b$ is divided by $(x - 1)(x + 2)$, the remainder is zero.

10. The integer 185 may be divided by 12 as follows: First divide 185 by 4 to obtain $185 = (46 \cdot 4) + 1$, and then divide the quotient, 46, by 3 to obtain $185 = [(15 \cdot 3) + 1]4 + 1$, or $185 = (15 \cdot 3 \cdot 4) + (1 \cdot 4) + 1$, or $185 = (15 \cdot 12) + 5$. Use such a procedure to find the quotient and remainder on dividing the following integers.
    (a) 833 by 15   (b) 479 by 28

11. The procedure of Exercise 10 can be applied to the division of polynomials, but synthetic division should be employed where the divisors are of the form $x - a$. Use this combination of procedures to perform each of the following divisions.
    (a) $x^2 - 4x + 2$ by $(x - 1)(x - 2)$
    (b) $2x^3 - 5x^2 + 4x - 7$ by $(x + 2)(x - 3)$
    (c) $x^5 - 5x^3 + 12x^2 - 10$ by $x^2 - 1$

Preparation for Section 8–4

Find $f(2)$, $f(-2)$, $f(\sqrt{3})$, $f(-1)$, and $f(\frac{1}{2})$ for each of the following.

1. $f(x) = x - 6$
2. $f(x) = 3x + 7$
3. $f(x) = x^2 - 1$
4. $f(x) = x^2 + 3x + 7$
5. $f(x) = 5x^2 + 3x - 8$
6. $f(x) = 2x^2 - \sqrt{2}x + 17$
7. $f(x) = x^3 + 4x^2 + x + 5$
8. $f(x) = x^4 - 3x^3 + 5x - 3$

8–4 POLYNOMIAL FUNCTIONS

A function f such that $f(x)$ is a polynomial in x is called a *polynomial function.* For example, the function f defined by

$$f(x) = x^3 + x^2 - x - 10$$

is a polynomial function.   The domain of a polynomial function is usually understood to be the set of all real numbers.   However, in the last section of this chapter, we shall consider polynomial functions which have the set of all complex numbers as their domain.

The polynomial $f(x)$ above can be divided by $x - 3$, yielding a quotient of $x^2 + 4x + 11$ and a remainder of 23, as shown by the following synthetic division.

$$\begin{array}{r|rrrr} 3 & 1 & 1 & -1 & -10 \\ & & 3 & 12 & 33 \\ \hline & 1 & 4 & 11 & 23 \end{array}$$

Hence,

$$f(x) = (x^2 + 4x + 11)(x - 3) + 23.$$

If we give x the value 3, then we obtain

$$f(3) = [3^2 + (4 \cdot 3) + 11](3 - 3) + 23 = (32 \cdot 0) + 23, \quad \text{or } 23.$$

In other words, $f(3)$ is the remainder when $f(x)$ is divided by $x - 3$. This result illustrates the following theorem.

REMAINDER THEOREM

If the polynomial $f(x)$ is divided by $x - r$, the remainder is $f(r)$.

The proof of this theorem is indicated in the example above.   Thus, if the polynomial $f(x)$ is divided by $x - r$, the quotient is some polynomial $q(x)$, and the remainder R is a polynomial that is either zero or of lower degree than $x - r$.   Since $x - r$ has degree 1, the remainder R is either 0 or of degree 0.   In either case, R is a constant polynomial.

$$f(x) = q(x)(x - r) + R$$

When we assign to x the value r, we get

$$f(r) = q(r)(r - r) + R = (q(r) \cdot 0) + R = 0 + R, \quad \text{or } R.$$

This proves the theorem.

The remainder theorem provides us with a convenient method of computing values of a polynomial function. It is frequently easier to divide synthetically by $x - r$ than to let $x = r$ in $f(x)$ when we wish to compute $f(r)$. Thus, to find $f(r)$, we need find only the remainder on dividing $f(x)$ by $x - r$. The remainder may be computed by synthetic division, as shown in the following problem.

Problem 1. If $f(x) = x^4 - 2x^2 - 7x + 6$, find $f(-2)$, $f(1)$, $f(2)$, and $f(5)$.

Solution. To obtain $f(-2)$, we find the remainder on dividing $f(x)$ by $x - (-2)$, as shown below. The other values of f are also computed below.

$$
\begin{array}{r|rrrrr}
-2 & 1 & 0 & -2 & -7 & 6 \\
   &   & -2 & 4 & -4 & 22 \\
\hline
   & 1 & -2 & 2 & -11 & 28
\end{array}
$$

Thus, $f(-2) = 28$.

$$
\begin{array}{r|rrrrr}
1 & 1 & 0 & -2 & -7 & 6 \\
  &   & 1 & 1 & -1 & -8 \\
\hline
  & 1 & 1 & -1 & -8 & -2
\end{array}
$$

Thus, $f(1) = -2$.

$$
\begin{array}{r|rrrrr}
2 & 1 & 0 & -2 & -7 & 6 \\
  &   & 2 & 4 & 4 & -6 \\
\hline
  & 1 & 2 & 2 & -3 & 0
\end{array}
$$

Thus, $f(2) = 0$.

$$
\begin{array}{r|rrrrr}
5 & 1 & 0 & -2 & -7 & 6 \\
  &   & 5 & 25 & 115 & 540 \\
\hline
  & 1 & 5 & 23 & 108 & 546
\end{array}
$$

Thus, $f(5) = 546$.

A number r is called a zero of the polynomial $f(x)$ if $f(r) = 0$; that is, r is a zero of $f(x)$ if r is a solution of the polynomial equation

$$f(x) = 0.$$

For example, in Problem 1, a zero of the polynomial $f(x)$ is 2 since it was shown that $f(2) = 0$.

According to the remainder theorem, if we divide the polynomial $f(x)$ by $x - r$, we obtain a quotient $q(x)$ and a remainder $f(r)$, that is,

$$f(x) = q(x)(x - r) + f(r).$$

Given that r is a zero of $f(x)$, then $f(r) = 0$ and

$$f(x) = q(x)(x - r) + 0,$$

or

$$f(x) = q(x)(x - r).$$

Hence, $x - r$ is a *divisor*, or *factor*, of $f(x)$ if $f(r) = 0$. Conversely, if $x - r$ is a divisor of $f(x)$, then the remainder obtained on dividing $f(x)$ by $x - r$ must be 0. This remainder is $f(r)$ by the remainder theorem; hence, $f(r) = 0$, and we have proved the following theorem.

FACTOR THEOREM

The polynomial $x - r$ is a divisor, or factor, of the polynomial $f(x)$ if, and only if, r is a zero of $f(x)$.

Problem 2. Which of the polynomials $x - 1$, $x + 1$, $x - \frac{1}{2}$, $x - 2$, and $x + 3$ are divisors of the polynomial

$$f(x) = 4x^3 + 16x^2 + 9x - 9?$$

Solution. We know that $x - 1$ will be a factor of $f(x)$ if 1 is a zero of $f(x)$. Since

$$f(1) = 4 + 16 + 9 - 9, \quad \text{or } 20,$$

1 is not a zero of $f(x)$. Hence, $x - 1$ is not a divisor of $f(x)$. Also,

$$f(-1) = -4 + 16 - 9 - 9, \quad \text{or } -6,$$

and -1 is not a zero of $f(x)$. Therefore, $x - (-1)$, or $x + 1$, is not a divisor of $f(x)$. Let us compute $f(\frac{1}{2})$, $f(2)$, and $f(-3)$ by synthetic division.

$\frac{1}{2}$	4	16	9	-9
		2	9	9
	4	18	18	0

Thus, $f(\frac{1}{2}) = 0$.

2	4	16	9	-9
		8	48	114
	4	24	57	105

Thus, $f(2) = 105$.

-3	4	16	9	-9
		-12	-12	9
	4	4	-3	0

Thus, $f(-3) = 0$.

Clearly, $\frac{1}{2}$ and -3 are zeros of $f(x)$, so that $x - \frac{1}{2}$ and $x + 3$ are divisors of $f(x)$. Since $f(2) \neq 0$, $x - 2$ is not a divisor of $f(x)$.

Exercises

1. (a) Given that $f(x) = 2x^3 - 3x^2 + 4x - 3$, find $f(0)$, $f(-2)$, $f(5)$, and $f(-4)$.

(b) Given that $q(y) = 12y^3 + 7y^2 - 14y + 3$, find $q(-2)$, $q(-3)$, $q(3)$, and $q(5)$.

2. (a) Given that $g(x) = x^4 - 7x^3 + 4x^2 + 5x$, find $g(0)$, $g(3)$, $g(-3)$, and $g(6)$.

(b) Given that $p(y) = y^5 - y + 3$, find $p(10)$, $p(-3)$, $p(1)$, and $p(2)$.

In Exercises 3–6, use synthetic division or substitution to find which, if any, of the numbers -3, -2, -1, 0, 1, 2, and 3 are zeros of the polynomials.

3. (a) $x - x^3$ (b) $x^3 - 7x + 6$

4. (a) $3x^3 + 8x^2 - 2x + 3$ (b) $3x^4 + 8x^3 + 6x^2 + 3x - 2$

5. (a) $x^3 + 3x^2 - x - 3$ (b) $y^3 + y + 1$

6. (a) $x^3 - 4x^2 + x + 6$ (b) $x^4 + x^3 - 3x^2 - 4x - 4$

Which of the polynomials $(x - 1)$, $(x + 1)$, $(x - 4)$, and $(x + 3)$ are divisors, or factors, of the following polynomials?

7. (a) $x^3 - 2x^2 - 11x + 12$ (b) $2x^3 + 3x^2 - 23x - 12$

8. (a) $2x^4 + x^3 + x^2 - x - 3$ (b) $x^4 + x^3 - 19x^2 + x - 20$

Use substitution to find which, if any, of the numbers $\sqrt{2}$, $\sqrt{3}$, $-\sqrt{2}$, and $-\sqrt{3}$ are zeros of the following polynomials.

9. (a) $x^3 + 3x^2 - 2x - 6$ (b) $x^4 - 5x^2 + 6$

10. (a) $x^3 + (\sqrt{6} - \sqrt{2} - \sqrt{3})x^2 + (\sqrt{6} - 3\sqrt{2} - 2\sqrt{3})x + 6$

(b) $x^3 - \sqrt{2}\,x^2 - 3x + 3\sqrt{2}$

If $f(-r) = f(r)$ for every r in the domain of f, the function is said to be an *even function*. If $f(-r) = -f(r)$ for every r in the domain of f, the function is said to be an *odd function*. For each of the following functions, find $f(1)$ and $f(-1)$, $f(2)$ and $f(-2)$, $f(k)$ and $f(-k)$, and then tell which are odd, which are even, and which are neither.

11. (a) $f(x) = x^4 + 3x^2 + 4$ (b) $f(x) = 2x^3 - 3x$

12. (a) $f(x) = 3x^4 - 2x^2 + x$ (b) $f(x) = x^6 + 3x^4 - 8$

13. (a) $f(x) = 2x^5 - x^2$ (b) $f(x) = 1 - x^2 - x^4$

14. (a) If all the exponents in a polynomial are even, is the polynomial an even function?

(b) If all the exponents in a polynomial are odd, is the polynomial an odd function?

15. (a) Is every polynomial function either odd or even? Illustrate your answer with an example.

(b) Is there any polynomial which is both odd and even?

16. Which, if any, of the numbers $2 + \sqrt{3}$, $3 + \sqrt{2}$, -3, $2 - \sqrt{3}$, and $3 - \sqrt{2}$ are zeros of the following polynomials?
    (a) $x^3 - x^2 - 11x + 3$
    (b) $x^4 - 10x^3 + 32x^2 - 34x + 7$
    (c) $x^3 - 5x^2 + x + 7$
    (d) $x^3 + (\sqrt{2} - \sqrt{3} - 5)x^2 + (6 + 3\sqrt{3} - 2\sqrt{2} - \sqrt{6})x$

17. If all the coefficients of a polynomial are integers and if the constant term is an odd integer, can an even integer be a zero of the polynomial? Can an odd integer be a zero? Justify your answers with specific illustrations.

18. Consider a third-degree polynomial of the form

$$p(x) = a_3x^3 + a_2x^2 + a_1x + a_0$$

with a_3, a_2, a_1, a_0 all integers.
    (a) Given that a_3, a_2, a_1, a_0 are all positive integers, what is the sign of each real zero of $p(x)$?
    (b) Given that a_3, a_2, a_1, a_0 are all negative integers, what is the sign of each real zero of $p(x)$?
    (c) Given that $a_0 = 1$ and r is an integral zero of $p(x)$, show that either $r = 1$ or $r = -1$.

8-5   INTEGRAL ZEROS OF INTEGRAL POLYNOMIALS

A polynomial is called an *integral polynomial* if all of its coefficients are integers. For example,

$$2x^2 - 3x + 1 \quad \text{and} \quad 7x - 5$$

are integral polynomials. We note that both the sum,

$$(2x^2 - 3x + 1) + (7x - 5) = 2x^2 + 4x - 4,$$

and the product,

$$(2x^2 - 3x + 1)(7x - 5) = 14x^3 - 31x^2 + 22x - 5,$$

of these two polynomials are also integral polynomials. It is clear from this example that the set of all integral polynomials is *closed* with respect to addition and multiplication. Thus, there is an *algebra of integral polynomials* contained in the algebra of polynomials. The basic axioms of our original algebra of polynomials are also valid for the algebra of integral polynomials. In particular, if an integer r is a zero of a polynomial $f(x)$, then r is called an *integral zero* of $f(x)$.

The problem in this section is that of finding integral zeros of integral polynomials. Let us attempt to develop a general procedure which, if followed, will yield all the integral zeros of an integral polynomial.

Problem 1. Find all the integral zeros of the integral polynomial

$$f(x) = 2x^3 - 5x^2 - 27x + 10.$$

Solution. We can try to solve this problem by computing $f(0)$, $f(1)$, $f(-1)$, $f(2)$, $f(-2)$, $f(3)$, $f(-3)$, and so on, until we find the zeros. For example, $f(0) = 10$, and therefore, 0 is not a zero. Also,

$$f(1) = 2 - 5 - 27 + 10, \quad \text{or} \ -20,$$

so that 1 is not a zero, and

$$f(-1) = 2(-1)^3 - 5(-1)^2 - 27(-1) + 10$$
$$= -2 - 5 + 27 + 10, \quad \text{or} \ 30,$$

so that -1 is not a zero. We could continue searching for integral zeros in this way for a long time without finding any, because some integral polynomials do not have any integral zeros.

There is a way of eliminating certain integers from consideration as zeros. For example, let us express $f(x)$ in the form

$$f(x) = x(2x^2 - 5x - 27) + 10.$$

Then the integer r is a zero of $f(x)$ if, and only if,

$$r(2r^2 - 5r - 27) + 10 = 0,$$

or, equivalently,

$$r(2r^2 - 5r - 27) = -10.$$

If r is an integer, then $2r^2 - 5r - 27$ must also be an integer because sums and products of integers are integers. By the equation above, r is a zero of $f(x)$ if, and only if, the product of the two integers r and $2r^2 - 5r - 27$ is -10. Therefore, for r to be an integral zero of $f(x)$, it must be a *divisor* of -10. Thus, the only *possible* integral zeros of $f(x)$ are the divisors of -10. Since

$$1, \quad 2, \quad 5, \quad 10, \quad -1, \quad -2, \quad -5, \quad -10$$

are all the integral divisors of -10 and 10, it follows that the only possible integral zeros of $f(x)$ are the eight integers listed above.

However, not all of these eight integers are zeros of $f(x)$, because 1 and -1 have already been shown not to be zeros. Since

$$f(10) = (2 \cdot 10^3) - (5 \cdot 10^2) - (27 \cdot 10) + 10,$$

and the first term, $2 \cdot 10^3$, is much larger than the sum of the other three, we see that the sum of all four terms of $f(10)$ cannot be zero. Therefore, 10 is not a zero of $f(x)$. Similarly, -10 is not a zero of $f(x)$.

We check by synthetic division to see which, if any, of the other four integers, 2, 5, -2, and -5, are zeros.

$$
\begin{array}{r|rrrr}
2 & 2 & -5 & -27 & 10 \\
  &   & 4 & -2 & -58 \\
\hline
  & 2 & -1 & -29 & -48
\end{array}
\qquad
\begin{array}{r|rrrr}
-2 & 2 & -5 & -27 & 10 \\
   &   & -4 & 18 & 18 \\
\hline
   & 2 & -9 & -9 & 28
\end{array}
$$

$$
\begin{array}{r|rrrr}
5 & 2 & -5 & -27 & 10 \\
  &   & 10 & 25 & -10 \\
\hline
  & 2 & 5 & -2 & 0
\end{array}
\qquad
\begin{array}{r|rrrr}
-5 & 2 & -5 & -27 & 10 \\
   &   & -10 & 75 & -240 \\
\hline
   & 2 & -15 & 48 & -230
\end{array}
$$

In only one case above, when $x = 5$, is the remainder 0. Hence, 5 is the only one of the four integers 2, 5, -2, -5 that is a zero of $f(x)$. We may conclude that 5 is the only integral zero of $f(x)$. Thus, we have solved our problem.

It is evident at a glance whether or not 0 is a zero of a polynomial; 0 is a zero if, and only if, the constant term of the polynomial is 0. Although we are not able to determine at a glance all the integral zeros of an integral polynomial, we can follow the procedure indicated in Problem 1 to determine the *possible* integral zeros. Thus, if

$$f(x) = a_n x^n + a_{n-1} x^{n-1} + \cdots + a_1 x + a_0$$

is an integral polynomial and r is an integral zero of $f(x)$, then

$$a_n r^n + a_{n-1} r^{n-1} + \cdots + a_1 r + a_0 = 0,$$
$$r(a_n r^{n-1} + a_{n-1} r^{n-2} + \cdots + a_1) + a_0 = 0,$$
$$r(a_n r^{n-1} + a_{n-1} r^{n-2} + \cdots + a_1) = -a_0.$$

Therefore, r must be a divisor of $-a_0$ or, alternatively, of a_0. This proves the following theorem.

INTEGRAL ZERO THEOREM

An integer is a zero of a given integral polynomial only if it is a divisor of the constant term of the polynomial.

We note that this theorem does *not* claim that every divisor, or even any divisor, of the constant term is a zero of the polynomial. For example, the only possible integral zeros of the integral polynomial $x^2 + x + 1$ are the divisors of the constant term 1, that is, 1 and -1. Since

$$1^2 + 1 + 1 = 3 \quad \text{and} \quad (-1)^2 + (-1) + 1 = 1,$$

neither 1 nor -1 is a zero. Consequently, the polynomial $x^2 + x + 1$ has no integral zeros.

Problem 2. Find the integral zeros of the integral polynomial

$$f(x) = 3x^3 - 17x^2 - 8x + 12.$$

Solution. According to the integral zero theorem, the possible integral zeros are the divisors of the constant term 12:

$$\pm 1, \quad \pm 2, \quad \pm 3, \quad \pm 4, \quad \pm 6, \quad \pm 12.$$

Perhaps you can see that 12 and -12 are not zeros, because the first term of $f(12)$ is much larger in absolute value than the sum of the other terms, and so is the first term of $f(-12)$. Since

$$f(1) = 3 - 17 - 8 + 12, \quad \text{or} \quad -10,$$

1 is not a zero. However,

$$f(-1) = -3 - 17 + 8 + 12, \quad \text{or} \quad 0,$$

and therefore, -1 is a zero.

Synthetic division can be used to show that 2, -2, 3, -3, 4, and -4 are not zeros. However, we shall leave the details to you. Let us check 6 and -6 as shown below.

6	3	-17	-8	12
		18	6	-12
	3	1	-2	0

-6	3	-17	-8	12
		-18	210	-1212
	3	-35	202	-1200

Evidently 6 is a zero, but -6 is not. Therefore,

$$\{-1, 6\}$$

is the set of all integral zeros of the given polynomial.

Problem 3. Find the integral zeros of the integral polynomial

$$x^3 + 2x^2 - 5x - 6.$$

Solution. By the integral zero theorem, the possible integral zeros are the divisors of the constant term -6:

$$\pm 1, \quad \pm 2, \quad \pm 3, \quad \pm 6.$$

Since $1^n = 1$ for every n we can find the value of $x^3 + 2x^2 - 5x - 6$ when $x = 1$ just by adding the coefficients:

$$1 + 2 - 5 - 6.$$

Since the sum of the coefficients is *not* zero, 1 is not a zero of $x^3 + 2x^2 - 5x - 6$.

Using synthetic division, we see that -1 is a zero of the polynomial.

$$
\begin{array}{r|rrrr}
-1 & 1 + 2 - 5 - 6 \\
   & \ \ - 1 - 1 + 6 \\
\hline
   & 1 + 1 - 6 + 0
\end{array}
$$

The synthetic division tells us that

$$x^3 + 2x^2 - 5x - 6 = (x + 1)(x^2 + x - 6).$$

Factoring $x^2 + x - 6$, we see that

$$x^3 + 2x^2 - 5x - 6 = (x + 1)(x + 3)(x - 2).$$

Hence -3 and 2 are also zeros of the given polynomial. Furthermore, because the third degree polynomial cannot be the product of more than three linear factors, we see that $\{-3, -1, 2\}$ is the complete set of integral zeros of $x^3 + 2x^2 - 5x - 6$.

Exercises

In Exercises 1–2, list the *possible* integral zeros of each polynomial. Then use synthetic division to see which, if any, actually are zeros of the polynomial.

1. (a) $2x^3 - x^2 - 13x - 6$ (b) $3x^3 + 23x^2 + 13x - 7$
2. (a) $6x^3 + 29x^2 - 6x - 5$ (b) $x^3 + x^2 - x - 1$

Find all the integral zeros of each of the following integral polynomials.

3. (a) $x^3 + 2x^2 - 2x - 4$ (b) $6x^3 - 67x^2 + 10x + 11$
4. (a) $15x^3 + 49x^2 + 8x - 12$ (b) $x^3 + x^2 + x - 1$

5. (a) $2x^4 - 25x^3 + 60x^2 + 23x + 36$

　　(b) $x^4 + 4x^3 - 17x^2 - 20x + 60$

6. (a) In Problem 2 on page 361, use synthetic division by $x - 6$ to write $3x^3 - 17x^2 - 8x + 12$ as a product of a linear and a quadratic polynomial. Can you factor the quadratic? What does it tell you about the zeros of the given third degree polynomial?

　　(b) In Problem 1 on page 359, use synthetic division by $x - 5$ to write $2x^3 - 5x^2 - 27x + 10$ as a product of a linear and a quadratic polynomial. Can you factor the quadratic? Can you find the zeros of the quadratic? What do you now know about the zeros of the given cubic (third degree) polynomial?

Find all the integral zeros, if any, of each of the following integral polynomials. If you can find nonintegral zeros, list them also.

7. $x^4 - 10x^3 + 35x^2 - 50x + 24$

8. $x^4 + 8x^3 + 13x^2 - 16x - 30$

9. $x^5 - 4x^4 + x^3 + 10x^2 - 4x - 8$

10. $x^4 - 12x^3 + 54x^2 - 68x + 81$

Find all the integral zeros of each of the following polynomials, and write each polynomial as a product of the factors you have obtained.

11. $x^4 + x^3 - 2x^2 + 4x - 24$

12. $3x^3 + 14x^2 - 72x + 64$

13. $x^3 - 4x^2 + 7x - 60$

14. $2x^3 - 5x^2 + 15x - 54$

15. $6x^4 + 23x^3 - 24x^2 - 68x + 48$

16. $7x^4 + 33x^3 - 181x^2 + 33x + 72$

17. If r is a zero of a real polynomial $p(x)$, then by the factor theorem, $p(x) = (x - r)q(x)$, where $q(x)$ is a polynomial of degree 1 less than the degree of $p(x)$. Show that

　　(a) if s is a zero of $q(x)$, then it is also a zero of $p(x)$.

　　(b) if $s \neq r$ and if s is a zero of $p(x)$, then s is a zero of $q(x)$.

18. We can use the results of Exercise 17 to decrease the number of steps in the search for integral zeros. We could have shortened Problem 2 on page 361 after we had found that -1 is a zero of $3x^3 - 17x^2 - 8x + 12$. By synthetic division we find that

$$3x^3 - 17x^2 - 8x + 12 = (x + 1)(3x^2 - 20x + 12).$$

Additional zeros of the cubic are also zeros of the quadratic polynomial $3x^2 - 20x + 12$, which we can factor as $(x - 6)(3x - 2)$. Thus, $3x^3 - 17x^2 - 8x + 12 = (x + 1)(x - 6)(3x - 2)$, and the set of zeros is $\{-1, 6, \frac{2}{3}\}$.

Find all the integral zeros of each of the following polynomials, using the factor theorem and the results of Exercise 17 to shorten your work. If you can find nonintegral zeros of the polynomial, list them also.

(a) $3x^3 - 4x^2 - 13x - 6$ (b) $x^3 + x^2 - 8x - 12$

(c) $x^3 - 8x^2 - 8x - 9$ (d) $2x^4 + 19x^3 - 8x^2 + 19x - 10$

8-6 RATIONAL ZEROS OF RATIONAL POLYNOMIALS

We shall call a polynomial $f(x)$ a *rational polynomial* if all the co-efficients of $f(x)$ are rational numbers. It is evident that the set of all rational polynomials is *closed* with respect to addition and multiplication, and that there is an algebra of rational polynomials as well as an algebra of integral polynomials. The basic axioms of our original algebra of polynomials are also valid for the algebra of rational polynomials. A zero r of a rational polynomial is called a *rational zero* if r is a rational number. In the preceding section, we were able to devise a method for finding all integral zeros of an integral polynomial. Now we shall indicate a similar method for determining all rational zeros of a rational polynomial.

Each rational polynomial $f(x)$ can be expressed as a product of a rational number and an integral polynomial $g(x)$. All we need do is consider each coefficient a_i of $f(x)$ as a quotient b_i/c_i of two integers and then find the least common multiple d of all denominators c_i. Then

$$f(x) = \frac{1}{d} g(x),$$

where all the coefficients of the polynomial $g(x)$ are now integers. For example, if

$$f(x) = \tfrac{1}{3}x^2 - \tfrac{3}{2}x + \tfrac{5}{6},$$

then the denominators 3, 2, and 6 of the coefficients have a least common multiple of 6. Hence,

$$f(x) = \tfrac{1}{6}(2x^2 - 9x + 5),$$

and the rational polynomial has been expressed as a product of the rational number $\tfrac{1}{6}$ and the integral polynomial $2x^2 - 9x + 5$.

If the rational polynomial $f(x)$ is expressed in the form

$$f(x) = \frac{1}{d}g(x)$$

as above, then for each real number r,

$$f(r) = \frac{1}{d}g(r).$$

Hence, $f(r) = 0$ if, and only if, $g(r) = 0$. Consequently, in looking for the rational zeros of the rational polynomial $f(x)$, we need only look for the rational zeros of the *integral* polynomial $g(x)$. Thus, let us consider the problem of finding all rational zeros of an integral polynomial.

Problem 1. Find all the rational zeros of the integral polynomial

$$g(x) = 6x^3 - x^2 - 2x - 15.$$

Solution. According to the integral zero theorem, the possible integral zeros of $g(x)$ are the divisors of -15:

$$\pm 1, \quad \pm 3, \quad \pm 5, \quad \pm 15.$$

You may readily verify that not one of these eight integers is a zero of $g(x)$.

On the other hand, the synthetic division

$$
\begin{array}{r|rrrr}
\frac{3}{2} & 6 & -1 & -2 & -15 \\
 & & 9 & 12 & 15 \\
\hline
 & 6 & 8 & 10 & 0
\end{array}
$$

shows that $\frac{3}{2}$ is a zero of $g(x)$.

Any rational number p/q, $q > 0$, expressed in lowest form is a zero of $g(x)$ if, and only if,

$$6\left(\frac{p}{q}\right)^3 - \left(\frac{p}{q}\right)^2 - 2\left(\frac{p}{q}\right) - 15 = 0,$$

or

$$6p^3 - p^2q - 2pq^2 - 15q^3 = 0. \tag{1}$$

By adding $15q^3$ to each side of Eq. (1) and factoring p out of the left side of the resulting equation, we obtain the equivalent equation

$$p(6p^2 - pq - 2q^2) = 15q^3.$$

The left side of this equation is expressed as a product of the two integers p and $6p^2 - pq - 2q^2$. The right side is an integer $15q^3$. Hence, p is a divisor of $15q^3$. However, we had assumed that p and q were relatively prime. Therefore, p must be a divisor of 15, and, hence of -15, the coefficient of q^3 in Eq. (1). If we start with Eq. (1), we can show that

$$6p^3 = q(p^2 + 2pq + 15q^2)$$

is an equivalent equation. By an argument similar to the one above, we see that the integer q is a divisor of $6p^3$ and hence, of 6, the coefficient of p^3.

Thus, we have shown that if the rational number p/q expressed in lowest form, with $q > 0$, is a zero of $g(x)$, then p must be a divisor of the constant term, -15, and q is a positive divisor of the leading coefficient, 6.

The possible values of p are ± 1, ± 3, ± 5, and ± 15; those of q are 1, 2, 3, and 6. Hence, the possible rational zeros of $g(x)$, other than integers, are

$$\pm \tfrac{1}{2}, \quad \pm \tfrac{1}{3}, \quad \pm \tfrac{1}{6}, \quad \pm \tfrac{3}{2}, \quad \pm \tfrac{5}{2}, \quad \pm \tfrac{5}{3}, \quad \pm \tfrac{5}{6}, \quad \pm \tfrac{15}{2}.$$

These represent all nonintegral values of p/q. We used synthetic division to show that $\tfrac{3}{2}$ is a zero of $g(x)$. This synthetic division enables us to factor the given cubic as follows:

$$6x^3 - x^2 - 2x - 15 = (x - \tfrac{3}{2})(6x^2 + 8x + 10).$$

Any number other than $\tfrac{3}{2}$ which is a zero of $6x^3 - x^2 - 2x - 15$ must be a zero of $6x^2 + 8x + 10$. The zeros of this quadratic, as of any other quadratic, are easily found in the following way.

$$6x^2 + 8x + 10 = 0$$
$$3x^2 + 4x + 5 = 0 \qquad\qquad \text{(Mult-A)}$$

$$x = \frac{-4 + \sqrt{-44}}{6} \quad \text{or} \quad x = \frac{-4 - \sqrt{-44}}{6} \quad \text{(Quadratic Formula)}$$

We see that $\tfrac{3}{2}$ is the only rational zero of $6x^3 - x^2 - 2x - 15$; in fact $\tfrac{3}{2}$ is the only real zero of this cubic.

The general theorem of integral polynomials illustrated by Problem 1 can be stated in the following way.

RATIONAL ZERO THEOREM

A rational number p/q, $q > 0$, expressed in lowest form, is a zero of the integral polynomial

$$g(x) = a_n x^n + a_{n-1} x^{n-1} + \cdots + a_1 x + a_0$$

only if p is a divisor of the constant term a_0 and q is a divisor of the leading coefficient a_n.

Problem 2. Find the rational zeros of the integral polynomial

$$g(x) = 10x^3 - 17x^2 - 7x + 2.$$

Solution. According to the rational zero theorem, the possible rational zeros have the form p/q, where p is a divisor of 2 and q is a divisor of 10. Consequently, p can be ± 1 or ± 2, and q can be 1, 2, 5, or 10. Thus, the possible rational zeros of $g(x)$ are

$$\pm 1, \quad \pm \tfrac{1}{2}, \quad \pm \tfrac{1}{5}, \quad \pm \tfrac{1}{10}, \quad \pm 2, \quad \pm \tfrac{2}{5}.$$

Since $g(1) = 10 - 17 - 7 + 2$ or -12 and $g(-1) = -10 - 17 + 7 + 2$ or -18, neither 1 nor -1 is a zero of $g(x)$. By the synthetic division given below, we see that

$$\{-\tfrac{1}{2}, \ \tfrac{1}{5}, \ 2\}$$

is the set of all rational zeros of $g(x)$.

$$
\begin{array}{r|rrrr}
\tfrac{1}{2} & 10 & -17 & -7 & 2 \\
 & & 5 & -6 & -\tfrac{13}{2} \\ \hline
 & 10 & -12 & -13 & -\tfrac{9}{2}
\end{array}
\qquad
\begin{array}{r|rrrr}
-\tfrac{1}{2} & 10 & -17 & -7 & 2 \\
 & & -5 & 11 & -2 \\ \hline
 & 10 & -22 & 4 & 0
\end{array}
$$

$$
\begin{array}{r|rrrr}
\tfrac{1}{5} & 10 & -17 & -7 & 2 \\
 & & 2 & -3 & -2 \\ \hline
 & 10 & -15 & -10 & 0
\end{array}
\qquad
\begin{array}{r|rrrr}
-\tfrac{1}{5} & 10 & -17 & -7 & 2 \\
 & & -2 & \tfrac{19}{5} & \\ \hline
 & 10 & -19 & -\tfrac{16}{5} &
\end{array}
$$

$$
\begin{array}{r|rrrr}
.1 & 10 & -17 & -7 & 2 \\
 & & 1 & -1.6 & \\ \hline
 & 10 & -16 & -8.6 &
\end{array}
\qquad
\begin{array}{r|rrrr}
-.1 & 10 & -17 & -7 & 2 \\
 & & -1 & 1.8 & \\ \hline
 & 10 & -18 & -5.2 &
\end{array}
$$

$$
\begin{array}{r|rrrr}
2 & 10 & -17 & -7 & 2 \\
 & & 20 & 6 & -2 \\ \hline
 & 10 & 3 & -1 & 0
\end{array}
\qquad
\begin{array}{r|rrrr}
-2 & 10 & -17 & -7 & 2 \\
 & & -20 & 74 & \\ \hline
 & 10 & -37 & 67 &
\end{array}
$$

$$\begin{array}{r|rrrr} .4 & 10 & -17 & -7 & 2 \\ & & 4 & -5.2 & \\ \hline & 10 & -13 & -12.2 & \end{array} \qquad \begin{array}{r|rrrr} -.4 & 10 & -17 & -7 & 2 \\ & & & -4 & 8.4 \\ \hline & 10 & -21 & 1.4 & \end{array}$$

You will note that we did not complete some of the divisions above, but stopped as soon as a nonintegral rational number appeared in the bottom row. Any further multiplication of this number and succeeding numbers by the rational number at the side will not yield an integer, and hence, the final remainder at the end of the row cannot be zero.

Another way to find the zeros is to factor the given polynomial (of degree n) using the first zero found and then work with the quotient (of degree $n - 1$) to find the remaining zeros. Thus the work in Problem 2 could be reduced to the following, assuming the zero $\frac{1}{5}$ is found first.

$$\begin{array}{r|rrrr} \frac{1}{5} & 10 & -17 & -7 & 2 \\ & & 2 & -3 & -2 \\ \hline & 10 & -15 & -10 & 0 \end{array}$$

$$\begin{aligned} 10x^3 - 17x^2 - 7x + 2 &= (x - \tfrac{1}{5})(10x^2 - 15x - 10) \\ &= (5x - 1)(2x^2 - 3x - 2) \\ &= (5x - 1)(2x + 1)(x - 2) \end{aligned}$$

Thus, the set of rational zeros is

$$\{\tfrac{1}{5}, \ -\tfrac{1}{2}, \ 2\}.$$

Exercises

In Exercises 1–4, list the possible rational zeros of each integral polynomial. Then find which actually are zeros of the polynomial.

1. (a) $2x^3 + x^2 + x - 1$ (b) $3x^3 + 5x^2 + 4x - 2$
2. (a) $10x^3 + 19x^2 - 5x - 6$ (b) $18x^3 - 21x^2 + 8x - 1$
3. (a) $20x^3 - 12x^2 - 3x + 2$ (b) $14x^4 - 45x^3 + 18x^2 + 12x - 5$
4. (a) $3x^3 - 13x^2 + 52x - 48$ (b) $4x^4 - 3x^3 + 12x^2 + 2x + 3$

Find all the rational zeros of each of the following polynomials.

5. (a) $6x^3 - 11x^2 + 7x - 6$
    (b) $2x^3 - 3x^2 + \frac{3}{2}x - \frac{1}{4}$
6. (a) $10x^4 + 19x^3 - 5x^2 + 19x - 15$
    (b) $12x^4 + 13x^3 - x^2 + 13x + 12$

7. (a) $3x^3 + 13x^2 + 3x - 4$
  (b) $x^4 + 4x^3 + 6x^2 + 4x + 1$
8. (a) $8x^4 - 28x^3 + 18x^2 + 27x - 27$
  (b) $2 - 3x - 12x^2 + 20x^3$
9. (a) $\frac{9}{8}x^4 - 3x^3 - x^2 + 4x + 4$
  (b) $x^3 + \frac{49}{30}x^2 - \frac{26}{15}x - 2$

---

10. Factor by the distributive law and then use synthetic division to find all the rational zeros of the following polynomials.
  (a) $20x^4 - 12x^3 - 3x^2 + 2x$
  (b) $12x^4 + 4x^3 - 3x^2 - x$

11. (a) Find the zeros of $2x^3 + 5x^2 - x - 6$.
  (b) Find the zeros of $2 + 5x - x^2 - 6x^3$.
  (c) Compare the zeros of the polynomials in parts (a) and (b).
  (d) If the zeros of $4x^3 + 3x^2 - 16x - 12$ are -2, $-\frac{3}{4}$, and 2, what do you expect the zeros of $4 + 3x - 16x^2 - 12x^3$ will be? Check to determine whether your answers are correct.

12. What relation do you think the zeros of

$$a_n x^n + a_{n-1}x^{n-1} + \cdots + a_1 x + a_0$$

have to the zeros of $a_n + a_{n-1}x + \cdots + a_1 x^{n-1} + a_0 x^n$? (Hint: Think about Exercise 11.)

13. Prove the rational zero theorem for $p(x) = a_3 x^3 + a_2 x^2 + a_1 x + a_0$.

Review for Sections 8–1 through 8–6

Perform the indicated operations.
1. $(7x^2 + 2x + 9) + (x^2 - 5x - 10)$
2. $(3x^2 - x - 1) + (x^2 + 4x - 11)$
3. $(x^3 - 4x^2 + 13) - (x^2 - 2x + 5)$
4. $(4x^4 + 3x^2 + 17) - (3x^3 + 2x^2 - 13)$
5. $(x^2 + 2x + 2)(x^2 - 3x + 1)$
6. $(2x^2 - 4x + 1)(3x^2 - x + 5)$

State the additive inverse of each of the following polynomials.
7. $7x^2 + x + 1$ 8. $3x^3 - 2x + 1$
9. $-4x^3 + 3x^2 + 17$ 10. $x^4 - 4$

Factor each of the following polynomials as indicated.

11. $x^3 + 6x^2 + 11x + 6$; first divide by $x + 1$

12. $x^3 - 6x^2 + 11x - 6$; first divide by $x - 1$

13. $x^3 + 6x^2 - 25x - 150$; first divide by $x - 5$

14. $x^5 + 6x^4 - 7x^3$; first divide by x^3

Use synthetic division to find the quotient and remainder in each of the following divisions.

15. $(4x^3 + 3x^2 + 2x + 1) \div (x + 3)$

16. $(x^3 - 10x^2 + 5x - 10) \div (x - 5)$

17. $(2x^3 + 2x^2 - 40x - 7) \div (x - 4)$

18. $(5x^3 - x^2 + x - 20) \div (x + 1)$

Find all the integral zeros of each of the following polynomials.

19. $x^3 - 2x^2 - 4x + 8$ **20.** $x^3 - 9x^2 + 26x - 24$

21. $3x^3 + 38x^2 + 113x - 42$ **22.** $5x^3 + 31x^2 + 51x + 9$

23. $x^4 + 6x^3 + 10x^2 - 3x - 14$

24. $x^5 - 5x^4 + 4x^3 - 20x^2 + 3x - 15$

Find the rational zeros of each of the following polynomials and write each polynomial as a product of the factors you have found.

25. $10x^3 + 21x^2 - 25x + 6$ **26.** $9x^3 - 19x - 10$

27. $12x^4 - 4x^3 + 31x^2 - 12x - 15$

28. $7x^4 + 22x^3 + 38x^2 + 5x$

29. $20x^4 + x^3 + 19x^2 + x - 1$

30. $30x^4 + 11x^3 + 6x^2 - 24x - 5$

Answers to Review for Sections 8–1 through 8–6

1. $8x^2 - 3x - 1$ **2.** $4x^2 + 3x - 12$

3. $x^3 - 5x^2 + 2x + 8$ **4.** $4x^4 - 3x^3 + x^2 + 30$

5. $x^4 - x^3 - 3x^2 - 4x + 2$ **6.** $6x^4 - 14x^3 + 17x^2 - 21x + 5$

7. $-7x^2 - x - 1$ **8.** $-3x^3 + 2x - 1$

9. $4x^3 - 3x^2 - 17$ **10.** $-x^4 + 4$

11. $(x + 1)(x + 3)(x + 2)$ **12.** $(x - 1)(x - 2)(x - 3)$

13. $(x - 5)(x + 5)(x + 6)$ **14.** $x^3(x + 7)(x - 1)$

15. $Q = 4x^2 - 9x + 29,\ R = -86$

16. $Q = x^2 - 5x - 20,\ R = -110$

17. $Q = 2x^2 + 10x,\ R = -7$

18. $Q = 5x^2 - 6x + 7,\ R = -27$

19. $2, -2$

20. $2, 3, 4$

21. $-6, -7$

22. -3

23. $-2, 1$

24. 5

25. $-3, \frac{2}{5}, \frac{1}{2}; \ (x + 3)(5x - 2)(2x - 1)$

26. $-\frac{2}{3}, -1, \frac{5}{3}; \ (3x + 2)(3x - 5)(x + 1)$

27. $-\frac{1}{2}, \frac{5}{6}; \ (2x + 1)(6x - 5)(x^2 + 3)$

28. $0, -\frac{1}{7}; \ x(7x + 1)(x^2 + 3x + 5)$

29. $-\frac{1}{4}, \frac{1}{5}; \ (4x + 1)(5x - 1)(x^2 + 1)$

30. $\frac{5}{6}, -\frac{1}{5}; \ (6x - 5)(5x + 1)(x^2 + x + 1)$

8-7   IRRATIONALITY OF ROOTS

In geometry, you may have used the unique factorization theorem to prove that certain real numbers are irrational. We can also use the rational zero theorem to prove that certain real numbers are irrational. The procedure used in a proof of this type is illustrated below.

Problem 1. Prove that $\sqrt{3}$ is an irrational number.

Solution. Since

$$(\sqrt{3})^2 - 3 = 0,$$

the number $\sqrt{3}$ is a zero of the integral polynomial

$$x^2 - 3.$$

According to the rational zero theorem, the only possible rational zeros of this polynomial are

$$\pm 1 \quad \text{and} \quad \pm 3.$$

By substitution, we see that not one of these four numbers is a zero of $x^2 - 3$. Therefore, the polynomial $x^2 - 3$ has no rational zeros. Hence, if $x^2 - 3$ does have real zeros, they must be irrational numbers. We know that $\sqrt{3}$ is a real zero of this polynomial. Consequently, $\sqrt{3}$ is an irrational number.

Problem 2. Find an integral polynomial of degree 3 having the three rational zeros $-\frac{1}{5}, \frac{2}{3}$, and 3.

Solution. The cubic polynomial

$$f(x) = (x + \tfrac{1}{5})(x - \tfrac{2}{3})(x - 3)$$

has the given numbers as zeros, as does the polynomial $15f(x)$:

$$
\begin{aligned}
15f(x) &= [5(x + \tfrac{1}{5})][3(x - \tfrac{2}{3})](x - 3) \\
&= (5x + 1)(3x - 2)(x - 3) \\
&= 15x^3 - 52x^2 + 19x + 6.
\end{aligned}
$$

Thus, $15f(x)$ is an integral polynomial of degree 3 with the given zeros.

Problem 3. Find an integral polynomial having the real number $\sqrt{5} - \sqrt{3}$ as a zero. Prove that $\sqrt{5} - \sqrt{3}$ is an irrational number.

Solution. If we begin with the polynomial $x - (\sqrt{5} - \sqrt{3})$, which has $\sqrt{5} - \sqrt{3}$ as a zero, and multiply it by other polynomials, we shall always get polynomials having $\sqrt{5} - \sqrt{3}$ as a zero. What we must do is multiply it by other polynomials so that the product has integral coefficients. To do this, we obtain differences of squares in the following way.

$$
\begin{aligned}
(x - \sqrt{5} + \sqrt{3})(x - \sqrt{5} - \sqrt{3}) &= (x - \sqrt{5})^2 - (\sqrt{3})^2 \\
&= x^2 - 2\sqrt{5}x + 5 - 3 \\
&= x^2 - 2\sqrt{5}x + 2
\end{aligned}
$$

$$
\begin{aligned}
(x^2 - 2\sqrt{5}x + 2)(x^2 + 2\sqrt{5}x + 2) &= (x^2 + 2)^2 - (2\sqrt{5}x)^2 \\
&= x^4 + 4x^2 + 4 - 20x^2 \\
&= x^4 - 16x^2 + 4
\end{aligned}
$$

Thus, the integral polynomial

$$g(x) = x^4 - 16x^2 + 4$$

has $\sqrt{5} - \sqrt{3}$ as one of its zeros. Does $g(x)$ have any rational zeros? No, since ± 1, ± 2, and ± 4 are its only possible rational zeros, and not one of these six numbers is a zero. Hence, $\sqrt{5} - \sqrt{3}$ must be an irrational zero of $g(x)$. This proves that $\sqrt{5} - \sqrt{3}$ is an irrational number. Incidentally, we have also proven that $\sqrt{5} + \sqrt{3}$ is an irrational number.

Exercises

In Exercises 1–3 find an integral polynomial of degree 3 for each of the given sets of zeros.

1. (a) $\{2, -2, 3\}$ (b) $\{\frac{1}{2}, \frac{3}{2}, -1\}$

2. (a) $\{3, -1, \frac{2}{5}\}$ (b) $\{-3, 1, -\frac{2}{5}\}$

3. (a) $\{\frac{1}{3}, -1, \frac{5}{2}\}$ (b) $\{\frac{2}{3}, 0, -\frac{3}{4}\}$

In Exercises 4–7 find an integral polynomial of degree 4 for each of the following sets of zeros.

4. (a) $\{1, 2, 3, 4\}$ (b) $\{1, 2, 4, -7\}$

5. (a) $\{1, \frac{1}{2}, \frac{1}{3}, \frac{1}{4}\}$ (b) $\{-\frac{2}{3}, \frac{2}{3}, \frac{1}{5}, -\frac{1}{5}\}$

6. (a) $\{1, -1, \frac{3}{4}, \frac{2}{5}\}$ (b) $\{2, -2, \frac{1}{2}, -\frac{1}{2}\}$

7. (a) $\{2, 0, -2\}$ (several possibilities)
    (b) $\{3, 0, -3\}$ (several possibilities)

For each of the following real numbers, find an integral polynomial which has that number as a zero. Use the rational zero theorem and your polynomial to prove that the given number is irrational.

8. (a) $\sqrt{2}$ (b) $\sqrt{5}$

9. (a) $3 - \sqrt{5}$ (b) $1 + \sqrt{2}$

10. (a) $\sqrt{7} - \sqrt{2}$ (b) $\sqrt{2} + \sqrt{3}$

11. (a) $\frac{1}{2} + \frac{1}{2}\sqrt{3}$ (b) $\frac{1}{2} - \frac{1}{2}\sqrt{3}$

12. (a) $\sqrt[3]{4}$ (b) $\sqrt[3]{2}$

---

13. Prove that each of the following numbers is irrational.

  (a) $\sqrt{6}$ (b) $\sqrt[3]{13}$

  (c) $\sqrt[n]{2}$, n any integer > 1 (d) $2 - \sqrt[3]{3}$

  (e) $\dfrac{1}{\sqrt[5]{2}}$

14. (a) Find an integral polynomial of degree three having zeros $\{2, 3, 5\}$.

  (b) Find an integral polynomial of degree three having zeros $\{\frac{1}{2}, \frac{1}{3}, \frac{1}{5}\}$.

  (c) How are the solution sets of (a) and (b) related?

  (d) How are the polynomials of (a) and (b) related?

8–8   FACTORING RATIONAL POLYNOMIALS

Every positive integer can be factored into a product of prime integers. For example,

$$60 = 2 \times 2 \times 3 \times 5.$$

We recall that an integer n greater than 1 is called a *prime* if n has no divisor d such that $1 < d < n$.

Similarly, every rational polynomial can be factored into a product of prime rational polynomials. A rational polynomial is called *prime* if it has no rational divisor $d(x)$ of positive degree less than the degree of $p(x)$. For example, the rational polynomial

$$p(x) = x^2 + x + 1$$

is prime, because it has no *rational* divisor of positive degree less than 2, that is, of degree 1. It has no rational divisor of degree 1 because it has no rational zero. Every rational polynomial of degree 1 is prime, since it cannot have a divisor of positive degree less than 1 because there is no positive integer less than 1.

Problem 1. Factor the polynomial

$$p(x) = x^3 + 2x^2 - 5x - 6$$

into a product of primes.

Solution. The synthetic division

$$
\begin{array}{r|rrrr}
2 & 1 & 2 & -5 & -6 \\
  &   & 2 & 8 & 6 \\
\hline
  & 1 & 4 & 3 & 0
\end{array}
$$

shows that 2 is a zero of $p(x)$, and therefore, $x - 2$ is a divisor of $p(x)$. Furthermore, it shows that

$$p(x) = (x - 2)(x^2 + 4x + 3).$$

However, $x^2 + 4x + 3$ is not a prime rational polynomial since

$$x^2 + 4x + 3 = (x + 1)(x + 3).$$

Hence, $p(x)$ is factored into a product of prime rational polynomials as follows:

$$p(x) = (x - 2)(x + 1)(x + 3).$$

Problem 2. Factor the following polynomial into a product of primes.

$$f(x) = 2x^3 - x^2 + 13x + 7$$

Solution. The possible rational zeros of $f(x)$ are listed below.

$$\pm 1, \quad \pm 7, \quad \pm\tfrac{1}{2}, \quad \pm\tfrac{7}{2}$$

Clearly, no odd integer can be a zero, because if we let x be an odd integer in $f(x)$, three of the resulting terms are odd integers and one is an even integer. Such a sum must be odd, and hence cannot be zero. Thus, we need not check ± 1 or ± 7. The synthetic division

$$
\begin{array}{r|rrrr}
-\tfrac{1}{2} & 2 & -1 & 13 & 7 \\
 & & -1 & 1 & -7 \\
\hline
 & 2 & -2 & 14 & 0
\end{array}
$$

shows that $-\tfrac{1}{2}$ is a zero of $f(x)$, and therefore, that $x - (-\tfrac{1}{2})$ is a factor. Thus,

$$f(x) = (x + \tfrac{1}{2})(2x^2 - 2x + 14). \tag{1}$$

We can factor the integer 2 out of the polynomial $2x^2 - 2x + 14$ and then multiply 2 and the factor $x + \tfrac{1}{2}$, obtaining first

$$(x + \tfrac{1}{2})(2)(x^2 - x + 7)$$

and then

$$f(x) = (2x + 1)(x^2 - x + 7). \tag{2}$$

We cannot factor $x^2 - x + 7$ further, since it has no rational zeros. Hence, either (1) or (2) above yields a factorization of $f(x)$ into a product of prime rational polynomials.

Problem 3. Factor the polynomial

$$p(x) = 2x^3 + x - 1$$

into a product of primes.

Solution. The only possible rational zeros of $p(x)$ are ± 1 and $\pm\tfrac{1}{2}$. We leave it to you to verify that not one of these four numbers is a zero of $p(x)$. Hence, $p(x)$ has no rational divisor of degree 1. Can $p(x)$ have a rational divisor $f(x)$ of degree 2? If it does, then the quotient obtained on dividing $p(x)$ by $f(x)$ is a rational polynomial $g(x)$ of degree 1, and

$$p(x) = f(x)g(x).$$

However, $p(x)$ would then have a rational divisor $g(x)$ of degree 1, contrary to our discovery that $p(x)$ has no rational divisor of degree 1. Therefore, $p(x)$ cannot have a rational divisor of degree 2. Consequently, $p(x)$ is a prime and cannot be factored.

We could factor the polynomial $p(x)$ of Problem 3 as follows:

$$p(x) = 2(x^3 + \tfrac{1}{2}x - \tfrac{1}{2}).$$

However, we are looking for a factorization in which each factor has a positive degree. The factor 2, on the other hand, has degree 0.

Exercises

Factor each of the following rational polynomials into a product of rational prime polynomials.

1. (a) $2x^2 + x - 6$ (b) $3x^2 - 6x - 9$
2. (a) $3x^2 - 5x - 9$ (b) $x^2 + 1$
3. (a) $x^3 - 1$ (b) $x^3 + 1$
4. (a) $2x^3 + 5x^2 - 22x + 15$ (b) $16x^4 - 14x^3 - 15x^2$
5. (a) $9x^3 + 21x^2 - 17x + 3$ (b) $4x^3 - 20x^2 + 17x - 4$
6. (a) $2x^3 + 3x^2 - 7x + 6$ (b) $x^3 + x^2 + x + 1$
7. (a) $x^3 + 3x^2 + 3x + 1$ (b) $x^4 + 8x^3 + 24x^2 + 32x + 16$
8. (a) $x^4 - 1$ (b) $2x^4 - 17x^2 - 9$
9. (a) $x^3 + x^2 - 3$ (b) $x^4 + 1$
10. (a) $8x^3 - 125$ (b) $27x^3 + 1$

Factor each of the following rational polynomials into a product of rational prime polynomials.

11. $3x^3 - 8x^2 + 11x - 10$
12. $x^4 - 11x^3 + 30x^2 - 8x$
13. $x^4 - 5x^2 + 6$
14. $6x^4 + 7x^3 + 12x^2 + x - 2$
15. $3x^4 - 20x^3 + 13x^2 - 6x$
16. $x^4 + x^3 - 2x^2 + x - 1$
17. $15x^4 + 9x^2 - 6$
18. $x^5 + 1$
19. $64x^6 - 1$
20. $64x^6 + 1$

8–9 FURTHER FACTORING

If a rational polynomial has degree 4 or more, then it is more difficult to factor it into a product of primes. This is illustrated below.

Problem. Factor the polynomial

$$g(x) = x^4 + 2x^3 - 8x^2 + 18x - 9$$

into a product of primes.

Solution. The possible rational zeros are ± 1, ± 3, and ± 9. You can quickly verify that not one of these integers is a zero. Hence, $g(x)$ has no linear rational factors. This does not necessarily mean that $g(x)$ is a prime rational polynomial, because it is possible that $g(x) = p(x)q(x)$, where $p(x)$ and $q(x)$ are prime rational polynomials of degree 2. Since the coefficient of x^4 in $g(x)$ is 1, we might try polynomials of the form $x^2 + ax + b$ and $x^2 + cx + d$ to see whether there are integers a, b, c, and d such that

$$g(x) = (x^2 + ax + b)(x^2 + cx + d).$$

Since

$$(x^2 + ax + b)(x^2 + cx + d)$$
$$= x^4 + (a + c)x^3 + (ac + b + d)x^2 + (ad + bc)x + bd,$$

we must have

$$x^4 + (a + c)x^3 + (ac + b + d)x^2 + (ad + bc)x + bd$$
$$= x^4 + 2x^3 - 8x^2 + 18x - 9.$$

These polynomials are equal if, and only if, corresponding coefficients are equal. Thus, the integers a, b, c, and d must be solutions of the following system of equations.

$$\begin{cases} a + c = 2 \\ ac + b + d = -8 \\ ad + bc = 18 \\ bd = -9 \end{cases}$$

If b and d are integers and $bd = -9$, then, assuming b to be the positive integer, we must have

$$b = 1,\ d = -9; \quad \text{or} \quad b = 3,\ d = -3; \quad \text{or} \quad b = 9,\ d = -1.$$

When we give these values to b and d as indicated below, then the first three equations of the system above reduce to the following equations.

$b = 1, d = -9$ $b = 3, d = -3$ $b = 9, d = -1$

$$\begin{cases} a + c = 2 \\ ac = 0 \\ -9a + c = 18 \end{cases} \qquad \begin{cases} a + c = 2 \\ ac = -8 \\ -a + c = 6 \end{cases} \qquad \begin{cases} a + c = 2 \\ ac = -16 \\ -a + 9c = 18 \end{cases}$$

The systems of linear equations taken from each set of equations above may be solved in the following way.

$$\begin{cases} a + c = 2 \\ -9a + c = 18 \end{cases} \qquad \begin{cases} a + c = 2 \\ -a + c = 6 \end{cases} \qquad \begin{cases} a + c = 2 \\ -a + 9c = 18 \end{cases}$$

$$-10a = 16 \qquad\qquad 2c = 8 \qquad\qquad 10c = 20$$

$$a = -\tfrac{8}{5}, \ c = \tfrac{18}{5} \qquad c = 4, \ a = -2 \qquad c = 2, \ a = 0$$

In only one of three cases where values are given to b and d is the value of ac what it should be, and that is the middle system. There $ac = -8$. Thus, $a = -2, b = 3, c = 4, d = -3$ is a solution of our system of equations, and

$$g(x) = (x^2 - 2x + 3)(x^2 + 4x - 3)$$

is a factorization of $g(x)$ into a product of prime rational polynomials.

Exercises

Factor each of the following rational polynomials into a product of rational prime polynomials.

1. (a) $x^4 + 3x^3 + 4x^2 + 9x + 3$
   (b) $x^4 - x^3 - 8x^2 + 6x + 8$

2. (a) $x^4 - x^3 - 13x^2 + x + 12$
   (b) $x^4 + 4x^3 - 7x^2 - 22x + 24$

3. (a) $x^4 + 2x^3 + 3x^2 + 2x + 1$
   (b) $x^4 + 3x^2 + 2$

4. (a) $x^4 + 7x^3 + x^2 - 63x - 90$
   (b) $x^4 - 4x^3 - x^2 + 16x - 12$

5. (a) $x^4 + 4x^3 - 16x^2 + 20x - 105$
   (b) $x^4 + 8x^3 + 16x^2 + 8x + 15$

6. (a) $x^4 - 9x^2 - 4x + 12$
   (b) $x^4 - 19x^2 - 6x + 72$

7. (a) $x^4 - 3x^3 + 4x^2 - 8x - 24$
   (b) $x^4 - 4x^3 + 6x^2 - 7x + 2$

Preparation for Section 8–10

Graph the following polynomials and find the zeros of each from your graph.

1. $f(x) = x^2 - 5x + 6$

2. $g(x) = x^2 + 6x - 7$

3. $p(x) = 3x^2 - 11x - 4$

4. $h(x) = 2x^2 + 7x - 15$

5. $f(x) = 6x^2 + 5x + 1$

6. $p(x) = x^2 + \frac{1}{2}x - 3$

8–10   IRRATIONAL ZEROS

Having developed a method for finding all rational zeros of a rational polynomial, we shall now try to find irrational zeros of a polynomial. Naturally, an *irrational zero* is a zero that is an irrational number. We can determine all the zeros of a quadratic polynomial by means of the quadratic formula. There are comparable formulas for finding all the zeros of a cubic or quartic polynomial, but we shall not present them here. This is as far as we can go, however, since it can be proved that there are no algebraic formulas for finding all the zeros of polynomials of degree 5 and higher. It is also true that there are no methods of the type described in the preceding two sections for determining irrational zeros of polynomials. For practical applications, it is often necessary to approximate the irrational zeros of a polynomial. There are many ways of doing this, one of which consists of the following steps.

The polynomial

$$p(x) = x^3 - 5x + 1$$

does not have any rational zeros. If we graph the polynomial equation $y = x^3 - 5x + 1$, we see that it probably has irrational zeros. This equation is graphed in the neighborhood of the origin in Fig. 8–1, with the aid of the following table of values.

x	-3	$-2\frac{1}{2}$	-2	$-1\frac{1}{2}$	-1	$-\frac{1}{2}$	0	$\frac{1}{2}$	1	$1\frac{1}{2}$	2	$2\frac{1}{2}$	3
y	-11	$-2\frac{1}{8}$	3	$5\frac{1}{8}$	5	$3\frac{3}{8}$	1	$-1\frac{3}{8}$	-3	$-3\frac{1}{8}$	-1	$4\frac{1}{8}$	13

The zeros of $p(x)$ are the x-coordinates of the points having y-coordinates 0; that is, the zeros of $p(x)$ are the x-coordinates of the points at which the graph intersects the x-axis.

If we assume that the graph of the equation $y = p(x)$ is a smooth connected curve such as that drawn in Fig. 8–1, then it is evident that there are three real zeros of $p(x)$, denoted by r_1, r_2, and r_3 in the figure.   From the graph, it is apparent that

$$-\tfrac{5}{2} < r_1 < -2,$$
$$0 < r_2 < \tfrac{1}{2},$$
$$2 < r_3 < \tfrac{5}{2}.$$

Since $p(x)$ has no rational zeros, each of the numbers r_1, r_2, and r_3 must be irrational. The inequalities above give us rational approximations of these zeros.

We can actually determine the approximate location of each zero by looking only at the table of values above. *Thus, there must be a zero between two numbers if the values of $p(x)$ at these two numbers have opposite sign.* Hence, it is clear that there is a zero r_1 of $p(x)$ between $-\tfrac{5}{2}$ and -2, since $p(-\tfrac{5}{2}) < 0$ and $p(-2) > 0$; and there must be a zero r_2 of $p(x)$ between 0 and $\tfrac{1}{2}$, since $p(0) > 0$ and $p(\tfrac{1}{2}) < 0$. Similarly, there is a third zero r_3 and $2 < r_3 < \tfrac{5}{2}$, since $p(2) < 0$ and $p(\tfrac{5}{2}) > 0$. Graphically, this means that the curve must cross the x-axis between a point of the curve above the x-axis and a point of the curve below the x-axis.

Each of the irrational zeros of the polynomial $p(x)$ above may be approximated more accurately by using linear interpolation.   For example, let us find a more accurate rational approximation of r_1. The straight line joining the points $A(-\tfrac{5}{2}, -\tfrac{17}{8})$ and $B(-2, 3)$ of Fig. 8–1 has slope

$$\frac{-\tfrac{17}{8} - 3}{-\tfrac{5}{2} + 2}, \quad \text{or} \quad \frac{41}{4}.$$

Figure 8–2 shows an enlarged picture of segment $\overline{AB}$. We choose as our next approximation of r_1 the coordinate of P, the point of intersection of segment $\overline{AB}$ and the x-axis. Since the slope of segment $\overline{PB}$ is $3/a$, where a is as indicated in Fig. 8–2, we must have

$$\frac{3}{a} = \frac{41}{4} \quad \text{and} \quad a = \frac{12}{41}, \quad \text{or } .3 \text{ approximately.}$$

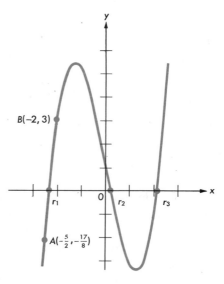

B(−2, 3)

$A(-\tfrac{5}{2}, -\tfrac{17}{8})$

FIGURE 8–1

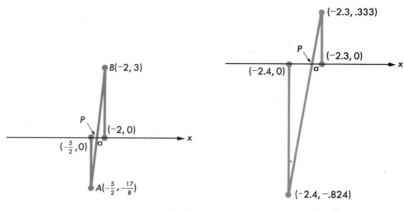

FIGURE 8–2   FIGURE 8–3

Hence, the x-coordinate of P is approximately $-2 - .3$, or -2.3.
Therefore,

$$r_1 \doteq -2.3.$$

To obtain a more accurate approximation of r_1, repeat this process
using numbers closer to r_1.

$$p(-2.4) = -.824, \quad p(-2.3) = .333$$

Hence, $-2.4 < r_1 < -2.3$. Now the line segment joining the points
$(-2.4, -.824)$ and $(-2.3, .333)$ has slope

$$\frac{-.824 - .333}{-2.4 + 2.3}, \quad \text{or } 11.57.$$

According to Fig. 8–3,

$$\frac{.333}{a} = 11.57 \quad \text{and} \quad a = \frac{.333}{11.57}, \quad \text{or } a \doteq .03.$$

Hence, $r_1 \doteq -2.3 - .03$, or $r_1 \doteq -2.33$.

You undoubtedly see how we could continue this process by computing $P(-2.34)$ and $P(-2.33)$ and once more using linear interpolation.

Exercises

In Exercises 1–2, locate zeros of each polynomial between successive integers.
Sketch the graph of $y = p(x)$.

1. (a) $p(x) = 3x^3 - 7x^2 - 6x + 14$
   (b) $p(x) = 2x^3 + x^2 - 10x - 5$
2. (a) $p(x) = 2x^3 - 3x^2 - 24x + 36$
   (b) $p(x) = 3x^3 + 8x^2 - 9x - 24$

3. Find one-decimal-place approximations of the irrational zeros of each of the following polynomials. Sketch their graphs.

(a) $x^3 - 3x^2 - x + 2$.　　　　　(b) $x^3 + 3x^2 + 4x + 5$

In Exercises 4–5 find a one-decimal-place approximation of the irrational zeros of each polynomial.

4. (a) $x^3 + x - 1$　　　　　　　(b) $x^3 + 3x^2 + 1$

5. (a) $x^3 - 2$　　　　　　　　　(b) $x^4 - 4x^3 + 2$

---

6. Find a two-decimal-place approximation of the real zero of $x^3 + x - 3$.

7. Find a two-decimal-place approximation of the positive real zero of $x^3 - 3x^2 - x - 6$.

8. Find a two-decimal-place approximation of the negative real zero of $x^3 + 3x^2 - 3x + 2$.

---

9. (a) If $p(x) = 6x^4 + 11x^3 - 4x - 1$, find $p(0)$ and $p(-1)$.

(b) Does $p(x)$ have a zero r such that $-1 < r < 0$?

(c) Find $p(-\frac{1}{3})$ and $p(-\frac{1}{2})$. Did you answer part (b) correctly?

10. Suppose that $p(x)$ is a real polynomial, $p(a) < 0$ and $p(b) > 0$.

(a) Does $p(x)$ have exactly one real zero between a and b?

(b) Does $p(x)$ have at least one real zero between a and b?

(c) Can $p(x)$ have an even number of real zeros between a and b?

(d) Can $p(x)$ have an odd number of real zeros between a and b?

Preparation for Section 8–11

Give the conjugate for each of the following complex numbers.

1. $5 + 8i$

2. $3 + i$

3. $4 - 5i$

4. $7 - i$

5. $\frac{1}{2}(2 + i)$

6. $\dfrac{5 - 2i}{3}$

Perform the indicated operations.

7. $(3 + i) + (5 - 4i)$　　　　　**8.** $(-8 - 5i) - (5 - 4i)$

9. $(7 - i)(3 + 4i)$　　　　　　**10.** $(-5 - 3i)(1 - 2i)$

*8–11   COMPLEX ZEROS OF REAL POLYNOMIALS

In this section, we shall discuss the complex zeros of a *real polynomial*, that is, of a polynomial whose coefficients are real numbers. According to the quadratic formula, every real quadratic polynomial has zeros. However, its zeros need not be real numbers. For example, the polynomial

$$x^2 - 4x + 5$$

has complex zeros

$$\frac{4 + \sqrt{-4}}{2} \quad \text{and} \quad \frac{4 - \sqrt{-4}}{2},$$

or

$$2 + i \quad \text{and} \quad 2 - i.$$

Since this polynomial has zeros $2 + i$ and $2 - i$, it has factors

$$x - (2 + i) \quad \text{and} \quad x - (2 - i)$$

according to the factor theorem:

$$x^2 - 4x + 5 = (x - 2 - i)(x - 2 + i).$$

One of the famous theorems of algebra, first proved in 1799 by the renowned German mathematician Gauss, states that *every polynomial of degree 1 or more has a zero.* Of course, the zeros of a polynomial need not be real numbers, as the example above shows. We shall not prove Gauss' theorem in this book, but we shall assume its truth.

If a real quadratic polynomial has two zeros, then it follows from the quadratic formula that both zeros are either real numbers or *conjugate complex numbers.* In the example above, $2 + i$ and $2 - i$ are conjugate complex numbers. Does a similar statement hold for real polynomials of degree higher than 2? Before we can answer this question, we must recall certain properties of conjugate complex numbers.

The complex number $a + bi$ has $a - bi$ as its conjugate. Let us denote the conjugate of each complex number r by $\bar{r}$. Thus,

$$\text{if } r = a + bi, \text{ then } \bar{r} = a - bi.$$

We are assuming, of course, that a and b are real numbers. For example,

$$\text{if } r = 5 + 4i, \text{ then } \bar{r} = 5 - 4i;$$

and

$$\text{if } s = 7 - 2i, \text{ then } \bar{s} = 7 + 2i.$$

Note that for the complex numbers r and s,

$$r + s = 12 + 2i, \quad \bar{r} + \bar{s} = 12 - 2i.$$

In other words, $\bar{r} + \bar{s}$ is the conjugate of $r + s$. Also,

$$rs = (35 - 8i^2) + (28i - 10i), \quad \text{or } 43 + 18i;$$
$$\overline{rs} = (35 - 8i^2) + (-28i + 10i), \quad \text{or } 43 - 18i.$$

Hence, $\overline{rs}$ is the conjugate of rs.

What we just demonstrated for two particular complex numbers can be shown to be valid for any two complex numbers. We state this result as follows.

If r and s are complex numbers, then the conjugate of their sum is the sum of their conjugates, and the conjugate of their product is the product of their conjugates. In symbols,

$$\overline{r + s} = \bar{r} + \bar{s} \quad \text{and} \quad \overline{rs} = \bar{r}\bar{s}.$$

Given three complex numbers r, s, and t, we have

$$\overline{r + s + t} = \overline{(r + s) + t} = \bar{r} + \bar{s} + \bar{t}.$$

A similar rule is valid for products. In general, it may be proved that *the conjugate of the sum of n complex numbers is the sum of their conjugates, and the conjugate of the product of n complex numbers is the product of their conjugates.* Consequently,

$$(\bar{r})^n = \overline{r^n}$$

for every complex number r and every positive integer n. The conjugate of a real number a (or $a + 0i$) is just a (or $a - 0i$). With these facts in mind, we can now prove the following theorem.

If $p(x)$ is a real polynomial and if r is a complex zero of $p(x)$, then $\bar{r}$ is also a zero of $p(x)$.

To prove this, let $p(x) = a_n x^n + a_{n-1} x^{n-1} + \cdots + a_1 x + a_0$, where the coefficients are real numbers. If t is any complex number, then

$$p(t) = a_n t^n + a_{n-1} t^{n-1} + \cdots + a_1 t + a_0,$$

$$\overline{p(t)} = \overline{a_n t^n + a_{n-1} t^{n-1} + \cdots + a_1 t + a_0}$$

$$= \overline{a_n t^n} + \overline{a_{n-1} t^{n-1}} + \cdots + \overline{a_1 t} + \overline{a_0}$$

$$= \overline{a_n}\,\overline{t^n} + \overline{a_{n-1}}\,\overline{t^{n-1}} + \cdots + \overline{a_1}\,\overline{t} + \overline{a_0}$$

$$= \overline{a_n}(\overline{t})^n + \overline{a_{n-1}}(\overline{t})^{n-1} + \cdots + \overline{a_1}\,\overline{t} + \overline{a_0}.$$

However, $\overline{a_n} = a_n$, $\overline{a_{n-1}} = a_{n-1}$, and so on, since the coefficients of $p(x)$ are real numbers. Hence,

$$\overline{p(t)} = a_n(\overline{t})^n + a_{n-1}(\overline{t})^{n-1} + \cdots + a_1 \overline{t} + a_0.$$

The right side of this equation is $p(\overline{t})$, that is, the value of the polynomial $p(x)$ at the complex number $\overline{t}$. Thus, we have proved that

$$\overline{p(t)} = p(\overline{t}).$$

This equation is true for every complex number t and, in particular, for each complex zero r of $p(x)$. Hence,

$$\overline{p(r)} = p(\overline{r}).$$

Since $p(r) = 0$ and $\overline{0} = 0$, we know that $\overline{p(r)} = 0$. Hence, $p(\overline{r}) = 0$ by the equation above. This result proves that $\overline{r}$ also is a zero of $p(x)$ and thus, proves the theorem. This theorem is sometimes stated in an alternative form:

Complex zeros of real polynomials occur in conjugate pairs.

To illustrate this theorem, consider the real polynomial

$$p(x) = 2x^3 - 3x^2 + 2x + 2.$$

Both $1 + i$ and $1 - i$ are zeros of $p(x)$, as shown in the following synthetic division.

$$
\begin{array}{r|rrrr}
1+i & 2 & -3 & 2 & 2 \\
    &   & 2+2i & -3+i & -2 \\
\hline
    & 2 & -1+2i & -1+i & 0 \\
1-i & 2 & -3 & 2 & 2 \\
    &   & 2-2i & -3-i & -2 \\
\hline
    & 2 & -1-2i & -1-i & 0
\end{array}
$$

Thus, both $x - (1 + i)$ and $x - (1 - i)$ are divisors of $p(x)$. Since they are two different divisors of $p(x)$ of degree 1, it follows that their product is also a divisor of $p(x)$. Thus

$$[x - (1 + i)][x - (1 - i)], \quad \text{or} \quad [(x - 1) - i][(x - 1) + i],$$

is a divisor of $p(x)$. This product equals $(x - 1)^2 - i^2$, or

$$x^2 - 2x + 2.$$

We note that the product of these two complex polynomials is a real polynomial. You can easily verify that

$$p(x) = (x^2 - 2x + 2)(2x + 1).$$

Thus, the polynomial $p(x)$ has two complex zeros, $1 + i$ and $1 - i$, and one real zero, $-\frac{1}{2}$.

If $p(x)$ is any real polynomial of degree 2 or more, having a complex zero $r = a + bi$, $b \neq 0$, then both r and $\bar{r}$ ($\bar{r} = a - bi$, $b \neq 0$) are zeros of $p(x)$ by the theorem above. Therefore, $x - r$ and $x - \bar{r}$ are distinct divisors of $p(x)$ by the factor theorem. Hence, their product

$$(x - r)(x - \bar{r}) = x^2 - (r + \bar{r})x + r\bar{r},$$

or

$$[x - (a + bi)][x - (a - bi)]$$
$$= x^2 - [(a + bi) + (a - bi)]x + (a + bi)(a - bi),$$

is a divisor of $p(x)$.

Since $r + \bar{r} = 2a$ and $r\bar{r} = a^2 + b^2$, the polynomial

$$f_1(x) = x^2 - 2ax + (a^2 + b^2)$$

is a *real polynomial*.

The polynomial $f_1(x)$ is a *prime real polynomial,* since it has no real factors of degree 1. Since $f_1(x)$ is a divisor of $p(x)$, and the quotient of a real polynomial by a real polynomial is real, we have

$$p(x) = f_1(x)q(x)$$

for some real polynomial $q(x)$.

If the real polynomial $q(x)$ is of positive degree, then it has a zero s by Gauss' theorem. If s is a real number, then $x - s$ is a real divisor of $q(x)$; if s is not real, then $q(x)$ has a real quadratic divisor $(x - s)(x - \bar{s})$. Thus,

$$q(x) = f_2(x)q_1(x),$$

where $f_2(x)$ is either $x - s$ or $(x - s)(x - \bar{s})$, whichever is real, and

$$p(x) = f_1(x)f_2(x)q_1(x).$$

We may continue this process with the real polynomial $q_1(x)$, provided that its degree is positive. Eventually, we will be able to factor $p(x)$ in the form

$$p(x) = f_1(x)f_2(x) \cdots f_n(x),$$

where each of the polynomials $f_1(x)$, $f_2(x)$, $\ldots$, $f_n(x)$ is real and of degree 1 or 2. Furthermore, each of these factors is a prime real polynomial in the sense that it cannot be further factored as a product of real polynomials of positive degree. This establishes the following property of real polynomials.

Every real polynomial of positive degree can be factored into a product of prime real polynomials, each of degree 1 or 2.

The prime real polynomials of degree 2 have conjugate complex zeros, whereas those of degree 1 have real zeros. For example,

$$p(x) = (x^2 - 2x + 2)(x^2 - 4x + 5)(2x - 3)$$

is factored into prime real polynomials. Thus,

$$x^2 - 2x + 2 \quad \text{has zeros} \quad 1 + i \quad \text{and} \quad 1 - i,$$
$$x^2 - 4x + 5 \quad \text{has zeros} \quad 2 + i \quad \text{and} \quad 2 - i,$$
$$2x - 3 \quad \text{has zero} \quad \tfrac{3}{2}.$$

If a real polynomial is of odd degree, such as the polynomial $p(x)$ above, and if $p(x) = f_1(x)f_2(x) \cdots f_n(x)$ where each of the factors $f_1(x), f_2(x), \ldots, f_n(x)$ is a real polynomial of degree 1 or 2, then some $f_i(x)$ must have degree 1, for otherwise, the degree of $p(x)$ would be

$$\overbrace{2 + 2 + \cdots + 2}^{n \text{ terms}}, \quad \text{or } 2n,$$

which is an even number, contrary to the assumption that $p(x)$ is of odd degree. Since some real factor of $p(x)$ has degree 1, $p(x)$ has a real zero by the factor theorem. We state this result in the following manner.

Every real polynomial of odd degree has at least one real zero.

Problem 1. Find the other zeros of the polynomial

$$p(x) = x^4 - 3x^3 + 6x^2 + 2x - 60$$

if one of the zeros is $1 - 3i$.

Solution. Because the coefficients of $p(x)$ are real, complex zeros occur in conjugate pairs. Therefore, if $1 - 3i$ is a zero of $p(x)$ so is $1 + 3i$.
   If $1 - 3i$ is a zero, then $x - (1 - 3i)$ is a factor. Also, since $1 + 3i$ is a zero, $x - (1 + 3i)$ is a factor. The product

$$[x - (1 - 3i)][x - (1 + 3i)]$$

must divide $p(x)$ since each factor does. The product

$$[x - (1 - 3i)][x - (1 + 3i)]$$

is equivalent to

$$[(x - 1) + 3i][(x - 1) - 3i]$$

which is equivalent to

$$[(x^2 - 2x + 1) + 9] \quad \text{or} \quad x^2 - 2x + 10.$$

By division we see that

$$
\begin{array}{r}
x^2 - x - 6 \\
x^2 - 2x + 10 \overline{\smash{\big)}\ x^4 - 3x^3 + 6x^2 + 2x - 60} \\
\underline{x^4 - 2x^3 + 10x^2} \\
-x^3 - 4x^2 + 2x \\
\underline{-x^3 + 2x^2 - 10x} \\
-6x^2 + 12x - 60 \\
\underline{-6x^2 + 12x - 60} \\
\end{array}
$$

Thus,

$$x^4 - 3x^3 + 6x^2 + 2x - 60 = (x^2 - 2x + 10)(x^2 - x - 6).$$

Since $x^2 - x - 6 = (x - 3)(x + 2)$, we know that 3 and -2 are zeros of $p(x)$. Hence the complete set of zeros of $p(x)$ is

$$\{3, -2, 1 + 3i, 1 - 3i\}.$$

Problem 2. Find a real polynomial $p(x)$ of smallest possible degree having $3 - i$ and $2i$ as zeros.

Solution. If $p(x)$ is to be real, $3 + i$ and $-2i$ must also be zeros. Hence $p(x)$ is the product of the four factors

$$p(x) = [x - (3 - i)][x - (3 + i)](x - 2i)(x + 2i),$$

so that

$$\begin{aligned} p(x) &= [(x - 3) + i][(x - 3) - i](x^2 + 4) \\ &= (x^2 - 6x + 9 + 1)(x^2 + 4) \\ &= (x^2 - 6x + 10)(x^2 + 4) \\ &= x^4 - 6x^3 + 14x^2 - 24x + 40. \end{aligned}$$

Thus the lowest degree for $p(x)$ is 4 because there are two pairs of complex conjugate zeros.

Exercises

In each of the exercises below, there is a real polynomial and one of its zeros. Find the other zeros, and express the polynomial as a product of real prime polynomials.

1. (a) $x^3 - 4x^2 + 9x - 10$; $1 - 2i$
   (b) $3x^3 - 2x^2 + 3x - 2$; i

2. (a) $x^3 - (6 + \sqrt{2})x^2 + (10 + 6\sqrt{2})x - 10\sqrt{2}$; $3 + i$
   (b) $x^4 + 1$; $\dfrac{\sqrt{2}}{2}(1 + i)$

3. (a) $2x^4 + 5x^3 + 4x^2 + 3$; $-\dfrac{3}{2} + \dfrac{\sqrt{3}}{2}i$
   (b) $x^3 + 8$; -2

4. (a) $x^4 - 8x^3 + 41x^2 - 100x + 100$; $2 + 4i$
   (b) $x^4 - 10x^3 + 50x^2 - 106x + 25$; $3 - 4i$

5. (a) $2x^4 - 2x^3 + 9x^2 + 4x - 26$; $\frac{1}{2} + \frac{5}{2}i$
   (b) $9x^4 - 6x^3 - 22x^2 + 18x - 15$; $\frac{1}{3} + \frac{2}{3}i$

In Exercises 6–10, find real polynomials of the smallest possible degree having the given numbers as zeros.

6. (a) $7 - 2i$ (b) $-\frac{1}{2} + \frac{3}{2}i$

7. (a) $1 + \sqrt{2}$ (b) $-2, \sqrt{3}$

8. (a) $0, i$ (b) $3 + 4i, 1$

9. (a) $-\frac{1}{2}, i + 5$ (b) $i + 1, i - 1$

10. (a) $1, i, 1 + i$ (b) $-2, -1, -i$

11. If $p(x) = x^3 - 3x^2 + 2ix + i - 1$, show that i is a zero but that $-i$ is not a zero. Does this contradict one of the theorems of this section?

12. Let $p(x) = a_0 + a_1x + a_2x^2 + \cdots + a_nx^n$ be a polynomial with complex coefficients, and let $q(x) = \bar{a}_0 + \bar{a}_1x + \bar{a}_2x^2 + \cdots + \bar{a}_nx^n$. If r is a complex zero of $p(x)$, prove that $\bar{r}$ is a zero of $q(x)$. Illustrate this result using the polynomial of Exercise 11.

13. Factor the polynomial $x^6 + 1$ into a product of real prime polynomials.

14. If r_1, r_2, and r_3 are the zeros of $x^3 + ax^2 + bx + c$, show that $r_1 + r_2 + r_3 = -a$ and $r_1r_2r_3 = -c$.

15. If r_1, r_2, r_3, and r_4 are the zeros of $x^4 + ax^3 + bx^2 + cx + d$, show that $r_1 + r_2 + r_3 + r_4 = -a$ and $r_1r_2r_3r_4 = d$.

EXTRA!

Some interesting relationships in the set of integers, as well as some shortcuts in arithmetic, can be found by studying the differences of squares of integers, that is, expressions such as $x^2 - y^2$ where x and y are integers.

Let us begin by considering the difference of the squares of two consecutive integers: $(n + 1)^2 - n^2$, n an integer. It can easily be seen that

$$(n + 1)^2 - n^2 = n^2 + 2n + 1 - n^2 = 2n + 1.$$

Thus,

$$(67)^2 - (66)^2 = 2(66) + 1 = 133.$$

If we increase each integer being squared by one, we have

$$(68)^2 - (67)^2 = 2(67) + 1 = 135,$$

and again

$$(69)^2 - (68)^2 = 2(68) + 1 = 137.$$

Does this pattern continue? Consider the following.

$$(n + 1)^2 - n^2 = 2n + 1$$
$$(n + 2)^2 - (n + 1)^2 = 2n + 3$$
$$(n + 3)^2 - (n + 2)^2 = 2n + 5$$

Thus we see that the differences between the squares of consecutive integers make up the set of positive odd numbers, $\{1, 3, 5, 7, \ldots\}$.

Now consider the difference of the squares of two integers which have a difference of two. It is easily seen that

$$(n + 2)^2 - n^2 = 4n + 4.$$

For example,

$$(50)^2 - (48)^2 = 4(48) + 4 = 196.$$

Again let us increase each integer being squared by one:

$$(51)^2 - (49)^2 = 4(49) + 4 = 200$$

and again,

$$(52)^2 - (50)^2 = 4(50) + 4 = 204.$$

Here the pattern seems to be that the differences of the squares of two integers which have a difference of two make up the set $\{4, 8, 12, 16, \ldots\}$.

$$(n + 2)^2 - n^2 = 4n + 4$$
$$(n + 3)^2 - (n + 1)^2 = 4n + 8$$
$$(n + 4)^2 - (n + 2)^2 = 4n + 12$$

We see that this is indeed the case.

In general, the difference of the squares of two integers which have a difference of k, is

$$(n + k)^2 - n^2 = 2kn + k^2.$$

Thus,

$$(35)^2 - (31)^2 = 2(4)(31) + 16 = 264.$$

In each of the following exercises find the first difference using a formula; then find the second difference using the first difference.

1. $(55)^2 - (54)^2$; $(56)^2 - (55)^2$
2. $(31)^2 - (30)^2$; $(32)^2 - (31)^2$
3. $(25)^2 - (24)^2$; $(24)^2 - (23)^2$
4. $(101)^2 - (100)^2$; $(100)^2 - (99)^2$
5. $(17)^2 - (16)^2$; $(19)^2 - (18)^2$
6. $(42)^2 - (41)^2$; $(40)^2 - (39)^2$
7. $(30)^2 - (28)^2$; $(31)^2 - (29)^2$
8. $(20)^2 - (18)^2$; $(19)^2 - (17)^2$

9. $(28)^2 - (26)^2$; $(26)^2 - (24)^2$

10. $(62)^2 - (60)^2$; $(60)^2 - (58)^2$

11. (a) Find a formula for the difference of the squares of two integers which have a difference of three.

   (b) Find a pattern for the differences of the squares of two integers which have a difference of three.

12. (a) Find a formula for the difference of the squares of two integers which have a difference of k, letting the smaller integer be $(n + 1)$. Compare this with the formula for $(n + k)^2 - n^2$.

   (b) Find a formula for the difference of the squares of two integers which have a difference of k, letting the smaller integer be $(n + 2)$. Compare this with the formulas for $(n + k)^2 - n^2$ and $(n + k + 1)^2 - (n + 1)^2$.

   (c) Find a pattern for the differences of the squares of two integers which have a difference of k.

HISTORICAL NOTE

Formulas for solving quadratic, cubic, and quartic polynomial equations were discovered in the sixteenth century. Despite the efforts of mathematicians in the seventeenth and eighteenth centuries, similar formulas for solving fifth- or higher-degree polynomial equations were not found. The memoir of J. L. Lagrange (1736–1813), *Reflexions sur la resolution algebrique des equations*, contained a systematic study of equation solving. This study was to prove extremely useful to the next generation of mathematicians who worked on the problem.

   Three names are connected with the ultimate solution of the problem of solving fifth- and higher-degree polynomial equations: Abel, Ruffini, and Galois. Although the Norwegian mathematician N. H. Abel (1802–1829) died before his twenty-seventh birthday, he made fundamental contributions to several fields of mathematics. In 1824, he published an algebraic proof of a most unusual theorem. His proof stopped all further attempts to find a formula which would give the solutions of a general quintic polynomial equation $x^5 + ax^4 + bx^3 + cx^2 + dx + e = 0$ in terms of powers and roots of its coefficients $a, b, c, d,$ and e. His theorem stated simply that there is no such formula for solving general polynomial equations of degree 5 or higher. An Italian physician, P. Ruffini, proved essentially the same result in 1813. However, Abel was not aware of Ruffini's work.

   One of the heartbreaking episodes of mathematical history is the story of the French mathematician E. Galois, who was killed in a political duel in 1832, a few months before his twenty-first birthday. Although he was a failure in school and in politics, he was reading the works of Lagrange at the age of sixteen and was discovering new results by the following year. He introduced the algebraic system called a *group*, and used it to give a definitive answer to the question of why polynomial equations of higher degree than 4 cannot be solved by a formula. He showed that if such an equation could be solved, then an associated finite group would have a certain structure. However, a group does not, in general, have this structure. His work led to an exhaustive study of group theory by later mathematicians, a study which is still going on at present.

KEY IDEAS AND KEY WORDS

A **polynomial** is an algebraic expression of the form

$$a_n x^n + a_{n-1} x^{n-1} + \cdots + a_1 x + a_0,$$

where n is a non-negative integer, x is a variable, and $a_n, a_{n-1}, \ldots, a_1, a_0$ are real or complex numbers. The numbers $a_0, a_1, \ldots, a_n$ are called the **coefficients** of the polynomial. In particular, a_n is called the **leading coefficient** and a_0 the **constant term.** If $a_n \neq 0$, then the polynomial is said to have **degree** n. The zero polynomial, 0, has no degree.

The set of all polynomials in a variable x with real or complex coefficients is **closed** under addition and multiplication. The five basic properties of addition and multiplication of the real number system, with the exception of the multiplicative inverse property, are valid for the algebra of polynomials.

For any given nonzero polynomials A and B, there exist unique polynomials Q and R such that $A = (B \cdot Q) + R$, with $R = 0$ or the degree of R less than the degree of B. We call Q the **quotient** and R the **remainder** on dividing A by B.

The **remainder theorem** states that if the polynomial $f(x)$ is divided by the polynomial $x - r$, then the remainder is $f(r)$.

The **factor theorem** states that the polynomial $x - r$ is a divisor, or factor, of a polynomial $f(x)$ if, and only if, $f(r) = 0$. We call r a **zero** of $f(x)$ if $f(r) = 0$.

A polynomial is called an **integral**, a **rational**, a **real**, or a **complex** polynomial depending upon whether its coefficients are integers, rational numbers, real numbers, or complex numbers respectively.

According to the **integral zero theorem**, an integer k is a zero of an integral polynomial only if k is a divisor of a_0, the constant term.

By the **rational zero theorem**, a rational number p/q expressed in lowest form is a zero of an integral polynomial only if p is a divisor of the constant term a_0 and q is a divisor of the leading coefficient a_n.

The **complex zeros** of a real polynomial occur in **conjugate pairs.** Therefore, every real polynomial of odd degree has at least one real zero.

CHAPTER REVIEW

1. Use synthetic division to find the quotient and the remainder when $4x^3 - 5x + 1$ is divided by each of the following.
   (a) $x - 2$ (b) $x + 3$

2. If $p(x) = 2x^3 - x^2 + 3x - 4$, find $p(-2)$, $p(1)$, $p(3)$, and $p(4)$.

3. Find the zeros of each of the following polynomials.
   (a) $6x^3 - x^2 - 12x - 5$ (b) $6x^4 - 11x^3 + 7x^2 - 22x + 24$

4. Find one-decimal-place approximations of the irrational zeros of the polynomial $3x^3 - 2x^2 - 11x + 7$. Graph the polynomial equation $y = 3x^3 - 2x^2 - 11x + 7$.

5. Find an integral polynomial of lowest possible degree for each of the following sets of zeros.
   (a) $\{\frac{1}{2}, 3, -\frac{2}{3}\}$ (b) $\{1 + \sqrt{3},\ 2i\}$

6. Prove that $\sqrt{2}/\sqrt{3}$ is irrational.

7. Factor each polynomial into a product of integral prime polynomials.
   (a) $x^4 + 2x^3 - 25x^2 - 26x + 120$ (b) $x^4 + 3x - 2$

8. The real polynomial

$$x^4 - 6x^3 + 29x^2 - 24x + 100$$

has complex zero $3 - 4i$. Find the other three zeros.

9. Illustrate the associative law of addition in the set of polynomials, using the three polynomials $8x^2 - 6$, $14x^2 - 4x + 8$, and $8x + 10$.

10. Illustrate the associative law of multiplication in the set of polynomials, using the three polynomials $3y - 9$, $3y + 9$, and $6y + 15$.

In Exercises 11–13, perform the indicated operations with polynomials.

11. $(x^3 + 3x^2 + 5x + 5) + (2x - 4)$

12. $(x^4 + x^2 + x)(x^4 + x^2 - x)$

13. $(3x^3 + 5x - 4)(3x^2 + 5x - 4)$

14. Determine k so that when $4x^3 - 2x^2 + 6x + 2k$ is divided by $2x - 2$, the remainder is 0.

15. Determine c and d so that when $2y^4 + 2y^3 - 14y^2 + 2cy + 2d$ is divided by $(y - 1)(2y + 4)$, the remainder is 0.

Which of the polynomials $(2x - 2)$, $(2x + 2)$, $(2x - 8)$, and $(2x + 6)$ are divisors of the following polynomials?

16. $2x^3 - 4x^2 - 22x + 24$

17. $4x^4 + 2x^3 + 2x^2 - 2x - 6$

18. $4x^3 + 6x^2 - 46x - 24$

19. $2x^4 + 2x^3 - 38x^2 + 2x - 40$

Find the rational zeros of each of the following polynomials.

20. $20x^3 - 34x^2 - 14x + 4$

21. $2x^4 - \frac{3}{2}x^3 + 6x^2 + x + \frac{3}{2}$

Find an integral polynomial of degree 4 for each of the following sets of zeros.

22. $\{1, 0, -1\}$ **23.** $\{\frac{1}{2}, -\frac{1}{2}, 1\}$

24. $\{1, 2, 4, -7\}$ **25.** $\{0, 1, -2, 3\}$

Determine the rational solutions of the following equations.

26. $2x^3 - 7x^2 - 7x + 30 = 0$

27. $2x^5 - 11x^4 + 65x^2 + 31x = 0$

28. $2x^4 - 3x^3 - 11x^2 + 3x + 9 = 0$

29. Use the fact that

$$x^8 - 6x^6 + 8x^4 + 6x^2 - 9$$

is divisible by $x^6 - 3x^4 - x^2 + 3$, which is, in turn, divisible by $x^2 - 3$, to write the eighth-degree polynomial as a product of four polynomials.

CHAPTER TEST

In Exercises 1 and 2, perform the indicated operations with polynomials.

1. $(3x^3 + 2x^2 + x + 2) + (\frac{1}{2}x^3 + 6x - 2)$

2. $0 \cdot (3x^3 + 5x^2 + 5x + 3)$

3. Given that

$$f(x) = x^5 - 3x^4 - x^2 + 7,$$

find $f(0)$, $f(1)$, and $f(-2)$.

4. Find the zeros of the polynomial

$$3x^3 - 4x^2 - 13x - 6.$$

5. Find an integral polynomial having zeros $\frac{3}{4}$ and $\sqrt{2}$.

6. Factor

$$6x^3 - 13x^2 + x + 2.$$

7 Prove that $\sqrt{2} + \sqrt{3}$ is an irrational number.

8. Factor

$$x^4 + 2x^3 - 4x^2 - 5x - 6.$$

CHAPTER

9

Elements
of Trigonometry

Objectives . . .

- To find the trigonometric functions
  of a given angle.
- To use the wrapping function and its
  properties to define the basic trigonometric concepts.
- To apply the properties of the circular
  functions in order to prove identities.
- To develop the properties of circular
  functions and their cofunctions.

9–1 TRIGONOMETRIC FUNCTIONS OF ACUTE ANGLES

Until recently, the branch of mathematics called trigonometry was primarily concerned with the measurement of triangles. The ratios of each side of a triangle to another side of the triangle are the original trigonometric functions of the angles of a triangle. In its modern meaning, trigonometry includes the study of a class of periodic functions and applications of these functions.

Every acute angle α may be considered to be an angle of some right triangle ABC, as indicated in Fig. 9–1. If the vertices of a triangle are designated by A, B, and C, then we shall frequently denote the lengths of the opposite sides by a, b, and c, respectively, and the angles at vertices A, B, and C by α, β, and γ, respectively. The small square at vertex C of Fig. 9–1 indicates that the angle at C is a right angle.

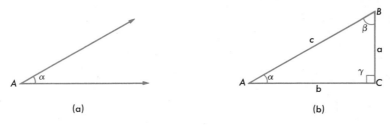

(a)   (b)

FIGURE 9–1

If α is an acute angle of the right triangle shown in Fig. 9–1, we can define the *sine* of α, the *cosine* of α, and the *tangent* of α in triangle ABC in the following manner.

$$sin\,\alpha = \frac{a}{c}, \quad cos\,\alpha = \frac{b}{c}, \quad tan\,\alpha = \frac{a}{b}$$

In this way, we can associate with each acute angle α three numbers: sin α, cos α, and tan α. Note that we have abbreviated sine to sin, cosine to cos, and tangent to tan.

Although it appears that sin α, cos α, and tan α could depend on the size of the right triangle containing angle α, this is not the case, for if $A'B'C'$ is another right triangle with α as an acute angle (see Fig. 9–2), then it follows that triangles ABC and $A'B'C'$ are similar. Hence,

$$\frac{a}{c} = \frac{a'}{c'}, \quad \frac{b}{c} = \frac{b'}{c'}, \quad \frac{a}{b} = \frac{a'}{b'}.$$

This proves that sin α, cos α, and tan α do not depend on the size of the right triangle containing angle α.

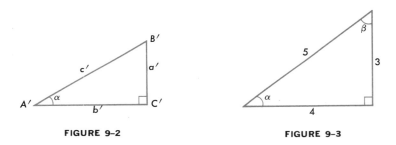

FIGURE 9–2   FIGURE 9–3

One of the simplest right triangles having sides of integral lengths is the right triangle with sides 3, 4, and 5, as shown in Fig. 9–3. If we denote the smaller acute angle by α and the larger acute angle by β, then according to the definitions above,

$$\sin \alpha = \tfrac{3}{5}, \quad \cos \alpha = \tfrac{4}{5}, \quad \tan \alpha = \tfrac{3}{4},$$
$$\sin \beta = \tfrac{4}{5}, \quad \cos \beta = \tfrac{3}{5}, \quad \tan \beta = \tfrac{4}{3}.$$

The correspondence that associates with each acute angle α the number sin α is a *function*, called the *sine*. This function has the set of all acute angles as its domain and the set of positive real numbers less than 1 as its range. Similarly, *cosine* and *tangent* are *functions* having the same domain. The three functions sine, cosine, and tangent are called *trigonometric functions.*

Problem 1. Find the trigonometric functions of an angle of measure 60°.

Solution. The hypotenuse is twice as long as the shorter leg in a 30°-60° right triangle. If we assume that the hypotenuse has length 2 and the shorter leg length 1, then the length b of the other leg is $\sqrt{3}$ since

$$2^2 = 1^2 + b^2 \quad \text{and} \quad b = \sqrt{3}$$

by the pythagorean theorem. When we look at Fig. 9–4, we see that

$$\sin 60° = \frac{\sqrt{3}}{2}, \quad \cos 60° = \frac{1}{2}, \quad \tan 60° = \frac{\sqrt{3}}{1}.$$

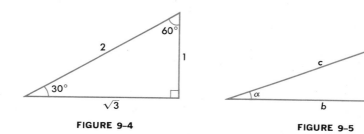

FIGURE 9–4   FIGURE 9–5

Problem 2. Find the values of the cos α and the tan α, given that α is acute and that sin α = .3.

Solution. Consider α as an angle of a right triangle (Fig. 9–5). The problem tells us that

$$\sin \alpha = \frac{a}{c} = .3.$$

Hence, $a = .3c$. Since $a^2 + b^2 = c^2$,

we have

$$b^2 = c^2 - a^2$$
$$= c^2 - (.3c)^2, \quad \text{or } .91c^2.$$

Thus,

$$b = c\sqrt{.91}.$$

Therefore,

$$\cos \alpha = \frac{b}{c} = \frac{c\sqrt{.91}}{c} = \sqrt{.91}, \quad \text{or } \frac{\sqrt{91}}{10},$$

$$\tan \alpha = \frac{a}{b} = \frac{.3c}{c\sqrt{.91}} = \frac{.3}{\sqrt{.91}}, \quad \text{or } \frac{3}{\sqrt{91}}, \quad \text{or } \frac{3\sqrt{91}}{91}.$$

Exercises

Find the trigonometric functions of each angle described in Exercise 1–6.

1. (a) An angle of measure 30°
   (b) An angle of measure 45°

2. (a) The two acute angles of the right triangle whose sides are 5, 12, and 13 units long
   (b) The two acute angles of the right triangle whose sides are 7, 24, and 25 units long

3. (a) The acute angle whose tangent is 12
   (b) The acute angle whose cosine is $\frac{1}{4}$

4. (a) The acute angle whose sine is .2
   (b) The acute angle whose cosine is .7

5. (a) The acute angle whose sine is .99
   (b) The acute angle whose cosine is .001

6. (a) The smaller acute angle of a right triangle with one leg of length 6 inches and with hypotenuse of length 9 inches
   (b) The larger acute angle of a right triangle with legs of 7 feet and 9 feet

7. (a) For an acute angle α of a right triangle, it is known that $\sin \alpha = \frac{3}{4}$ and that the length of the leg opposite angle α is 12. Find the lengths of the hypotenuse and the other leg.
   (b) For an acute angle α of a right triangle, it is known that $\cos \alpha = \frac{2}{3}$ and that the length of the leg adjacent to angle α is 10. Find the lengths of the hypotenuse and the other leg.

---

8. In $\triangle ABC$, the angle at A has measure 30° and the lengths of the two sides including angle A are 50 and 130, as shown in the figure.

   (a) Find the length, h, of the altitude drawn to the base $\overline{AB}$ and find the area of $\triangle ABC$.

   (b) Show that $\triangle ABC$ is *not* a right triangle

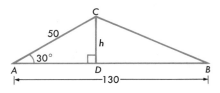

---

9. Prove that for each acute angle α, $(\sin \alpha)^2 + (\cos \alpha)^2 = 1$.

10. Prove that for each acute angle α,

$$\tan \alpha = \frac{\sin \alpha}{\cos \alpha}.$$

11. What is the measure of α if the tangent of α is equal to its own reciprocal?

12. Prove that if α and β are complementary angles, then

    (a) $\sin \alpha = \cos \beta$.

    (b) $\cos \alpha = \sin \beta$.

9-2 THE WRAPPING FUNCTION

Another way to approach the trigonometric functions is to relate them to points on a unit circle (that is, a circle of radius 1). In this approach, the domains of the sine and cosine functions are the set of all real numbers, rather than a set of acute angles. When considered in this way, the trigonometric functions are often called *circular functions*. We place the center of a unit circle at the origin of a cartesian coordinate system, and then place a number line (the s-axis) parallel to the y-axis and touching the unit circle at point $(1, 0)$, as shown in Fig. 9-6. We assume that all three number lines (the x-axis, the y-axis, and the s-axis) have the same unit of length.

Now imagine that the s-axis is an infinitely long thread which can be wrapped around the circle. The piece above the x-axis can be wrapped in a counterclockwise manner, and the piece below the x-axis can be wrapped in a clockwise manner. Then each point on the s-axis can be made to coincide with a point on the circle. In other words, this process defines a function W, called the *wrapping function*, which associates with each real number s (as the coordinate of a point on the s-axis) a *point* $W(s)$ on the unit circle. Because the thread is infinitely long and the circle has finite circumference 2π, the thread can be wrapped around the circle infinitely many times.

Each arc $\overset{\frown}{AB}$ of a unit circle has a length. For example, the arc $\overset{\frown}{AB}$

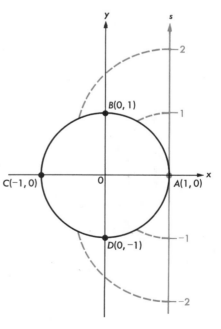

FIGURE 9-6

of Fig. 9–6 is a quarter circle, and hence, its length is $2\pi/4$, or $\pi/2$. Similarly, arc $\overset{\frown}{AC}$ is a semicircle with length π, and counterclockwise arc $\overset{\frown}{AD}$ is a three-quarter circle with length $3\pi/2$. Thus,

$$W(0) = A(1, 0),$$
$$W\left(\frac{\pi}{2}\right) = B(0, 1),$$
$$W(\pi) = C(-1, 0),$$
$$W\left(\frac{3\pi}{2}\right) = D(0, -1),$$
$$W(2\pi) = A(1, 0).$$

If $s > 2\pi$, the piece of thread of length s is wrapped around the circle more than once. For example,

$$W(3\pi) = C(-1, 0).$$

If the negative s-axis is wrapped around the circle, as shown in Fig. 9–7, we see that

$$W\left(-\frac{\pi}{2}\right) = D(0, -1),$$
$$W(-\pi) = C(-1, 0),$$
$$W\left(-\frac{3\pi}{2}\right) = B(0, 1),$$
$$W(-2\pi) = A(1, 0),$$
$$W(-3\pi) = C(-1, 0),$$

and so on.

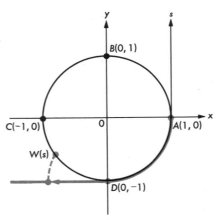

FIGURE 9–7

If we increase or decrease the length of a piece of thread by 2π, we end up at the same point on the unit circle. Thus, for every real number s,

$$W(s) = W(s + 2\pi), \quad W(s) = W(s - 2\pi).$$

On the other hand, if $0 < c < 2\pi$,

$$W(s) \neq W(s + c), \quad W(s) \neq W(s - c).$$

Thus, the function W repeats itself every 2π, and 2π is the least positive number for which this is true. For this reason, we call the function W *periodic* and the number 2π its *period*.

The wrapping function W is periodic with period 2π.

If $0 \leq s < 2\pi$, then $W(s)$ is the point on the unit circle such that the arc from A to $W(s)$, when traced counterclockwise, has length s. If $s > 2\pi$, then we subtract an integral multiple of 2π from s so that the difference is between 0 and 2π. In this manner, we can express $W(s)$ as $W(t)$ for some number t, where $0 \leq t < 2\pi$, as shown in Fig. 9–8. If $s < 0$, then we add an integral multiple of 2π to s so that the sum t is between 0 and 2π. In either case, $W(s) = W(t)$ by the periodicity of W.

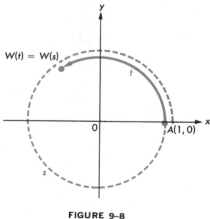

FIGURE 9–8

Problem 1. Find $W\left(\dfrac{\pi}{4}\right)$.

Solution. Since arc $\overset{\frown}{AP}$ is half of arc $\overset{\frown}{AB}$ (Fig. 9–9), the measure of $\angle POA$ must be 45°, and $\triangle OPQ$ is a 45° right triangle. We constructed the circle with a radius of 1; therefore, $\overline{OP}$ has length 1. We know that

$$OQ = QP$$

and

$$(OP)^2 = (QP)^2 + (OQ)^2.$$

Therefore,

$$QP = \frac{\sqrt{2}}{2}$$

and

$$W\left(\frac{\pi}{4}\right) = \left(\frac{\sqrt{2}}{2}, \frac{\sqrt{2}}{2}\right).$$

Problem 2. Find $W\left(-\frac{3\pi}{4}\right)$.

Solution. The point

$$W\left(-\frac{3\pi}{4}\right)$$

is halfway between the points $W(\pi)$ and $W(3\pi/2)$. We know from our previous work that the coordinates of all points in the third quadrant are negative. Since the measure of $\angle POQ$ is 45°, $\triangle OPQ$ is a 45° right triangle. (See Fig. 9–10.)

$$W\left(-\frac{3\pi}{4}\right) = \left(-\frac{\sqrt{2}}{2}, -\frac{\sqrt{2}}{2}\right)$$

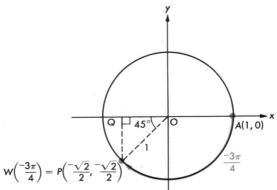

FIGURE 9-10

Problem 3. Find $W\left(\dfrac{\pi}{6}\right)$.

Solution. Since arc $\overset{\frown}{AP}$ is a third of arc $\overset{\frown}{AB}$ (Fig. 9–11), the measure of $\angle POA$ is 30° and $\triangle OPQ$ is a 30°–60° right triangle. Therefore,

$$QP = .5, \quad OQ = \frac{\sqrt{3}}{2} \quad \text{and} \quad W\left(\frac{\pi}{6}\right) = \left(\frac{\sqrt{3}}{2}, \frac{1}{2}\right).$$

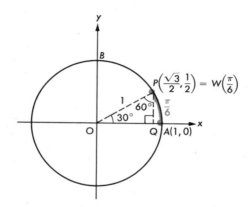

FIGURE 9–11

Problem 4. Find $W\left(\dfrac{21\pi}{4}\right)$ and $W\left(-\dfrac{11\pi}{2}\right)$.

Solution. If we subtract $2(2\pi)$, or 4π, from $21\pi/4$, we get a number t between 0 and 2π:

$$t = \frac{21\pi}{4} - 4\pi, \quad \text{or} \quad \frac{5\pi}{4}.$$

By the periodicity of W,

$$W\left(\frac{21\pi}{4}\right) = W\left(\frac{5\pi}{4}\right).$$

Since $W(5\pi/4)$ is the same point as $W(-3\pi/4)$, as shown in Fig. 9–10,

$$W\left(\frac{21\pi}{4}\right) = \left(-\frac{\sqrt{2}}{2}, -\frac{\sqrt{2}}{2}\right).$$

We must add $3(2\pi)$, or 6π, to $-(11\pi)/2$ in order to obtain a number t between 0 and 2π:

$$t = -\frac{11}{2}\pi + 6\pi = \frac{\pi}{2}.$$

By the periodicity of W,

$$W\left(-\frac{11\pi}{2}\right) = W\left(\frac{\pi}{2}\right), \quad \text{or } (0, 1).$$

Exercises

Complete the following tables.

1. (a)

s	0	$\frac{\pi}{6}$	$\frac{\pi}{4}$	$\frac{\pi}{3}$	$\frac{\pi}{2}$
$W(s)$	$(1, 0)$	$(?, ?)$	$(?, ?)$	$(?, ?)$	$(0, 1)$

(b)

s	$\frac{2\pi}{3}$	$\frac{3\pi}{4}$	$\frac{5\pi}{6}$	π
$W(s)$	$(?, ?)$	$(?, ?)$	$(?, ?)$	$(-1, 0)$

2. (a)

s	$\frac{7\pi}{6}$	$\frac{5\pi}{4}$	$\frac{4\pi}{3}$	$\frac{3\pi}{2}$
$W(s)$	$(?, ?)$	$(?, ?)$	$(?, ?)$	$(0, -1)$

(b)

s	$\frac{5\pi}{3}$	$\frac{7\pi}{4}$	$\frac{11\pi}{6}$	2π
$W(s)$	$(?, ?)$	$(?, ?)$	$(?, ?)$	$(1, 0)$

3. Fill in the bottom row with real numbers t which lie in the interval $0 \leqq t < 2\pi$ and have the property $W(t) = W(s)$.

(a)

s	3π	$\frac{7\pi}{2}$	4π	$\frac{11\pi}{2}$	7π	10π
t	?	?	?	?	?	?

(b)

s	-2π	$-\frac{5\pi}{2}$	-3π	-5π	-7π	$-\frac{15\pi}{2}$
t	?	?	?	?	?	?

Find a number t such that $0 \leqq t < 2\pi$ and $W(t) = W(s)$.

4. (a) $s = \frac{13\pi}{6}$ **(b)** $s = \frac{13\pi}{3}$

5. (a) $s = \dfrac{19\pi}{6}$ (b) $s = \dfrac{3\pi}{4}$

6. (a) $s = -\dfrac{22\pi}{3}$ (b) $s = -\dfrac{15\pi}{4}$

7. (a) For each number s in Exercises 4(a), 5(a), 6(a), find the coordinates of the point $W(s)$.

    (b) For each number s in Exercises 4(b), 5(b), 6(b), find the coordinates of the point $W(s)$.

Find the coordinates of the point $P = W(s)$ for each value of s.

8. $s = -\dfrac{14\pi}{3}$ **9.** $s = \dfrac{11\pi}{3}$ **10.** $s = \dfrac{27\pi}{4}$

11. $s = -\dfrac{7\pi}{4}$ **12** $s = \dfrac{41\pi}{6}$ **13.** $s = \dfrac{35\pi}{6}$

14. $s = \dfrac{47\pi}{4}$ **15.** $s = \dfrac{9\pi}{2}$ **16.** $s = -\dfrac{11\pi}{3}$

17. $s = -\dfrac{27\pi}{4}$ **18.** $s = \dfrac{23\pi}{6}$ **19.** $s = \dfrac{22\pi}{3}$

9–3 PROPERTIES OF THE WRAPPING FUNCTION

For every real number s, the points $W(s)$ and $W(-s)$ are mirror images of each other, as shown in Fig. 9–12. This relationship can be stated as follows:

$$\text{If } W(s) = (x, y), \quad \text{then } W(-s) = (x, -y). \tag{1}$$

For example,

$$W\left(\frac{3\pi}{4}\right) = \left(-\frac{\sqrt{2}}{2}, \frac{\sqrt{2}}{2}\right)$$

and

$$W\left(-\frac{3\pi}{4}\right) = \left(-\frac{\sqrt{2}}{2}, -\frac{\sqrt{2}}{2}\right).$$

The points $W(s)$ and $W(s + \pi/2)$ are also related. To illustrate this relation, let us consider $s = \pi/6$. Then $s + \pi/2 = 2\pi/3$. Since

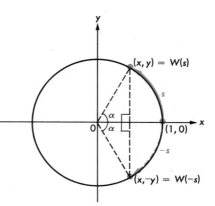

FIGURE 9–12

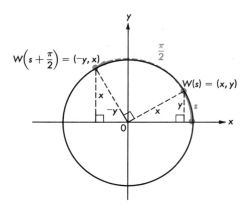

FIGURE 9-13

$s = \pi/6$, we can use the information we know about a 30°–60° right triangle (see Fig. 9–13) to find that

$$W\left(\frac{\pi}{6}\right) = \left(\frac{\sqrt{3}}{2}, \frac{1}{2}\right) \quad \text{and} \quad W\left(\frac{2\pi}{3}\right) = \left(-\frac{1}{2}, \frac{\sqrt{3}}{2}\right).$$

This relationship between $W(s)$ and $W(s + \pi/2)$ will always hold because the triangles involved will always be congruent. We state this relationship in the following way.

$$\textit{If } W(s) = (x, y), \textit{ then } W\left(s + \frac{\pi}{2}\right) = (-y, x). \qquad (2)$$

In other words, the x-coordinate of $W(s)$ becomes the y-coordinate of $W(s + \pi/2)$, and the negative of the y-coordinate of $W(s)$ becomes the x-coordinate of $W(s + \pi/2)$.

Since

$$s + \pi = \left(s + \frac{\pi}{2}\right) + \frac{\pi}{2},$$

we can use relationship (2) twice to obtain $W(s + \pi)$: If

$$W(s) = (x, y),$$

then

$$W\left(s + \frac{\pi}{2}\right) = (-y, x)$$

and

$$W\left(\left(s + \frac{\pi}{2}\right) + \frac{\pi}{2}\right) = (-x, -y).$$

Also, $W(s + \pi) = W(s - \pi)$ by the periodicity of W. Thus, we have the following result.

If $W(s) = (x, y)$, then $W(s + \pi) = W(s - \pi) = (-x, -y)$.   (3)

We can use relationships (2) and (3) to find functional values of many other combinations of s and $\pi/2$. For example, if

$$W(s + \pi/2) = (-y, x),$$

then $W(s - \pi/2) = W((s + \pi/2) - \pi) = (y, -x)$ by relationship (3). Thus, by relationship (2), we have the following.

If $W(s) = (x, y)$, then $W\left(s - \dfrac{\pi}{2}\right) = (y, -x)$.   (4)

Problem. If $W(s) = (x, y)$, what is $W(\pi/2 - s)$?

Solution. If $W(s) = (x, y)$, then

$$W\left(s - \frac{\pi}{2}\right) = (y, -x)$$

and

$$W\left(\frac{\pi}{2} - s\right) = W\left(-\left(s - \frac{\pi}{2}\right)\right) = (y, x).$$

Exercises

In Exercises 1–5, find the coordinates of each indicated point.

1. (a) $W\left(\dfrac{3\pi}{4}\right)$ (b) $W\left(-\dfrac{13\pi}{4}\right)$

2. (a) $W\left(-\dfrac{2\pi}{3}\right)$ (b) $W\left(\dfrac{4\pi}{3}\right)$

3. (a) $W\left(\dfrac{7\pi}{6}\right)$ (b) $W\left(\dfrac{31\pi}{6}\right)$

4. (a) $W\left(-\dfrac{3\pi}{4}\right)$ (b) $W(19\pi)$

5. (a) $W(18\pi)$ (b) $W(3\pi)$

6. If the points $W(s)$ and $W(s')$ have the same coordinates, how are s and s' related?

7. Complete the following table.

s	0	$\dfrac{\pi}{6}$	$\dfrac{\pi}{4}$	$\dfrac{\pi}{3}$
$W(s)$	$(1, 0)$	$\left(\dfrac{\sqrt{3}}{2}, \dfrac{1}{2}\right)$	$\left(\dfrac{\sqrt{2}}{2}, \dfrac{\sqrt{2}}{2}\right)$	$\left(\dfrac{1}{2}, \dfrac{\sqrt{3}}{2}\right)$
$W(-s)$	$(?, ?)$	$(?, ?)$	$(?, ?)$	$(\_?\_, \_?\_)$
$s + \dfrac{\pi}{2}$	$?$	$?$	$?$	$?$
$W\left(s + \dfrac{\pi}{2}\right)$	$(?, ?)$	$(?, ?)$	$(?, ?)$	$(?, ?)$

s	$\dfrac{\pi}{2}$	$\dfrac{2\pi}{3}$	$\dfrac{5\pi}{6}$	$\dfrac{3\pi}{4}$
$W(s)$	$(0, 1)$	$(?, ?)$	$(?, ?)$	$(?, ?)$
$W(-s)$	$(?, ?)$	$(?, ?)$	$(?, ?)$	$(?, ?)$
$s + \dfrac{\pi}{2}$	$?$	$?$	$?$	$?$
$W\left(s + \dfrac{\pi}{2}\right)$	$(?, ?)$	$(?, ?)$	$(?, ?)$	$(?, ?)$

8. Suppose that s is a number between $\pi/2$ and π. Make a drawing like that of Fig. 9–12 to show the relationship between $W(s)$ and $W(-s)$.

9. Verify the following relationship for $s = 0$, $s = \pi/2$, $s = \pi$, and $s = 3\pi/2$.

$$\text{If } W(s) = (x, y), \text{ then } W(-s) = (x, -y).$$

10. Locate the point $P = W(\pi/4)$ on a graph of the unit circle and label this point with its coordinates. On the same graph, locate the following points and give their coordinates.

$$Q = W\left(\frac{3\pi}{4}\right), \quad R = W\left(\frac{5\pi}{4}\right), \quad S = W\left(\frac{7\pi}{4}\right)$$

On your sketch, draw dotted lines to help you find the coordinates of each point. Verify that the following relationship applied to P, Q, R, and S will yield coordinates of points Q, R, S, and P, respectively.

$$\text{If } W(s) = (x, y) \text{ then } W\left(s + \frac{\pi}{2}\right) = (-y, x).$$

11. On a graph of the unit circle, show the relationship between the points $W(s)$ and $W(s \pm \pi)$. Derive the following relationship from your figure.

$$\text{If } W(s) = (x, y), \text{ then } W(s + \pi) = W(s - \pi) = (-x, -y).$$

12. (a) Locate the point

$$P = W\left(\frac{\pi}{6}\right)$$

on a graph of the unit circle and label this point with its coordinate. On the same graph, locate the point

$$Q = W\left(\frac{7\pi}{6}\right)$$

and give its coordinates. Verify that if relationship (3) on page 409 is applied to P and Q, respectively, it will yield coordinates of the points Q and P, respectively.

(b) Follow the directions of part (a), using points

$$P = W\left(\frac{5\pi}{6}\right) \quad \text{and} \quad Q = W\left(\frac{11\pi}{6}\right).$$

13. Use relationships (1) and (3) on pages 407 and 409 to find $W(\pi - s)$, given that $W(s) = (x, y)$.

9-4   THE SINE AND COSINE

We recall that the wrapping function W associates with each number s a unique point $W(s)$ on the unit circle (Fig. 9–14). The coordinates of $W(s)$ are also functions of s; therefore, we can make the following definitions.

Definition of sine and cosine

$$W(s) = (\textit{cosine s, sine s}) \quad \textit{for every real number s}$$

According to the definition above, the x-coordinate of a point $W(s)$ on the unit circle is the cos s and the y-coordinate is the sin s, that is

$$\cos s = x \quad \text{and} \quad \sin s = y.$$

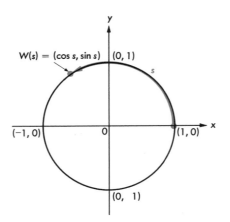

FIGURE 9-14

The function W is periodic with period 2π. Knowing this, we can show the truth of the following statement.

The sine and cosine are periodic functions; each has period 2π.

Problem 1. Find the sine and cosine of $\pi/4$, $\pi/3$, and $\pi/2$.

Solution. In Fig. 9-9, we saw that $W(\pi/4) = (\sqrt{2}/2, \sqrt{2}/2)$. Hence

$$\sin\frac{\pi}{4} = \frac{\sqrt{2}}{2}, \quad \cos\frac{\pi}{4} = \frac{\sqrt{2}}{2}.$$

$W(\pi/3) = (1/2, \sqrt{3}/2)$. (See Fig. 9-15.) Therefore,

$$\sin\frac{\pi}{3} = \frac{\sqrt{3}}{2}, \quad \cos\frac{\pi}{3} = \frac{1}{2}.$$

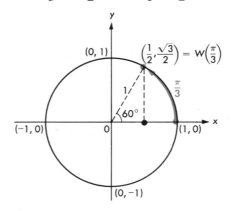

FIGURE 9-15

Since $W(\pi/2) = (0, 1)$, we have

$$\sin \frac{\pi}{2} = 1, \quad \cos \frac{\pi}{2} = 0.$$

Problem 2. Find the sine and cosine of $55\pi/4$ and $-10\pi/3$.

Solution. The greatest integral multiple of 2π contained in $55\pi/4$ is 12π. Therefore,

$$W\left(\frac{55\pi}{4}\right) = W\left(\frac{55\pi}{4} - (6 \cdot 2\pi)\right),$$

$$= W\left(\frac{7\pi}{4}\right).$$

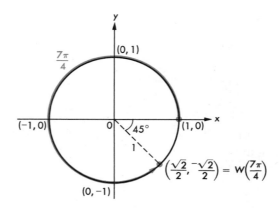

FIGURE 9–16

According to Fig 9–16, $W(7\pi/4) = (\sqrt{2}/2, -\sqrt{2}/2)$. Thus,

$$\sin \frac{55\pi}{4} = -\frac{\sqrt{2}}{2}, \quad \cos \frac{55\pi}{4} = \frac{\sqrt{2}}{2}.$$

By the periodicity of W, we have

$$W\left(-\frac{10\pi}{3}\right) = W\left(4\pi - \frac{10\pi}{3}\right),$$

$$= W\left(\frac{2\pi}{3}\right).$$

According to Fig. 9–17, $W\left(\frac{2\pi}{3}\right) = \left(-\frac{1}{2}, \frac{\sqrt{3}}{2}\right).$

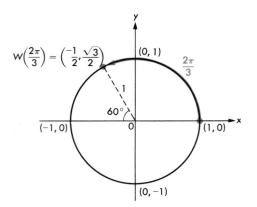

FIGURE 9-17

Thus,

$$\sin\left(-\frac{10\pi}{3}\right) = \frac{\sqrt{3}}{2}, \quad \cos\left(-\frac{10\pi}{3}\right) = -\frac{1}{2}.$$

The unit circle has equation

$$x^2 + y^2 = 1.$$

Therefore, for each real number s, the point $W(s)$ on the unit circle has coordinates (cos s, sin s) which are a solution of the above equation. This can be stated in the following way.

FIRST FUNDAMENTAL IDENTITY

$$sin^2\ s + cos^2\ s = 1 \quad \textit{for every real number } s \qquad \textit{(FI-1)}$$

Note that we write $\sin^2 s$ for $(\sin s)^2$ and $\cos^2 s$ for $(\cos s)^2$. The first fundamental identity is an example of an equation which is true for all numbers in the domains of the functions. In trigonometry, such an equation is frequently called an *identity*.

It follows from the first fundamental identity that $\sin^2 s \leqq 1$ and $\cos^2 s \leqq 1$. Hence,

$$-1 \leqq sin\ s \leqq 1 \quad \textit{for every real number } s,$$
$$-1 \leqq cos\ s \leqq 1 \quad \textit{for every real number } s.$$

In other words, the interval $\{x \mid -1 \leqq x \leqq 1\}$ is the *range* of the cosine and $\{y \mid -1 \leqq y \leqq 1\}$ is the range of the sine.

Exercises

For each s in Exercises 1–2, find $W(s)$, and give $\sin s$ and $\cos s$.

1. (a) $\dfrac{9\pi}{4}$ (b) $\dfrac{5\pi}{6}$

2. (a) $-\dfrac{\pi}{6}$ (b) $\dfrac{4\pi}{3}$

Find each of the following.

3. (a) $\sin \dfrac{9\pi}{4}$ (b) $\cos\left(-\dfrac{5\pi}{6}\right)$

4. (a) $\cos \dfrac{7\pi}{3}$ (b) $\sin \dfrac{13\pi}{4}$

5. (a) $\cos \dfrac{3\pi}{2}$ (b) $\cos \dfrac{17\pi}{6}$

6. (a) $\sin \dfrac{5\pi}{6}$ (b) $\sin(-3\pi)$

7. (a) $\sin\left(-\dfrac{5\pi}{6}\right)$ (b) $\cos 4\pi$

8. Complete the following table by telling whether the $\sin s$ and $\cos s$ are positive or negative numbers in each of the four quadrants in a cartesian coordinate system.

		I	II	III	IV
(a)	$\sin s$	+	?	?	?
(b)	$\cos s$	+	?	?	?

9. (a) When we say $\sin s = 1$, we mean that the y-coordinate of $W(s)$ is 1. Draw a sketch of the unit circle and locate all such points. How many points have this property?
   (b) For what values of s in the interval $0 \leq s < 2\pi$ is $\cos s = 1$?

---

10. (a) If $\sin s = \frac{1}{2}$, use (FI-1) to find the two possible values of $\cos s$.
    (b) Since $\sin s$ in part (a) is positive, the point $W(s)$ must be in the first or second quadrant. Why?
    (c) If $\sin s = \frac{1}{2}$ and $\pi/2 < s < \pi$, what is $\cos s$?
    (d) Draw a sketch and find s for part (c).

11. (a) If $-\pi/2 < s < 0$, is $\cos s$ positive or negative?
    (b) Given that s is in the interval $-\pi/2 < s < 0$ and that $\cos s = \frac{3}{5}$, use (FI-1) to find $\sin s$.

Review for Sections 9–1 through 9–4

Find the trigonometric functions (sine, cosine, tangent) of each of the following angles.

1. The acute angle whose tangent is 7

2. The acute angle whose cosine is $\frac{2}{5}$

3. The acute angle whose sine is $\frac{3}{4}$

4. The acute angle whose tangent is 1

5. The acute angle whose sine is .4

6. The acute angle whose cosine is .8

7. The acute angle whose sine is .15

8. The acute angle whose cosine is .01

Find the coordinates of the point $P = W(s)$, where W is the wrapping function, for each value of s.

9. $s = \dfrac{\pi}{2}$ 　　　　　　　　　　 **10.** $s = -\dfrac{\pi}{2}$

11. $s = 3\pi$ 　　　　　　　　　　 **12.** $s = -3\pi$

13. $s = \dfrac{7\pi}{4}$ 　　　　　　　　　　 **14.** $s = \dfrac{5\pi}{6}$

15. $s = -\dfrac{9\pi}{2}$ 　　　　　　　　　　 **16.** $s = -\dfrac{7\pi}{2}$

17. $s = \dfrac{19\pi}{4}$ 　　　　　　　　　　 **18.** $s = \dfrac{11\pi}{4}$

19. $s = -\dfrac{17\pi}{3}$ 　　　　　　　　　　 **20.** $s = \dfrac{13\pi}{6}$

For each of the following values of s, find $P_1 = W(s)$, $P_2 = W(-s)$, $P_3 = W\left(s + \dfrac{\pi}{2}\right)$, $P_4 = W(s + \pi)$, $P_5 = W(s - \pi)$, and $P_6 = W\left(s - \dfrac{\pi}{2}\right)$.

21. $s = 2\pi$ 　　　　　　　　　　 **22.** $s = 3\pi$

23. $s = -\dfrac{13\pi}{6}$ 　　　　　　　　　　 **24.** $s = \dfrac{19\pi}{6}$

25. $s = \dfrac{11\pi}{4}$ 　　　　　　　　　　 **26.** $s = \dfrac{7\pi}{2}$

For each of the following values of s, find $W(s)$, $\sin s$ and $\cos s$.

27. $s = 6\pi$ 　　　　　　　　　　 **28.** $s = 7\pi$

29. $s = \dfrac{5\pi}{4}$ 　　　　　　　　　　 **30.** $s = -\dfrac{3\pi}{2}$

31. $s = \dfrac{7\pi}{6}$ 　　　　　　　　　　 **32.** $s = \dfrac{5\pi}{3}$

Answers to Review for Sections 9–1 through 9–4

1. $\sin \alpha = \dfrac{7\sqrt{2}}{10}$, $\cos \alpha = \dfrac{\sqrt{2}}{10}$ **2.** $\sin \alpha = \dfrac{\sqrt{21}}{5}$, $\tan \alpha = \dfrac{\sqrt{21}}{2}$

3. $\cos \alpha = \dfrac{\sqrt{7}}{4}$, $\tan \alpha = \dfrac{3\sqrt{7}}{7}$ **4.** $\sin \alpha = \dfrac{\sqrt{2}}{2}$, $\cos \alpha = \dfrac{\sqrt{2}}{2}$

5. $\cos \alpha = \dfrac{\sqrt{21}}{5}$, $\tan \alpha = \dfrac{2\sqrt{21}}{21}$ **6.** $\sin \alpha = .6$, $\tan \alpha = .75$

7. $\cos \alpha = \dfrac{\sqrt{391}}{20}$, $\tan \alpha = \dfrac{3\sqrt{391}}{391}$

8. $\sin \alpha = \dfrac{3\sqrt{1111}}{100}$, $\tan \alpha = 3\sqrt{1111}$

9. $(0, 1)$ **10.** $(0, -1)$

11. $(-1, 0)$ **12.** $(-1, 0)$

13. $\left(\dfrac{\sqrt{2}}{2}, -\dfrac{\sqrt{2}}{2} \right)$ **14.** $\left(-\dfrac{\sqrt{3}}{2}, \dfrac{1}{2} \right)$

15. $(0, -1)$ **16.** $(0, 1)$

17. $\left(-\dfrac{\sqrt{2}}{2}, \dfrac{\sqrt{2}}{2} \right)$ **18.** $\left(-\dfrac{\sqrt{2}}{2}, \dfrac{\sqrt{2}}{2} \right)$

19. $\left(\dfrac{1}{2}, \dfrac{\sqrt{3}}{2} \right)$ **20.** $\left(\dfrac{\sqrt{3}}{2}, \dfrac{1}{2} \right)$

21. $P_1 = (1, 0)$, $P_2 = (1, 0)$, $P_3 = (0, 1)$, $P_4 = (-1, 0)$, $P_5 = (-1, 0)$, $P_6 = (0, -1)$

22. $P_1 = (-1, 0)$, $P_2 = (-1, 0)$, $P_3 = (0, -1)$, $P_4 = (1, 0)$, $P_5 = (1, 0)$, $P_6 = (0, 1)$

23. $P_1 = \left(\dfrac{\sqrt{3}}{2}, -\dfrac{1}{2} \right)$, $\quad P_2 = \left(\dfrac{\sqrt{3}}{2}, \dfrac{1}{2} \right)$, $\quad P_3 = \left(\dfrac{1}{2}, \dfrac{\sqrt{3}}{2} \right)$,

$P_4 = \left(-\dfrac{\sqrt{3}}{2}, \dfrac{1}{2} \right)$, $\quad P_5 = \left(-\dfrac{\sqrt{3}}{2}, \dfrac{1}{2} \right)$, $\quad P_6 = \left(-\dfrac{1}{2}, -\dfrac{\sqrt{3}}{2} \right)$

24. $P_1 = \left(-\dfrac{\sqrt{3}}{2}, -\dfrac{1}{2} \right)$, $\quad P_2 = \left(-\dfrac{\sqrt{3}}{2}, \dfrac{1}{2} \right)$, $\quad P_3 = \left(\dfrac{1}{2}, -\dfrac{\sqrt{3}}{2} \right)$,

$P_4 = \left(\dfrac{\sqrt{3}}{2}, \dfrac{1}{2} \right)$, $\quad P_5 = \left(\dfrac{\sqrt{3}}{2}, \dfrac{1}{2} \right)$, $\quad P_6 = \left(-\dfrac{1}{2}, \dfrac{\sqrt{3}}{2} \right)$

25. $P_1 = \left(-\dfrac{\sqrt{2}}{2}, \dfrac{\sqrt{2}}{2} \right)$, $\quad P_2 = \left(-\dfrac{\sqrt{2}}{2}, -\dfrac{\sqrt{2}}{2} \right)$,

$P_3 = \left(-\dfrac{\sqrt{2}}{2}, -\dfrac{\sqrt{2}}{2} \right)$, $\quad P_4 = \left(\dfrac{\sqrt{2}}{2}, -\dfrac{\sqrt{2}}{2} \right)$,

$P_5 = \left(\dfrac{\sqrt{2}}{2}, -\dfrac{\sqrt{2}}{2} \right)$, $\quad P_6 = \left(\dfrac{\sqrt{2}}{2}, \dfrac{\sqrt{2}}{2} \right)$

26. $P_1 = (0, -1)$, $P_2 = (0, 1)$, $P_3 = (1, 0)$, $P_4 = (0, 1)$, $P_5 = (0, 1)$,
$P_6 = (-1, 0)$

27. $W(s) = (1, 0)$, $\sin s = 0$, $\cos s = 1$

28. $W(s) = (-1, 0)$, $\sin s = 0$, $\cos s = -1$

29. $W(s) = \left(-\dfrac{\sqrt{2}}{2}, -\dfrac{\sqrt{2}}{2} \right)$, $\sin s = -\dfrac{\sqrt{2}}{2}$, $\cos s = -\dfrac{\sqrt{2}}{2}$

30. $W(s) = (0, 1)$, $\sin s = 1$, $\cos s = 0$

31. $W(s) = \left(-\dfrac{\sqrt{3}}{2}, -\dfrac{1}{2} \right)$, $\sin s = -\dfrac{1}{2}$, $\cos s = -\dfrac{\sqrt{3}}{2}$

32. $W(s) = \left(\dfrac{1}{2}, -\dfrac{\sqrt{3}}{2} \right)$, $\sin s = -\dfrac{\sqrt{3}}{2}$, $\cos s = \dfrac{1}{2}$

9–5 PROPERTIES OF SINE AND COSINE

Many identities follow from the properties of the wrapping function given in Section 9–4. The first fundamental identity, (FI-1), was stated in Section 9–4. The following are some other fundamental identities.

$$sin\ (-s)\ =\ -sin\ s \qquad\qquad (FI\text{-}2)$$

$$cos\ (-s)\ =\ cos\ s \qquad\qquad (FI\text{-}3)$$

These follow directly from relationship (1) on page 407.

We call f an *odd function* if $f(-x) = -f(x)$ for every x in the domain of f. We call f an *even function* if $f(-x) = f(x)$ for every x in the domain of f. By the second fundamental identity, *sine is an odd function*, and by the third fundamental identity, *cosine is an even function*.

If $W(s) = (\cos s, \sin s)$, then $W(s + \pi/2) = (-\sin s, \cos s)$ by the second relationship on page 408. This leads us to the fourth and fifth fundamental identities.

$$sin\left(s + \frac{\pi}{2} \right) = cos\ s \qquad\qquad (FI\text{-}4)$$

$$cos\left(s + \frac{\pi}{2} \right) = -sin\ s \qquad\qquad (FI\text{-}5)$$

Other identities are given below.

$$sin\ (s \pm \pi) = -sin\ s \qquad \text{(FI-6)}$$

$$cos\ (s \pm \pi) = -cos\ s \qquad \text{(FI-7)}$$

$$sin\left(s - \frac{\pi}{2}\right) = -cos\ s \qquad \text{(FI-8)}$$

$$cos\left(s - \frac{\pi}{2}\right) = sin\ s \qquad \text{(FI-9)}$$

Problem. Find $\sin 4\pi/3$ and $\cos 7\pi/4$.

Solution.

$$\sin \frac{4\pi}{3} = \sin\left(\frac{\pi}{3} + \pi\right) \qquad\qquad \cos \frac{7\pi}{4} = \cos\left(\frac{3\pi}{4} + \pi\right)$$

$$= -\sin \frac{\pi}{3} \qquad\qquad\qquad = -\cos \frac{3\pi}{4}$$

$$= -\frac{\sqrt{3}}{2} \qquad\qquad\qquad = -\cos\left(\frac{\pi}{4} + \frac{\pi}{2}\right)$$

$$\qquad\qquad\qquad\qquad\qquad = \sin \frac{\pi}{4}$$

$$\qquad\qquad\qquad\qquad\qquad = \frac{\sqrt{2}}{2}$$

The fundamental identities derived in this section will be used in the next chapter. Of those listed, the second, third, sixth, and seventh are the most useful in application and are easiest to recall from the properties of the wrapping function W. For example,

$$\sin\left(-\frac{10\pi}{3}\right) = -\sin \frac{10\pi}{3} \qquad \text{(FI-2)}$$

$$= -\sin\left(\frac{10\pi}{3} - 2\pi\right)$$

$$= -\sin \frac{4\pi}{3}$$

$$= -\left(-\sin \frac{\pi}{3}\right) \qquad \text{(FI-6)}$$

$$= \frac{\sqrt{3}}{2}.$$

In solving the following exercises, you may find it more useful to learn these formulas rather than to refer to them in the text.

Exercises

Evaluate each of the following.

1. (a) $\sin\left(-\dfrac{5\pi}{4}\right)$ (b) $\cos\left(-\dfrac{7\pi}{6}\right)$

2. (a) $\cos\dfrac{19\pi}{6}$ (b) $\sin\left(-23\pi\right)$

3. (a) $\sin\left(-\dfrac{11\pi}{3}\right)$ (b) $\cos\left(-17\pi\right)$

4. (a) $\cos\left(-\dfrac{11\pi}{3}\right)$ (b) $\sin\left(-\dfrac{17\pi}{6}\right)$

5. (a) $\sin\dfrac{5\pi}{3}$ (b) $\cos\dfrac{11\pi}{6}$

6. (a) $\sin\dfrac{7\pi}{4}$ (b) $\cos\dfrac{2\pi}{3}$

7. (a) $\sin\dfrac{4\pi}{3}$ (b) $\cos\dfrac{29\pi}{6}$

8. (a) $\cos\left(-\dfrac{5\pi}{6}\right)$ (b) $\sin\left(-\dfrac{11\pi}{6}\right)$

9. (a) $\cos\left(-\dfrac{5\pi}{3}\right)$ (b) $\sin\left(-\dfrac{5\pi}{6}\right)$

State whether each of the following functions is odd, even, or neither.

10. $f(x) = 3x^3 - 4x$ 11. $f(x) = 2x^6 + 4x^4 - 8$

12. $f(x) = 6x^5 - 2x^2$ 13. $f(x) = 1 - x^3 - 4x^5$

14. Derive (FI-8) and (FI-9) from relationship (4) on page 409.

15. Derive (FI-6) and (FI-7) from relationship (3) on page 409.

16. (a) Consider the polynomial function f, defined by

$$f(x) = x^5 - 3x^3 + 4x.$$

Show that f is an *odd* function.

(b) Show that the polynomial function g, defined by

$$g(x) = 3x^4 + 2x^2 - 5,$$

is an *even* function.

(c) Consider the polynomial function h, defined by

$$h(x) = x^3 - 3x^2 + x - 2.$$

Is h odd? Is h even?

17. (a) Make a verbal statement about all *odd* polynomial functions by generalizing Exercise 16(a).
   (b) Make a verbal statement about all *even* polynomial functions by generalizing Exercise 16(b).
   (c) Make a verbal statement about polynomial functions that are neither odd nor even by generalizing Exercise 16(c).

---

18. (a) Use (FI-2) and (FI-6) to prove that $\sin(\pi - s) = \sin s$.
   (b) Prove that $\cos(\pi - s) = -\cos s$.

9-6   THE OTHER TRIGONOMETRIC FUNCTIONS

For convenience, certain combinations of the sine and cosine are given names.

$$tangent\ s = \frac{sine\ s}{cosine\ s}$$

$$cotangent\ s = \frac{cosine\ s}{sine\ s}$$

$$secant\ s = \frac{1}{cosine\ s}$$

$$cosecant\ s = \frac{1}{sine\ s}$$

The domain of each of these four new functions is the set of all real numbers, excluding those numbers for which the function in the denominator is 0. For example,

$$\left\{ s \mid s \neq \frac{\pi}{2} + n\pi,\ n \text{ an integer} \right\}$$

is the domain of both the tangent and the secant.

Problem 1. Find the circular functions of $\pi/4$ and $\pi/3$.

Solution.

$$\sin \frac{\pi}{4} = \frac{\sqrt{2}}{2},$$
$$\sin \frac{\pi}{3} = \frac{\sqrt{3}}{2},$$

$$\cos \frac{\pi}{4} = \frac{\sqrt{2}}{2},$$
$$\cos \frac{\pi}{3} = \frac{1}{2},$$

$$\tan \frac{\pi}{4} = \frac{\frac{\sqrt{2}}{2}}{\frac{\sqrt{2}}{2}} = 1,$$
$$\tan \frac{\pi}{3} = \frac{\frac{\sqrt{3}}{2}}{\frac{1}{2}} = \sqrt{3},$$

$$\cot \frac{\pi}{4} = \frac{\frac{\sqrt{2}}{2}}{\frac{\sqrt{2}}{2}} = 1,$$
$$\cot \frac{\pi}{3} = \frac{\frac{1}{2}}{\frac{\sqrt{3}}{2}} = \frac{\sqrt{3}}{3},$$

$$\sec \frac{\pi}{4} = \frac{1}{\frac{\sqrt{2}}{2}} = \sqrt{2},$$
$$\sec \frac{\pi}{3} = \frac{1}{\frac{1}{2}} = 2,$$

$$\csc \frac{\pi}{4} = \frac{1}{\frac{\sqrt{2}}{2}} = \sqrt{2},$$
$$\csc \frac{\pi}{3} = \frac{1}{\frac{\sqrt{3}}{2}} = \frac{2}{3}\sqrt{3}.$$

Observe that we have abbreviated tangent to tan, cotangent to cot, secant to sec, and cosecant to csc.

We shall leave the proof of the following identities for the exercises.

$$sec^2 s = 1 + tan^2 s \qquad (FI\text{-}10)$$
$$csc^2 s = 1 + cot^2 s \qquad (FI\text{-}11)$$

Problem 2. If $\pi < s < 3\pi/2$ and $\tan s = \frac{1}{2}$, find the other trigonometric functions of s.

Solution. First,

$$\cot s = 2.$$

By the tenth fundamental identity, $\sec^2 s = \frac{5}{4}$. Since $\cos s < 0$ if $\pi < s < 3\pi/2$, the $\sec s$ must be less than 0 also. Hence,

$$\sec s = -\frac{\sqrt{5}}{2}.$$

Therefore,

$$\cos s = -\frac{2}{\sqrt{5}} = -\frac{2\sqrt{5}}{5},$$

$$\sin s = \cos s \tan s = -\frac{\sqrt{5}}{5},$$

$$\csc s = -\sqrt{5}.$$

Problem 3. Simplify the expression

$$\frac{1}{1 - \sin s} + \frac{1}{1 + \sin s}.$$

Solution. We proceed as follows:

$$\frac{1}{1 - \sin s} + \frac{1}{1 + \sin s} = \frac{(1 + \sin s) + (1 - \sin s)}{(1 - \sin s)(1 + \sin s)}$$

$$= \frac{2}{1 - \sin^2 s}.$$

Since $1 - \sin^2 s = \cos^2 s$ by the first fundamental identity, and $\sec^2 s = 1/\cos^2 s$, we obtain

$$\frac{2}{\cos^2 s}, \quad \text{or } 2\sec^2 s,$$

as a simplified form of the given expression.

Problem 4. Prove that the following equation is an identity.

$$\csc s - \sin s = \cos s \cot s$$

Solution. What we really wish to show is that the expressions on the two sides of this equation are equivalent, that is, that one may be changed into the other by use of the fundamental identities. One way of doing this is shown on the following page.

$$\csc s - \sin s = \frac{1}{\sin s} - \sin s$$

$$= \frac{1 - \sin^2 s}{\sin s}$$

$$= \frac{\cos^2 s}{\sin s}$$

$$= \cos s \cdot \frac{\cos s}{\sin s}$$

$$= \cos s \cot s$$

Hence, $\csc s - \sin s = \cos s \cot s$ for every s in the common domain of the cotangent and the cosecant.

Exercises

In Exercises 1–5, find the other five trigonometric functions of s.

1. (a) $\cos s = \dfrac{\sqrt{5}}{5}$ and $0 < s < \dfrac{\pi}{2}$

  (b) $\sin s = \dfrac{3\sqrt{10}}{10}$ and $0 < s < \pi$

2. (a) $\cos s = \dfrac{1}{\sqrt{2}}$ and $0 < s < \dfrac{\pi}{2}$ (b) $\sin s = \dfrac{1}{2}$ and $\dfrac{\pi}{2} < s < \pi$

3. (a) $\tan s = -2$ and $\dfrac{3\pi}{2} < s < 2\pi$ (b) $\sin s = -1$

4. (a) $\sec s = -\sqrt{2}$ and $\tan s < 0$ (b) $\csc s = 3$ and $\cos s < 0$

5. (a) $\tan s = 1$ and $\sin s < 0$ (b) $\cos s = -1$

Complete the table by telling whether the tangent, cotangent, secant, and cosecant are positive or negative numbers in the four quadrants of a cartesian coordinate system.

		I	II	III	IV
6. (a)	tangent	+	?	?	?
(b)	cotangent	+	?	?	?
7. (a)	secant	+	?	?	?
(b)	cosecant	+	?	?	?

8. (a) What is the range of $\sin s$?
  (b) What is the range of $\cos s$?

9. (a) What is the range of cot s?

(b) What is the range of sec s?

In Exercise 10, use a sketch of the unit circle.

10. (a) Describe the behavior of the tangent function in the interval

$$\left\{ s \mid 0 \leqq s < \frac{\pi}{2} \right\} .$$

(b) Describe the behavior of the tangent function in the interval

$$\left\{ s \mid \frac{\pi}{2} < s \leqq \pi \right\} .$$

(c) What is the range of the tangent function; that is, what is the set of values of tan s?

Simplify each of the following expressions.

11. cos s tan s

12. $\sec^2 s - \tan^2 s$

13. $\dfrac{1}{\sec s - \tan s} - \dfrac{1}{\sec s + \tan s}$

14. $\dfrac{\cot s}{\csc s}$

15. sec s − sin s tan s

16. $\cot^2 s - \csc^2 s$

Prove that each of the following equations is an identity.

17. $(\sin s + \cos s)^2 = 1 + 2 \sin s \cos s$

18. $\dfrac{\sin s}{\csc s - \cot s} + \dfrac{\sin s}{\csc s + \cot s} = 2$

19. $\dfrac{\sin s}{1 - \cos s} = \dfrac{1 + \cos s}{\sin s}$

20. sin s cos s − sec s sin s = −$\sin^2 s$ tan s

21. tan s + cot s = sec s csc s

22. $\dfrac{\cos s}{1 + \sin s} = \sec s - \tan s$

---

23. Show that the tangent function is an odd function.

24. Derive (FI-11).

25. Derive (FI-10). (Hint: Divide both sides of the equation in (FI-1) by $\cos^2 s$.)

9–7   RADIAN MEASURE AND GENERAL ANGLES

In trigonometry, it is convenient for us to think of an angle in a more general way than we did in geometry. We still say that an angle is composed of two rays in a plane having a common endpoint V, called the vertex of the angle. However, let us suppose that we keep V fixed and rotate one of these rays to another position in the given plane. Then the angle is *swept out.* The ray with which we start is called the *initial side* of the angle, and the ray with which we end is called the *terminal side.* The curved arrow in Fig. 9–18 indicates that in the formation of the angle, initial side I is rotated in a counterclockwise direction to terminal side T. An angle α is said to be in *standard position* relative to a cartesian coordinate system in a plane if the vertex of α is at the origin and the initial side of α is along the positive x-axis.

FIGURE 9–18

We shall assign a measure to each angle in the following way. The measure will be a positive number if the angle is formed by a counterclockwise rotation, and a negative number if the angle is formed by a clockwise rotation. There are two common ways of measuring angles: by degrees and by radians.

Definition of radian measure of an angle

The length of arc swept out by an angle α on the unit circle is called the radian measure of α.

Since the circumference of a unit circle is 2π, an angle formed by one revolution (in a counterclockwise direction) of the terminal side has a radian measure of 2π. If the terminal side is rotated more than one complete revolution, the angle formed will have a radian measure of more than 2π. A straight angle has a radian measure π, and a right angle has radian measure $\pi/2$.

The measure of α is 1 radian if the arc of the unit circle swept out by α is of length 1 and if α is formed by a counterclockwise rotation. (See Fig. 9–19.) If the arc swept out by α had length 2, then α would

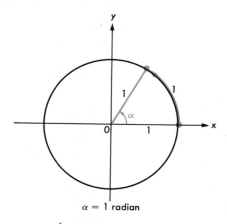

$\alpha = 1$ radian

FIGURE 9-19

have radian measure 2 or -2, depending on whether α was formed by a counterclockwise or a clockwise rotation. From now on, when we write $\alpha = 2$ without stating units, we mean that α has measure 2 radians. (See Fig. 9-20.)

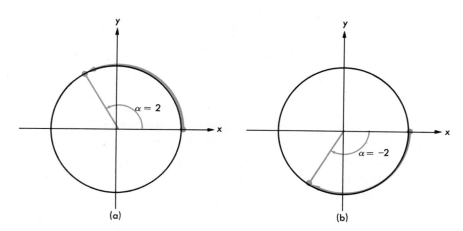

FIGURE 9-20

If we start with the fact that a straight angle has measure 180°, or π radians, the formula

$$r = \frac{\pi}{180} d$$

gives the radian measure r of an angle in terms of its degree measure d.

We can solve the above formula for d in terms of r, obtaining

$$d = \frac{180}{\pi} r,$$

which gives the degree measure d of an angle in terms of its radian measure r. For example,

$$\text{if } r = \frac{\pi}{6}, \text{ then } d = 30°;$$

$$\text{if } r = 1, \text{ then } d = \frac{180}{\pi} \doteq 57.3°.$$

In other words $57.3° \doteq 1$ radian.

The first two columns of the Table of Values of Trigonometric Functions in the Appendix give the approximate radian measures of angles of measure $0°, 1°, 2°, \ldots, 89°, 90°$. Since π is irrational, it follows that if the degree measure of an angle is a rational number, then the radian measure is irrational, and vice versa.

The trigonometric functions of a general angle can now be defined in the following way.

Definition of the trigonometric functions of a general angle

If angle α has radian measure s, then we define

$$sin \; \alpha = sin \; s \quad and \quad cos \; \alpha = cos \; s.$$

The other functions of a general angle α are defined in terms of the sine α and cosine α, as before. For example, $\tan \alpha = \sin \alpha / \cos \alpha$.

If angle α is acute, and if α is in standard position as shown in Fig. 9–21, then α is an angle of right triangle ABC. Hence,

$$\sin \alpha = \frac{y}{1}, \quad \cos \alpha = \frac{x}{1}$$

by the definitions of the sine and cosine of an acute angle in Section 9–1. On the other hand, if α has radian measure s, then $W(s)$ is the point B. Since $W(s) = (\cos s, \sin s)$ and $B = (x, y)$, we have $x = \cos s$

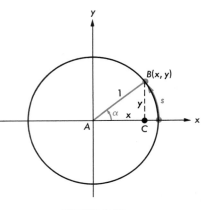

FIGURE 9–21

and $y = \sin s$. Thus,

$$\sin \alpha = \sin s, \quad \cos \alpha = \cos s,$$

and the two definitions of sine and cosine agree for acute angles.

From now on, we shall consider the domains of the trigonometric functions as either a set of general angles or as a set of real numbers, whichever is more convenient. Whenever we write sin 30°, we mean the sine of an angle of measure 30°. If we write sin 3, we mean the sine of the number 3, or, equivalently, the sine of an angle of measure 3 radians.

The Table in the Appendix lists three-decimal-place approximations of $\sin \alpha$, $\cos \alpha$, and $\tan \alpha$ for $\alpha = 0°, 1°, 2°, \ldots, 89°, 90°$. For example,

$$\sin 24° \doteq .407, \quad \cos 44° \doteq .719, \quad \tan 77° \doteq 4.331.$$

Exercises

Given the radian measure, find the degree measure for each angle below.

1. (a) $\dfrac{2\pi}{3}$　　　　　　　　　　　　(b) $-\dfrac{\pi}{4}$

2. (a) $-\dfrac{\pi}{3}$　　　　　　　　　　　(b) $\dfrac{22\pi}{3}$

3. (a) $\dfrac{8\pi}{9}$　　　　　　　　　　　(b) $\dfrac{7\pi}{4}$

4. (a) 2　　　　　　　　　　　　　(b) $\dfrac{34\pi}{3}$

Given the degree measure, find the radian measure for each angle below.

5. (a) $-90°$　　　　　　　　　　　(b) 40°

6. (a) 450°　　　　　　　　　　　(b) $-60°$

7. (a) 200°　　　　　　　　　　　(b) 450°

8. (a) 330°　　　　　　　　　　　(b) $-150°$

In each of the following exercises, sketch the angle in standard position, and find the three trigonometric functions: sine, cosine, and tangent.

9. 30°　　　　　　10. $-150°$　　　　　　11. $-90°$

12. 45°　　　　　　13. 120°　　　　　　14. $-60°$

15. 570°　　　　　　16. $-210°$　　　　　　17. 0°

18. 370°　　　　　　19. $-280°$　　　　　　20. 756°

In Exercises 21–26, find the sine and cosine of each number.

21. .628   **22.** .942   **23.** .803

24. .401   **25.** .262   **26.** 1.501

27. Show that the radian measure of α is

$$\frac{a}{r}.$$

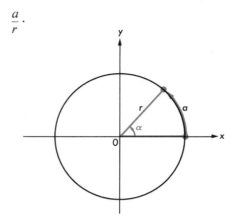

9-8 FUNCTIONS AND COFUNCTIONS

If an acute angle has measure α degrees, then its *complement* has measure $90 - \alpha$ degrees. Similarly, if an acute angle has radian measure s, then its complement has radian measure $\pi/2 - s$. The trigonometric functions of a number and its complement are related in the following way.

$$\sin\left(\frac{\pi}{2} - s\right) = \sin\left(-\left(s - \frac{\pi}{2}\right)\right)$$

$$= -\sin\left(s - \frac{\pi}{2}\right) \qquad \text{(FI-2)}$$

$$= \cos s \qquad \text{(FI-8)}$$

$$\cos\left(\frac{\pi}{2} - s\right) = \cos\left(-\left(s - \frac{\pi}{2}\right)\right)$$

$$= \cos\left(s - \frac{\pi}{2}\right) \qquad \text{(FI-3)}$$

$$= \sin s \qquad \text{(FI-9)}$$

Since these equations are true for every number s, they are identities.

$$sin\left(\frac{\pi}{2} - s\right) = cos\ s, \quad cos\left(\frac{\pi}{2} - s\right) = sin\ s \qquad \textit{(FI-12)}$$

Similar identities can be derived for the other trigonometric functions.

$$tan\left(\frac{\pi}{2} - s\right) = cot\ s, \quad cot\left(\frac{\pi}{2} - s\right) = tan\ s \quad \text{(FI-13)}$$

$$sec\left(\frac{\pi}{2} - s\right) = csc\ s, \quad csc\left(\frac{\pi}{2} - s\right) = sec\ s \quad \text{(FI-14)}$$

The sine and cosine are called *cofunctions* of each other; that is, cosine is the cofunction of sine, and sine is the cofunction of cosine. Similarly, the tangent and cotangent are cofunctions, and the secant and cosecant are cofunctions. In terms of cofunctions, the twelfth, thirteenth, and fourteenth fundamental identities can be expressed as follows: If f is any one of the six trigonometric functions and cof is its cofunction, then

$$f\left(\frac{\pi}{2} - s\right) = cof\ s.$$

For example,

$$\sin\frac{\pi}{6} = \cos\left(\frac{\pi}{2} - \frac{\pi}{6}\right) = \cos\frac{\pi}{3},$$

$$\cot\frac{3\pi}{8} = \tan\left(\frac{\pi}{2} - \frac{3\pi}{8}\right) = \tan\frac{\pi}{8},$$

$$\sec 42° = \csc(90° - 42°) = \csc 48°.$$

If an angle has measure α between 0° and 180°, then its *supplement* has measure $180 - \alpha$ degrees. Similarly, if an acute angle has radian measure s, then its supplement has radian measure $\pi - s$. Using the second, third, sixth, and seventh fundamental identities, we can easily establish the following identity.

$$sin\ (\pi - s) = sin\ s, \quad cos\ (\pi - s) = -cos\ s \quad \text{(FI-15)}$$

For example,

$$\cos\frac{5\pi}{6} = \cos\left(\pi - \frac{\pi}{6}\right) = -\cos\frac{\pi}{6},$$

$$= -\frac{\sqrt{3}}{2}.$$

Exercises

Using the Table of Values of Trigonometric Functions, when necessary, find the value of the following functions.

1. (a) $\sin \frac{2}{3}\pi$ (b) $\tan \frac{3}{4}\pi$

2. (a) $\cos \frac{5}{6}\pi$ (b) $\sin \dfrac{13\pi}{6}$

3. (a) $\cos \dfrac{9\pi}{4}$ (b) $\tan 3\pi$

4. (a) $\cos \dfrac{8\pi}{3}$ (b) $\sec \dfrac{11\pi}{4}$

5. (a) $\cos 113°$ (b) $\sin 170°$

6. (a) $\tan 151°$ (b) $\cos 94°$

7. (a) $\tan 91°$ (b) $\sin 150°$

8. (a) $\sin 130°$ (b) $\cos 95°$

9. (a) $\tan 113°$ (b) $\tan 463°$

10. (a) $\cos 540°$ (b) $\cos 455°$

11. (a) $\sin 450°$ (b) $\sin 350°$

Fill in the blanks in each of the following problems.

12. (a) $\cos \dfrac{\pi}{10} = \sin$ __?__   (b) $\csc \dfrac{2\pi}{3} = \sec$ __?__

13. (a) $\tan 48° = \cot$ __?__   (b) $\sin 40° = \cos$ __?__

14. (a) $\sin \dfrac{\pi}{4} = \cos$ __?__   (b) $\cot 63° = \tan$ __?__

15. (a) $\sec \dfrac{\pi}{3} = \csc$ __?__   (b) $\tan \dfrac{\pi}{6} = \cot$ __?__

16. (a) $\csc 46° = \sec$ __?__   (b) $\cos 19° = \sin$ __?__

---

17. Using the Table of Values of Trigonometric Functions, when necessary, give the values of the trigonometric functions in Exercises 12–16.

Find the complement of each of the following angles for the given radian measure. Give a three-decimal-place approximation for the sine and cosine of each angle and its complement.

18. .646   **19.** 1.047   **20.** 1.309

21. .314   **22.** 1.204   **23.** 1.431

---

24. From (FI-15), derive similar identities relating the other four trigonometric functions of s and $\pi - s$.

KEY IDEAS AND KEY WORDS

The trigonometric (or circular) functions are defined in terms of the **wrapping function W,** which assigns to each real number s a point $W(s)$ on a unit circle. By definition of **sine** and **cosine,** the coordinates of $W(s)$ are (cos s, sin s). The other trigonometric functions, **tangent, cotangent, secant,** and **cosecant,** are defined in terms of sine and cosine:

$$\tan s = \frac{\sin s}{\cos s}, \qquad \cot s = \frac{\cos s}{\sin s},$$

$$\sec s = \frac{1}{\cos s}, \qquad \csc s = \frac{1}{\sin s}.$$

The sine and cosine are **periodic functions** with period 2π. In other words, the following equations are true for every real number s.

$$\sin s = \sin (s + 2\pi), \qquad \cos s = \cos (s + 2\pi)$$

The following are the **fundamental identities.**

$\sin^2 s + \cos^2 s = 1$ **(FI-1)**

$\sin (-s) = -\sin s$ **(FI-2)**

$\cos (-s) = \cos s$ **(FI-3)**

$\sin \left(s + \dfrac{\pi}{2}\right) = \cos s$ **(FI-4)**

$\cos \left(s + \dfrac{\pi}{2}\right) = -\sin s$ **(FI-5)**

$\sin (s \pm \pi) = -\sin s$ **(FI-6)**

$\cos (s \pm \pi) = -\cos s$ **(FI-7)**

$\sin \left(s - \dfrac{\pi}{2}\right) = -\cos s$ **(FI-8)**

$\cos \left(s - \dfrac{\pi}{2}\right) = \sin s$ **(FI-9)**

$\sec^2 s = 1 + \tan^2 s$ **(FI-10)**

$\csc^2 s = 1 + \cot^2 s$ **(FI-11)**

$\sin \left(\dfrac{\pi}{2} - s\right) = \cos s, \qquad \cos \left(\dfrac{\pi}{2} - s\right) = \sin s$ **(FI-12)**

$\tan \left(\dfrac{\pi}{2} - s\right) = \cot s, \qquad \cot \left(\dfrac{\pi}{2} - s\right) = \tan s$ **(FI-13)**

$\sec \left(\dfrac{\pi}{2} - s\right) = \csc s, \qquad \csc \left(\dfrac{\pi}{2} - s\right) = \sec s$ **(FI-14)**

$\sin (\pi - s) = \sin s, \qquad \cos (\pi - s) = -\cos s$ **(FI-15)**

If α sweeps out an arc of the unit circle of length s, then we call s the **radian measure** of angle α. Then π radians $= 180°$.

CHAPTER REVIEW

In Exercises 1–15, find each number.

1. $\sin(-\pi)$ **2.** $\tan\dfrac{2\pi}{3}$ **3.** $\cos\dfrac{\pi}{2}$

4. $\sec\dfrac{3\pi}{4}$ **5.** $\sin(-5\pi)$ **6.** $\sin\left(-\dfrac{7\pi}{6}\right)$

7. $\tan\dfrac{7\pi}{4}$ **8.** $\cos 180°$ **9.** $\sin 270$

10. $\sec 210°$ **11.** $\tan 225°$ **12.** $\csc 240°$

13. $\cot 135°$ **14.** $\sin\left(-\dfrac{9\pi}{2}\right)$ **15.** $\cos\left(-\dfrac{11\pi}{6}\right)$

16. Show that

$$W\left(\frac{11\pi}{4}\right) = W\left(-\frac{5\pi}{4}\right).$$

17. Given that

$$W\left(\frac{\pi}{4}\right) = P,$$

determine the coordinates (x, y) of P.

18. Show that if n is an integer, then $W(s + 2\pi n) = W(s)$.

19. Graph $W(s)$ for

$$s = \frac{7\pi}{6}, \quad -\frac{5\pi}{6}, \quad \frac{5\pi}{12}, \quad \frac{21\pi}{4}, \quad 17\pi, \quad -\frac{5\pi}{4}, \quad 2, \quad -3.$$

20. Are there real numbers s such that $\sin s = 2$?

Simplify each of the following expressions.

21. $\sec s \cos s - \cos^2 s$

22. $\dfrac{\cot^2 s}{1 - \sin^2 s}$

23. $\dfrac{\cot^2 s}{1 + \cot^2 s}$

24. $1 - \dfrac{\sin^2 s}{1 + \cos s}$

25. $\dfrac{\tan^2 s + 1}{\cot^2 s + 1}$

Prove the following identities.

26. $\sin s \sec s \cot s = 1$

27. $\cos^4 s - \sin^4 s = \cos^2 s - \sin^2 s$

28. $\cot^2 s - \cos^2 s = \cos^2 s \cot^2 s$

29. $\dfrac{\cos s}{1 + \sin s} + \dfrac{1 + \sin s}{\cos s} = 2 \sec s$

30. $\dfrac{1 - \tan^2 s}{1 - \cot^2 s} = 1 - \sec^2 s$

Find the values of the following trigonometric functions. In each case, convert radian measure to degree measure.

31. $\cos\left(-\dfrac{\pi}{3}\right)$ **32.** $\sin\dfrac{7\pi}{6}$ **33.** $\tan\left(-\dfrac{3\pi}{4}\right)$ **34.** $\cot\left(-\dfrac{\pi}{2}\right)$

Express each of the following in terms of a trigonometric function of s.

35. $\sin(90° + s)$ **36.** $\cos(180° - s)$

37. $\sin(180° + s)$ **38.** $\cos(360° - s)$

39. $\sin(-s)$ **40.** $\sin\left(\dfrac{\pi}{2} - s\right)$

41. $\tan(\pi + s)$

In Exercises 42–46, which of the functions are odd? Which are even? Which are neither odd nor even?

42. $f(x) = \sec x$ **43.** $f(x) = x \sin x$

44. $f(x) = \sin x$ **45.** $f(x) = x \cos x$

46. $f(x) = x + \cos x$

CHAPTER TEST

1. Fill in the following table of values of the sine, cosine, and tangent functions of an acute angle. Illustrate your answers with sketches of appropriate right triangles.

θ	30°	45°	60°
$\sin\theta$	?	?	?
$\cos\theta$	?	?	?
$\tan\theta$	?	?	?

Find each number in Exercises 2–7.

2. $\sin 120°$ **3.** $\cos 135°$ **4.** $\tan 150°$

5. $\sin\dfrac{5\pi}{4}$ **6.** $\sin\left(-\dfrac{2\pi}{3}\right)$ **7.** $\cos\left(-\dfrac{\pi}{2}\right)$

8. (a) Given that $W\left(\dfrac{\pi}{3}\right) = Q$, determine the coordinates of Q.

   (b) What are the coordinates of $W\left(-\dfrac{\pi}{3}\right)$?

Prove each of the following identities.

9. $\sec s \csc s - 2 \cos s \csc s = \tan s - \cot s$

10. $(\sec^2 s)(1 - \cos^2 s) = \tan^2 s$

CHAPTER 10

Topics in Trigonometry

Objectives . . .

- To apply the law of sines and cosines to the solution of triangles.
- To derive addition formulas and half-angle formulas for the circular functions.
- To solve trigonometric equations.
- To apply notions of periodicity to the study of trigonometric functions.
- To associate numbers with functions in order to develop the inverse trigonometric functions.

10–1 LAW OF COSINES

The sides and angles of every triangle are related in several ways; these relationships will be discussed in this section. Since the sum of the measures of the angles of a triangle is 180°, each angle of a triangle has a measure between 0° and 180°. Let ABC be a given triangle, and let a coordinate system be placed in the plane of the triangle so that angle α at vertex A is in standard position. Then the vertices of the given triangle will have the coordinates shown in Fig. 10–1.

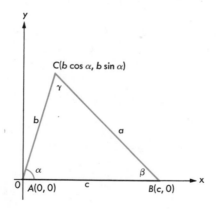

FIGURE 10–1

According to the distance formula, a, the distance between points B and C is given by

$$a = \sqrt{(b \cos \alpha - c)^2 + (b \sin \alpha - 0)^2}.$$

Hence,

$$a^2 = b^2 (\cos \alpha)^2 - 2bc \cos \alpha + c^2 + b^2 (\sin \alpha)^2,$$
$$a^2 = b^2 (\cos^2 \alpha + \sin^2 \alpha) + c^2 - 2bc \cos \alpha,$$

and since $\cos^2 \alpha + \sin^2 \alpha = 1$,

$$a^2 = b^2 + c^2 - 2bc \cos \alpha.$$

This is a proof of the following law.

LAW OF COSINES

If α, β, and γ are the angles of a triangle and a, b, and c are the lengths of the respective opposite sides, then

$$a^2 = b^2 + c^2 - 2bc \cos \alpha.$$

We can interchange a and b, and α and β, to obtain the formula

$$b^2 = a^2 + c^2 - 2ac \cos \beta.$$

In a similar way, we can interchange a and c, and α and γ, to obtain the formula

$$c^2 = a^2 + b^2 - 2ab \cos \gamma.$$

The law of cosines is sometimes called the generalized pythagorean theorem. For example, if $\alpha = 90°$, then $\cos \alpha = 0$, and the law of cosines becomes the pythagorean theorem: $a^2 = b^2 + c^2$.

Problem 1. Find a for the triangle in Fig. 10–2.

Solution. By the law of cosines,

$$a^2 = 3^2 + 4^2 - (2 \cdot 3 \cdot 4 \cos 60°).$$

Since $\cos 60° = \frac{1}{2}$,

$$a^2 = 9 + 16 - 12,$$
$$a^2 = 13,$$

and $a = \sqrt{13}$.

This problem illustrates one of the principal uses of the law of cosines. The law helps us find the length of one side of a triangle if we are given the lengths of the other two sides and the measure of the angle formed by them.

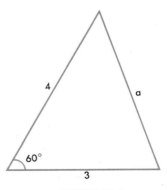

FIGURE 10–2

Problem 2. If the sides of a triangle have lengths 12, 9, and 5, find approximate measures of the angles.

Solution. If the vertices and angles of this triangle are labeled as shown in Fig. 10–3, then by the law of cosines,

$$12^2 = 9^2 + 5^2 - (2 \cdot 9 \cdot 5 \cos \alpha),$$
$$144 = 81 + 25 - (90 \cos \alpha),$$
$$\cos \alpha = -\tfrac{38}{90}.$$

Thus, $\cos \alpha \doteq -.422.$ The fact that $\cos \alpha$ is negative indicates that α is obtuse. Since $\cos (180° - \alpha)$ $= -\cos \alpha \doteq .422$, we see that $(180° - \alpha) \doteq 65°$ and $\alpha \doteq 115°$.

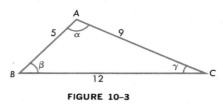

FIGURE 10-3

We can find the other angles of triangle ABC in a similar way. Thus,

$$9^2 = 12^2 + 5^2 - (2 \cdot 5 \cdot 12 \cos \beta),$$
$$\cos \beta = \tfrac{88}{120}, \quad \text{or } .733.$$

Hence, $\beta \doteq 43°$. Now γ has measure $180 - (115 + 43)°$, or $\gamma \doteq 22°$. Thus, the angles of the triangle are $\alpha \doteq 115°$, $\beta \doteq 43°$, $\gamma \doteq 22°$.

Exercises

In Exercises 1–5, A, B, and C designate the vertices of a triangle; α, β, and γ designate the measures of the corresponding angles; and a, b, and c designate the lengths of the corresponding opposite sides.

1. (a) Find c, given that $b = 4$, $a = \sqrt{3}$, $\gamma = 150°$.
   (b) Find c, given that $a = 3$, $b = 7$, $\gamma = 40°$.
2. (a) Find α, given that $a = 4$, $b = 6$, $c = 7$.
   (b) Find α, given that $a = 3$, $b = 4$, $c = 6$.
3. (a) Find c, given that $a = 5$, $b = 5\sqrt{2}$, $\gamma = 45°$.
   (b) Find a, given that $b = 3$, $c = 4$, $\alpha = 120°$.
4. (a) Find c, given that $a = 5$, $b = 5\sqrt{2}$, $\gamma = 135°$.
   (b) Find a, given that $b = 3$, $c = 2$, $\alpha = 60°$.
5. (a) Find the smallest angle, given that $a : b : c = 2 : 3 : 4$.
   (b) Find β, given that $a = 10$, $c = 8$, $b = 6$.

---

6. A parallelogram with one angle of measure 120° has sides of length 50 feet and 80 feet. Find the length of the shorter diagonal.

7. The sides of a parallelogram are 40 feet and 70 feet long, and the smallest angle has measure 36°. Find the length of the longer diagonal.

8. A triangular lot bounded by three streets has a frontage of 300 feet on one street, 250 feet on the second, and 420 feet on the third street. Find the measure of the smallest angle between two streets bounding the lot.

9. Two planes, one flying at 450 miles per hour and the other at 300 miles per hour, left an airport at the same time. Three hours later, they were 1200 miles apart. What was the measure of the angle between their flight paths?

10. Draw $\triangle ABC$ with an obtuse angle at A in standard position. Follow the method of the proof in the text to prove the law of cosines for this triangle.

11. Prove that if $\triangle ABC$ has an obtuse angle at C, then $c^2 > a^2 + b^2$.

10–2   LAW OF SINES

Each triangle T has an area $A(T)$, given by

$$A(T) = \tfrac{1}{2}bh,$$

where h is the length of the altitude of the triangle drawn from vertex B. If α is acute, then $\sin \alpha = h/c$ and

$$h = c \sin \alpha$$

from Fig. 10–4. This suggests the following formula.

FORMULA FOR THE AREA OF A TRIANGLE T

$$A(T) = \frac{1}{2}bc \ sin \ \alpha$$

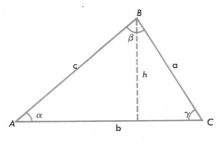

FIGURE 10–4

Although we proved this formula on the assumption that α is acute, the formula is valid even if $\alpha = 90°$ or $\alpha > 90°$. Thus, if $\alpha = 90°$, then $\sin \alpha = 1$. The formula $A(T) = \frac{1}{2}bc$ is the one most frequently used in finding the area of a right triangle. In the exercises, you will be asked to prove that the general formula is true when $\alpha > 90°$.

The formula for $A(T)$ is true for any two sides and the included angle. Thus, we also have

$$A(T) = \tfrac{1}{2}ac \sin \beta.$$

From these two formulas for $A(T)$, we obtain the true equation

$$\tfrac{1}{2}bc \sin \alpha = \tfrac{1}{2}ac \sin \beta,$$

or, multiplying each side by $2/abc$, we have

$$\frac{\sin \alpha}{a} = \frac{\sin \beta}{b}.$$

This is a proof of the following important law.

LAW OF SINES

If α, β, and γ are the angles of a triangle, and a, b, and c are the lengths of the respective opposite sides, then

$$\frac{\sin \alpha}{a} = \frac{\sin \beta}{b}.$$

We may interchange b and c, and β and γ, to obtain the law of sines in another form:

$$\frac{\sin \alpha}{a} = \frac{\sin \gamma}{c}.$$

Problem 1. Find the length of a for $\triangle ABC$, shown in Fig. 10–5.

Solution. By the law of sines,

$$\frac{\sin 30°}{a} = \frac{\sin 45°}{10}.$$

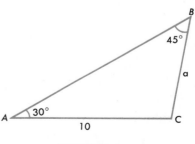

FIGURE 10–5

Since

$$\sin 30° = \tfrac{1}{2} \text{ and } \sin 45° = \frac{\sqrt{2}}{2},$$

we obtain

$$a = 5\sqrt{2}.$$

This problem shows that we can use the law of sines to find the length of one side of a triangle if we are given the length of another side and the measures of two angles of the triangle.

Problem 2. We can also use the law of sines to find the other parts of a triangle if we are given the lengths of two sides and the measure of an angle opposite one of them. For example, let $\alpha = 30°$, $a = 8$, and $b = 12$. Find the other angles and the third side of the triangle.

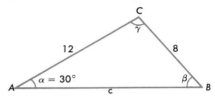

FIGURE 10–6

Solution. If the vertices and angles of the triangle are labeled as shown in Fig. 10–6, then by the law of sines,

$$\frac{\sin 30°}{8} = \frac{\sin \beta}{12}.$$

Since $\sin 30° = \tfrac{1}{2}$,

$$\sin \beta = \tfrac{3}{4}, \quad \text{or } .75.$$

From the Table of Values of Trigonometric Functions in the Appendix, we see that $\beta \doteq 49°$. Now γ has measure $180° - (30 + 49)°$, or $\gamma \doteq 101°$.

If c is the third side of the triangle, then

$$\frac{\sin 101°}{c} = \frac{\sin 30°}{8}.$$

We can find $\sin 101°$, using the identity

$$\sin (180 - \gamma)° = \sin \gamma.$$

Therefore,

$$\sin 101° = \sin (180 - 101)°, \quad \text{or } \sin 79°.$$

From the Table in the Appendix, sin 79° ≐ .982. Hence,

$$\frac{.982}{c} = \frac{.5}{8}$$

and

$$c \doteq 15.7.$$

Thus, the other angles of the triangle in Fig. 10–6 are $\beta \doteq 49°$ and $\gamma \doteq 101°$, and the other side is $c \doteq 15.7$.

However, since sin $(180° - \beta) =$ sin β, then $(180 - 49)°$, or $131°$, is also an angle with sine of .75. Thus, $\beta \doteq 131°$ is another possible solution. In other words, the problem has two possible solutions. The second solution is shown in Fig. 10–7.

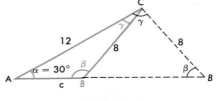

FIGURE 10–7

In this case, γ has measure $180 - (30 + 131)$ degrees, or $\gamma \doteq 19°$. To find c, we have

$$\frac{\sin 19°}{c} = \frac{\sin 30°}{8}.$$

From the Table, sin 19° ≐ .326. Hence, $c \doteq 5.2$. The other angles of the triangle in Fig. 10–7 are $\beta \doteq 131°$, $\gamma \doteq 19°$, and the other side is $c \doteq 5.2$.

The law of sines is ideally suited for logarithmic computation. Thus, from the law of sines, we have

$$\log\left(\frac{\sin \alpha}{a}\right) = \log\left(\frac{\sin \beta}{b}\right),$$

or

$$\log \sin \alpha - \log a = \log \sin \beta - \log b.$$

Given values of three of the four variables in the equation above, we can quickly compute the value of the other variable. This is illustrated in the following problem.

Problem 3. Vertices A and B of $\triangle ABC$ are on one bank of a river and vertex C is on the opposite bank, as shown in Fig. 10–8. The distance between A and B is 200 feet, and the angles at A and B have measures 33° and 63°, respectively. Find the distance between C and A, and the distance between C and B. Also, find the width of the river.

Solution. The angle at C has measure $180° - (33 + 63)°$, or 84°. If b designates the distance from A to C, then

$$\frac{\sin 63°}{b} = \frac{\sin 84°}{200}$$

by the law of sines. From the Table, we find that $\sin 63° \doteq .891$ and $\sin 84° \doteq .995$. Therefore,

$$\log .891 - \log b = \log .995 - \log 200,$$

or

$$\log b = \log 200 + \log .891 - \log .995.$$

From the Table of Common Logarithms, $\log 200 \doteq .3010 + 2$ and $\log .891 \doteq .9499 - 1$. Therefore,

$$\log 200 + \log .891 \doteq 1.2509 + 1.$$

Also, $\log .995 \doteq .9978 - 1$. Therefore,

$$\log 200 + \log .891 - \log .995 = \log b \doteq .2531 + 2.$$

Hence, by the Table of Common Logarithms,

$$b \doteq 179 \text{ feet.}$$

If a denotes the distance from B to C in Fig. 10–8, then

$$\frac{\sin 33°}{a} = \frac{\sin 84°}{200} .$$

Since $\sin 33° \doteq .545$, we have

$$\log a = \log 200 + \log .545 - \log .995.$$

From the Table of Common Logarithms,

$$\log 200 + \log .545 - \log .995 = \log a \doteq .0396 + 2.$$

Hence, by the Table of Common Logarithms,

$$a \doteq 110 \text{ feet.}$$

If w denotes the width of the river, then

$$\sin 33° = \frac{w}{b}$$

and

$$\log w = \log b + \log \sin 33°.$$

From our previous work,

$$\log b = 2.2531$$

and

$$\log \sin 33° = .7364 - 1.$$

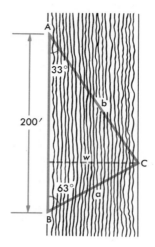

Therefore, $\log w = \log b + \log \sin 33° = 2.9895 - 1$, or 1.9895. Hence, $w \doteq 97.6$ feet.

FIGURE 10–8

Exercises

In each exercise of Exercises 1–11, A, B, and C designate the vertices of a triangle; α, β, and γ designate the measures of the corresponding angles; and a, b, and c designate the lengths of the corresponding opposite sides.

1. (a) Find c, given that $\alpha = 60°$, $\beta = 75°$, $a = 5\sqrt{6}$.
   (b) Find b, given that $\alpha = 50°$, $\gamma = 55°$, $a = 30$.

2. (a) Find γ, given that $b = 7$, $c = 10$, $\beta = 30°$.
   (b) Find γ, given that $b = 7$, $c = 10$, $\alpha = 30°$.

3. (a) Find γ, given that $a = 4$, $b = 5$, $\beta = 30°$.
   (b) Find β, given that $a = 12$, $b = 8\sqrt{3}$, $\alpha = 60°$.

4. (a) Find a, given that $\alpha = 30°$, $\beta = 135°$, $b = 10\sqrt{2}$.
   (b) Find c, given that $\alpha = 30°$, $\beta = 105°$, $a = 3\sqrt{2}$.

5. (a) Find the areas of the two possible triangles of Exercise 2(a).
   (b) Find the area of the triangle in Exercise 2(b).

6. (a) Given that $\beta = 60°$, $a = 10$, $b = 9\sqrt{3}$, find the other side and the angles of the triangle.
   (b) Given that $\beta = 30°$, $b = 9$, $c = 15$, find the other side and the angles of the triangle.

7. (a) Find the area of the triangle of Exercise 6(a).
   (b) Find the area or areas of the triangle or triangles of Exercise 6(b).

8. (a) Find c, given that $\alpha = 110°$, $\beta = 55°$, $a = 30$.
   (b) Find a, given that $\beta = 28°$, $\gamma = 41°$, $c = 100$.

9. (a) Find c, given that $\alpha = 37°$, $\beta = 53°$, $a = 60$.
   (b) Find γ, given that $a = 9$, $c = 10$, $\alpha = 55°$.

10. (a) Find b and then α, given that $a = 12$, $c = 9$, $\beta = 63°$.
   (b) Find b, α, and γ, given that $a = \sqrt{2}$, $c = 8$, $\beta = 45°$.

11. (a) Find the area of the triangle in Exercise 10(a).
   (b) Find the area of the triangle in Exercise 10(b).

---

12. A telegraph pole casts a shadow 40 feet long when the angle of elevation of the sun is 63°. The pole leans 15° from the vertical, directly toward the sun. Find the length of the pole.

13. From a ship, the angle of elevation of a point A at the top of a cliff is 21°. After the ship has sailed 2500 feet directly toward the foot of the cliff, the angle of elevation of A is 47°. Find the height of the cliff.

14. A 10-foot ladder must make an angle of 30° with the ground if it is to reach a certain window. What angle must a 20-foot ladder make with the ground to reach the same window?

15. Prove that the following formula for the area of a triangle T is true if $\alpha > 90°$.

$$A(T) = \tfrac{1}{2}bc \sin \alpha$$

16. A surveyor runs a line due east from A to B, but he cannot continue the line in an easterly direction because of an obstacle. Therefore, he runs a line 800 feet long from B to C in a direction 24° east of south, and then runs another line CD in a direction 47° east of north. How long should CD be if D is to be due east of B?

17. The two diagonals of a parallelogram have lengths 10 and 7. The diagonals meet at a 60° angle. Find the lengths of the sides of the parallelogram and the measure of its angles.

18. On a coordinate plane, plot the three points

$$A(-2, 7), \quad B(6, 1), \quad C(-6, -4)$$

and draw $\triangle ABC$. Find the measure of the three angles of this triangle.

19. Find length a in the figure.

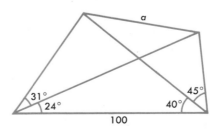

20. (a) Find a formula for the area of a parallelogram with two of its adjacent sides of length b and c, given that the included angle of the sides has a measure of α.

(b) Find the area of the parallelogram, given that $b = 365$, $c = 489$, $\alpha = 132°$.

21. In the figure, $PABC$ is a parallelogram with two adjacent sides of length 300 and 450 forming a 47° angle. The arrows suggest an application to the following physical problem: Two forces, one of 300 pounds and the other of 450 pounds, acting on an object at P with a 47° angle between their

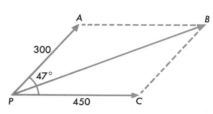

directions, have the same effect as one force acting on P in the direction of the diagonal PB. The length of the diagonal gives the magnitude of this resultant force. Find the magnitude of the resultant force and the measure of the angle it makes with the 450-pound force.

22. A regular polygon of n sides is inscribed in a circle of radius r. Using trigonometric functions, derive a formula for the perimeter of the polygon.

23. Given that k is the proportionality number $\sin \alpha/a$, encountered in the law of sines, and that $r = 1/(2k)$, prove that r is the radius of the circle circumscribed about $\triangle ABC$.

10–3 THE ADDITION FORMULAS

In this section, we shall develop formulas for finding trigonometric functions of *sums* and *differences* of numbers. For any real numbers u and v, there correspond points $W(u)$ and $W(v)$ on the unit circle, as shown in Fig. 10–9. If $0 < u < v < 2\pi$, then the arc from $W(u)$ to $W(v)$ has length $v - u$. Therefore, there is a central angle α of the circle whose radian measure is $v - u$.

We can follow the method used in proving the law of cosines to show that the distance d between points $W(u)$ and $W(v)$ can be given by the equation

$$d^2 = 1^2 + 1^2 - (2 \cdot 1 \cdot 1 \cdot \cos \alpha)$$
$$= 2 - 2 \cos \alpha.$$

Since α has radian measure $v - u$, we have proved that

$$d^2 = 2 - 2 \cos (v - u).$$

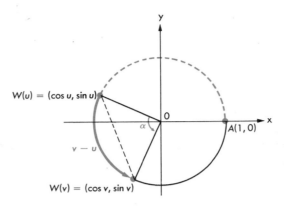

FIGURE 10-9

On the other hand, we can compute the distance between $W(u)$ and $W(v)$ by using the distance formula.

$$
\begin{aligned}
d^2 &= (\cos v - \cos u)^2 + (\sin v - \sin u)^2 \\
&= \cos^2 v - 2 \cos v \cos u + \cos^2 u \\
&\quad + \sin^2 v - 2 \sin v \sin u + \sin^2 u \\
&= (\sin^2 u + \cos^2 u) + (\sin^2 v + \cos^2 v) \\
&\quad - 2(\cos v \cos u + \sin v \sin u) \\
&= 1 + 1 - 2(\cos v \cos u + \sin v \sin u)
\end{aligned}
$$

We now have two different formulas for the distance between points $W(u)$ and $W(v)$ which we combine to obtain the equation

$$
2 - 2 \cos (v - u) = 2 - 2(\cos v \cos u + \sin v \sin u).
$$

By simplifying, we obtain the first *addition formula* of trigonometry.

FIRST ADDITION FORMULA

$$
\cos (v - u) = \cos v \cos u + \sin v \sin u \qquad (A\text{-}1)
$$

Although the first addition formula, (A-1), was proved on the assumption that $0 < u < v < 2\pi$, it can be shown that it is true for all values of u and v. Although we have used the term *radian measure* in the proof of the first addition formula, the formula continues to be true if we think of u and v as the degree measure of angles.

The following problem indicates how the first addition formula can be used to find the cosine of certain angles and numbers.

Problem 1. Find cos 15°.

Solution. Because 15 = 45 − 30 and we know the sine and cosine of angles of measure 45° and 30°, we can use the first addition formula to find cos 15°.

$$\cos 15° = \cos 45° \cos 30° + \sin 45° \sin 30°$$

We substitute the known values of the sine and cosine of 45° and 30° and obtain

$$\cos 15° = \left(\frac{\sqrt{2}}{2} \cdot \frac{\sqrt{3}}{2}\right) + \left(\frac{\sqrt{2}}{2} \cdot \frac{1}{2}\right),$$

or

$$\cos 15° = \tfrac{1}{4}(\sqrt{6} + \sqrt{2}).$$

This is the exact value of cos 15°. Using the Table of Square Roots, we obtain

$$\sqrt{6} \doteq 2.449 \quad \text{and} \quad \sqrt{2} \doteq 1.414.$$

Hence,

$$\cos 15° \doteq \tfrac{1}{4}(3.863), \text{ or } .966.$$

Does this result agree with the entry in the Table of Values of Trigonometric Functions?

The addition formulas given below can be derived from the first addition formula, (A-1). However, instead of including the proofs, we shall outline them in the exercises.

SECOND, THIRD, AND FOURTH ADDITION FORMULAS

$$\cos (v + u) = \cos v \cos u - \sin v \sin u \qquad (A\text{-}2)$$

$$\sin (v - u) = \sin v \cos u - \cos v \sin u \qquad (A\text{-}3)$$

$$\sin (v + u) = \sin v \cos u + \cos v \sin u \qquad (A\text{-}4)$$

Problem 2. Find $\sin \dfrac{11\pi}{12}$.

Solution. Since

$$\frac{11\pi}{12} = \frac{2\pi}{3} + \frac{\pi}{4},$$

$$\sin \frac{11\pi}{12} = \sin\left(\frac{2\pi}{3} + \frac{\pi}{4}\right)$$

$$= \sin \frac{2\pi}{3} \cos \frac{\pi}{4} + \cos \frac{2\pi}{3} \sin \frac{\pi}{4}$$

$$= \left(\frac{\sqrt{3}}{2} \cdot \frac{\sqrt{2}}{2}\right) + \left(-\frac{1}{2} \cdot \frac{\sqrt{2}}{2}\right)$$

$$= \frac{1}{4}(\sqrt{6} - \sqrt{2}).$$

Exercises

Find the exact value of each of the following.

1. (a) $\sin 15°$ (b) $\tan 15°$

2. (a) $\sin 75°$ (b) $\cos 75°$

3. (a) $\tan 75°$ (b) $\tan 195°$

4. (a) $\sin 105°$ (b) $\tan 105°$

5. (a) $\cos \dfrac{7\pi}{12}$ (b) $\tan \dfrac{7\pi}{12}$

6. (a) $\tan \dfrac{29\pi}{12}$ (b) $\tan \dfrac{5\pi}{12}$

7. (a) Given that $\sin u = \frac{2}{3}$ and $\cos v = \frac{3}{7}$, with $\pi/2 < u < \pi$ and $0 < v < \pi/2$, find each of the following.

   $\cos (u + v)$ $\sin (u + v)$ $\tan (u + v)$

   (b) Given that $\csc u = \frac{7}{3}$, $\cos u < 0$, $\tan v = -\frac{3}{2}$, and $\cos v > 0$, find each of the following.

   $\sin (u - v)$ $\cos (u - v)$ $\tan (u - v)$

8. (a) If $\sin u = \frac{3}{5}$ and $\cos v = \frac{5}{13}$, with $\pi/2 < u < \pi$ and $0 < v < \pi/2$, find each of the following.

   $\cos (u + v)$ $\sin (u + v)$ $\tan (u + v)$

   (b) If $\sec u = \frac{25}{7}$, $\tan u < 0$, $\tan v = -\frac{4}{3}$, and $\sin v > 0$, find each of the following.

   $\cos (u - v)$ $\sin (u - v)$ $\tan (u - v)$

Use the addition formulas to simplify each of the following.

9. (a) $\cos\left(\dfrac{3\pi}{2} - u\right)$ (b) $\sin\left(2\pi - u\right)$

10. (a) $\tan\left(\pi - u\right)$ (b) $\cos\left(u + \dfrac{3\pi}{2}\right)$

11. (a) $\cos\left(\pi - u\right)$ (b) $\tan\left(\dfrac{5\pi}{2} + u\right)$

---

12. Use the formulas $\cos\left(\pi/2 - v\right) = \sin v$, $\sin\left(\pi/2 - v\right) = \cos v$, and (A-1) to prove formula (A-4). The proof consists of writing $\sin\left(v + u\right)$ first as $\cos\left[\pi/2 - \left(v + u\right)\right]$ and then as $\cos\left[\left(\pi/2 - v\right) - u\right]$.

13. Use the formulas $\cos\left(-u\right) = \cos u$, $\sin\left(-u\right) = -\sin u$, and (A-1) to prove (A-2). This proof consists of writing $\cos\left(v + u\right)$ as $\cos\left[v - \left(-u\right)\right]$.

14. Prove formula (A-3).

15. Use the fundamental identity $\tan s = \sin s/\cos s$, (A-2), and (A-4) to show that

(a) $\tan\left(v + u\right) = \dfrac{\sin v \cos u + \cos v \sin u}{\cos v \cos u - \sin v \sin u}$.

(b) $\tan\left(v + u\right) = \dfrac{\tan v + \tan u}{1 - \tan v \tan u}$.

16. Use the formula $\tan\left(-u\right) = -\tan u$ and the formula of Exercise 15(b) to show that

$$\tan\left(v - u\right) = \dfrac{\tan v - \tan u}{1 + \tan v \tan u}.$$

Prove each of the following identities.

17. $\cos\left(u + v\right)\cos\left(u - v\right) = \cos^2 u - \sin^2 v$

18. $\sin\left(u + v\right)\sin\left(u - v\right) = \sin^2 u - \sin^2 v$

19. $\cos\left(\dfrac{\pi}{4} - u\right) = \dfrac{1}{\sqrt{2}}\left(\cos u + \sin u\right)$

20. $\dfrac{\cos\left(u + v\right)}{\cos\left(u - v\right)} = \dfrac{1 - \tan u \tan v}{1 + \tan u \tan v}$

Use the fundamental identities of Section 9–5 and the addition formulas in this section to prove each of the following.

21. (FI-4) **22.** (FI-5) **23.** (FI-6)

24. (FI-7) **25.** (FI-8) **26.** (FI-9)

10-4   DOUBLE-ANGLE AND HALF-ANGLE FORMULAS

If in the second addition formula, (A-2), we let $u = v$, then we obtain the equation

$$\cos (v + v) = \cos v \cos v - \sin v \sin v,$$

which is equivalent to the equation below.

FIRST DOUBLE-ANGLE FORMULA

$$cos\ 2v\ =\ cos^2 v\ -\ sin^2 v \qquad\qquad (D\text{-}1)$$

If we know $\cos v$ and $\sin v$, we can use the first double-angle formula, (D-1), to find $\cos 2v$. The second double-angle formula can be derived from the fourth addition formula, (A-4).

SECOND DOUBLE-ANGLE FORMULA

$$sin\ 2v\ =\ 2\ sin\ v\ cos\ v \qquad\qquad (D\text{-}2)$$

Problem 1. Given that $0 < v < \pi/2$ and that $\sin v = \frac{5}{6}$, find $\sin 2v$ and $\cos 2v$.

Solution. Before we can use the first and second double-angle formulas, we must find $\cos v$. By the first fundamental identity,

$$\sin^2 v + \cos^2 v = 1.$$

Then

$$\cos^2 v = 1 - \sin^2 v = 1 - (\tfrac{5}{6})^2, \quad \text{or } \tfrac{11}{36}.$$

Hence,

$$\cos v = \frac{\sqrt{11}}{6} \quad \text{or} \quad \cos v = -\frac{\sqrt{11}}{6}.$$

However, since $0 < v < \pi/2$, $\cos v > 0$. Thus, $\cos v = \sqrt{11}/6$. Now we can use the double angle-formulas to obtain

$$\sin 2v = 2 \cdot \frac{5}{6} \cdot \frac{\sqrt{11}}{6}, \quad \text{or } \frac{5\sqrt{11}}{18},$$

$$\cos 2v = \left(\frac{\sqrt{11}}{6}\right)^2 - \left(\frac{5}{6}\right)^2,$$

$$\cos 2v = \frac{11}{36} - \frac{25}{36}, \quad \text{or} \quad -\frac{14}{36}, \quad \text{or} \quad -\frac{7}{18}.$$

Two different forms of the first double-angle formula can be obtained by using the first fundamental identity, (FI-1). Thus, if we replace $\cos^2 v$ by $1 - \sin^2 v$ in the first double-angle formula, we get

$$\cos 2v = 1 - 2 \sin^2 v. \tag{1}$$

If we replace $\sin^2 v$ by $1 - \cos^2 v$, we get

$$\cos 2v = 2 \cos^2 v - 1. \tag{2}$$

Formulas (1) and (2) can be solved for $\sin^2 v$ and $\cos^2 v$, respectively:

$$\sin^2 v = \tfrac{1}{2}(1 - \cos 2v),$$
$$\cos^2 v = \tfrac{1}{2}(1 + \cos 2v).$$

If we let $u = 2v$, and hence, $v = u/2$, in the identities above, we obtain the *half-angle formulas* below.

FIRST AND SECOND HALF-ANGLE FORMULAS

$$\cos^2 \frac{u}{2} = \frac{1}{2}(1 + \cos u) \tag{H-1}$$

$$\sin^2 \frac{u}{2} = \frac{1}{2}(1 - \cos u) \tag{H-2}$$

If we know $\cos u$ and the quadrant in which $W(u/2)$ lies, we can use the first and second half-angle formulas to find $\sin u/2$ and $\cos u/2$, as illustrated in Problem 2.

Problem 2. Find the sine and cosine of $5\pi/8$.

Solution. If we let $u = 5\pi/4$,

$$\sin^2 \frac{5\pi}{8} = \frac{1}{2}\left(1 - \cos \frac{5\pi}{4}\right)$$

$$= \frac{1}{2}\left[1 - \left(-\frac{\sqrt{2}}{2}\right)\right]$$

$$= \frac{1}{4}(2 + \sqrt{2}).$$

Since $W(5\pi/8)$ is in the second quadrant and the sine is positive in this quadrant,

$$\sin \frac{5\pi}{8} = \frac{1}{2}\sqrt{2 + \sqrt{2}}.$$

Similarly,

$$\cos^2 \frac{5\pi}{8} = \frac{1}{4}(2 - \sqrt{2})$$

and

$$\cos \frac{5\pi}{8} = -\frac{1}{2}\sqrt{2 - \sqrt{2}},$$

since the cosine is negative in the second quadrant.

Exercises

Given that $\cos u = \frac{3}{5}$ and $0 < u < \pi/2$, evaluate each of the following.

1. (a) $\sin u$ (b) $\tan u$

2. (a) $\sin 2u$ (b) $\cos 2u$

3. (a) $\tan 2u$ (b) $\sin \dfrac{u}{2}$

4. (a) $\cos \dfrac{u}{2}$ (b) $\tan \dfrac{u}{2}$

Given that $\sin u = \frac{5}{13}$ and $\pi/2 < u < \pi$, evaluate each of the following.

5. (a) $\cos u$ (b) $\sin 2u$

6. (a) $\tan 2u$ (b) $\sin \dfrac{u}{2}$

Given that $\tan u = \frac{24}{7}$ and $\sin u < 0$, evaluate each of the following.

7. (a) $\sin u$ (b) $\cos u$

8. (a) $\cos 2u$ (b) $\tan \dfrac{u}{2}$

Given that $\sec u = \frac{7}{5}$ and $\tan u < 0$, evaluate each trigonometric function.

9. (a) $\sin u$ (b) $\sin 2u$

10. (a) $\tan 2u$ (b) $\tan \dfrac{u}{2}$

11. (a) Use the half-angle formulas to find the values of the six trigonometric functions of the angle with measure $15°$.

    (b) Use the half-angle formulas to find the values of the six trigonometric functions of the angle with measure $22\frac{1}{2}°$.

12. (a) Find a formula for $\tan^2 u/2$ in terms of $\cos u$.
(b) Show that

$$\tan \frac{u}{2} = \frac{1 - \cos u}{\sin u}.$$

13. (a) Derive (D-2) from (A-4).
(b) Use (D-1) and (D-2) to show that

$$\tan 2v = \frac{2 \tan v}{1 - \tan^2 v}.$$

14. Show that $\sin 3u = 3 \sin u - 4 \sin^3 u$. (Hint: $3u = 2u + u$.)

Prove each of the following identities.

15. $\cos 3u = 4 \cos^3 u - 3 \cos u$

16. $\sqrt{1 + \sin 2u} = |\sin u + \cos u|$

17. $\dfrac{\cos 2\delta}{\sin \delta} - \dfrac{\sin 2\delta}{\cos \delta} = \dfrac{2 \cos 3\delta}{\sin 2\delta}$

18. $\dfrac{1 + \tan^2 \phi}{2 \tan \phi} = \csc 2\phi$

19. $\dfrac{\sin 2\theta}{1 - \cos 2\theta} = \cot \theta$

Given that α, β, and γ are the angles of a triangle, prove the identities in Exercises 20 and 21.

20. $\tan \alpha + \tan \beta + \tan \gamma = \tan \alpha \tan \beta \tan \gamma$

21. $\tan \dfrac{\alpha}{2} \tan \dfrac{\beta}{2} + \tan \dfrac{\beta}{2} \tan \dfrac{\gamma}{2} + \tan \dfrac{\gamma}{2} \tan \dfrac{\alpha}{2} = 1$

---

22. Given triangle ABC and point D on $\overline{AB}$ as shown in the figure,
(a) show that triangle ABC is similar to triangle CBD with proportionality factor r.
(b) show that the length of $\overline{DB}$ is r^2.
(c) show that $2r = \sqrt{5} - 1$.
(d) show that $\beta = 2\alpha$.
(e) show that α has measure 36°.
(f) show that $\sin \alpha = \frac{1}{4}\sqrt{10 - 2\sqrt{5}}$.
(g) show that $\cos \alpha = \frac{1}{4}(1 + \sqrt{5})$.
(h) find the trigonometric functions of β.

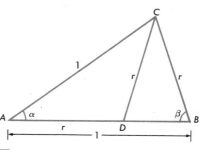

Review for Sections 10–1 through 10–4

1. Find a, given that $c = 5$, $b = 8$, $\alpha = 90°$.

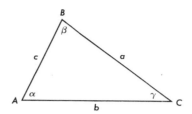

2. Find b, given that $c = 3$, $a = 4$, $\beta = 120°$.
3. Find c, given that $a = 3\sqrt{2}$, $b = 9$, $\gamma = 45°$.
4. Find α, given that $a = 10$, $b = 12$, $c = 6$.
5. Find β, given that $a = 9$, $b = 10$, $c = 5$.
6. Find γ, given that $a = 5\sqrt{2}$, $b = 6\sqrt{2}$, $c = 10$.
7. Find a, given that $\beta = 75°$, $\gamma = 45°$, $c = 8$.
8. Find c, given that $\alpha = 15°$, $\beta = 135°$, $b = 5$.
9. Find α, given that $a = 5\sqrt{2}$, $b = 5$, $\beta = 45°$.
10. Find β, given that $b = 2\sqrt{3}$, $c = 6$, $\gamma = 120°$.
11. Given that $a = 10$, $b = 10\sqrt{2}$, $\alpha = 30°$, find the other side and the angles of the triangle. Find the area of the triangle or triangles.
12. Given $a = 3\sqrt{3}$, $c = 3\sqrt{2}$, $\gamma = 45°$, find the other side and the angles of the triangle. Find the area of the triangle or triangles.

For Exercises 13–16, use parallelogram *EFGH*.

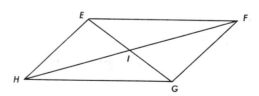

13. Find EG, given that $EF = 8$, $EH = 5$, $\angle FGH = 120°$.
14. Find HF, given that $EH = 10\sqrt{2}$, $GH = 15$, $\angle EFG = 45°$.
15. Find $\angle FEH$, given $EF = 4$, $HI = 3$, $\angle EHF = 20°$.
16. Find $\angle FEG$, given $EF = 5\sqrt{2}$, $FH = 10$, $\angle EIF = 135°$.

Find the exact value of each of the following.

17. $\cos 15°$ **18.** $\cos 105°$

19. $\sin 165°$ **20.** $\tan 165°$

21. $\sin \dfrac{7\pi}{8}$

22. $\tan \dfrac{7\pi}{8}$

23. $\cos \dfrac{5\pi}{12}$

24. $\tan \dfrac{5\pi}{12}$

If $\sin u = \frac{4}{5}$ and $\cos v = \frac{12}{13}$, with $\dfrac{\pi}{2} < u < \pi$ and $0 < v < \dfrac{\pi}{2}$, find each of the following.

25. $\sin (u + v)$

26. $\cos (u - v)$

27. $\tan (u + v)$

28. $\tan (u - v)$

29. $\sin 2u$

30. $\cos \dfrac{u}{2}$

31. $\tan 2v$

32. $\cot \dfrac{v}{2}$

33. Use the half-angle formulas to find the values of the six trigonometric functions of the angle with measure $67\frac{1}{2}°$.

Simplify the following.

34. $\dfrac{2 - 2 \cos u}{4 \cos^2 \dfrac{u}{2}}$

35. $\dfrac{1 - 2 \sin^2 v}{4 \sin^2 v \cos^2 v}$

Answers to Review for Sections 10–1 through 10–4

1. $a = \sqrt{89} \doteq 9.43$

2. $b = \sqrt{13} \doteq 3.61$

3. $c = 3\sqrt{5} \doteq 6.71$

4. $\alpha \doteq 56°$

5. $\beta \doteq 86°$

6. $\gamma \doteq 79°$

7. $a = 4\sqrt{6} \doteq 9.80$

8. $c = \frac{5}{2}\sqrt{2} \doteq 3.54$

9. $\alpha = 90°$

10. $\beta = 30°$

11. $\beta = 45°$, $\gamma = 105°$, $c \doteq 19.32$, area $\doteq 68.30$ sq units; or $\beta = 135°$, $\gamma = 15°$, $c \doteq 5.18$, area $\doteq 18.31$ sq units

12. $\alpha = 60°$, $\beta = 75°$, $b \doteq 5.80$, area $\doteq 10.65$ sq units; or $\alpha = 120°$, $\beta = 15°$, $b \doteq 1.55$, area $\doteq 2.85$ sq units

13. $EG = 7$

14. $HF = 5\sqrt{29} \doteq 26.93$

15. $\angle FEH \doteq 31°$

16. $\angle FEG = 30°$

17. $\frac{1}{4}(\sqrt{2} + \sqrt{6})$

18. $\frac{1}{4}(\sqrt{2} - \sqrt{6})$

19. $\frac{1}{4}(\sqrt{6} - \sqrt{2})$

20. $-2 + \sqrt{3}$

21. $\frac{1}{2}\sqrt{2 - \sqrt{2}}$

22. $\sqrt{2} - 1$

23. $\frac{1}{4}(\sqrt{6} - \sqrt{2})$

24. $2 + \sqrt{3}$

25. $\frac{33}{65}$

26. $-\frac{16}{65}$

27. $-\frac{33}{56}$

28. $-\frac{63}{16}$

29. $-\frac{24}{25}$ **30.** $\dfrac{\sqrt{5}}{5}$

31. $\frac{120}{119}$ **32.** 5

33. $\sin 67\frac{1}{2}° = \frac{1}{2}\sqrt{2 + \sqrt{2}},\quad \cos 67\frac{1}{2}° = \frac{1}{2}\sqrt{2 - \sqrt{2}},$
$\tan 67\frac{1}{2}° = \sqrt{2} + 1,\qquad \cot 67\frac{1}{2}° = \sqrt{2} - 1,$
$\sec 67\frac{1}{2}° = \sqrt{4 + 2\sqrt{2}},\quad \csc 67\frac{1}{2}° = \sqrt{4 - 2\sqrt{2}}$

34. $\tan^2 \dfrac{u}{2}$ or $\dfrac{1 - \cos u}{1 + \cos u}$ **35.** $\csc 2v \cot 2v$

10–5 TRIGONOMETRIC EQUATIONS

An equation that involves trigonometric functions, such as

$$2 \sin^2 x - \sin x - 1 = 0,$$

is called a *trigonometric equation.* If this trigonometric equation has any solutions, then it has infinitely many, since the trigonometric functions are all periodic. Therefore, in solving such an equation, we shall seek the solutions in one period of the functions involved unless we are instructed otherwise.

Problem 1. Solve the equation $2 \sin^2 x - \sin x - 1 = 0$.

Solution. Let us find every number x, with $0 \le x < 2\pi$, for which this equation is true. Basically, the given equation is quadratic in $\sin x$:

$$2(\sin x)^2 - (\sin x) - 1 = 0.$$

In other words, it has the same form as the quadratic equation

$$2y^2 - y - 1 = 0.$$

We solve these two equations side by side to illustrate that the method is the same.

$$2y^2 - y - 1 = 0 \qquad 2 \sin^2 x - \sin x - 1 = 0$$
$$(2y + 1)(y - 1) = 0 \qquad (2 \sin x + 1)(\sin x - 1) = 0$$

The solution set of each of these equations is given below.

$$\{y \mid 2y + 1 = 0\} \cup \{y \mid y - 1 = 0\}$$
$$\{-\tfrac{1}{2}\} \cup \{1\}, \quad \text{or} \quad \{-\tfrac{1}{2}, 1\}$$
$$\{x \mid 2 \sin x + 1 = 0\} \cup \{x \mid \sin x - 1 = 0\}$$
$$\{x \mid \sin x = -\tfrac{1}{2}\} \cup \{x \mid \sin x = 1\}$$

For $0 \leqq x < 2\pi$, the equation

$$\sin x = -\frac{1}{2} \quad \text{has solution set} \quad \left\{\pi + \frac{\pi}{6},\ 2\pi - \frac{\pi}{6}\right\},$$

and the equation

$$\sin x = 1 \quad \text{has solution set} \quad \left\{\frac{\pi}{2}\right\}.$$

Hence, $\{\pi/2,\ 7\pi/6,\ 11\pi/6\}$ is the solution set of the given trigonometric equation in one period of the sine.

Problem 2. Solve the equation $\sin^2 x = 1 + 2\cos x$.

Solution. We can obtain an equivalent equation containing only cosines by replacing $\sin^2 x$ by $1 - \cos^2 x$, according to the first fundamental identity, (FI-1).

$$1 - \cos^2 x = 1 + 2\cos x$$

This equation is equivalent, in turn, to each of the following.

$$-\cos^2 x = 2\cos x$$
$$0 = \cos^2 x + 2\cos x$$
$$0 = \cos x(\cos x + 2)$$

Hence, the solution set of the given equation is

$$\{x \mid \cos x = 0\} \cup \{x \mid \cos x + 2 = 0\}.$$

Since $-1 \leqq \cos x \leqq 1$ for every x, the equation $\cos x + 2 = 0$ has solution set $\emptyset$. Thus, the solution set is

$$\{x \mid \cos x = 0\}.$$

If $0 \leqq x < 2\pi$, then the solution set is $\{\pi/2,\ 3\pi/2\}$.

Exercises

Solve each of the following trigonometric equations for $0 \leqq x < 2\pi$.

1. (a) $\sin x = \frac{1}{2}$ (b) $2\sin^2 x - 5\sin x - 3 = 0$

2. (a) $4\sin^2 x = 3$ (b) $\cos 2x = 1$

3. (a) $4\sin x \cos x = 1$ (b) $3\cos 4x = 5$

4. (a) $2\cos\left(x + \frac{\pi}{3}\right) = 1$ (b) $2\tan x = 1 - \tan^2 x$

5. (a) $2 \cos x = -\sqrt{3}$ (b) $\tan^2 x = 1$
6. (a) $\tan^2 x - 3 \tan x + 2 = 0$ (b) $\cos^2 x - 1 = 2 \sin x$
7. (a) $\cos x - 2 \sin^2 x + 1 = 0$ (b) $2 \sin 3x = 1$
8. (a) $3 \tan^2 \left(x + \frac{\pi}{4} \right) = 1$ (b) $2 \cos \left(2x + \frac{\pi}{2} \right) = 1$
9. (a) $2 \sin x + 2 \cos x = \tan x + 1$
   (b) $\sin x \cos x + 1 = \sin x + \cos x$
10. (a) $\tan^2 x + 4 \tan x = 1$ (b) $4 \sin x + 3 \cos x = 5$
11. (a) $4 \cos^2 4x = 3$ (b) $5 \cos^2 x = \cos x$
12. (a) $\sin x \cos x = 2 \cos x$ (b) $\sin^2 x = 3 \cos^2 x$
13. (a) $4 \cos^2 (3x + \pi) = 1$ (b) $(\sin x + 2)(\tan 2x + 1) = 0$

In Exercises 14–19, solve each trigonometric equation for $0 \leqq x < 2\pi$.

14. $4 \sin^2 x + 1 = 3 \tan^2 x$

15. $\sin x = \cos x$

16. $\sin 3x \cos x + \cos 3x \sin x = 1$

17. $\sqrt{3} \sin 3x + \cos 3x = 2$

18. Solve the following system of trigonometric equations for all ordered pairs (x, y) having $0 \leqq x < 2\pi$.

$$\begin{cases} y = 2 - 2 \sin x \\ y = 2 \sin x \end{cases}$$

19. Find the solution set of the following system of equations.

$$\begin{cases} y = \sin x - 1 \\ y^2 = \frac{1}{2} \sin x \end{cases}$$

10–6   GRAPHS OF THE TRIGONOMETRIC FUNCTIONS

Every reader of this book has probably seen a *sine curve*, either on the screen of an oscilloscope or in some related way. In this section, we shall sketch the sine curve and the other trigonometric curves.

Because of the periodicity of the sine and cosine, we need only graph each function over one period in order to be able to describe its graph completely. Actually, since

$$\sin (\pi + s) = -\sin s,$$

the graph of the sine from π to 2π is the "negative" of its graph from 0 to π. The same is true for the cosine. Thus, we can get a rough idea of the graph of the sine function from the short table of values below.

x	0	$\dfrac{\pi}{6}$	$\dfrac{\pi}{3}$	$\dfrac{\pi}{2}$	$\dfrac{2\pi}{3}$	$\dfrac{5\pi}{6}$	π
$\sin x$	0	$\dfrac{1}{2}$	$\dfrac{\sqrt{3}}{2}$	1	$\dfrac{\sqrt{3}}{2}$	$\dfrac{1}{2}$	0

We have sketched the graph of the sine function from -3π to 3π in Fig. 10–10, using this table and our remarks above.

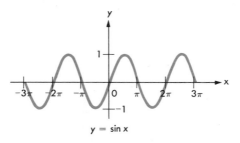

$$y = \sin x$$

FIGURE 10–10

The *cosine curve* is often described as being "90° out of phase" with the sine curve. Thus, if we move the sine curve of Fig. 10–10 a distance of $\pi/2$ units (equivalent to 90°) to the left, the resulting curve is the graph of the cosine function. We can see that this is so by using the fourth addition formula, (A-4), and letting $v = x$ and $u = \pi/2$.

$$\sin\left(x + \frac{\pi}{2}\right) = \sin x \cos \frac{\pi}{2} + \cos x \sin \frac{\pi}{2}$$

$$= \sin x \cdot 0 + \cos x \cdot 1$$

Hence,

$$\cos x = \sin\left(x + \frac{\pi}{2}\right).$$

The cosine curve is sketched in Fig. 10–11.

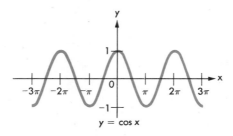

$$y = \cos x$$

FIGURE 10–11

The tangent function has a smaller period than either the sine or the cosine. Because

$$\tan x = \tan (x + \pi)$$

for every real number x, and π is the smallest positive number for which such an equation is true, the period of the tangent function is π. If we recall that the range of the tangent function is the set of all real numbers, then we realize that the graph of the tangent function is unbounded. The graph consists of an infinite number of branches, which are all alike. One of these branches occurs between $x = -\pi/2$ and $x = \pi/2$.

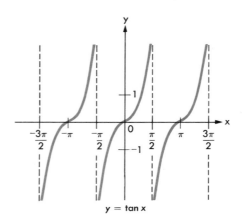

$y = \tan x$

FIGURE 10-12

The lines $x = \pi/2$, $x = 3\pi/2$, $x = -\pi/2$, $x = -3\pi/2$, and so on, are called *asymptotes* of the graph. We have sketched the graph in Fig. 10-12, using the Table of Values of Trigonometric Functions in the Appendix. Since

$$\text{secant } x = \frac{1}{\cos x},$$

the domain of the secant is the set

$$\{x \mid \cos x \neq 0\} = \left\{x \mid x \neq \frac{2n + 1}{2} \pi, \ n \text{ an integer}\right\}.$$

Also, since $|\cos x| \leq 1$, we have $|\sec x| \geq 1$ for every number x in its domain. In fact, the range of secant is the set

$$\{y \mid y \geq 1\} \cup \{y \mid y \leq -1\}.$$

We can graph the secant from the cosine by taking reciprocals of ordinates. For every point (a, b) on the graph of the cosine, with $b \neq 0$, the point $(a, 1/b)$ is on the graph of the secant. Thus, as $|b|$ gets closer to zero, $|1/b|$ gets larger. In other words, the vertical lines $x = (2n + 1)\pi/2$, $n = 0, \pm 1, \pm 2,$ ..., are asymptotes of the graph. A sketch of the graph is shown in Fig. 10-13.

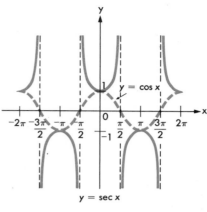

$y = \sec x$

FIGURE 10-13

Exercises

1. (a) Graph the cotangent function.
   (b) Graph the cosecant function.

2. (a) On the same set of axes, sketch graphs of each of the following equations.

   $$y = \sin x \qquad y = -\sin x \qquad y = \sin(-x)$$

   (b) On the same set of axes, sketch graphs of each of the following equations.

   $$y = \cos x \qquad y = 2 \cos x \qquad y = 2 + \cos x$$

---

3. Graph the sine curve and the cosine curve on the same set of axes. Complete the following table and then graph the equation

$$y = \sin x + \cos x.$$

x	0	$\dfrac{\pi}{4}$	$\dfrac{\pi}{2}$	$\dfrac{3\pi}{4}$	π	$\dfrac{5\pi}{4}$	$\dfrac{3\pi}{2}$	$\dfrac{7\pi}{4}$	2π
$\sin x + \cos x$	$0 + 1$	$\dfrac{\sqrt{2}}{2} + \dfrac{\sqrt{2}}{2}$	?	?	?	?	?	?	?

---

4. Make a table of values for plotting the graph of the equation $y = \sin 2x$. For x, use the numbers in the interval $0 \leq x < \pi/2$ which are integral multiples of $\pi/12$. Make your graph cover the interval $0 \leq x < 2\pi$. Compare this graph with that of the equation $y = \sin x$.

5. Sketch a graph of the equation $y = \sin x$. On the same set of axes, graph the equation $y = \sin (x + \pi)$. How can the graph of $y = \sin x$ be shifted to produce the graph of $y = \sin (x + \pi)$?

10-7 AMPLITUDES AND PERIODS OF TRIGONOMETRIC FUNCTIONS

Equations of the form

$$y = a \sin bx, \quad a \text{ and } b \text{ positive numbers,}$$

are commonplace in the theory of electricity and wave motion. Let us analyze the graph of such an equation by analyzing the function f, defined by

$$f(x) = a \sin bx, \quad a \text{ and } b \text{ positive numbers.}$$

The range of f is the set

$$\{y \mid -a \leqq y \leqq a\}.$$

This is so because the range of the sine function is the set

$$\{y \mid -1 \leqq y \leqq 1\}.$$

We call a the *amplitude* of the function f. In the same way, we call $|a|$ the amplitude of the functions $a \sin bx$ and $a \cos bx$, whether a is positive or not.

To show that f is periodic, we seek the smallest positive number k such that

$$f(x + k) = f(x) \quad \text{for every number } x.$$

In this case, since $f(x + k) = a \sin [b(x + k)] = a \sin (bx + bk)$, we want to find the smallest positive number k such that

$$\sin (bx + bk) = \sin bx \quad \text{for every number } x.$$

However, the sine function has period 2π. Therefore, the smallest positive number bk such that $\sin bx = \sin (bx + bk)$ for every number x is 2π. Hence, $bk = 2\pi$ and $k = 2\pi/b$.

In other words, the function f, defined by

$$f(x) = a \sin bx, \quad a \text{ and } b \text{ positive numbers,}$$

is periodic with period $2\pi/b$. In the same way, if b is not positive, $a \sin bx$ and $a \cos bx$ are periodic with period $2\pi/|b|$.

Problem 1. Discuss and sketch the graph of the equation

$$y = 2 \sin 3x.$$

Solution. From our remarks above, we know that the function f, defined by

$$f(x) = 2 \sin 3x,$$

has amplitude 2 and period $2\pi/3$. Thus, we can sketch its graph from the following table of values. (See Fig. 10–14.)

x	0	$\dfrac{\pi}{18}$	$\dfrac{\pi}{9}$	$\dfrac{\pi}{6}$	$\dfrac{2\pi}{9}$	$\dfrac{5\pi}{18}$	$\dfrac{\pi}{3}$
$2 \sin 3x$	0	1	$\sqrt{3}$	2	$\sqrt{3}$	1	0

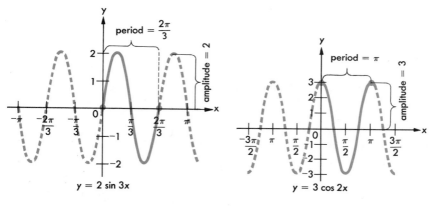

FIGURE 10–14   FIGURE 10–15

Problem 2. Discuss and sketch the graph of the equation

$$y = 3 \cos 2x.$$

Solution. The function g, defined by

$$g(x) = 3 \cos 2x,$$

has amplitude 3 and period $2\pi/2$, or π. Thus, we can sketch its graph from the following table of values. (See Fig. 10–15.)

x	0	$\dfrac{\pi}{12}$	$\dfrac{\pi}{6}$	$\dfrac{\pi}{4}$	$\dfrac{\pi}{3}$	$\dfrac{5\pi}{12}$	$\dfrac{\pi}{2}$
$3 \cos 2x$	3	$\dfrac{3\sqrt{3}}{2}$	$\dfrac{3}{2}$	0	$-\dfrac{3}{2}$	$-\dfrac{3\sqrt{3}}{2}$	-3

Problem 3. Discuss and sketch the graph of the equation

$$y = 2 \sin 3x + 3 \cos 2x.$$

Solution. The function h, defined by

$$h(x) = 2 \sin 3x + 3 \cos 2x,$$

is simply the sum of the functions f and g, defined in Problems 1 and 2, respectively. Although 2π is not the period of f or g, these functions do repeat their values every 2π. Hence, the function h repeats its values every 2π. Therefore, the function h is periodic with period less than or equal to 2π. Because the graph of f has three identical pieces in the interval $\{x \mid 0 \leq x \leq 2\pi\}$ and the graph of g has two such pieces in this interval, we can argue that the graph of h has the greatest common divisor of two and three, or one, identical piece, in an interval of 2π. In other words, h has period 2π.

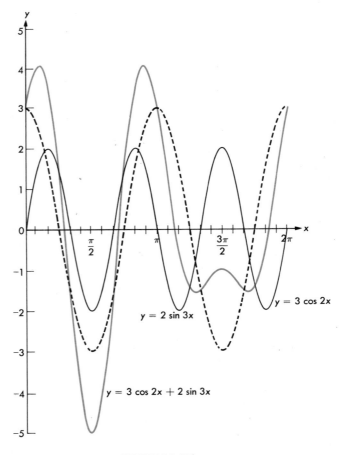

FIGURE 10-16

We can construct the graph of h from the graphs of f and g by the method of adding ordinates. This method is illustrated by a few points in the table below. The graph of the function is shown in Fig. 10–16.

x	0	$\dfrac{\pi}{6}$	$\dfrac{\pi}{3}$
$2 \sin 3x + 3 \cos 2x$	$0 + 3$	$2 + \dfrac{3}{2}$	$0 + -\dfrac{3}{2}$
$h(x)$	3	$\dfrac{7}{2}$	$-\dfrac{3}{2}$

Exercises

Give the period and amplitude of each function, and then graph the function.

1. (a) $y = \sin(-x)$ (b) $y = -3 \cos x$

2. (a) $y = 4 \sin x$ (b) $y = 3 \sin 2x$

3. (a) $y = 4 \cos \dfrac{2x}{3}$ (b) $y = \sin\left(\dfrac{x}{2}\right)$

4. (a) $y = 3\,|\cos x|$ (b) $y = -2\,|\sin x|$

5. (a) $y = 3 - 3 \cos x$ (b) $y = 3 + 3 \sin x$

6. (a) $y = \sin\left(x - \dfrac{\pi}{2}\right)$ (b) $y = \sin 2(x - \pi)$

7. (a) $y = 2 \sin(x - \pi)$ (b) $y = 3 \sin(\pi - x)$

Give the period of each function and then graph the function.

8. $y = \sin x + \sin 2x$

9. $y = \sin x + \cos x$

10. $y = \sin 2x + \cos 3x$

11. Sketch the graph of the equation $y = \tan x$, and use it to sketch the graph of the equation $y = \tan(x + \pi/2)$ on the same axes.

12. Graph the function $y = 2 \sin \pi x$, and give its period and amplitude.

13. If a, b, and c are numbers such that $a^2 + b^2 = c^2$, and if s is a number such that $\sin s = b/c$ and $\cos s = a/c$, prove that

$$a \sin x + b \cos x = c \sin(x + s)$$

for every real number x.

Use your answer to Exercise 13 to rewrite each of the following equations, and then graph the equation.

14. $y = \sqrt{3} \sin x + \cos x$ **15.** $y = \sin x - \cos x$

10–8 INVERSE TRIGONOMETRIC FUNCTIONS

For each number x in the interval $I = \{x \mid -1 \leq x \leq 1\}$, there exists an arc $\overparen{AP}$ of length s, with $0 \leq s \leq \pi$, as shown in Fig. 10–17. Since $x = \cos s$, it is natural to call s the *arc whose cosine is* x and denote s by *arccosine x.*

Definition of arccosine

arccosine $x = s$, *where* $\cos s = x$ *and* $0 \leq s \leq \pi$

The domain of arccosine is the interval $-1 \leq x \leq 1$.

Similarly, for each number y in $J = \{y \mid -1 \leq y \leq 1\}$, there exists an arc $\overparen{AP}$ of length s, with $-\pi/2 \leq s \leq \pi/2$, as shown in Fig. 10–18. The arc $\overparen{AP}$ is understood to have a positive length if P is above the x-axis and a negative length if P is below the x-axis. Both cases are shown in Fig. 10–18. Since $y = \sin s$ in either case, we call s the *arcsine y.*

Definition of arcsine

arcsine $y = s$, *where* $\sin s = y$ *and* $-\dfrac{\pi}{2} \leq s \leq \dfrac{\pi}{2}$

The domain of arcsine is the interval $-1 \leq y \leq 1$.

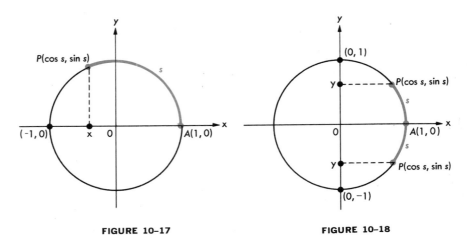

FIGURE 10–17   FIGURE 10–18

In the same way that we abbreviated sine and cosine, we shall abbreviate arccosine to *arccos* and arcsine to *arcsin.*

Problem. Find $\arccos \frac{1}{2}$, $\arcsin 1$, $\arccos\left(-\frac{\sqrt{2}}{2}\right)$, and $\arcsin\left(-\frac{\sqrt{3}}{2}\right)$.

Solution. Since

$$\cos \frac{\pi}{3} = \frac{1}{2} \text{ and } 0 \leq \frac{\pi}{3} \leq \pi, \arccos \frac{1}{2} = \frac{\pi}{3}.$$

Since

$$\sin \frac{\pi}{2} = 1 \text{ and } -\frac{\pi}{2} \leq \frac{\pi}{2} \leq \frac{\pi}{2}, \arcsin 1 = \frac{\pi}{2}.$$

Since

$$\cos \frac{3\pi}{4} = -\frac{\sqrt{2}}{2} \text{ and } 0 \leq \frac{3\pi}{4} \leq \pi, \arccos\left(-\frac{\sqrt{2}}{2}\right) = \frac{3\pi}{4}.$$

Since

$$\sin\left(-\frac{\pi}{3}\right) = -\frac{\sqrt{3}}{2} \text{ and } -\frac{\pi}{2} \leq -\frac{\pi}{3} \leq \frac{\pi}{2}, \arcsin\left(-\frac{\sqrt{3}}{2}\right) = -\frac{\pi}{3}.$$

The cosine and arccosine functions are related to each other by the following equations.

$$\cos (arccos\ x) = x \text{ for every number } x \text{ in } \{x \mid -1 \leq x \leq 1\}$$
$$arccos (\cos s) = s \text{ for every number } s \text{ in } \{s \mid 0 \leq s \leq \pi\}$$

If f and g are functions defined by

$$f(s) = \cos s, \text{ domain } f = \{s \mid 0 \leq s \leq \pi\},$$
$$g(x) = \arccos x, \text{ domain } g = \{x \mid -1 \leq x \leq 1\},$$

$$f(g(x)) = x \text{ for all } x \text{ in domain } g,$$
$$g(f(s)) = s \text{ for all } s \text{ in domain } f.$$

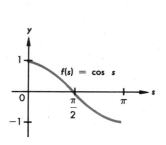
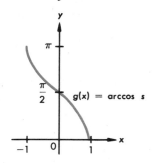

FIGURE 10–19

Any two functions f and g which are related in this way are called *inverse functions*. It is important to realize f *is not the cosine function*, since the domain of f is $\{s \mid 0 \leq s \leq \pi\}$ whereas the domain of cosine is the set of all real numbers. However, f and cosine have the same values over the domain of f. The graphs of f and g are shown in Fig. 10–19.

The sine and arcsine functions satisfy similar equations.

$$sin\ (arcsin\ y) = y\ for\ every\ number\ y\ in\ \{y \mid -1 \leq y \leq 1\}$$

$$arcsin\ (sin\ s) = s\ for\ every\ number\ s\ in\ \left\{s \mid -\frac{\pi}{2} \leq s \leq \frac{\pi}{2}\right\}$$

Therefore, if we define functions f and g by

$$f(s) = sin\ s,\ domain\ f = \left\{s \mid -\frac{\pi}{2} \leq s \leq \frac{\pi}{2}\right\},$$

$$g(x) = arcsin\ x,\ domain\ g = \{x \mid -1 \leq x \leq 1\},$$

the functions f and g are inverses of each other. These functions are graphed in Fig. 10–20.

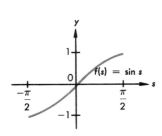
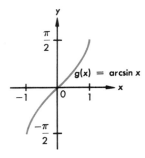

FIGURE 10-20

Each trigonometric function has an arc-function defined in a way similar to those above. For example, we have the following definition of arctangent.

Definition of arctangent

$$arctan\ x = y,\ where\ tan\ y = x\ and\ -\frac{\pi}{2} < y < \frac{\pi}{2}$$

The domain of arctangent is the set R of all real numbers.

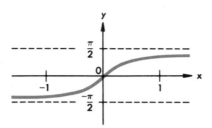

FIGURE 10-21

The graph of the arctangent function is the graph of the equation

$$x = \tan y, \qquad -\frac{\pi}{2} < y < \frac{\pi}{2},$$

as shown in Fig. 10–21.

Exercises

Find each of the following. Use the Table of Values of Trigonometric Functions, if necessary.

1. (a) $\arcsin \dfrac{\sqrt{3}}{2}$ (b) $\arctan(-\sqrt{2})$

2. (a) $\arccos(-1)$ (b) $\arctan \sqrt{3}$

3. (a) $\arcsin 0$ (b) $\arcsin \frac{3}{5}$

4. (a) $\arccos(-\frac{4}{5})$ (b) $\arctan(-\frac{5}{12})$

5. (a) $\arcsin \frac{1}{2}$ (b) $\arccos\left(-\dfrac{\sqrt{3}}{2}\right)$

6. (a) $\arctan 10$ (b) $\arcsin\left(-\dfrac{1}{\sqrt{2}}\right)$

7. (a) $\arccos(-\frac{1}{2})$ (b) $\arccos 0$

8. (a) $\arctan \sqrt{2}$ (b) $\arcsin \frac{2}{3}$

9. (a) $\arcsin \frac{4}{5}$ (b) $\arctan(-12)$

Find arctan (tan s) for each given number s.

10. (a) $s = \dfrac{\pi}{4}$ (b) $s = \dfrac{5\pi}{4}$

11. (a) $s = -\dfrac{7\pi}{4}$ (b) $s = -\dfrac{3\pi}{4}$

12. (a) $s = -\dfrac{\pi}{4}$ (b) $s = \dfrac{3\pi}{4}$

13. (a) $s = \dfrac{11\pi}{4}$ (b) $s = -\dfrac{9\pi}{4}$

Evaluate each of the following.

14. (a) $\sin (\arctan -1)$
    (b) $\csc (\arcsin \tfrac{1}{2})$

15. (a) $\cot (\arccos -\tfrac{3}{5})$
    (b) $\tan (\arcsin \tfrac{7}{25})$

16. (a) $\tan (\arctan -1)$
    (b) $\cos (\arctan -1)$

17. (a) $\sec \left(\arcsin -\dfrac{\sqrt{3}}{2} \right)$

    (b) $\sin \left(\arccos -\dfrac{5}{13} \right)$

---

18. For which numbers s in Exercises 10–13 is $\arctan (\tan s) = s$?

19. For which numbers s is $\arctan (\tan s) = s$?

20. For which numbers x is $\tan (\arctan x) = x$?

Complete each of the following statements:

21. Sin $(\arcsin x) = x$ for every number x in the set

$$\{x \mid \underline{\quad ?\quad}\}.$$

22. Arcsin $(\sin s) = s$ for every number s in the set

$$\{s \mid \underline{\quad ?\quad}\}.$$

Show that each equation in Exercises 23 and 24 is true.

23. Arcsin $\tfrac{12}{13} + \arcsin \tfrac{4}{5} = \arccos -\tfrac{33}{65}$

24. $2 \arctan \tfrac{1}{3} + \arctan \tfrac{1}{7} = \arctan 1$

25. Find the solution set of the equation

$$\arctan 3x + \arctan x = \arctan 2.$$

26. Prove the following identity.

$$\arctan \frac{1}{5} + \arctan \frac{2}{3} = \frac{\pi}{4}$$

*10–9 TRIGONOMETRIC FORM OF COMPLEX NUMBERS

Every complex number has the form $a + bi$ where a and b are real numbers and $i^2 = -1$. As we saw in Chapter 4, the complex numbers can be used as coordinates in the complex number plane. Thus, each point P having coordinates (a, b) in a cartesian coordinate system has coordinate $a + bi$ in the associated complex number plane. If P is not the origin, that is, if $a + bi \neq 0$, then P is on the terminal side of some angle θ in standard position, as shown in Fig. 10–22. If

$$r = |a + bi| = \sqrt{a^2 + b^2},$$

then

$$\frac{a}{\cos \theta} = \frac{r}{1} \quad \text{and} \quad \frac{b}{\sin \theta} = \frac{r}{1}$$

by the definition of similar triangles. Hence,

$$a = r \cos \theta, \quad b = r \sin \theta$$

and

$$a + bi = r \cos \theta + (r \sin \theta)i,$$

or

$$a + bi = r(\cos \theta + i \sin \theta).$$

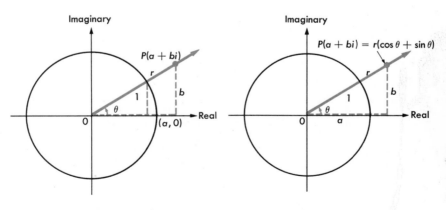

FIGURE 10–22   FIGURE 10–23

We call $r(\cos \theta + i \sin \theta)$ a *trigonometric form* of the complex number $a + bi$. (See Fig. 10–23.) In a trigonometric form of $a + bi$, the positive number r is the *absolute value* of $a + bi$ and θ is an *angle* associated with $a + bi$.   The number 0 has trigonometric form $0(\cos \theta + i \sin \theta)$ for any angle θ.

Problem 1. Find a trigonometric form of each of the following.

(a) 4   (b) $-3i$

(c) $2 + 2i$ (d) $1 - \sqrt{3}i$

Solution. Each of these complex numbers is plotted in Fig. 10–24. We read the following trigonometric forms from the figure.

(a) $4 = 4(\cos 0° + i \sin 0°)$

(b) $-3i = 3(\cos 270° + i \sin 270°)$

(c) $2 + 2i = 2\sqrt{2}\,(\cos 45° + i \sin 45°)$

(d) $1 - \sqrt{3}i = 2(\cos -60° + i \sin -60°)$

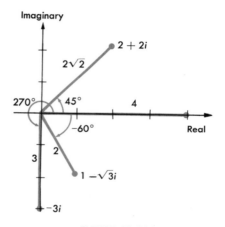

FIGURE 10-24

The angle θ is not unique because the sine and cosine are periodic functions. For example, we could just as well have expressed $1 - \sqrt{3}i$ in the trigonometric form

$$1 - \sqrt{3}i = 2(\cos 300° + i \sin 300°)$$

since $\sin -60° = \sin 300°$ and $\cos -60° = \cos 300°$.

If w and z are two complex numbers having trigonometric forms

$$w = r(\cos \theta + i \sin \theta),$$
$$z = s(\cos \phi + i \sin \phi),$$

then a trigonometric form of their product wz may be found by multiplying the two complex numbers and using the second and fourth addition formulas.

$$wz = r(\cos \theta + i \sin \theta) \cdot s(\cos \phi + i \sin \phi)$$
$$= rs(\cos \theta + i \sin \theta)(\cos \phi + i \sin \phi)$$
$$= rs[(\cos \theta \cos \phi - \sin \theta \sin \phi) + i(\cos \theta \sin \phi + \sin \theta \cos \phi)]$$

Thus,

$$wz = rs[\cos (\theta + \phi) + i \sin (\theta + \phi)].$$

This result can be stated in words in the following manner.

A trigonometric form of the product of two complex numbers is found by multiplying absolute values and adding angles of the two complex numbers.

The following theorem is named after De Moivre, a seventeenth-century French mathematician.

De MOIVRE'S THEOREM

$$[r(\cos \theta + i \sin \theta)]^n = r^n(\cos n\theta + i \sin n\theta)$$

for every real number r, every angle θ, and every positive integer n

We shall postpone the proof of this theorem until Chapter 13.

Problem 2. Use De Moivre's theorem to find

(a) $(2 + 2i)^5$. (b) $(1 - \sqrt{3}i)^6$.

Solution.
(a) By Problem 1, $2 + 2i = 2\sqrt{2} (\cos 45° + i \sin 45°)$. Hence, by De Moivre's theorem,

$$(2 + 2i)^5 = [2\sqrt{2} (\cos 45° + i \sin 45°)]^5$$
$$= (2\sqrt{2})^5[\cos (5 \cdot 45°) + i \sin (5 \cdot 45°)]$$
$$= 128\sqrt{2} (\cos 225° + i \sin 225°).$$

Since both $\sin 225°$ and $\cos 225°$ are equal to $-\sqrt{2}/2$, we have

$$(2 + 2i)^5 = 128\sqrt{2}\left(-\frac{\sqrt{2}}{2} - i\frac{\sqrt{2}}{2}\right)$$
$$= -128 - 128i.$$

(b) By Problem 1, $1 - \sqrt{3}\, i = 2(\cos -60° + i \sin -60°)$. Hence, by De Moivre's theorem,

$$(1 - \sqrt{3}i)^6 = 2^6[\cos (6 \cdot -60°) + i \sin (6 \cdot -60°)]$$
$$= 64(\cos -360° + i \sin -360°).$$

Since $\cos -360° = 1$ and $\sin -360° = 0$, we obtain

$$(1 - \sqrt{3}i)^6 = 64.$$

In other words, $1 - \sqrt{3}\, i$ is a complex sixth root of 64. Incidentally, 2 and -2 are the only real sixth roots of 64.

The following problem shows the way in which we can use De Moivre's theorem to find roots of complex numbers.

Problem 3. Find the square roots of

(a) $i.$ (b) $-2 + 2\sqrt{3}i.$

Solution.
(a) The complex number i has trigonometric form

$$i = \cos 90° + i \sin 90°.$$

If $r(\cos \theta + i \sin \theta)$ is a square root of i, then its square must be i:

$$[r(\cos \theta + i \sin \theta)]^2 = \cos 90° + i \sin 90°.$$

Hence, using De Moivre's theorem, we must have

$$r^2(\cos 2\theta + i \sin 2\theta) = \cos 90° + i \sin 90°.$$

In Section 4–2 of Chapter 4, we saw that $a + bi = c + di$ if, and only if, $a = c$ and $b = d$. Thus, $r = 1$ and $2\theta = 90°$, or $\theta = 45°$, and the resulting complex number,

$$1(\cos 45° + i \sin 45°),$$

will be a square root of i. Consequently, $\sqrt{2}/2 + i\sqrt{2}/2$ is a square root of i. Given one square root of a number, the only other square root is the negative of the first one. Hence,

$$\frac{\sqrt{2}}{2} + \frac{\sqrt{2}}{2} i \quad \text{and} \quad -\frac{\sqrt{2}}{2} - \frac{\sqrt{2}}{2} i$$

are the square roots of i.

(b) The trigonometric form of $-2 + 2\sqrt{3}i$ is $4(\cos 120° + i \sin 120°)$. If

$$[r(\cos \theta + i \sin \theta)]^2 = 4(\cos 120° + i \sin 120°),$$

then

$$r^2(\cos 2\theta + i \sin 2\theta) = 4(\cos 120° + i \sin 120°),$$

with $r = 2$ and $\theta = 60°$. Thus,

$$2(\cos 60° + i \sin 60°), \quad \text{or} \quad 2\left(\frac{1}{2} + \frac{\sqrt{3}}{2}i\right),$$

is a square root of $-2 + 2\sqrt{3}i$. Hence, the two square roots of $-2 + 2\sqrt{3}i$ are

$$1 + \sqrt{3}i \quad \text{and} \quad -1 - \sqrt{3}i.$$

Exercises

Find a trigonometric form of each of the following complex numbers.

1. (a) $-1 + \sqrt{3}i$ (b) $\sqrt{2} - \sqrt{2}i$
2. (a) $2i$ (b) -5
3. (a) $-5i$ (b) $-1 - i$
4. (a) $\sqrt{3} + 3i$ (b) π
5. (a) $\dfrac{\pi}{2}$ (b) $5 - 5i$

Find the product of each of the following pairs of complex numbers, and write the product in the form $a + bi$.

6. (a) $3(\cos 20° + i \sin 20°)$ and $4(\cos 70° + i \sin 70°)$
   (b) $\frac{1}{2}(\cos 42° + i \sin 42°)$ and $6(\cos -42° + i \sin -42°)$
7. (a) $5(\cos 15° + i \sin 15°)$ and $4(\cos 165° + i \sin 165°)$
   (b) $2(\cos 10° + i \sin 10°)$ and $7(\cos 50° + i \sin 50°)$
8. (a) $3(\cos 300° + i \sin 300°)$ and $5(\cos 330° + i \sin 330°)$
   (b) $2(\cos 20° + i \sin 20°)$ and $3(\cos 25° + i \sin 25°)$

Use De Moivre's theorem to find each of the following.

9. $[2(\cos 30° + i \sin 30°)]^3$ 10. $[\sqrt[3]{3}(\cos 20° + i \sin 20°)]^9$
11. $(2 - 2i)^4$ 12. $(\sqrt{3} + i)^6$

13. $(-3 + \sqrt{3}i)^3$ **14.** $(-3 - 3i)^3$

15. $(\sqrt{2} + \sqrt{2}i)^7$ **16.** $(\sqrt[5]{3} - \sqrt[5]{3}i)^{10}$

In Exercises 17–22, use De Moivre's theorem to find each of the following.

17. The cube roots of $27i$

18. The square roots of $-4i$

19. The eighth roots of 16

20. The cube roots of -8

21. The fourth roots of i

22. The fifth roots of $3 - \sqrt{3}i$, leaving your answers in trigonometric form

23. (a) Find the sixth roots of 1.
   (b) Which of the roots in part (a) are also cube roots of 1?
   (c) Which of the roots in part (a) are also square roots of 1?

24. Prove De Moivre's theorem (a) for $n = 3$ and (b) for $n = 4$.

EXTRA!

A sundial measures the angle of shadow that the sun makes against a raised object on the sundial. Thus, it seems that trigonometry would be useful in constructing an accurate sundial. One method of doing this is as follows.*

The face of the sundial should, of course, be horizontal, and should lie in a north-south direction so that twelve o'clock (the most natural starting point) is pointing north on the north-south line. Then the shadow-producing pole, or pin, called the *style*, should be set on this north-south line so that it makes an angle with the face of the sundial equal to the latitude of the geographic location where it is being constructed. This is because latitude is the angle of the North Star above the horizon; and thus, the style will be pointing at the North Star and the axis of the style will be parallel to the axis about which the sun appears to rotate. In this way the sundial will be accurate in all seasons of the year.

To mark off a scale on the face of the sundial, the following formula is used.

   tangent (shadow angle) = sine (latitude) × tangent (hour angle)

Since we have twelve o'clock as the starting point, we can find the correct place for one o'clock as follows. One hour is $\frac{1}{24}$ of a complete revolution of the earth: $\frac{1}{24} \times 360° = 15°$. This is the hour angle. Thus,

   tan (shadow angle) = sin (latitude) × tan 15°.

* W. C. Vergara, *Mathematics in Everyday Things*, (New York: Harper & Bros., 1959).

Using a table of values of trigonometric functions, the shadow angle can be determined; the measure of the shadow angle is then used to mark off one o'clock (that is, the angle between the line marking twelve o'clock and one o'clock is the shadow angle).

Continuing in the same way, the hour angle for two o'clock is 30°. Solving

$$\tan \text{ (shadow angle)} = \sin \text{ (latitude)} \times \tan 30°$$

for the shadow angle will give the angle between the line marking twelve o'clock and two o'clock.

Using the latitude of your geographic location, find the shadow angles needed to mark off each hour (one o'clock to twelve o'clock) on a sundial.

KEY IDEAS AND KEY WORDS

If α, β, and γ are the angles and a, b, and c are the lengths of the respective opposite sides of a triangle, then each of the following laws is true.

Law of cosines

$$a^2 = b^2 + c^2 - 2bc \cos \alpha$$

Law of sines

$$\frac{\sin \alpha}{a} = \frac{\sin \beta}{b}$$

The **addition formulas** relate the trigonometric functions of sums and differences of two numbers (or angles) to the functions of the individual numbers (or angles). These formulas can be stated in the following manner.

First, second, third, and fourth addition formulas

$$\cos (v - u) = \cos v \cos u + \sin v \sin u \qquad \text{(A-1)}$$
$$\cos (v + u) = \cos v \cos u - \sin v \sin u \qquad \text{(A-2)}$$
$$\sin (v - u) = \sin v \cos u - \cos v \sin u \qquad \text{(A-3)}$$
$$\sin (v + u) = \sin v \cos u + \cos v \sin u \qquad \text{(A-4)}$$

Special instances of the addition formulas are the double-angle formulas and the half-angle formulas.

First and second double-angle formulas

$$\cos 2v = \cos^2 v - \sin^2 v \qquad\qquad \text{(D-1)}$$

$$\sin 2v = 2 \sin v \cos v \qquad\qquad \text{(D-2)}$$

First and second half-angle formulas

$$\cos^2 \frac{u}{2} = \frac{1}{2} (1 + \cos u) \qquad\qquad \text{(H-1)}$$

$$\sin^2 \frac{u}{2} = \frac{1}{2} (1 - \cos u) \qquad\qquad \text{(H-2)}$$

The **inverse trigonometric functions, arcsine, arccosine,** and **arctangent,** are defined in the following way.

$$\arcsin x = s, \text{ where } \sin s = x \text{ and } -\frac{\pi}{2} \leq s \leq \frac{\pi}{2}$$

$$\arccos x = s, \text{ where } \cos s = x \text{ and } 0 \leq s \leq \pi$$

$$\arctan x = s, \text{ where } \tan s = x \text{ and } -\frac{\pi}{2} < s < \frac{\pi}{2}$$

CHAPTER REVIEW

In Exercises 1–4, $\triangle ABC$ has sides of lengths a, b, and c with opposite angles α, β, and γ.

1. Find c, given that $a = 3$, $b = 2$, $\gamma = 120°$.

2. Find α, given that $a = 5$, $b = 7$, $c = 8$.

3. Find a, given that $\alpha = 30°$, $\beta = 105°$, $c = 10$.

4. Find the area of the triangle in Exercise 1.

If $\sin u = \frac{2}{7}$ and $\cos v = \frac{7}{11}$, with $\pi/2 < u < \pi$ and $0 < v < \pi/2$, find each of the following.

5. $\cos (u - v)$

6. $\sin (u - v)$

7. $\tan (u - v)$

If $\cos u = \frac{3}{10}$, $\tan u < 0$, $\tan v = -\frac{10}{17}$, and $\sin v > 0$, find each of the following.

8. $\sin (u + v)$

9. $\cos (u + v)$

10. $\tan (u + v)$

Use the half-angle formulas to find the sine, cosine, and tangent of each of the following.

11. $\dfrac{\pi}{8}$ **12.** $\dfrac{3\pi}{8}$

Use the double-angle formulas to find the sine, cosine, and tangent of each of the following.

13. $\dfrac{2\pi}{3}$ **14.** $\dfrac{5\pi}{3}$

Given $\cos v = -\frac{2}{3}$, with $\pi/2 < v < \pi$, find each of the following.

15. $\sin 2v$ **16.** $\tan \frac{1}{2}v$

Simplify each of the following expressions.

17. $\dfrac{\cos 2x}{\cos x + \sin x}$

18. $\sin x \cos 2x + \cos x \sin 2x$

19. $\sin 2x \tan x + \cos 2x$

20. $2 \sin^2 \dfrac{x}{2} + \cos x$

For each of the following, find the solution set which lies within the interval $0 \le x < 2\pi$.

21. $2 \sin^2 x - 5 \sin x - 3 = 0$

22. $\cos^2 x - 2 \cos x = 0$

23. $\sec^2 x - \tan x = 1$

Draw the graph and state the period and amplitude of each of the following functions.

24. $f(x) = 5 \sin 4x$

25. $g(x) = 3 \cos 2x$

26. $h(x) = 3(1 + \cos 2x)$

Find each of the following.

27. $\arcsin \frac{3}{2}$ **28.** $\arccos \left(-\frac{1}{2}\right)$

29. $\arctan (-1)$ **30.** $\arcsin \left(-\frac{1}{2}\right)$

31. $\arccos (-1)$ **32.** $\tan \left(\arccos -\frac{3}{7}\right)$

33. $\sec \left(\arcsin -\frac{1}{2}\right)$ **34.** $\cot \left(\arccot -1\right)$

In Exercises 35–38, prove each identity.

35. $\csc 2\theta + \cot 2\theta = \cot \theta$

36. $\dfrac{2 \tan \theta}{1 + \tan^2 \theta} = \sin 2\theta$

37. $\cos^4 u - \sin^4 u = \cos 2u$

38. $\dfrac{2 \sin^2 u - 1}{\sin u \cos u} = \tan u - \cot u$

In Exercises 39 and 40, show that each equation is true.

39. $\arctan 2 - \arctan 1 = \arctan \frac{1}{3}$

40. $\arcsin \frac{4}{5} = \pi - 2 \arctan 2$

41. Find the sixth roots of 64.

42. (a) Express the following complex number in trigonometric form.

$$-\frac{1}{\sqrt{2}} + \frac{1}{\sqrt{2}} i$$

   (b) Find, in trigonometric form, the cube roots of the complex number of part (a).

   (c) Express one of the roots in part (b) in the form $a + bi$.

43. (a) If an arc 10 feet long subtends an angle of 2 radians at the center of a circle, find its radius.

   (b) Find the area of the circular sector in part (a).

44. City B is due north of City A. To fly from city A to city B, one must take a plane from city A to city C, which is 50° east of north from A at a distance of 150 miles, and then fly 200 miles to city B. How far due north is City B from City A?

45. A parallelogram has two sides of lengths 50 and 100. One angle of the parallelogram has measure 120°. Find the length of the longer diagonal and the angle made by this diagonal and the longer side.

CHAPTER TEST

1. Find the longer diagonal of a parallelogram having sides of lengths 10 and 15 and one angle of measure 60°.

2. Find α in $\triangle ABC$, given that $a = 2$, $b = 1$, $\beta = \pi/3$.

3. Find the area of $\triangle ABC$, given that $a = 2$, $b = 4$, $\gamma = 30°$.

4. From the addition formulas, $\cos (v + u) = \cos v \cos u - \sin v \sin u$ and $\sin (u + v) = \sin v \cos u + \cos v \sin u$, derive the double-angle formulas for sine and cosine.

In Exercises 5 and 6, prove each identity.

5. $\sin 2\theta = \tan \theta (1 + \cos 2\theta)$

6. $\dfrac{\cos (v - u) + \sin (v + u)}{\cos u + \sin u} = \cos v + \sin v$

7. For the following equation, find the part of the solution set that lies in the interval $0 \leqq x < 2\pi$.

$$2 \sin^2 x - 5 \sin x - 3 = 0$$

8. Graph the function $f(x) = 3 \sin 2x$, using that part of the domain of f for which $0 \leqq x < 2\pi$.

In Exercises 9–11, find each number.

9. arcsin (-1) 10. arccos 0   11. arctan $(-\frac{1}{2})$

12. A vertical telegraph pole is supported by two guy wires, each running from the top of the pole to the ground. One wire is 70 feet long and makes an angle of 55° with the ground. If the second wire is 60 feet long, what angle does it make with the ground?

CHAPTER **11**

Problems of Counting

Objectives...

- To build tree diagrams to verify the sequential counting principle.
- To apply the theory of combinations to counting groups of distinct objects.
- To apply the theory of permutations to counting arrangements of distinct objects.
- To develop formulas for finding permutations and combinations.
- To apply combinations to the proof of the binomial theorem.

11–1 SEQUENTIAL COUNTING PRINCIPLE

The procedure for solving a counting problem is usually twofold. First, we devise a *scheme* for listing the set of objects to be counted; then we look for *patterns* in this scheme so that we can compute the count without actually pointing to the objects one by one. This procedure is implemented by some basic counting principles which we shall illustrate in the following problems.

Problem 1. Consider a set of four discs in which the discs are numbered 1, 2, 3, and 4. How many two-digit numbers can be represented by placing two discs side by side?

Solution. We might choose any one of the four discs as a start. Then to the right of this disc we could place any one of the three remaining discs. The *tree diagram* of Fig. 11–1 suggests our scheme.

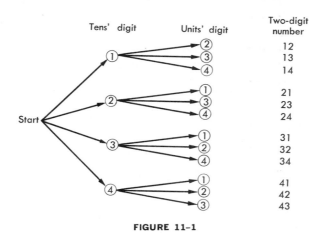

FIGURE 11-1

The arrows drawn from the word "start" point to the four possible discs of our first choice. The numeral on each of these discs will be a tens' digit of our number. Three arrows are drawn from each disc of our first choice, indicating the possible discs of our second choice. Our second choice must be different from our first choice. The numeral on each disc of our second choice will be a units' digit of our number. To the right of the tree, we have listed the numbers represented by our various choices. This list is formed by reading off the digits in order along each path (that is, along a succession of branches) of the tree. The total number of two-digit numbers so formed is 12, the total number of paths. The total number of paths is the product of the number of arrows drawn in the first stage and the number of arrows drawn from one disc in the second stage.

If more than two actions are performed, then the tree will have more than two branching stages, as the following problem illustrates.

Problem 2. How many four-digit numbers can be formed with the set of four discs of Problem 1?

Solution. The tree diagram used to count the number of possibilities in this problem has four branching stages: The stages represent, in turn, the choice of the thousands' digit of the number, the hundreds' digit, the tens' digit, and finally the units' digit.

Since there are four arrows drawn in the first stage, three arrows drawn from each disc in the second stage, two arrows drawn from each disc in the third stage, and one arrow drawn from each disc in the final stage, there are $4 \cdot 3 \cdot 2 \cdot 1$, or 24, paths in this tree. Thus, 24 four-digit numbers can be formed. It should be noted that there are many other orders in which the four actions can be performed. We might select the tens' digit first (4 ways), the hundreds' digit second (3 ways), the units' digit third (2 ways), and finally the thousands' digit (1 way). The number of paths is nonetheless $4 \cdot 3 \cdot 2 \cdot 1$, or 24.

A succession of two or more actions performed in a definite order is called a *sequence* of actions. The number of possible results of a sequence of actions in a given problem may often be counted by using the following fundamental principle.

SEQUENTIAL COUNTING PRINCIPLE

Given that two or more actions are performed in a definite order, that the first action produces m possible results, and that for each of these results, the second action produces n possible results, and that for each of these results, the third action produces p results, and so on, then the number of possible results of this sequence of actions is the product of the numbers m, n, p, and so on.

Each action referred to in the sequential counting principle is performed at a *branching stage* of a tree diagram, and each result of a sequence of actions is a *path* of the diagram. Problem 3 is another example of this principle.

Problem 3. How many two-digit numbers can be formed if only the digits 1, 2, 3, and 4 are used?

Solution. This problem might at first glance appear to be the same as Problem 1. However, the number 44 fulfills the conditions of this problem but not those of Problem 1, where two *different* discs had to be used to form each number. If we let the first action be that of selecting the tens' digit and the second action be that of selecting the units' digit of our number, then there are 4 possible results of the first action, and for each of these results there are 4 possible results of the second action. Hence, there are 4 × 4, or 16, possible results of this sequence of actions; that is, there are 16 two-digit numbers that can be formed.

The tree diagram for Problem 3 is similar to that drawn in Fig. 11-1 for Problem 1. The difference is that four branches, instead of three, are drawn in the second stage from each first-stage endpoint.

Exercises

1. (a) If you are given a set of five discs, numbered 1, 3, 5, 6, and 9, how many two-digit numbers can you represent by placing two discs side by side? how many three-digit numbers can you represent by placing three discs side by side? how many four-digit numbers can you represent by placing four discs in a row? how many five-digit numbers can you represent by placing five discs in a row?

   (b) Given the set of digits {1, 3, 6, 8, 9} and the condition that repetition of digits is not allowed, how many two-digit numbers can be formed? how many even two-digit numbers can be formed? how many three-digit numbers can be formed? how many odd three-digit numbers can be formed?

2. (a) Given the set of digits {4, 5, 6}, how many two-digit numbers can be formed? how many even two-digit numbers can be formed? how many odd two-digit numbers can be formed?
      Draw a tree diagram showing how many even two-digit numbers can be formed.

   (b) Given that repetition of digits is allowed, answer each question in Exercise 1(b).

3. (a) John and Tom had their birthdays guessed by a mind reader at a carnival. The mind reader wrote the month and day of each boy's birthday on the same card. Ignore leap years in answering the questions below.

How many possible guesses can the mind reader make in writing the card?

If the mind reader is told that the boys have different birthdays, how many guesses can he make?

   (b) The mind reader in Exercise 3(a) above is told that both boys were born in June.

How many possible guesses can the mind reader make in writing the card?

If the mind reader is told that the boys have different birthdays, how many guesses can he make?

4. How many four-digit numbers can be formed if only the digits 1, 2, 3, and 4 are used, if each number must begin and end with an even digit, and

   (a) if repetition of digits is not allowed?

   (b) if repetition of digits is allowed?

5. (a) In how many different ways can a student answer a multiple-choice exam, if the exam consists of five questions and each question has three possibilities which are listed as *a*, *b*, and *c*?

   (b) Answer the question in part (a), assuming that the student never makes the same lettered choice for two consecutive answers.

6. John's mother always puts in his lunch box one white-bread sandwich, one brown-bread sandwich, a piece of fruit, and a dessert. Her sandwich fillings are peanut butter, jam, egg salad, cheese, ham, and sliced chicken. For fruit, she selects a banana, an orange, an apple, or a pear. Her desserts are chocolate cake and molasses cookies.

   (a) If his mother puts a different filling in each sandwich, how many lunches can John have before he eats the same lunch twice?

   (b) If she does not always use a different filling in each sandwich, how many different lunches can John have?

In Exercises 7 and 8, Jane tosses a penny, a dime, and a quarter, in turn. We designate the result of each toss with *H* for heads and *T* for tails. Make a tree diagram that shows the results of Jane's tosses. At the end of each path, write three letters to indicate the result of the sequence of tosses. Thus, *HTH* will be at the end of one path indicating that the penny landed *H*, the dime landed *T*, and the quarter landed *H*.

7. (a) How many results are there?

   (b) In how many of the results do exactly two heads show?

8. (a) In how many of the results do three heads show?

   (b) In how many of the results do at least two heads show?

In Exercises 9–15, numbers are to be formed from the digits 0, 1, 2, 3, 4, 5, 6, 7, 8, and 9, without repetition of digits. The first digit of each number must, of course, be nonzero.

9. How many three-digit numbers can be formed starting with the digit 1?

10. How many three-digit numbers can be formed?

11. How many five-digit numbers can be formed that end with the digit 0?

12. How many five-digit numbers can be formed so that the last digit is an even number but not zero?

13. How many even five-digit numbers can be formed?

14. How many three-digit numbers can be formed to satisfy the requirement that each number is less than 300?

15. How many odd five-digit numbers can be formed with digits alternating odd and even?

11–2   ALTERNATIVE CASES PRINCIPLE

The next problem illustrates the need for separating some counting problems into various cases, called *mutually exclusive cases*, before applying the sequential counting principle.

Problem. If repetition of digits is not allowed, how many numbers can be formed by using the digits 5, 6, 7, and 8?

Solution. We can form one-digit numbers, two-digit numbers, three-digit numbers, and four-digit numbers; each of these mutually exclusive cases involves a different sequence of actions, starting with one action for one-digit numbers and ending with four actions for four-digit numbers. Using the sequential counting principle, we determine the number of results of the sequence of actions in each case below.

Cases	Count
One-digit numbers	4
Two-digit numbers	$4 \cdot 3$, or 12
Three-digit numbers	$4 \cdot 3 \cdot 2$, or 24
Four-digit numbers	$4 \cdot 3 \cdot 2 \cdot 1$, or 24

If tree diagrams are drawn, the first case has a one-stage tree, the second case a two-stage tree, the third case a three-stage tree, and the fourth case a four-stage tree. To obtain the solution of the problem, we find the *sum* of the counts listed above: $4 + 12 + 24 + 24$, or 64. Thus, 64 different numbers can be formed.

The four cases of this problem are called mutually exclusive since each case refers to a type of number entirely different from those in the other cases. In other words, the appearance of a number in one set *excludes* the possibility of its being in the set of another case. Thus, each number is a one-digit, or a two-digit, or a three-digit, or a four-digit number, but it cannot be more than one of these types at once.

We have illustrated the following fundamental principle for counting mutually exclusive cases.

ALTERNATIVE CASES PRINCIPLE

If an action can be analyzed into several mutually exclusive cases, say into cases 1, 2, 3, and so on, and if there are m possible results of performing the action in case 1, n possible results of performing the action in case 2, p possible results of performing the action in case 3, and so on, then the total number of possible results of the action is the sum of the numbers m, n, p, and so on.

Exercises

1. (a) How many numbers of three or fewer digits can be formed if only the numerals 1, 2, and 3 are used and if repetition of digits is not allowed? if repetition of digits is allowed? if no number can be greater than 200?

   (b) How many *odd* numbers can be formed using only the digits 5, 6, 7, 8 if repetition of digits is not allowed? if repetition of digits is allowed? if no number can be 700 or greater?

2. (a) If only the digits 2, 3, 6, 7, and 9 are used and if repetition of digits is allowed, how many numbers of no more than five digits can be formed?

   How many of these numbers are even?

   How many of these numbers are three-digit numbers?

   (b) Numbers are formed using any of the digits 0, 1, 2, 3, . . . , 9 but no repetition of digits is allowed.

   How many three-digit numbers can be formed?

   How many numbers formed satisfy the requirement that each number must be less than 300?

   How many three-digit numbers can be formed with digits alternating odd-even-odd or even-odd-even?

3. (a) How many different individuals can there be, each with two initials and no two with the same ordered pair of initials?

How many different members can there be in an organization if each person has three initials and no two persons have the same initials in the same order?

How many different monograms should an embroiderer prepare so that he will have a monogram for any person with either two or three initials?

(b) There are exactly four different roads from town A to town B and three from town B to town C. There are also two routes from town A to town C that bypass town B.

How many possible routes are there from A to C that bypass B?

How many possible routes are there from A to C that pass through B?

How many possible routes are there from A to C?

How many possible routes are there from A to C and back to A?

Consider a pair of dice that consists of a red die and a green die. The red die and then the green die are thrown, and the number of dots showing on the top face of each is noted.

4. Make a list that has an ordered pair representing the result of each sequence; the first member of each ordered pair will represent the number of dots showing on the red die. You should have 36 different pairs in your list.

5. In Exercise 4, how many results are there in which the total number of dots showing is 7?

6. In Exercise 4, how many results are there in which the total number of dots showing is 11?

7. In Exercise 4, how many results are there in which the total number of dots showing is 7 or 11?

8. In Exercise 4, how many results are there in which the total number of dots showing is less than or equal to 4?

Suppose that license plates for certain years always start with two letters which may be alike. The letters are followed by four numerals, which can be the digits 0, 1, 2, ..., 9. Repetition of digits is allowed. (You may give your answers with products of integers indicated instead of computed.)

9. How many different license plates can be issued if no zeros are permitted to appear between the letters and the first nonzero numeral?

10. How many different license plates can be issued without the restriction made in Exercise 9?

11. How many different license plates can be issued without the restriction made in Exercise 9 if there is no repetition of letters and no repetitions of numerals?

12. How many different license plates are available, under the conditions stated in Exercise 11 if the letters I, O, and Q are not used?

11-3 COMBINATIONS AND PERMUTATIONS

If a set S consists of the first five letters of the alphabet, then we may use set notation to indicate S:

$$S = \{a, b, c, d, e\}.$$

In this notation, *the order in which we write the elements of S is immaterial.* Thus, we could just as well indicate the elements of the set S in another order. For example, $S = \{a, c, e, b, d\}$.

In listing the elements of a set, we never display any element more than once. For example, we would never write $\{3, 3, 3\}$ for the set of digits of the number 333. Rather, we would write $\{3\}$ and say that the number 333 was formed by repeated use of the single digit 3 of the set $\{3\}$.

Consider the subsets

$$U = \{a, c, e\}, \quad V = \{c, b\}, \quad W = \{a\}$$

of the set $S = \{a, b, c, d, e\}$.

Since the subset W of S has exactly one element, we shall call it a 1-subset of S. Similarly, U is called a 3-subset and V is called a 2-subset of S, according to the following definition.

Definition of a combination

If S is a set with n elements and if T is a subset of S containing r elements, then T is called an r-subset of S. Such a set T is also called a combination of r objects from a set of n objects.

We note that an n-subset of a set of n objects is the set itself. Also, we never speak of a combination of r objects from a set of n objects unless $r \leqq n$.

Problem 1. List all possible combinations of three letters from the set S:

$$S = \{a, b, c, d\}.$$

Solution. It is helpful to use an organized procedure rather than to proceed at random. Therefore, we shall pick one letter, say a, and list all of the combinations of three letters that contain this letter.

$$\{a, b, c\} \qquad \{a, c, d\}$$
$$\{a, b, d\}$$

Notice that we did not list $\{a, c, b\}$ in the second column because the set $\{a, c, b\}$ is the same as the set $\{a, b, c\}$, which we had already listed. Now let us list the sets containing b that we have not already listed.

$$\{b, c, d\}$$

Thus, the total number of combinations of three letters from S is 4. An easy way to check is to see if we used each letter an equal number of times. In this case, each letter is used 3 times.

Sometimes we are interested in indicating a specific order for the objects of a set. For example, the outcome of a race is announced by listing the names of the participants in the order in which they finish the race. Thus, the list

Tom,   Frank,   Joe,   Archibald

indicates that Tom won the race, Frank was second, Joe was third, and Archibald was last. Such strings of elements are called *arrangements* of elements from a set.

As another example, the expressions *abcde* and *aabcb* are arrangements of five elements taken from the set $\{a, b, c, d, e, f\}$. The arrangement *abcde* is called an *arrangement of five elements without repetition,* and *aabcb* is called an *arrangement of five elements with repetition.*

Another way of designating arrangements follows the notation for *ordered pairs* of numbers. Thus, the arrangement *aabcb* may be written as (a, a, b, c, b). We call (a, a, b, c, b) an *ordered 5-tuple.* In general, if an arrangement of r elements $a_1, a_2, \ldots, a_r$ of a set is taken in the order in which we have written them, then this arrangement is designated by the *ordered r-tuple* $(a_1, a_2, \ldots, a_r)$. Two ordered r-tuples $(a_1, a_2, \ldots, a_r)$ and $(b_1, b_2, \ldots, b_r)$ of elements of a set are equal if, and only if, $a_1 = b_1$, $a_2 = b_2$, $\ldots$, $a_r = b_r$. For example, the ordered 3-tuples $(1, 2, 3)$ and $(1, 2, 3)$ are equal, but the ordered 3-tuples $(1, 2, 3)$ and $(2, 1, 3)$ are different. Each numeral for an integer consists of an ordered r-tuple of digits.

Arrangements without repetition are called permutations. In this definition, r and n are positive integers with $r \leq n$.

Definition of a permutation

A permutation of r objects from a set of n objects is an arrangement without repetition of r objects from the set of n objects.

Problem 2. List all possible permutations of three objects from the set

$$S = \{a, b, c, d\}.$$

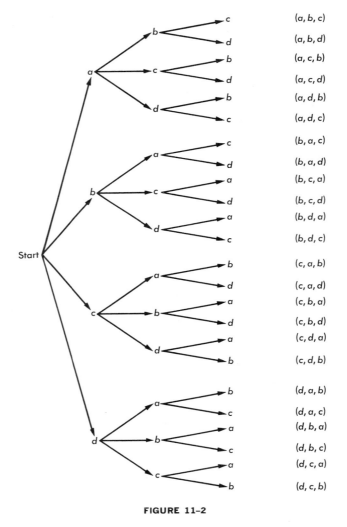

FIGURE 11–2

Solution. The tree diagram of Fig. 11–2 illustrates the three actions involved in selecting each permutation. According to the sequential

counting principle, we count the number of permutations and obtain
$4 \cdot 3 \cdot 2$, or 24.

Exercises

1. (a) In four columns, list the set of all permutations of the 3 elements of
each combination found in Problem 1 (page 492). How does your
list of 24 permutations compare with that in Problem 2 (page 494)?
   (b) List all possible combinations of two objects from the set
$T = \{w, x, y, z\}$. List all possible permutations of two objects
from T.

2. (a) Five students, Bob, Charles, Dick, Elsie, and Jane, are candidates for
membership on a committee which will have three members.

   Make a list of all possible committees.

   Make a list of all possible committees which have Bob, Dick, and one
of the girls as members.
   (b) Committees having 3 men each are to be formed from a list of 6 men
denoted by A, B, C, D, E, and F.

   Make a list of all possible committees.

   Make a list of all possible committees, given that A agrees to serve
only if E also serves.

3. (a) In this exercise, you are to form numbers with digits from the set
$\{6, 7, 8, 9\}$. Repetition of digits is not allowed.

   Make a list of all possible two-digit numbers.

   Make a list of all possible even three-digit numbers.

   Make a list of all possible even four-digit numbers in which even and
odd digits alternate.
   (b) A four-faced die can be made by writing the numbers 1, 2, 3, and 4 on
the faces of a regular tetrahedron. Two such dice are manufactured,
one painted blue and the other yellow, and both are tossed once. The
number read is that on the face which lands facing down.

   Make a list of all possible ways in which the pair of dice can land,
listing each way as an ordered pair of numbers.

   Make a list of all possible ways in which the pair of dice can land
with the sum of the numbers less than 6.

4. (a) Using the symbols H and T for heads and tails, respectively, make a
list of all possible results of tossing a penny 3 times in succession.
   (b) A one-act play has 2 parts for boys and 2 parts for girls. Make a list
of all possible casts for the play, choosing members from the following set of applicants.

$\{$Alice, Bob, Charles, Diane, Elsie, Frank, George$\}$

5. (a) Set $S = \{K, P, O, H, V\}$ is to be partitioned into two subsets. The first subset will contain two elements of S, and the second subset will contain the remaining three elements of S. For example, $\{\{K, O\}, \{P, H, V\}\}$ is one such partition. Make a list of all such partitions of S.

(b) The element V is removed from the set S, and the remaining set of four elements is partitioned into two subsets, each containing two elements. Make a list of all such partitions.

6. In a psychology experiment, a rat is placed at the entrance of a T maze, from which he runs either to the left, L, or the right, R. (See the figure.)

(a) Suppose that this experiment is performed 3 times. List the possible paths of the rat (for example, LRL, and so on).

(b) If food is always placed at L, how many of these paths could the rat take to receive food at least 2 of the 3 times?

(c) Suppose that the food is placed at L, R, and L, in turn, and answer the question in part (b).

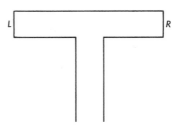

7. State whether each of the following lists is a list of combinations, a list of permutations, or a list of elements of neither type.

(a) A list of all possible ways of placing 6 people in a line for a photograph

(b) A list of all possible football teams formed from a squad of 25 men, each of whom is versatile enough to play any position

(c) A list of all possible bridge hands

(d) A list of all possible ways of placing 3 books on a shelf when 9 different books are available

(e) A list of all possible selections of 3 books from a reading list containing 9 recommended books

(f) A list of all possible ways in which 2 ordinary dice can land in 1 toss of the dice

(g) A list of all the three-digit numbers in which no digits are repeated

(h) A list, from 10 contestants, of the winners of first, second, and third prizes

11–4   FORMULAS FOR COUNTING PERMUTATIONS AND COMBINATIONS

In the problems of the preceding section, we saw that the *number* of permutations of 3 objects from a set of 4 objects is 24, and the *number* of combinations of 3 objects from a set of 4 objects is 4. It is convenient to introduce symbols for such numbers. Thus, let

$_nP_r$ denote the number of permutations of r objects from a set of n objects;

$_nC_r$ denote the number of combinations of r objects from a set of n objects.

Using this notation, we know from the preceding section that

$$_4P_3 = 24$$

and

$$_4C_3 = 4.$$

Other symbols commonly used are P_r^n and $P(n, r)$ instead of $_nP_r$; and C_r^n, $C(n, r)$, and $\binom{n}{r}$ in place of $_nC_r$.

Problem 1. Find $_nP_r$.

Solution. We are asked to find the number of permutations of r objects from a set consisting of n objects. We can imagine the r stages of a tree diagram that could be used to list all such permutations. There are n branches in the first stage; for each branch of the first stage, there are $n - 1$ branches in the second stage; for each branch of the second stage, there are $n - 2$ branches in the third stage; and so on. By the sequential counting principle, the total number of permutations of r objects from a set of n objects is

$$\overbrace{_nP_r = n \cdot (n - 1) \cdot (n - 2) \cdot \ldots}^{r \text{ factors}}$$

In the sequence that starts out

$$n, \quad n - 1, \quad n - 2, \quad n - 3, \quad n - 4, \quad \ldots,$$

the second element is $n - 1$, the third is $n - 2$, and the fifth is $n - 4$. It follows that the rth element is $n - (r - 1)$, or $n - r + 1$. Thus, the number of permutations of r objects from a set of n objects is given by the following formula.

$$_nP_r = n(n - 1)(n - 2) \cdot \ldots \cdot (n - r + 1)$$

Remember that $_nP_r$ is represented as a product of r successive integers, the largest of which is n.

For example, $_5P_3$ is a product of 3 successive integers, the largest of which is 5, that is,

$$_5P_3 = 5 \cdot 4 \cdot 3, \quad \text{or } 60.$$

Also,

$$_{10}P_4 = 10 \cdot 9 \cdot 8 \cdot 7, \quad \text{or } 5040,$$
$$_{52}P_{13} = 52 \cdot 51 \cdot 50 \cdot \ldots \cdot (52 - 13 + 1)$$

$$\underbrace{= 52 \cdot 51 \cdot 50 \cdot \ldots \cdot 40.}_{\text{13 factors}}$$

The formula for the number of permutations of n objects from a set of n objects is of particular interest. If we let $r = n$ in the formula above for $_nP_r$, then $n - r + 1 = n - n + 1$, or 1, and

$$_nP_n = n \cdot (n - 1) \cdot (n - 2) \cdot \ldots \cdot 1.$$

In other words, $_nP_n$ is the *product of the first n positive integers*.

Problem 2. Find $_5C_2$.

Solution. We can imagine the set of five objects to be $S = \{a, b, c, d, e\}$. Let us determine how $_5P_2$ and $_5C_2$ are related. The number of permutations of 2 objects from the set S is

$$_5P_2 = 5 \cdot 4, \quad \text{or } 20.$$

Note that there are two permutations of each 2-subset of S; that is, the permutations of the 2-subset $\{b, e\}$ of S are (b, e) and (e, b). Since there are $_5C_2$ 2-subsets of S and since there are two permutations of each 2-subset, there are $2 \cdot _5C_2$ permutations of two objects from the set S, that is,

$$2 \cdot _5C_2 = _5P_2$$

and

$$_5C_2 = \frac{_5P_2}{2} = \frac{20}{2}, \quad \text{or } 10.$$

Similarly, we may obtain a formula for $_nC_r$ from that for $_nP_r$ by performing a two-action procedure to count the number of permutations having r objects from a set of n objects. The first action is to select an r-subset from the set of n objects, and the second action is to form permutations of all r objects of the r-subset. There are $_nC_r$ r-subsets and $_rP_r$ permutations of the r-objects of each of these subsets. Hence, by the sequential counting principle there are

$$_nC_r \cdot {}_rP_r$$

permutations of r objects from a set of n objects. Because we know that the above product is $_nP_r$, we have the following formula for the number of combinations of r objects from a set S consisting of n objects.

$$_nC_r \cdot {}_rP_r = {}_nP_r, \quad or \quad _nC_r = \frac{_nP_r}{_rP_r}$$

For example,

$$_4C_3 = \frac{_4P_3}{_3P_3}$$

$$= \frac{4 \cdot 3 \cdot 2}{3 \cdot 2 \cdot 1}, \quad \text{or } 4.$$

$$_7C_4 = \frac{_7P_4}{_4P_4}$$

$$= \frac{7 \cdot 6 \cdot 5 \cdot 4}{4 \cdot 3 \cdot 2 \cdot 1}$$

$$= 7 \cdot 5, \quad \text{or } 35.$$

There are 4 combinations of 3 objects from a set of 4 objects.

There are 35 combinations of 4 objects from a set of 7 objects.

Exercises

Evaluate each of the following.

1. (a) $_{10}P_3$ (b) $\frac{_9P_4}{_4P_4}$

2. (a) $_9C_4$ (b) $_9C_1$

3. (a) $_9C_9$ (b) $_4P_4$

4. How many four-digit numbers can be formed if repetition of digits is not allowed and if only the numerals shown are used?
   (a) 1, 2, 3, 4?   (b) 0, 1, 2, 3?

5. (a) Answer Exercise 4(a) allowing for repetition.
   (b) Answer Exercise 4(b) allowing for repetition.

6. (a) $_8P_3$ (b) $_7P_7$

7. (a) $_{16}P_1$ (b) $_{20}C_{20}$

8. (a) $_{16}C_1$ (b) $_9C_5$

9. (a) From a set of 10 different entries in a contest, 3 are to be chosen to receive first, second, and third prize. In how many ways can these prizes be awarded?

   (b) A panel consisting of 1 girl and 2 boys is to be elected from a slate consisting of 5 girls and 10 boys. How many different panels are possible?

10. (a) How many different committees of 4 students can be formed from 8 students?

   How many of these contain one particular student A?

   How many committees include A and exclude B?

   How many include both A and B?

   How many exclude both A and B?

   (b) A small class consists of 3 boys and 5 girls.

   In how many ways can they all be seated in a row if both end seats are occupied by boys?

   In how many ways can a committee of 3 be chosen from the class?

   How many of these committees of three will contain 1 boy and 2 girls?

   How many of these committees of three will contain 3 boys?

   How many of these committees of three will contain 3 girls?

11. (a) How many committees of 4 people can be formed from a group of 10 people?

   (b) In how many ways can 6 different books be arranged on a shelf?

---

12. (a) Suppose that a penny is tossed 5 times and that the succession of results is represented by H's and T's. Determine how many different sequences of results of the 5 tosses are possible. In how many of these sequences is a head showing on both the first and last toss?

   (b) Out of a group of 10 boys and 7 girls, 3 boys and 2 girls are to be selected to represent a school. In how many ways can the selection be made?

13. (a) Given that $_nP_5 = 6(_nP_3)$, find n.

   (b) Given that $_nP_5 = 6720$, find $_nC_5$.

14. (a) In how many ways can 7 people be lined up in one row for a photograph?

   (b) In how many ways can the 7 people be lined up if one of them, say C, has to be in the middle?

   (c) How many lineups of the 7 people have C in the middle and two other people, A and B, always taking the end positions?

15. John has 3 boxes, one red, one white, and one blue. He has 9 different objects. In how many ways can he put 3 objects in each box? (Hint: This is a three-stage counting process, involving one stage for each box and using combinations at each stage.)

16. If the 3 boxes in Exercise 15 are colored red and are indistinguishable, then it makes no difference in which box John puts a particular set of 3 objects. In how many ways can he now put 3 of his 9 different objects in each box?

17. (a) In how many ways can 4 different books be arranged on a shelf?
(b) From a group of 8 students, how many different committees of 4 students can be formed?

18. (a) If there is no repetition of letters, how many three-letter arrangements can be made from the letters in the word "cloudy"?
(b) Answer part (a) allowing for repetition of letters.

19. One section of each of the eleventh grade English, algebra, and Latin courses will be meeting at 9 A.M., 11 A.M., and 1 P.M. In how many ways can a student arrange his schedule so that he can take these three courses?

20. At each of the times, 7, 7:30, 8, and 8:30 P.M., there are always three different half-hour programs on different channels: a Western, a mystery, and a musical show. No program scheduled on one channel ever appears on another channel.
(a) In how many ways can a person spend his evening hours from 7 to 9 P.M. if he watches television?
(b) In how many ways can he watch shows from 7 to 9 P.M. and never see a Western?
(c) In how many ways can he watch shows from 7 to 9 P.M. and see at least one Western?
(d) In how many ways can he watch shows from 7 to 9 P.M. and see nothing but Westerns?

21. In how many ways can 7 people line up if two of them, A and B, always stand next to each other?

22. From a set of books consisting of 3 different novels and 5 different biographies, 2 novels and 3 biographies are selected.
(a) How many selections are there?
(b) In how many different ways can the books selected be lined up on a shelf?

---

23. (a) Find the sum $_4C_4 + {_4C_3} + {_4C_2} + {_4C_1}$.
(b) Interpret the sum in part (a) in terms of counting the number of nonempty subsets of a set of 4 objects.
(c) Make a tree diagram to check your answer to part (b), using the set $\{a, b, c, d\}$. Use four branching stages, one for each element, writing a if a is to be a member of the subset, and writing $\bar{a}$ if a is not to be a member, and so on.

24. The circular disc shown at the right is to be pinned through its center to a board and spun around this center pin. The numbers 1, 2, 3, 4 are to be assigned to the four points marked with crosses. In how many ways can this be done? (Hint: The assignments (1, 2, 3, 4) and (2, 3, 4, 1) produce the same effect when the disc is spun.)

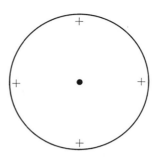

25. Consider that the *rim* of the disc in Exercise 24 represents a bracelet that has no clasp, and the points marked with crosses indicate the position of 4 round beads of different colors. How many possible bracelets are there? (Hint: Remember to turn the bracelet over.)

26. In how many arrangements can 6 people be seated in 6 chairs placed at a round table
(a) if one particular position is designated as head of the table?
(b) without the restriction in part (a)?

11–5   FACTORIALS

The formulas for $_nP_r$ and $_nC_r$ may be written in a simpler way if we use the notation of factorials.

THE NOTATION OF FACTORIALS

For each positive integer n, the product of the first n positive integers is called n factorial and is denoted by n!.

$$n! = n(n - 1)(n - 2) \cdot \ldots \cdot 2 \cdot 1$$

For example,

$$1! = 1,$$
$$2! = 2 \cdot 1, \quad \text{or } 2,$$
$$3! = 3 \cdot 2 \cdot 1, \quad \text{or } 6,$$
$$6! = 6 \cdot 5 \cdot 4 \cdot 3 \cdot 2 \cdot 1, \quad \text{or } 720.$$

The factorial numbers grow large very rapidly as we extend this list. For example,

$$10! = 3,628,800.$$

If we know the value of the factorial of an integer, we can quickly compute the value of the factorial of the next integer. For example,

$$7! = 7 \cdot 6 \cdot 5 \cdot 4 \cdot 3 \cdot 2 \cdot 1$$
$$= 7 \cdot 6!$$
$$= 7 \cdot 720, \quad \text{or} \quad 5040.$$

In other words,

$$(n + 1)! = (n + 1) \cdot n!$$

for every positive integer n.

The formula for $_nP_r$ can be expressed in factorials. We recall that

$$_nP_n = n!,$$

but if $r < n$, then

$$_nP_r = n(n - 1)(n - 2) \cdot \ldots \cdot (n - r + 1),$$

$$_nP_r = \frac{n(n - 1)(n - 2) \cdot \ldots \cdot (n - r + 1)(n - r)(n - r - 1) \cdot \ldots \cdot 2 \cdot 1}{(n - r)(n - r - 1) \cdot \ldots \cdot 2 \cdot 1},$$

$$_nP_r = \frac{n!}{(n - r)!}.$$

For example,

$$_7P_2 = \frac{7!}{5!} = 42.$$

In evaluating $_7P_2$, we do not compute 7! and 5! and then divide 7! by 5!. Instead, we proceed in the following way.

$$\frac{7!}{5!} = \frac{7 \cdot 6 \cdot 5 \cdot 4 \cdot 3 \cdot 2 \cdot 1}{5 \cdot 4 \cdot 3 \cdot 2 \cdot 1}$$

$$\frac{7!}{5!} = 7 \cdot 6$$

In general,

$$_nP_r = \frac{n!}{(n - r)!} = n(n - 1) \cdot \ldots \cdot (n - r + 1).$$

The formula

$$_nP_r = \frac{n!}{(n - r)!}$$

is valid as long as $r < n$. If we let $r = n$ in this formula, we obtain the equation

$$_nP_n = \frac{n!}{(n - n)!},$$

$$\text{or } _nP_n = \frac{n!}{0!}.$$

We can define 0! so that the equation above is true. Since $_nP_n = n!$, we define

$$0! = 1.$$

With 0! defined in this way, the formula

$$_nP_r = \frac{n!}{(n - r)!}$$

is true for every pair n, r of positive integers, provided that $r \leq n$.

We can also find a formula in terms of factorials for the number of combinations of r objects from a set of n objects. From the preceding section,

$$_nC_r = \frac{_nP_r}{_rP_r}.$$

Hence,

$$_nC_r = \frac{n!/(n - r)!}{r!},$$

or

$$_nC_r = \frac{n!}{r!(n - r)!}.$$

This is called the *symmetric form* of the formula for $_nC_r$. It is valid for every pair r, n of positive integers when $r \leq n$. For example,

$$_7C_2 = \frac{7!}{2!5!}.$$

Thus,

$$_7C_2 = \frac{7 \cdot 6}{2 \cdot 1}, \text{ or } 21.$$

The equation $_nC_r = {_nC_{n-r}}$ is verified by using the symmetric form of the formula for $_nC_r$.

$$_nC_r = \frac{n!}{r!(n-r)!}$$

$$_nC_{n-r} = \frac{n!}{(n-r)!(n-(n-r))!}, \quad \text{or} \quad \frac{n!}{(n-r)!r!}$$

Hence,

$$_nC_r = {_nC_{n-r}}.$$

Thus,

$$_{90}C_{88} = {_{90}C_2}, \quad \text{or } 4005.$$

For convenience, we *define* $_nC_0$ to be equal to $_nC_n$. Since $_nC_n = 1$, we have

$$_nC_0 = 1$$

by definition. Therefore, the formula

$$_nC_r = {_nC_{n-r}}$$

is true for every positive integer n and every nonnegative integer r with $r \leq n$.

Exercises

Evaluate each of the following.

1. (a) $\dfrac{6!}{2!3!}$

   (b) $\dfrac{8!}{7!}$

2. (a) $_{1000}C_0$

   (b) $_{1000}C_{999}$

Simplify of each the following.

3. (a) $\dfrac{300!262!}{260!302!}$

   (b) $8! - 7!$

4. (a) $_8C_6 \cdot {_6C_4} \cdot {_4C_2} \cdot {_2C_2}$

   (b) $_7C_5 \cdot {_5C_3} \cdot {_3C_1}$

5. (a) $\dfrac{(n+3)!}{n!}$

   (b) $(n - r - 2)!(n - r - 1)(n - r)$

6. (a) $\dfrac{(n-2)!}{n!}$

   (b) $_nC_{n-2}$

7. (a) $\dfrac{(2n)!}{n!}$

   (b) $\dfrac{(3n)!}{n!}$

8. (a) Given that $_nC_7 = {_nC_5}$, find the value of $_nC_9$.

(b) Given that $_nC_{12} = {_nC_8}$, find $_nC_{17}$ and $_{22}C_n$.

9. (a) Show that $_nC_{r-1} + {_nC_r} = {_{n+1}C_r}$.

(b) Given the following, find n.

$$\frac{n!}{(n-3)!} = 210$$

10. (a) Show that

$$\frac{1}{n!} + \frac{1}{(n+1)!} = \frac{n+2}{(n+1)!}.$$

(b) Show that

$$_{n+1}C_{r+1} = {_nC_r} + {_nC_{r+1}}.$$

---

11. In how many ways can 8 different novels be arranged on a shelf?

12. From the set $\{1, 2, 3, 4, 5, 6\}$, in how many ways can one choose two numbers whose sum is even?

13. In how many ways can 5 students,

George, John, Charles, Mary, Joanne,

stand in a line in which boys and girls alternate?

14. Answer the question in Exercise 13 for 6 students, supposing that another girl, Ruth, joins the group.

---

15. In how many ways can 8 different keys be put on a key ring which is made so that the keys slide around the complete ring?

16. Remembering that a number is divisible by 9 only if the sum of its digits is divisible by 9, and given that repetition of digits is allowed, how many three-digit numbers, each divisible by 9, can be formed if only the numbers 0, 1, 3, 6, 8, 9 are used?

17. Given n points in a plane, no three of which are collinear, how many lines can be drawn joining the points in pairs?

18. Derive the formula

$$_nC_r = {_nC_{n-r}}$$

by considering the lists of objects for which each side of the equality provides the count.

11-6   THE BINOMIAL THEOREM

In this section, we shall show how our counting techniques can be used to derive an important formula of algebra. This formula is used to raise a binomial, such as $x + y$, to a positive integral power. For example, we may check by multiplication that each of the following formulas is true.

$$(x + y)^2 = x^2 + 2xy + y^2$$
$$(x + y)^3 = x^3 + 3x^2y + 3xy^2 + y^3$$
$$(x + y)^4 = x^4 + 4x^3y + 6x^2y^2 + 4xy^3 + y^4$$
$$(x + y)^5 = x^5 + 5x^4y + 10x^3y^2 + 10x^2y^3 + 5xy^4 + y^5$$

The coefficients of the various terms appearing on the right side of each equation above are called *binomial coefficients.* Thus, the last equation has binomial coefficients

$$1, \quad 5, \quad 10, \quad 10, \quad 5, \quad 1,$$

in that order. Note the symmetric way in which the numbers appear in this 6-tuple.

For each positive integer n,

$$(x + y)^n = \overbrace{(x + y) \cdot (x + y) \cdot \ldots \cdot (x + y)}^{n \text{ factors}}.$$

Using the distributive law, we can multiply out the right side of this equation in the following way. First, select an x or y from each of the n binomial factors and multiply the n chosen quantities together. Then make another selection of an x or a y from each of the n binomial factors and multiply them together, and continue this process until you have made your selections in every possible way. Finally, add together all the products so formed. The result will be a formula for $(x + y)^n$.

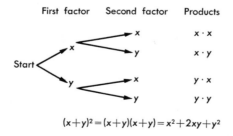

$$(x+y)^2 = (x+y)(x+y) = x^2 + 2xy + y^2$$

FIGURE 11-3

The tree diagram of Fig. 11–3 illustrates the above procedure for finding $(x + y)^2$. Hence,

$$(x + y)^2 = x^2 + 2xy + y^2.$$

We find $(x + y)^3$ in a similar way, as shown by the tree diagram in Fig. 11–4.

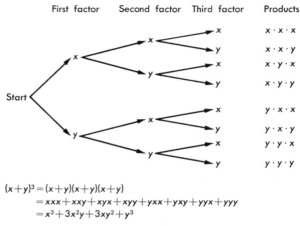

$$(x+y)^3 = (x+y)(x+y)(x+y)$$
$$= xxx + xxy + xyx + xyy + yxx + yxy + yyx + yyy$$
$$= x^3 + 3x^2y + 3xy^2 + y^3$$

FIGURE 11–4

The products occurring in the last column of Fig. 11–4 are of four different types:

$$x^3, \quad x^2y, \quad xy^2, \quad y^3.$$

Hence, the expanded form of $(x + y)^3$ is a sum of terms of these types; the number of terms of each type is the coefficient of the term in the sum. A method of finding the binomial coefficients of the expanded form of $(x + y)^3$ without the aid of a tree diagram is indicated in the table. In this table and throughout the rest of the chapter, we shall use the symbol

$$\binom{n}{r} \quad instead \; of \quad {}_nC_r.$$

We recall that by definition, ${}_nC_0 = 1$. Hence, by definition, $\binom{n}{0} = 1$.

$(x + y)(x + y)(x + y)$		
Type of term	Procedure	Number of ways
x^3	Select x from every factor, y from no factor.	1, or $\binom{3}{0}$
x^2y	Select y from exactly one factor.	$\binom{3}{1}$
xy^2	Select y from exactly two factors.	$\binom{3}{2}$
y^3	Select y from every factor.	$\binom{3}{3}$

According to the above table,

$$(x + y)^3 = \binom{3}{0}x^3 + \binom{3}{1}x^2y + \binom{3}{2}xy^2 + \binom{3}{3}y^3.$$

This result agrees with our previous formula for $(x + y)^3$, since

$$\binom{3}{0} = 1, \qquad\qquad \binom{3}{1} = \frac{3}{1}, \text{ or } 3,$$

$$\binom{3}{2} = \frac{3 \cdot 2}{2 \cdot 1}, \text{ or } 3, \qquad\qquad \binom{3}{3} = \frac{3 \cdot 2 \cdot 1}{3 \cdot 2 \cdot 1}, \text{ or } 1.$$

The pattern for the expansion of

$$(x + y)^n$$

is suggested by this example. We state it in the form of a theorem.

THE BINOMIAL THEOREM

For every pair x, y of real numbers and every positive integer n,

$$(x + y)^n =$$

$$\binom{n}{0}x^n + \binom{n}{1}x^{n-1}y + \binom{n}{2}x^{n-2}y^2 + \cdots + \binom{n}{k}x^{n-k}y^k + \cdots$$

$$+ \binom{n}{n-2}x^2y^{n-2} + \binom{n}{n-1}xy^{n-1} + \binom{n}{n}y^n.$$

The expansion above for $(x + y)^n$ is easy to remember if we keep in mind the succession of terms. Each term has the form

$$\binom{n}{k}x^{n-k}y^k.$$

To obtain all the terms, we let k assume the successive values 0, 1, 2, $\ldots$, n. Note that the sum of the degrees of x and y in each term is n since $(n - k) + k = n$.

Problem 1. Expand

$$(2a + 3b)^3$$

by the binomial theorem and simplify the terms of the expansion.

Solution. The expressions $2a$ and $3b$ can be substituted for x and y in the formula for the binomial expansion. We have

$$(2a + 3b)^3 = \binom{3}{0}(2a)^3 + \binom{3}{1}(2a)^2(3b) + \binom{3}{2}(2a)(3b)^2 + \binom{3}{3}(3b)^3$$

$$= 1(8a^3) + 3(4a^2)(3b) + 3(2a)(9b^2) + 1(27b^3)$$

$$= 8a^3 + 36a^2b + 54ab^2 + 27b^3.$$

Problem 2. Expand $(3c^2 - d)^4$ and simplify.

Solution. We write $3c^2 - d$ as $3c^2 + (-d)$ so that $3c^2$ can be the x of the formula and $-d$ can be the y. Then

$$(3c^2 - d)^4 = \binom{4}{0}(3c^2)^4 + \binom{4}{1}(3c^2)^3(-d) + \binom{4}{2}(3c^2)^2(-d)^2$$

$$+ \binom{4}{3}(3c^2)(-d)^3 + \binom{4}{4}(-d)^4$$

$$= 1(81c^8) + 4(27c^6)(-d) + 6(9c^4)(d^2)$$

$$+ 4(3c^2)(-d^3) + 1(d^4)$$

$$= 81c^8 - 108c^6d + 54c^4d^2 - 12c^2d^3 + d^4.$$

Exercises

Use the binomial theorem to expand each expression, and then simplify.

1. (a) $(x - y)^8$ (b) $(p - q)^5$
2. (a) $(a + b)^7$ (b) $(x + y)^6$
3. (a) $(1 + x)^5$ (b) $(1 - x)^5$
4. (a) $(1 - .02)^3$ (b) $(1 + .01)^4$
5. (a) $(1 + x^2)^3$ (b) $(1 - x^2)^4$
6. (a) $(3x - 2y)^3$ (b) $(4x - 3y)^4$
7. (a) In the simplification of the expansion of $(2a - b)^8$, the exponent of b in a particular term is 3.
   Is this term the third or fourth in the expansion?
   What is the complete term including its sign?
   Write the complete term of the expansion which has 6 as the exponent of b.
   (b) In the simplification of the expansion $(3a - 2b)^7$, the exponent of b in a particular term is 4.
   Is this term the fourth or fifth in the expansion?
   What is the complete term with its sign?
   Write the complete term of the expansion which has 6 as the exponent of b.

Without writing out the entire expansion in any of the following cases, find the specified terms in their simplest forms.

8. (a) The fifth term of the expansion of $(7x - 2y)^6$
   (b) The third term of the expansion of $(2c + \frac{1}{2}d)^7$

9. (a) The term in the expansion of

$$\left(x - \frac{1}{x}\right)^8$$

   which does not contain an x.
   (b) Write the term in the expansion of

$$\left(\frac{1}{x^2} - 2x^2\right)^6$$

   which does not contain an x.

10. (a) Write the two middle terms in the expansion of

$$\left(\frac{2}{3}a - \frac{3}{2}b\right)^7 .$$

   (b) Write the two middle terms in the expansion of

$$\left(\frac{2}{5}x - \frac{2}{7}y\right)^9 .$$

Write and simplify each of the following.

11. (a) The first three terms in the expansion of $(x\sqrt{x} + 2)^5$
   (b) The first five terms in the expansion of $(3 - 2\sqrt{x})^7$

12. (a) Show that the first four terms of the binomial expansion can be written in the form

$$(x + y)^n = x^n + \frac{n}{1}x^{n-1}y + \frac{n(n-1)}{1 \cdot 2}x^{n-2}y^2$$

$$+ \frac{n(n-1)(n-2)}{1 \cdot 2 \cdot 3}x^{n-3}y^3 + \cdots$$

   (b) Write the next two terms of the expansion begun in part (a).

13. (a) Use the first three terms of the binomial expansion of $(1 - .01)^5$ to find an approximation of $(.99)^5$.
   (b) Compute an approximation of $(1.04)^6$.
   (c) Check your approximations in parts (a) and (b) by using logarithms.

11-7 PASCAL'S TRIANGLE

We are now in a position to explain the symmetry noted in the set of binomial coefficients of the expansion of $(x + y)^n$. In this expansion, the coefficients, in the order in which they appear in the binomial theorem, are

$$\binom{n}{0}, \ \binom{n}{1}, \ \binom{n}{2}, \ \binom{n}{3}, \ \ldots, \ \binom{n}{n-3}, \ \binom{n}{n-2}, \ \binom{n}{n-1}, \ \binom{n}{n}.$$

The first coefficient is equal to the last; the second is equal to the next to the last; the third is equal to the third from the last; and so on. Remember that

$$\binom{n}{k} = \binom{n}{n-k}$$

for every value of k, with $0 \leq k \leq n$.

The symmetry of the binomial coefficients is often displayed in the form given below.

$(x + y)^1$ $\qquad\qquad\qquad \binom{1}{0} \quad \binom{1}{1}$

$(x + y)^2$ $\qquad\qquad \binom{2}{0} \quad \binom{2}{1} \quad \binom{2}{2}$

$(x + y)^3$ $\qquad\quad \binom{3}{0} \quad \binom{3}{1} \quad \binom{3}{2} \quad \binom{3}{3}$

$(x + y)^4$ $\qquad \binom{4}{0} \quad \binom{4}{1} \quad \binom{4}{2} \quad \binom{4}{3} \quad \binom{4}{4}$

$(x + y)^5$ $\quad \binom{5}{0} \quad \binom{5}{1} \quad \binom{5}{2} \quad \binom{5}{3} \quad \binom{5}{4} \quad \binom{5}{5}$

If we enter the value of each combination symbol in the array above and place a 1 at the top of the array, we obtain the triangular array started below. This infinite triangular array of numbers is called *Pascal's triangle* in honor of the French mathematician and philosopher Blaise Pascal (1623–1662).

```
                  1
               1     1
            1     2     1
         1     3     3     1
      1     4     6     4     1
   1     5    10    10     5     1
   _     _     _     _     _     _     _
```

If you look at the simplified form of the binomial expansions in Problems 1 and 2 on pages 509 and 510, you will see that the simplified coefficients do not exhibit the symmetry of Pascal's triangle of binomial coefficients. In Problem 1, for example, the coefficients of this expansion lack symmetry because the coefficients 2 and 3 of the expressions $2a$ and $3b$ appear in the expansion in various powers.

Exercises

1. (a) Use Pascal's triangle to obtain the binomial expansion of $(2a + 3b)^4$. Simplify the resulting expression.
   (b) Use Pascal's triangle to obtain the binomial expansion of $(2a - b)^5$ and simplify the resulting expression.
2. (a) Obtain the binomial expansion of $(x - 2y)^5$ and simplify.
   (b) Obtain the binomial expansion of $(x + 2y)^4$ and simplify.
3. (a) Given a principal of \$100 invested at compound interest at the yearly rate of 4%, with interest compounded quarterly, use the binomial theorem to find the amount of money in the account at the end of 1 year. (Hint: At the end of the first quarter-year, the amount is $100(1 + .01)$; after the second quarter-year, it is $100(1 + .01)^2$; and so on.)
   (b) Expand $\left(x + \dfrac{1}{x}\right)^3$.

---

4. By evaluating each of the binomial symbols, show that the equation

$$\binom{n + 1}{r} = \binom{n}{r - 1} + \binom{n}{r}$$

is true for every integer $n > 1$ and every integer r, with $1 \leqq r \leqq n$.
5. Use the results of Exercise 4 to extend the triangle in the text to include the row of coefficients for $(x + y)^8$.

---

6. (a) Use the binomial expansion of $(1 + 1)^n$ to show that if n is a positive integer, then

$$2^n = \binom{n}{0} + \binom{n}{1} + \binom{n}{2} + \cdots + \binom{n}{n}.$$

(b) Since $\binom{n}{0} = 1$, the expression

$$\binom{n}{1} + \binom{n}{2} + \binom{n}{3} + \cdots + \binom{n}{n} = 2^n - 1$$

is equivalent to the equation in part (a). Explain how the equation immediately above gives a formula for the total number of nonempty subsets of a set of n objects.

(c) Test the formula of part (b) by listing the nonempty subsets of each of the following sets: $\{a\}$, $\{a, b\}$, $\{a, b, c\}$, and $\{a, b, c, d\}$.

7. (a) Use the binomial theorem to expand $(1 - 1)^n$ to show that

$$\binom{n}{0} - \binom{n}{1} + \binom{n}{2} - \binom{n}{3} + \cdots + (-1)^n \binom{n}{n} = 0.$$

(b) Test the formula in part (a) for several rows of Pascal's triangle.

KEY IDEAS AND KEY WORDS

There are two fundamental counting principles.

Sequential counting principle

Given that two or more actions are performed in a definite order, that the first action produces m possible results, and that for each of these results, the second action produces n possible results, and that for each of these results, the third action produces p results, and so on, then the number of possible results of this sequence of actions is the product of the numbers m, n, p, and so on.

Alternative cases principle

If an action can be analyzed into several mutually exclusive cases, say into cases 1, 2, 3, and so on, and if there are m possible results of performing the action in case 1, n possible results of performing the action in case 2, p possible results of performing the action in case 3, and so on, then the total number of possible results of the action is the sum of the numbers m, n, p, and so on.

A subset T of a set S with n elements is called an **r-subset** of S if T contains r elements. Subset T is also called a **combination** of r-objects from a set of n objects. The symbols

$$_nC_r \quad \text{and} \quad \binom{n}{r}$$

are used to denote the **number of combinations** of r objects from a set of n objects.

A **permutation** of r objects from a set S of n objects is an arrangement without repetition of r objects from S. The symbol $_nP_r$ denotes the **number of permutations** of r objects from a set of n objects.

If we use the **factorial notation**

$$n! = n(n-1)(n-2) \cdot \ldots \cdot 2 \cdot 1,$$

we can obtain the following formulas.

$$_nP_r = n(n-1)(n-2) \cdot \ldots \cdot (n-r+1) = \frac{n!}{(n-r)!}$$

$$_nC_r = \frac{_nP_r}{_rP_r} = \frac{n!}{r!(n-r)!}$$

$$_nC_r = {_nC_{n-r}}$$

The **binomial theorem** states that the equation

$$(x+y)^n = \binom{n}{0}x^n + \binom{n}{1}x^{n-1}y + \cdots + \binom{n}{k}x^{n-k}y^k + \cdots + \binom{n}{n}y^n$$

is true for all real numbers x and y and every positive integer n.

CHAPTER REVIEW

In Exercises 1–9, evaluate each expression.

1. $\dfrac{1000!}{988!}$

2. $_{200}C_{198}$

3. $\dbinom{5}{4}\dbinom{10}{8}$

4. $_{10}P_3$

5. $\dfrac{8!}{2!6!}$

6. $_{1000}C_{1000}$

7. $\dfrac{100!}{2!98!}$

8. $\dbinom{27}{0}$

9. $\dbinom{107}{1}$

10. (a) How many committees of 2 people can be formed from a group of 10?
   (b) How many committees of 2 or more people can be formed from a group of 10?

11. How many three-digit numbers can be formed if numerals from the set $\{0, 1, 2, 3, 4\}$ are used and
   (a) if no repetition of digits is allowed?
   (b) if repetition is allowed?
   (c) if repetition is allowed and the numbers must be even integers?

12. (a) From a collection of 6 novels and 5 nonfiction books, how many different selections of 2 novels and 3 nonfiction books can be made?
   (b) In how many ways can your selection of books be arranged on a shelf if the novels are separated from the nonfiction books?
   (c) In how many ways can your selection be arranged on the shelf if the restriction of part (b) is removed?

Use the binomial theorem to expand each of the following, and then simplify.

13. $(2x + 5y)^3$

14. $(1 - x)^4$

15. $(x - y)^7$

16. $(2x + 3y)^4$

17. $\left(\dfrac{x}{y} - 1\right)^5$

18. $(2x + y)^4$

19. $\left(3x - \dfrac{1}{2}y\right)^5$

20. $\left(\dfrac{a}{2} - \dfrac{b}{3}\right)^4$

21. $\left(x + \dfrac{1}{2}y\right)^5$

22. $\left(\dfrac{1}{2}t + \dfrac{1}{3}v\right)^4$

23. $(x + \sqrt{y})^{10}$

24. $(a - 2b)^5$

Write and simplify each of the following.

25. The fourth term in the expansion of $(2x - 3y^2)^8$

26. The term of the expansion of $[x - (2/x)]^6$ which does not contain an x

27. The second term of $(3x + 2y)^5$

28. The third term of $(\frac{1}{2}x + y)^6$

29. The middle term of $(x^2 - y^2)^4$

30. The fifth term of $(2 - 3t)^7$

31. The sixth term of $(3\sqrt{x} + \sqrt[5]{y})^5$

CHAPTER TEST

1. Evaluate $\dfrac{5! + 4!}{6!}$.

2. Evaluate $_{20}C_{17}$.

3. Evaluate $_4C_0 \cdot {}_3C_2 + {}_4C_1 \cdot {}_3C_1 + {}_4C_2 \cdot {}_3C_0$.

4, Express the following as a quotient with factorials only.

$$_{11}C_4 \cdot {}_7C_3 \cdot {}_4C_2 \cdot {}_2C_2$$

5. How many three-digit numbers can be formed if only numerals from the set $\{1, 2, 3, 4\}$ are used and if
   (a) repetition of numerals is not allowed?
   (b) repetition is allowed?

6. If 3 girls and 4 boys are lined up in a row for a photograph, how many arrangements are possible? In how many of these arrangements do boys and girls alternate?

7. Using the binomial theorem, expand and simplify $(x^2 - 2y)^4$.

8. Find the coefficient of y^6 in the expansion of $(5x - 2y)^7$ and simplify.

CHAPTER 12

Probability

Objectives . . .

- To relate the mathematical definition of probability to our common experience.
- To apply probability theory to the binomial distribution.
- To define the concept of dependent and independent events.
- To apply probability concepts to application in business and science.

Conversation is sprinkled with statements such as "Smith will probably be elected mayor," "Chances are good that today will be another hot one," and "It's a toss-up between the two teams." In the first two statements, the speaker feels that a particular outcome, while not guaranteed, is more likely to happen than not. The third statement indicates that the speaker has no such intuition concerning what may happen.

In many instances, more precise statements about outcomes can be made. For example, suppose that the letter A is painted on each of five faces of a cube and the letter B is painted on the sixth face. If the cube is rolled on a tabletop, then it is far more likely that an A, rather than a B, will appear on top when the cube stops rolling. The fact that there are five chances out of six for an A to be on top may be translated into the following mathematical statement: The probability of an A is $\frac{5}{6}$.

Problem 1. An ordinary die is rolled once. (a) What is the probability of a 3 on the top face of the die? (b) What is the probability of a number less than or equal to 3 on the top face?

Solution. The faces of an ordinary die are numbered 1 through 6. In a roll of the die, it seems natural to expect that one particular face is as likely to appear on top as any other face. Of these *six* equally weighted possibilities, just *one* leads to the case of a 3 on top. Thus, for part (a), we say that the probability of a 3 is $\frac{1}{6}$.

The number on the top face will be less than or equal to 3 if it is either a 1, 2 or a 3. Thus, the probability for part (b) is $\frac{3}{6}$, or $\frac{1}{2}$.

Problem 2. An urn contains 100 balls which differ only in color. Of these 100 balls, 75 are red and 25 are white. One ball is drawn from the urn. (a) What is the probability that the ball drawn from the urn is red? (b) What is the probability that the ball drawn is white?

Solution. There is an equal chance that any one of the 100 balls will be selected from the urn. Because there are 75 red balls and 25 white balls, 75 of these cases will result in a red ball being drawn and 25 in a white ball being drawn. Hence, the answers to (a) and (b) are $\frac{75}{100}$, or $\frac{3}{4}$, and $\frac{25}{100}$, or $\frac{1}{4}$, respectively.

Problem 3. From a set of four discs numbered 1, 2, 3, and 4, respectively, two discs are selected at random and placed side by side to form a two-digit number. (a) What is the probability that the discs selected will form the two-digit number 32? (b) What is the probability that they will form a two-digit number which does not contain the digit 2?

Solution. This problem differs from the first two problems in that a set of equally weighted outcomes is not immediately apparent. We select two discs from the given four discs and place the two that are selected side by side. The phrase *at random* suggests that we consider all such possible selections as equally likely. From the counting principles of the last chapter, we know that there are $4 \cdot 3$, or 12, ordered pairs of discs that could be so presented. Only one of these pairs would result in the two-digit number 32, so we say that the probability of this result is $\frac{1}{12}$. In part (b), several of the pairs would not contain the digit 2 (for example, 34, 41, 14, and so on). Resorting again to elementary counting practices, we see that $3 \cdot 2$, or 6, of the pairs do *not* contain the digit 2. Thus, the answer to the question in part (b) is $\frac{6}{12}$, or $\frac{1}{2}$.

Exercises

Analyze each of the following problems in a way that will enable you to give the same weight to each outcome of a set of all possible outcomes. Then determine the number of equally likely cases that lead to the correct result.

In Exercises 1–3 a green die and a red die are each rolled once and their top faces noted. Make a table of the 36 possible outcomes, writing each outcome as an ordered pair, the first number of the pair being the number of dots on the top face of the green die, the second number of the pair, the number of dots on the top face of the red die. Arrange the pairs in a rectangular array, the first row containing all pairs with 1 as the first number, the second row with pairs having 2 as the first number, etc.

1. (a) What is the probability of a 6 on the top face of each die?

(b) What is the probability of "snake eyes," that is, of a 1 on the top face of each die?

2. (a) What is the probability of a 5 on the top face of the red die and a 6 on the green die?

(b) What is the probability of a 5 on the top face of one die and a 6 on the other?

3. (a) What is the probability of a total of 11 on the two top faces?

(b) What is the probability of a total of 7 on the two top faces?

4. A nickel and a dime are each tossed once and their top faces noted. Make a list showing all possible outcomes, writing them as ordered pairs, the first number of the pair being the nickel's top face.

(a) What is the probability of heads on both coins?

(b) What is the probability of tails on both coins?

5. (a) Suppose that a card is drawn from a well-shuffled bridge deck containing 52 cards. What is the probability of an ace? a spade? the ace of spades?

(b) Suppose that a card is drawn from a well-shuffled bridge deck from which the red aces and red queens have been removed. What is the probability of an ace? a heart? the queen of spades?

6. (a) An ordinary die is painted and the numbers changed so that two opposite faces bear a 1, two other opposite faces bear a 2, and the remaining faces bear a 3. If the die is rolled once, what is the probability of a 2 on the top face? of either a 1 or a 2?

(b) On a trick die, the face that ordinarily bears a 1 has a 6 painted on it, but the other faces are unchanged. If the die is rolled once, what is the probability of an odd number on the top face? of an even number?

7. (a) From a set of five discs numbered 1, 2, 3, 4, 5, respectively, one disc is selected at random and the number on its face recorded. The disc is then returned to the set. Following the same procedure, a second selection is made and a two-digit number is recorded. What is the probability of the two-digit number 41 being recorded? What is the probability of a two-digit *even* number being recorded?

(b) There are four roads connecting towns A and B and three roads connecting towns B and C. In addition, there are two roads which bypass B to connect A and C. If a person selects a route, at random, to get from A to C, what is the probability of a route that bypasses B?

8. (a) From a set of nine discs numbered from 1 to 9, one disc is selected at random. What is the probability of a prime number on the disc? (Note: 1 is not considered to be a prime number.) What is the probability of an odd number on the disc? of a multiple of 3 as the number on the disc?

(b) From a set of six discs numbered from 1 to 6, two discs are selected at random and placed side by side to form a two-digit number. What is the probability of an *odd* two-digit number? of a two-digit number less than 30? of a two-digit number such that the sum of its digits is 7?

12–2   EVENTS IN FINITE PROBABILITY SPACES WITH EQUIPROBABLE WEIGHTS

Each of the problems in the first section concerns an experiment that is performed with a set of objects. In the problems on pages 519 and 520, a die is rolled, a ball is drawn from an urn, and two discs are selected and placed side by side. Each experiment results in a finite set of possible outcomes. We are willing to give equal weight to each of these outcomes, that is, we agree that the set with which we are working is a set of equally likely outcomes. A set of outcomes in which equal weight is assigned to each outcome is called a *finite probability space with equiprobable weights*. It is customary to call the outcomes *points* of the space. Thus, the space in Problem 1 on page 519 has 6 equally weighted points and the space in Problem 3 on page 520 has 12 such points, each of which is an ordered pair of numbers.

Probability questions arising from such experiments concern various *events*, such as *top face* 3 or *top face a number less than or equal to* 3. In this terminology, events are *subsets* of the probability space of the experiment. Thus, in Problem 1 on page 519, the event *top face* 3 is the subset $\{3\}$ of the probability space, and the event *top face less than or equal to* 3 is the subset $\{1, 2, 3\}$. The numbers we gave as *probabilities* for these two events were $\frac{1}{6}$ and $\frac{3}{6}$, or $\frac{1}{2}$, respectively. These numbers are ratios of the number of points in the corresponding event to the total number of points in the space.

Definition of the probability of an event

In an experiment, if S is the finite probability space with equiprobable weights and E is a subset of S, then we may define the probability of an event E, denoted by P(E), in the following manner.

$$P(E) = \frac{\text{number of points in } E}{\text{number of points in } S}$$

When we attempt to answer a probability question, we first specify the probability space. This enables us to count the total number of equally likely outcomes, or points, of the space, and the number of points in various subsets of this space. Since E is a subset of S, it follows from the definition that the probability of an event is a number between 0 and 1. If E is the space S, we have $P(E) = 1$, but if E is the empty set, then $P(E) = 0$. As an example of probability 1 or 0, consider the toss of a fake coin with heads on both sides; what is the probability of a head? of a tail?

Exercises

In the following exercises be sure *first* to specify the probability space.

1. (a) Using ordered triples and denoting the coordinates by the symbols H or T, list the 8 equally likely outcomes of an experiment in which 3 pennies are tossed. What is the probability of 3 heads? 2 heads and 1 tail? 1 head and 2 tails? no heads?

    (b) An urn contains 100 balls, of which 20 are white, 20 green, and 60 red. A set of 2 balls is drawn from the urn. What is the probability of drawing 2 green balls? 1 green ball and 1 red ball? 2 balls which are not green? 2 balls of different color?

2. (a) Two girls and three boys are lined up in a row for a picture. If each arrangement has equiprobable weight, what is the probability that the boys and girls alternate? (Hint: Let points of S be permutations of 5 individuals out of a group of 5 people.)

    (b) All possible numbers having one or two digits are formed from the digits 1, 2, 3, and 4, and no digits are repeated. Each resulting number is written on a separate disc. From the collection of discs, one disc is drawn at random. What is the probability of a digit 3 in the number on the disc selected?

3. (a) A set of 2 cards is drawn at random from a deck of 52 cards. How many possibilities are there for such a draw? What is the probability of a draw of 2 jacks? What is the probability of a draw with 1 jack and 1 queen?

    (b) From a group of 3 girls and 4 boys, a committee of two members is to be chosen. If each committee has equiprobable weight, what is the probability of a committee consisting of a boy and a girl? 2 boys? 2 girls?

4. (a) Five discs, numbered 1 to 5, are selected one at a time at random. What is the probability that the discs are drawn in the order 1, 2, 3, 4, 5? What is the probability that the first two discs are 1, 2, in that order?

    (b) If a red die and a green die are thrown, what is the probability that the red die shows a number greater than 3 and the green die shows a a number less than 3?

5. (a) How many three-digit numbers can be formed, using only numerals from the set $\{1, 2, 3, 4, 5\}$ if repetition of digits is not allowed?

(b) From the set of possible three-digit numbers in part (a), one element is chosen at random. What is the probability of a number beginning with the digit 1? beginning with an even digit?

6. (a) Answer the question of Exercise 5(a), given that repetition of digits is allowed.
   (b) Answer the question of Exercise 5(b), given that repetition of digits is allowed.

---

7. In a family of 3 children, what is the probability of all 3 children being boys? What is the probability of 2 girls and 1 boy? 2 boys and 1 girl? 3 girls?

8. A lot of 50 items contains 5 defective and 45 nondefective items. A sample set of 3 of these items is selected from the lot and tested. What is the probability that all 3 items in the sample are defective? that none are defective? that exactly 1 is defective? that at least 2 are defective?

9. A lunch counter has 6 seats, numbered 1 to 6. Three people come in and take seats, at random, at the empty counter. What is the probability that the seats numbered 1, 2, and 3 are occupied? that 3 seats are occupied and that there are no empty seats between any two of them?

10. From a group of five students, A, B, C, D, E, a committee of three is chosen by lot.
    (a) How many possible committees can be so formed?
    (b) What is the probability that A is on the committee?

11. In one roll of a pair of ordinary dice, what is the probability of a total of 7 or 11?

12-3 COMPLEMENTARY EVENTS AND ADDITION THEOREMS

Since events are subsets of a probability space, we may use the algebra of subsets to answer probability questions. A useful device for picturing the relationships between various subsets of a set is the Venn diagram, named in honor of the English logician, John Venn (1834–1883).

For example, let $S = \{a, b, c, d, e, f\}$ be a probability space of six equally likely outcomes, and let A be the following subset of S.

$$A = \{a, b, c, d\}$$

In Fig. 12–1, the six points which comprise set S are enclosed in a rectangle and the four points of S which comprise the subset A are enclosed in the circle labeled A. By definition, the probability of A, $P(A)$, is $\frac{4}{6}$, or $\frac{2}{3}$. The points of S which are not in A also form a subset

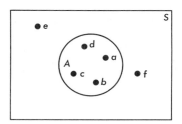

FIGURE 12-1

$\overline{A}$, called the *complement of A*. In Fig. 12–1, the points of $\overline{A}$ are those points of S *outside* the circle A, that is, $\overline{A} = \{e, f\}$.   Note that $P(\overline{A}) = \frac{2}{6}$, or $\frac{1}{3}$, which is $1 - P(A)$, or $1 - \frac{2}{3}$. In fact, the following theorem is true for any subset A of a probability space S.

THEOREM ON COMPLEMENTARY EVENTS

If A is an event in the probability space S, and $\overline{A}$ is its complement, then $P(\overline{A}) = 1 - P(A)$.

Proof. Let $n(S)$ be the number of points in the probability space S. Let $n(A)$ and $n(\overline{A})$ be the number of points in A and $\overline{A}$, respectively. Then $n(A) + n(\overline{A}) = n(S)$, since $\overline{A}$ contains all the points of S not in A. Hence, we have

$$n(\overline{A}) = n(S) - n(A),$$

and upon dividing both sides of this equation by $n(S)$,

$$P(\overline{A}) = 1 - P(A).$$

Before illustrating the usefulness of this theorem, we shall state a second probability theorem.

ADDITION THEOREM OF PROBABILITIES

If A and B are subsets of a probability space S, then

$$P(A \cup B) = P(A) + P(B) - P(A \cap B).$$

In particular, *if $A \cap B$ is the empty set, then*

$$P(A \cup B) = P(A) + P(B).$$

Proof. Recall that the *union*, $A \cup B$, of subsets A and B is the set consisting of all points in A or B and that the *intersection*, $A \cap B$, is the set of all points that are common to both A and B. Let $n(A)$, $n(B)$, $n(A \cup B)$, and $n(A \cap B)$ be the number of points of S in each of the corresponding subsets, A, B, $A \cup B$, and $A \cap B$. From the

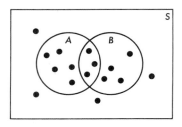

FIGURE 12-2

Venn diagram in Fig. 12–2, we see that adding the numbers $n(A)$ and $n(B)$ counts the points in $A \cap B$ twice. Thus,

$$n(A) + n(B) - n(A \cap B)$$

gives us the correct number of points in $A \cup B$, that is,

$$n(A \cup B) = n(A) + n(B) - n(A \cap B).$$

After dividing both sides of this equation by $n(S)$, we obtain

$$P(A \cup B) = P(A) + P(B) - P(A \cap B).$$

If $A \cap B$ is the empty set, we have $P(A \cap B) = 0$, so that the addition formula becomes

$$P(A \cup B) = P(A) + P(B) \quad \text{if} \quad A \cap B = \emptyset.$$

Sets A and B for which $A \cap B = \emptyset$ are called *disjoint* sets. In probability terminology, disjoint sets A and B, representing events in a probability space, are called *mutually exclusive events.*

Definition of mutually exclusive events

If A and B are sets in a probability space and $A \cap B = \emptyset$, then A and B are called mutually exclusive events.

The event $A \cup B$, representing the union of any two events A, B of a probability space, can be called the event *at least one of A or B,* and the event $A \cap B$ can be called *both A and B.*

Problem. In a single roll of two dice, what is the probability of at least one six on the top faces?

Solution. In Exercises 1 through 3 of Section 12–1, we analyzed an experiment in which there are 36 equally likely outcomes from a toss of two dice. The event A, *at least one six*, consists of those ordered pairs with first coordinate 6, or second coordinate 6, or possibly both coordinates 6. The complementary event, $\overline{A}$, is the set of all ordered pairs in which *neither* coordinate is 6. By elementary counting procedures, we quickly compute

$$n(\overline{A}) = 5 \cdot 5, \quad \text{or } 25,$$

so that $P(\overline{A}) = \frac{25}{36}$, and hence, $P(A) = 1 - P(\overline{A})$, or $\frac{11}{36}$, according to the theorem on complementary events.

In this problem, we could have represented the event A as

$$A = B_1 \cup B_2,$$

where B_1 is the event *six on the first die*, and B_2 is the event *six on the second die*. Then $n(B_1) = n(B_2) = 6$ and $n(B_1 \cap B_2) = 1$, so that by the addition theorem of probabilities,

$$P(A) = P(B_1) + P(B_2) - P(B_1 \cap B_2)$$
$$= \tfrac{6}{36} + \tfrac{6}{36} - \tfrac{1}{36}, \quad \text{or } \tfrac{11}{36}.$$

Exercises

1. (a) In tossing two dice, what is the probability of a sum of numbers different from 7 on the top faces?
   (b) In tossing three pennies, what is the probability of at least one head showing?

2. (a) If a single card is drawn from a bridge deck of 52 cards, what is the probability of an ace or a spade? of a heart or a spade?
   (b) If a single card is drawn from a bridge deck of 52 cards, what is the probability of a jack or a heart? of a jack or a queen?

3. (a) A high school has 100 students, of whom 50 are enrolled in French, 30 are enrolled in Latin, and 20 are enrolled in both French and Latin.
   (i) Make a Venn diagram, letting S represent the set of 100 students and enclosing subsets F and L in two overlapping circles in S. In the set $F \cap L$, write the number of students taking both French and Latin: $n(F \cap L)$. Then write the number of elements in each of the remaining three regions in the rectangle S. These regions represent sets $F \cap \overline{L}$ (students taking French, but not Latin), $\overline{F} \cap L$ (students taking Latin, but not French), and $\overline{F} \cap \overline{L}$ (students taking neither French nor Latin).

(ii) If one student is chosen at random from the class, what is the probability that the student chosen is taking at least one of the languages? is taking neither language?

(b) In a group of 100 girls, 40 are blondes and the rest are brunettes. Fifty of the girls have blue eyes, and the others have brown eyes. There are 10 blue-eyed blondes.

(i) Make a Venn diagram, letting S represent the set of 100 girls and enclosing subsets E (blue-eyed) and B (blonde) in two overlapping circles in S. In the set $E \cap B$, write the number of blue-eyed blondes. Then write the numbers of elements in each of the remaining three regions of S: blondes who are not blue-eyed, girls who have blue eyes but are not blonde, and brunettes who are not blue-eyed.

(ii) If a boy dates one of these 100 girls, choosing her name by lot, what are his chances of going out with a brown-eyed brunette?

4. (a) Suppose that we are given more information about the class described in Exercise 3(a): 20 students take German, 5 take both French and German, 8 take both German and Latin, and 3 take all three languages.

(i) Make a Venn diagram with three overlapping circles representing sets L, F, and G (German). Working from the inside of the circles to the outside, compute the number of elements of the eight disjoint sets in S.

(ii) What is the probability that a student selected at random from the class is a student of French, but is not a student of either of the other two languages? is a student of none of these three languages?

(b) The registrar of a school of 500 students reports the following enrollments: French, 300; German, 200; Latin, 180. He reports that duplication of names occurs in 70 cases with French and German, in 80 cases with French and Latin, in 60 cases with German and Latin, and that there are 50 students taking all three languages.

(i) Can you make a Venn diagram to show this?

(ii) Why is there reason to question his arithmetic?

---

5. From the set of 4 aces of a bridge deck of 52 cards, 2 are drawn at random. What is the probability that in the pair selected, at least 1 of the cards is a red ace?

6. A carton containing 12 eggs has 1 rotten egg. If three eggs are chosen at random from the box, what is the probability that the rotten egg will be one of the eggs chosen?

7. If a fair coin is tossed 5 times, how many equally weighted outcomes are there? What is the probability that at least 1 head will show in the 5 tosses? at most 1 head?

8. A certain class of 80 students boasts 20 honor students and 30 school athletes. Forty students in the class do not indulge in sports and are not honor students. If a student is selected at random to represent the class, what is the probability that he is both an honor student and a school athlete? that he is in at least one of these two special categories?

---

9. A group of 250 people is classified according to nationality (native or foreign); age group (adult or child); sex (male or female). In the group, there are 20 native children of whom 10 are boys. There are 30 native males and 40 foreign men. Of the whole group, 100 are native, 100 are children, and 100 are males. In selecting one person at random from this group, what is the probability that the person selected is
(a) a native woman?   (b) a foreign girl?

10. An integer is chosen at random from the first 20 positive integers. What is the probability that the integer chosen is divisible by 4 or by 6? (Try to do this exercise in two ways.)

12-4 INDEPENDENT EVENTS

We shall now consider two different, but related, experiments. Suppose we have an urn containing 3 red balls and 4 white balls.

Experiment 1. Two balls are drawn in succession from the urn, and the first ball *is not* replaced before the second is drawn.

Experiment 2. Two balls are drawn in succession from the urn, and the first ball *is* replaced before the second is drawn.

In each experiment, what are the probabilities of the following events?
(a) A, first ball red
(b) B, second ball red
(c) $A \cap B$, both balls red

Solution. In Experiment 1, we take a sample space, S_1, consisting of the set of all ordered pairs, without replacement of balls, from the set of 7 balls. We use equiprobable assignment of weights to the points in S_1. Therefore, $n(S_1) = 7 \cdot 6$, or 42.
Event A consists of all ordered pairs of the form (R, R) or (R, W):

$$n(A) = (3 \cdot 2) + (3 \cdot 4), \quad \text{or } 18,$$
$$P(A) = \tfrac{18}{42}, \quad \text{or } \tfrac{3}{7}.$$

Event B consists of all ordered pairs of the form (R, R) or (W, R):

$$n(B) = (3 \cdot 2) + (4 \cdot 3) = 18,$$
$$P(B) = \tfrac{18}{42}, \quad \text{or } \tfrac{3}{7}.$$

The elements of $A \cap B$ consist only of ordered pairs of the type (R, R):

$$n(A \cap B) = 3 \cdot 2, \quad \text{or} \quad 6,$$
$$P(A \cap B) = \tfrac{6}{42}, \quad \text{or} \quad \tfrac{1}{7}.$$

In Experiment 2, we take a sample space S_2 consisting of the set of all ordered pairs, with replacement of balls, from the set of 7 balls. We use equiprobable assignment of weights to the points in S_2. Therefore,

$$n(S_2) = 7 \cdot 7, \quad \text{or} \quad 49,$$
$$n(A) = (3 \cdot 3) + (3 \cdot 4), \quad \text{or} \quad 21,$$
$$P(A) = \tfrac{21}{49}, \quad \text{or} \quad \tfrac{3}{7},$$
$$n(B) = (3 \cdot 3) + (4 \cdot 3), \quad \text{or} \quad 21,$$
$$P(B) = \tfrac{21}{49}, \quad \text{or} \quad \tfrac{3}{7},$$
$$n(A \cap B) = 3 \cdot 3, \quad \text{or} \quad 9,$$
$$P(A \cap B) = \tfrac{9}{49}.$$

Notice that in each experiment, the probability of a red ball on the second draw is the same as that of a red ball on the first draw. This seems obvious in the second experiment because the first ball is replaced before the second is drawn. However, it is less obvious in the first experiment because the chances of drawing a red ball on the second draw seem to depend on the color of the first ball drawn.

The difference between the two experiments becomes evident when we try to relate the probability of the event $A \cap B$, both balls red, to the probabilities of the separate events A and B. In Experiment 2, we see that

$$P(A \cap B) = P(A) \cdot P(B) \quad \text{since} \quad \tfrac{9}{49} = \tfrac{3}{7} \cdot \tfrac{3}{7}.$$

In other words, if we know only the probabilities of events A and B, we can find the probability of $A \cap B$ by multiplying these two probabilities. This illustrates the following property of pairs of events.

Definition of independent events

Two events A and B in a sample space S are said to be independent if, and only if,

$$P(A \cap B) = P(A) \cdot P(B).$$

In Experiment 1, we see that

$$P(A \cap B) \neq P(A) \cdot P(B) \quad \text{since} \quad \tfrac{1}{7} \neq \tfrac{3}{7} \cdot \tfrac{3}{7}.$$

Thus, in this experiment, A and B are *dependent*, rather than *independent*, events. The definition above may be extended to more than two events.

Three events A, B, and C of a sample space S are said to be completely independent if, and only if, any two of these events are independent and

$$P(A \cap B \cap C) = P(A) \cdot P(B) \cdot P(C).$$

Four events A, B, C, and D are said to be completely independent if, and only if, any three of the events are completely independent and

$$P(A \cap B \cap C \cap D) = P(A) \cdot P(B) \cdot P(C) \cdot P(D).$$

We could extend the definition to include any finite number of events.

Exercises

1. (a) Two fair coins are tossed. Let A be the event *not more than one head* and B the event *at least one of each face*. Show that A and B are dependent events.

   Three fair coins are tossed. Let A' and B' be the events in this space corresponding to the events A and B above. Are A' and B' independent or dependent events?

   (b) Three fair coins are tossed. Let A be the event *at least two heads*, let B be the event *at most two heads*, and let C be the event *same face on all three coins*.

   Compute $P(A)$, $P(B)$, $P(C)$, $P(A \cap C)$, and $P(B \cap C)$.
   Are events A and C independent?
   Are events B and C independent?

2. (a) Two dice are tossed. Show that the event *even on first die* and the event *both dice fall alike* are independent.

   (b) A die is tossed 3 times. What is the probability that the first toss will show odd, the second toss even, and the third toss a six?

3. (a) A die is tossed 3 times. Let event A be all ordered triples resulting from an even first toss (e, x, x); let event B be those resulting from an odd second toss (x, o, x); let event C be those resulting from a six on the third toss $(x, x, 6)$; let S be the sample space. Find each of the following:

   $$n(S), \quad n(A), \quad n(B), \quad n(C), \quad n(A \cap B),$$
   $$n(A \cap C), \quad n(B \cap C), \quad n(A \cap B \cap C).$$

   Are the three events A, B, and C completely independent?

   (b) The table below shows a two-way classification of a group of 100 people according to sex and age.

	45 or older	less than 45	Total
Men	39	21	60
Women	26	14	40
Total	65	35	100

The marginal totals on the right of the table are the totals of the rows and the marginal totals at the bottom of the table are the totals of the columns. Suppose that a person is chosen, at random, from this group and let D be the event *45 or older* and M the event *male*. Are the events D and M independent? Are D and $\overline{M}$? $\overline{D}$ and M? $\overline{D}$ and $\overline{M}$?

---

4. (a) One card is drawn from a bridge deck of 52 cards. Let A be the event *ace* and B be the event *spade*. Show that events A and B are independent. Are A and B mutually exclusive?

   (b) Let C be the event *king* in the experiment of part (a). Show that events A and C are mutually exclusive and are not independent.

5. Using the definitions of independence and of mutually exclusive events, prove the following statement: If A and B are independent events, then they are not mutually exclusive. Assume that $P(A) \neq 0$ and $P(B) \neq 0$.

6. Each of the three-digit code numbers 100, 010, 001, and 111 is written on a disc. From the set of 4 discs, one is chosen at random. Let A_1, A_2, and A_3 be the events *first digit* 1, *second digit* 1, and *third digit* 1, respectively. Show that each pair of events A_1 and A_2, A_1 and A_3, A_2 and A_3 is independent but that the set of all three events is not a completely independent set.

7. In a certain school, examination results showed that 12% of the students failed French, 10% failed chemistry, and 2% failed both French and chemistry. A student is selected, at random, from the school roll. Are the events *student failed French* and *student failed chemistry* independent?

12–5 BINOMIAL DISTRIBUTION

The principal usefulness of the concept of independence is that it allows us to compute the probability of an intersection of several events once we know the probability of each of these individual events. An example of this is given by the *independent trials process.*

Suppose that an experiment is performed n times and that care is taken to make certain that the same conditions apply each time. This gives us a set of *n independent trials of an experiment*, or an *independent trials process.* Examples of independent trials processes are coin tossing, dice throwing, and repeated drawing of balls with replacement. Because of the independence property, the probability space of such a process can be built sequentially. In other words, probabilities can be assigned to the points of the space by *multiplying* the probabilities of the points of the common spaces of the independent trials.

Problem 1. It is believed that, of a large group of people, opinions on a certain proposal are divided so that about 60% of the people are for the proposal and about 40% are against it. If 5 people are chosen at random and asked their opinion, what is the probability that of these 5 people, 3 are for and 2 are against the proposal?

Solution. If we assume that the 5 individuals do not influence one another in giving their answers, we may consider this an independent trials process, consisting of 5 trials in which a person is asked his opinion. On each trial there is a 60%, or $\frac{3}{5}$, probability of response for the proposal and a 40%, or $\frac{2}{5}$, probability of response against it. As we perform the 5 trials, we shall work with arrangements of the type *FFFAA*, *FFAFA*, and so on, representing sequences of replies for and against. Since the trials are independent, we have

$$P(FFFAA) = \tfrac{3}{5} \cdot \tfrac{3}{5} \cdot \tfrac{3}{5} \cdot \tfrac{2}{5} \cdot \tfrac{2}{5}, \quad \text{or} \quad (\tfrac{3}{5})^3(\tfrac{2}{5})^2,$$

$$P(FFAFA) = \tfrac{3}{5} \cdot \tfrac{3}{5} \cdot \tfrac{2}{5} \cdot \tfrac{3}{5} \cdot \tfrac{2}{5}, \quad \text{or} \quad (\tfrac{3}{5})^3(\tfrac{2}{5})^2,$$

and so on. Since *each* sequence of replies is to have 3 *F*'s and 2 *A*'s, the probability of any one of these sequences will be the same as the two we computed: $(\tfrac{3}{5})^3(\tfrac{2}{5})^2$. Hence, to complete this problem, we need to *count* the number of sequences, each of which has 3 *F*'s and 2 *A*'s. This is a problem in *combinations*, since we want the number of ways of selecting a 3-subset of the spaces numbered 1 to 5. We shall put the *F*'s in these spaces, and use the remaining 2 spaces for *A*'s. There are $\binom{5}{3}$ such combinations and the answer to our question is

$$\binom{5}{3}(\tfrac{3}{5})^3(\tfrac{2}{5})^2, \quad \text{or} \quad \tfrac{216}{625}.$$

Problem 1 belongs to a large class of experiments involving independent trials processes for which there exist formulas for computing probabilities. The most famous of these formulas is given in the following theorem.

BINOMIAL DISTRIBUTION THEOREM

If a sequence of n independent trials of an experiment is performed, and if each trial results in one of two possible outcomes, called success and failure, with the probability of success given to be p and that of failure given to be q, then the probability of exactly k successes in the n trials is

$$\binom{n}{k} p^k q^{n-k} \quad \text{for} \quad k = 0, 1, 2, \ldots, n.$$

Proof. Since the sum of the probabilities of the outcomes of each trial must be 1, we have $p + q = 1$, or

$$q = 1 - p.$$

Suppose that R is the event of exactly k successes in n trials in the probability space of all ordered n-tuples selected from the set $\{S, F\}$, where S stands for success and F for failure. Then one point of R is

$$\underbrace{SS \cdots S}_{k \text{ symbols}} \quad \underbrace{FF \cdots F}_{n-k \text{ symbols.}}$$

Because the trials are independent, the probability assigned to this point is

$$p^k q^{n-k}.$$

The number of arrangements of the k S's and $(n - k)$ F's in an ordered n-tuple is the number of combinations of k objects from a set of n objects,

$$\binom{n}{k}.$$

Hence,

$$P(R) = \binom{n}{k} p^k q^{n-k},$$

as stated in the theorem.

An easy way to remember the binomial distribution theorem is to expand $(q + p)^n$ by the binomial theorem:

$$(q + p)^n$$
$$= \binom{n}{0} q^n + \binom{n}{1} q^{n-1} p + \cdots + \binom{n}{k} q^{n-k} p^k + \cdots + \binom{n}{n} p^n.$$

Then the term containing p^k is the probability of exactly k successes in n trials of our experiment. Since $q + p = 1$, the sum of the probabilities in the binomial distribution is 1.

A sequence of independent trials of the same experiment, each trial having *success* and *failure* as its two possible outcomes, is often called a *sequence of Bernoulli trials,* named for the Swiss mathematician James Bernoulli (1654–1705).

Problem 2. Find the probability of obtaining more than 2 but fewer than 6 successes in 12 Bernoulli trials of an experiment in which the probability of success in each trial is $\frac{1}{3}$.

Solution. The event A, more than 2 but fewer than 6 successes, consists of the three mutually exclusive events; B, exactly 3 successes; C, exactly 4 successes; and D, exactly 5 successes. Hence,

$$P(A) = P(B) + P(C) + P(D)$$
$$= \binom{12}{3}\left(\frac{1}{3}\right)^3\left(\frac{2}{3}\right)^9 + \binom{12}{4}\left(\frac{1}{3}\right)^4\left(\frac{2}{3}\right)^8 + \binom{12}{5}\left(\frac{1}{3}\right)^5\left(\frac{2}{3}\right)^7.$$

This expression simplifies to

$$P(A) = \frac{1331 \times 2^8}{3^{12}}.$$

Using logarithms, we obtain

$$\begin{aligned} \log P(A) &= \log 1331 + 8 \log 2 - 12 \log 3 \\ &\doteq 3.1242 + 2.4080 - 5.7252 \\ &\doteq .8070 - 1. \end{aligned}$$

Hence,

$$P(A) \doteq .641.$$

Problem 3. How many times must a coin be tossed for the chances to be 99% or better that at least 1 head shows?

Solution. If we take n Bernoulli trials with probability of success $\frac{1}{2}$ on each trial and if A is the event *at least one head*, then we wish to determine the smallest positive integer n such that

$$P(A) \geq .99.$$

It is easier to work with the complementary event $\overline{A}$, *no head shows*,

$$P(\overline{A}) = \binom{n}{0}\left(\frac{1}{2}\right)^0\left(\frac{1}{2}\right)^n = \left(\frac{1}{2}\right)^n.$$

Using $P(A) = 1 - P(\overline{A})$, we obtain

$$1 - \left(\frac{1}{2}\right)^n \geq .99.$$

We must find the smallest possible integer n that is a solution of this inequality. The inequalities below are equivalent to the one above.

$$.01 \geq (\tfrac{1}{2})^n$$
$$2^n \geq 100$$

The smallest positive integer n such that $2^n \geqq 100$ is 7. Therefore, the coin must be tossed 7 times to make the chances 99% or better of at least 1 head showing.

Exercises

1. (a) A coin is tossed 5 times. Using the binomial distribution formulas, find the probability of the events A, *exactly four heads*, and B, *at least one head*.

   (b) A die is rolled 4 times. Using the binomial distribution formulas, find the probability of the events A, *exactly 3 sixes*, and B, *at least one six*.

2. (a) What is the probability of getting 3 or more sixes in 4 tosses of a die? of getting at most 3 sixes in the 4 throws?

   (b) A coin is tossed 5 times. What is the probability of heads appearing 3 or more times? of at most 3 heads appearing?

3. (a) A baseball player's batting average is .250. What is the probability that he gets exactly 2 hits in 4 times at bat? that he gets at least 1 hit in 4 times at bat?

   (b) A certain team has probability $\frac{2}{3}$ of winning whenever it plays. What is the probability that the team will win exactly 4 out of 5 games? that the team will win at most 4 out of 5 games? that the team will win 4 games out of 5 if it has already won the first 2 games of the series of 5 games?

4. (a) Expand $(.6 + .4)^4$ and interpret each term of this expansion as a probability in the space of a specified number of Bernoulli trials of a particular experiment. Do *not* simplify each term in the expansion.

   (b) Expand the binomial $(.8 + .2)^4$ and interpret each term of this expansion as a probability in the space of a specified number of Bernoulli trials of a particular experiment. Do *not* simplify each term in the expansion.

5. (a) Ten students are polled to determine their approval or disapproval of a suggested design for the class ring. If the opinions of the class as a whole are equally divided on this issue, what is the probability that 8 or more of the students polled say that they approve?

   (b) What is the probability of obtaining at least one six in 4 tosses of a fair die? of obtaining at least one double-six in 24 tosses of two fair die?

6. (a) How many tosses of a fair coin are required if the probability that at least 1 head will appear is to be greater than $\frac{9}{10}$?

   (b) How many times must a fair die be thrown to make the probability greater than $\frac{9}{10}$ that at least one six shows?

7. Over a period of time, it is found that 10% of the fuses produced by a certain manufacturing process are defective. Using logarithms to compute your answers, find the probability that in a sample of 10 fuses selected from the production line there will be
   (a) no defectives.
   (b) at least 1 defective.
   (c) at most 1 defective.

8. Three independent trials of an experiment are performed. Each trial results in one of two outcomes, success or failure. Let p be the (unknown) probability of success on each trial.
   (a) Use the binomial distribution formulas to obtain a formula giving the probability P of at most 1 success in the 3 trials as a function of p; call this result $P(p)$.
   (b) Make a table of values of your function P, listing $P(p)$ for $p = .1$, .2, .3, .4, .5, .6, .7, .8, .9. Find also $P(0)$ and $P(1)$ and interpret these two probabilities in terms of the experiment being performed.
   (c) Graph the function P from your table of values in part (b), using the horizontal axis for values of p and the vertical axis for values of $P(p)$.
   (d) Describe briefly how the probability of at most 1 success in 3 Bernoulli trials changes as the success probability p for each trial increases.

*12–6   AN APPLICATION OF THE BINOMIAL DISTRIBUTION TO DECISION MAKING

The inspection of manufactured articles in a factory might be considered a sequence of Bernoulli trials. The two outcomes for each article inspected could be either acceptance, if the article is satisfactory, or rejection, if it is defective. The probability that an article will be rejected is called the *process average fraction defective*. The following problem corrects a fallacy often committed in interpreting the meaning of process average fraction defective.

Problem. In a certain manufacturing process, the process average fraction defective is $\frac{1}{20}$. Is it correct to infer from this number that there is exactly 1 defective in each run of 20?

Solution. To answer this question, let A be the event *exactly 1 defective in each 20 trials* in a Bernoulli model for which $n = 20$ and $p = .05$.

$$P(A) = \binom{20}{1} (.05)(.95)^{19}$$

$$\doteq .3725$$

Hence, the chances are only about 3 in 8 that a run of 20 produces exactly 1 defective.

The purpose of factory inspection is to determine, on the basis of probability considerations, whether the production process is running satisfactorily or not. Those in charge of production set up a *decision plan* based on an inspection process. Thus in the manufacturing process of the problem above, one such plan might be: "Inspect a run of 20 articles. If exactly one defective article is found, judge the process to be satisfactory; otherwise overhaul the machinery." The solution to the above problem shows that such a plan would result in giving an approval to production about $\frac{3}{8} \doteq .3725$ of the time when the actual process average fraction defective is $\frac{1}{20}$ and deciding to overhaul $\frac{5}{8}$ or more than half of the time such a plan was used. It is clear that this plan is not a very sensible one from the point of requiring overhaul when inspection shows 0 defectives in the sample inspected! A better plan might be to give an approval if *one or fewer* defective articles appear in the sample. For this event B, we have

$$P(B) = \binom{20}{1}(.05)(.95)^{19} + (.95)^{20} \doteq .7263$$

which would be the probability of approval leaving a probability of .2737 for overhaul under the assumption of a process average defective of $\frac{1}{20}$.

Other probability considerations the manufacturer would be interested in, even for the better plan just discussed, would involve the chances for the two alternatives of approval or rejection-and-overhaul if the process average defective had, somehow, drastically changed, say to $\frac{1}{10}$ instead of $\frac{1}{20}$. He could compute the probabilities in the same way to guide him in evaluating his decision plan.

In the following three exercises, these ideas are illustrated using small numbers of trials to avoid heavy computation for you. Even so, computation will be facilitated if tables of binomial distributions are used. A section of such a table for 10 Bernoulli trials is given below. The column headings of the table list various values of the success probability p for binomial distributions with $n = 10$, and the row leaders list the successive values of k from 0 to 10. For example, the entry .146 in column $p = .25$ and row $k = 4$ gives the probability to three decimal places of exactly 4 successes in 10 Bernoulli trials when, in each of these trials, the success probability is $p = .25$, that is,

$$\binom{10}{4}(.25)^4(.75)^6 \doteq .146.$$

k \ p	.1	.25	.50	.75	.90
0	.349	.056	.001	.000	.000
1	.387	.188	.010	.000	.000
2	.194	.282	.044	.000	.000
3	.057	.250	.117	.003	.000
4	.011	.146	.205	.016	.000
5	.001	.058	.246	.058	.001
6	.000	.016	.205	.146	.011
7	.000	.003	.117	.250	.057
8	.000	.000	.044	.282	.194
9	.000	.000	.010	.188	.387
10	.000	.000	.001	.056	.349

Exercises

1. Ten articles are selected at different times during the day at a factory producing large quantities of the product. If 2 or fewer defectives are found, the day's run is judged ready to sell. If more than 2 defectives are found, the day's run is subject to further inspection and the machinery is overhauled.
   (a) What is the probability that the day's run will be accepted when the actual process average fraction defective is .50?
   (b) What is the probability that the day's run will be accepted when the actual process average fraction defective is .75?
   (c) What is the probability that the day's run will be accepted when the actual process average fraction defective is .90?
   (d) What is the probability that the decision to overhaul the machinery will be made when the actual process average fraction defective is .1?
   (e) What is the probability that the decision to overhaul the machinery will be made when the actual process average fraction defective is .25?

2. Joy claims that she can call the toss of a fair coin correctly more than half the time. To test her claim, you can devise the following experiment and decision plan. You will toss the coin 10 times, each time asking Joy to state in advance which way the coin will land. If she is correct 7 or more of the 10 times, you will agree with her claim; otherwise, you

will say she is just guessing. Using the table of binomial probabilities given in the text, answer the following questions.

(a) Under the decision plan, what is the probability that you will give Joy credit for her claim when she is actually just guessing each time?

(b) Under your plan, what is the probability that you will accuse Joy of just guessing when she actually has a *success probability* (probability of being right in calling a toss) of $\frac{3}{4}$?

3. The standard treatment for a certain disease leads to cures in $\frac{1}{4}$ of the cases. A new treatment is devised which is said to produce cures in $\frac{3}{4}$ of the cases. The new treatment is tested on 10 people having the disease. If 7 or more are cured, the new treatment will be adopted. If 3 or fewer people are cured, the new treatment will be discarded as not worth further research. If the number cured is 4, 5, or 6, then judgment on the new treatment will be deferred but studies investigating its properties will continue.

(a) Find the probability of *each* of these 3 possible actions, given that the new treatment is no more effective than the original treatment, that is, given that $p = \frac{1}{4}$ for the 10 Bernoulli trials.

(b) Find the probabilities of each of the actions if the new treatment is actually as effective as claimed.

EXTRA!

One of the famous problems in the field of probability is the so-called birthday problem.

Problem. A clerk registering voters notices that in a group of 20 or 30 people, he frequently finds at least two people who have the same birthday. Explain why this is so.

Solution. In attempting to explain this phenomenon, let us ignore those people born on February 29, that is, let us assume that there are 365 days in each year.

Before dealing with the clerk's observation, we consider the following simpler problem. In a random group of 3 people, what is the probability that at least 2 have the same birthday? To answer this question, we conduct the experiment of asking each person the date of his birthday. Then an appropriate space S is the set of all ordered triples, with repetition, of the first 365 positive integers. These integers represent the days of the year from January 1 through December 31. Thus, we have

$$n(S) = 365 \cdot 365 \cdot 365, \quad \text{or} \quad 365^3.$$

The event A whose probability we are trying to find is *at least two birthdays the same*. Rather than finding $P(A)$, let us find $P(\overline{A})$, where $\overline{A}$ is the complementary event *all three birthdays different*. We may derive $P(\overline{A})$ in the following way. Since $\overline{A}$ is the set of all ordered triples in S, without repetition, we have

$$n(\overline{A}) = {}_{365}P_3, \quad \text{or } 365 \cdot 364 \cdot 363.$$

Hence,

$$P(\overline{A}) = \frac{365 \cdot 364 \cdot 363}{365^3}, \quad \text{or } \frac{364 \cdot 363}{365^2}.$$

Finally, since A and $\overline{A}$ are complementary sets in S,

$$P(A) = 1 - P(\overline{A}) = 1 - \frac{364 \cdot 363}{365^2}, \quad \text{or } \frac{1093}{133,225}.$$

Since $P(A) \doteq .008$, we conclude that there is less than 1 chance in 100 that at least 2 of the group of 3 people have the same birthday.

If we start with a random group of r people and ask each person the date of his birthday, then this experiment suggests a sample space S of ordered r-tuples, with repetition, from the first 365 positive integers and

$$n(S) = 365^r.$$

If A is the event *at least two birthdays the same*, then the complementary event $\overline{A}$ is *all r birthdays different*. In the same way that we found $P(\overline{A})$ above, we obtain

$$P(\overline{A}) = \frac{365 \cdot 364 \cdot \ldots \cdot (365 - r + 1)}{365^r},$$

$$P(A) = 1 - P(\overline{A}).$$

It is not easy to compute $P(A)$ if r is large. Of course, $P(\overline{A})$ can be approximated by means of logarithms if r is not too large.

To return to the original problem, it may be shown that

$$P(\overline{A}) \doteq .493 \quad \text{if} \quad r = 23,$$
$$P(A) \doteq .507 \quad \text{if} \quad r = 23.$$

In other words, in a group of 23 people, the probability that at least two people have the same birthday is greater than $\frac{1}{2}$. Consequently, the clerk's observations are supported by the theory of probability. Incidentally, if a group contains 60 people, the probability that at least two people have the same birthday exceeds .99.

1. Find to 2 significant digits the probability that in a group of 6 people, at least 2 have the same birthday.

2. (a) If you are in a room containing 5 people, what is the probability that at least 1 person will have the same birthday as yours? (Note: This is *not* the same birthday problem as that in this section.)

   (b) How large a group of people is needed for the probability to be greater than $\frac{1}{2}$ that at least 1 of the group will have the same birthday as yours?

HISTORICAL NOTE

It is generally believed that the science of probability originated in the correspondence between two great mathematicians of the seventeenth century, Pascal (1623–1662) and Fermat (1601–1665). These two men began to exchange ideas when they were asked questions by the French nobleman, Chevalier de Méré, whose gambling experiences seemed to contradict his attempts at mathematical reasoning about dice and cards. However, Sydney Gould†, in a recent translation of Cardan's *Liber de Ludo Aleae* (*Book on Games of Chance*), written around 1520, makes a strong case for beginning the historical study of probability with the colorful figure of Cardan.

The theory of probability has attracted the attention of many outstanding mathematicians in its brief history. Important contributions were made by the famous mathematical family of Bernoulli, by De Moivre (1667–1754) and Laplace (1749–1827), and by the Russian mathematicians Chebyshev (1821–1894), Markov (1856–1922), and Liapunov (1858–1918). Today, probability, together with its related branches of research, such as mathematical statistics, game theory, and operations research, is an important field of study in mathematics.

KEY IDEAS AND KEY WORDS

A set of all possible outcomes of an experiment in which each outcome is given equal weight is called a **probability space with equiprobable measure.** Each possible outcome of such an experiment is called a **point** of the space. If S is the probability space of such an experiment and E is a subset of S, then we may define the probability of an event E, denoted by $P(E)$, in the following manner.

$$P(E) = \frac{\text{number of points in E}}{\text{number of points in S}}, \quad \text{or} \quad \frac{n(E)}{n(S)}$$

If A and B are events in a probability space S, we have the following related events: $\overline{A}$, the **complement** of A; $A \cup B$, the **union** of A and B; and $A \cap B$, the **intersection** of A and B. Furthermore, we have

$$P(\overline{A}) = 1 - P(A),$$

and

$$P(A \cup B) = P(A) + P(B) - P(A \cap B).$$

---

† *The Book on Games of Chance*, Gerolamo Cardano (Cardan), translated by Sydney H. Gould, (New York: Holt, Rinehart and Winston, Inc., 1961).

If $A \cap B = \emptyset$, the empty set, we say that A and B are **mutually exclusive events**. In this particular case, $P(A \cap B) = P(\emptyset)$, or 0, and we have

$$P(A \cup B) = P(A) + P(B) \quad \text{when} \quad A \cap B = \emptyset.$$

Two events A and B are said to be **independent events** if

$$P(A \cap B) = P(A) \cdot P(B).$$

Events which are not independent are called **dependent events**.

A sequence of independent trials of an event in which each trial results in success or failure, with probability of success p on each trial, is called a sequence of **Bernoulli trials**. The **binomial distribution theorem** states that in a sequence of n Bernoulli trials with probability of success p, the probability of *exactly* k successes in the n trials is given by

$$\binom{n}{k} p^k (1 - p)^{n-k} \quad \text{for} \quad k = 0, 1, 2, \ldots, n.$$

CHAPTER REVIEW

1. In tossing four coins, what is the probability of
   (a) exactly 3 heads?   (b) at least 3 heads?   (c) at most 1 head?

2. An algebra class is composed of 7 blondes and 11 brunettes. Of the 9 boys in the class, 5 are brunettes. One class member is selected at random. What is the probability that the individual selected is a blond girl?

3. Assuming equal probability for boy or girl, what is the probability in a 3-child family of 2 boys and a girl?

4. A bargain counter has 4 pair of socks, but the socks of each pair have become separated. If you pull out 2 socks at random, what is the probability that they form a matching pair?

5. Let A and B be two independent events with $P(A \cap B) = \frac{1}{6}$ and $P(A \cup B) = \frac{2}{3}$. Find $P(A)$ and $P(B)$. Is there more than one possible answer?

6. In the World Series, the first team to win 4 games is the winner. Suppose that the stronger of two teams has probability $\frac{2}{3}$ of winning each game, independent of the outcome of any other game. Assume that a game cannot end in a tie. Show that the probability that the series will end in 4 games is 0.21, correct to two decimal places.

7. (a) How many committees of 5 students can be formed from a class of 7 girls and 8 boys?
   (b) What is the probability that 1 particular boy, A, will be a member of this committee?
   (c) What is the probability that this committee will have more boys than girls?

8. If 3 cards are drawn from the suit of 13 hearts, what is the probability that the selection will contain the ace or the king, or both?

9. What is the probability of getting at least one 6 in 4 tosses of an ordinary die? of getting exactly one 6 in the 4 tosses?

10. A set of balls numbered from 1 to 15 is placed in an urn and 2 balls are drawn simultaneously. What is the probability that the sum of their numbers is 10?

11. If in Exercise 10, one ball is drawn and replaced and then a second ball drawn, what is the probability that the sum of the numbers is 10?

12. Let *A* be the event *head on first coin* and *B* be the event *coins show different faces* in the probability space of a toss of two ordinary coins. Show that *A* and *B* are independent events.

CHAPTER TEST

1. A small club has 10 members of whom 6 are lawyers, 3 are liars, and 3 of the members are neither lawyers nor liars. If one slip of paper is selected from a hat containing the 10 names on slips of paper, what is the probability that the name selected will be that of a lawyer-liar?

2. From an urn containing 5 white and 3 red balls, 3 balls are drawn. There is no replacement of balls.
(a) How many possible subsets of 3 balls can be drawn?
(b) What is the probability of drawing 2 white balls and 1 red ball?
(c) What is the probability of drawing 3 red balls?
(d) What is the probability of drawing at least 1 red ball?

3. A fair die is rolled 4 times. Use the binomial distribution formulas to find the probability of rolling
(a) exactly 3 sixes.
(b) at most 3 sixes.
(c) no sixes.
(d) not more than 1 six.

4. Three boys and three girls are lined up in a row for a picture.
(a) How many arrangements of the 6 people are there?
(b) What is the probability of the girls and boys being lined up in the following order: *GBGBGB*?
(c) What is the probability of boys and girls alternating in the lineup?

5. If *A* and *B* are independent events in a probability space *S* such that $P(A \cap B) = \frac{1}{6}$ when $n(S) = 18$ and $n(B) = 9$, find each of the following.
(a) $P(B)$
(b) $P(A)$
(c) $n(A)$

CUMULATIVE REVIEW III

1. The cubic polynomial $4x^3 + 3x^2 + ax + b$, with a and b real numbers, has $-1 + i\sqrt{3}$ as a zero. Find the other zeros and determine the values of a and b.

2. If you have 6 pairs of shoes, in how many ways could you choose a right shoe and a left shoe which do not form a pair?

3. Let U be the set of all points (x, y) in a rectangular coordinate plane, and let

$$D = \{(x, y) \mid x^2 + y^2 \leq 4\},$$
$$L = \{(x, y) \mid x + y = 2\},$$
$$R = \{(x, y) \mid x + y > 2\}.$$

Graph each of the following sets in U.
(a) D (b) L
(c) $D \cap L$ (d) $R \cap L$
(e) R (f) $D \cap R$

4. Three dice are rolled.
(a) What is the probability that their sum is greater than or equal to 16?
(b) What is the probability that their sum is less than or equal to 17?

5. Find the set of zeros for each of the following polynomials, and write each polynomial as a product of real prime factors.
(a) $x^3 - 4x^2 + x + 6$ (b) $2x^3 + 5x^2 - x - 1$
(c) $x^4 - 6x^3 + 10x^2 - 6x + 9$ (d) $4x^4 + x^2 - 3x + 1$

6. Three colors of paint are available for painting a group of 10 houses, and there are 5 houses on each side of a street. Each house is to be painted 1 color only. How many ways of painting the houses are there if at most 2 different colors are to be used for the houses on the same side of the street?

7. Approximate to one-decimal-place accuracy a positive real zero of the polynomial $x^3 - 3x - 3$.

8. If A is an event in a sample space with probability $\frac{2}{3}$, we say that the odds for A are 2:1 and the odds against A are 1:2. In general, for an event E with probability $p > \frac{1}{2}$, the odds for E are $p:q$, where $q = 1 - p$; if E has probability $p < \frac{1}{2}$, the odds against E are $q:p$; if E has probability $p = \frac{1}{2}$, the odds are 1:1, or *the odds are even*.
(a) Suppose that you throw a pair of dice once. Find the odds against obtaining a total less than 5.
(b) Suppose that A and B play the following game: A draws a card from an ordinary bridge deck and then B draws a card from the remaining set of cards. If the cards are of the same suit, B wins; otherwise, A wins. What are the odds in favor of A?

9. Determine the values of a and b so that $2x^3 - x^2 + ax + b$ will be divisible by $(x + 2)(x - 4)$.

10. Find the solution set for the system of equations

$$\begin{cases} x^2 - y = 2, \\ y^2 - x = 2. \end{cases}$$

11. Express $(1 + i)^{10}$ as a complex number in the form $a + bi$.

12. In shuffling a deck of 52 cards, 4 are accidentally dropped. What is the probability that the missing cards are all of the same suit?

13. Prove that $\sqrt[4]{6}$ is irrational.

14. What is the probability of a one appearing on the top face twice in 6 tosses of an ordinary die?

15. (a) If $2 - i$ and $\sqrt{3}$ are zeros of the polynomial

$$x^5 - 4x^4 + 2x^3 + 12x^2 - 15x,$$

what are the other zeros?

(b) Write an equation of a rational polynomial of lowest possible degree having -2 and $4 + \sqrt{5}$ as two of its zeros.

16. How many three-digit numbers greater than 200 can be formed with the digits 1, 2, 3, 4, 5, and 6 if repetition of digits is not allowed?

17. Jane asks 7 people to come to a party at her house.
(a) In how many ways can she select the 7 people from a group of 10 acquaintances?
(b) In how many ways can she make her selection if 2 of the 10 people refuse to attend the party together?

18. In the sample space of 2 throws of a die, let A, B, and C be the following events.

A, odd number on the first throw

B, odd number on the second throw

C, odd sum on the two throws

Show that any pair of the set of events A, B, C is independent, but that this is not a completely independent set of three events.

19. What values must m and n have if the polynomial $x^2 + 3x + 4$ is to be a factor of $x^4 + mx^2 + n$?

20. A triangle has vertices $P(0, 0)$, $Q(12, 0)$, and $R(6, -6\sqrt{3})$. The midpoints of the three sides are joined to form a triangle with vertices A, B, and C. Find the perimeter of triangles PQR and ABC.

21. Graph $y = 2^x + 1$ and $y = 2^x$ on the same set of axes.

22. Graph $y = 2^{x+1}$ and $y = 2^x$ on the same set of axes.

23. Given that triangle ABC is isosceles, with $AB = BC = a$, $AC = b$, and angle ABC of measure $20°$, show that $a^3 + b^3 = 3a^2b$.

24. If s and t are numbers such that $0 \le s < t \le \pi/2$, show that

$$\sin\left(\frac{s + t}{2}\right) > \frac{\sin s + \sin t}{2}.$$

What does this imply about the graph of the sine?

25. Given that r is an irrational number and that a, b, c, and d are rational numbers, under what conditions on a, b, c, and d is the number

$$\frac{(ar + b)}{(cr + d)}$$

also rational?

26. Let a, b, c, and d be distinct integers and

$$p(x) = (x - a)(x - b)(x - c)(x - d) - 4.$$

If it is known that the polynomial $p(x)$ has a rational zero r, then show that r must equal

$$\frac{(a + b + c + d)}{4}.$$

27. Graph the system of inequalities

$$\begin{cases} |y| \le \sqrt{x^2 + 9}, \\ -\sqrt{y^2 + 9} \le x \le \sqrt{y^2 + 9}. \end{cases}$$

28. Graph the solution set of the following system of inequalities.

$$\begin{cases} 4y^2 - x^2 + 16y \le 0 \\ 9x^2 + y^2 - 2y > 24 \end{cases}$$

29. Draw and describe the graph of each of the following inequalities.

(a) $x^2 > y^2 + 4$
(c) $x \le \sqrt{y^2 + 4}$

(b) $|x| < y^2 + 4$
(d) $|x| \ge \sqrt{y^2 + 4}$

30. For what values of k does the graph of $y^2 = k^2$ intersect the graph of

$$\frac{y^2}{a^2} - \frac{x^2}{b^2} = 1$$

in at least two points?

CHAPTER 13

Mathematical Induction

Objectives . . .

- To develop formulas for finding sums of arithmetic and geometric series.
- To apply series formulas to the case of the infinite geometric series.
- To develop the concept of mathematical induction.
- To prove basic theorems about natural numbers by using mathematical induction.

13–1   ARITHMETIC SERIES

A sum of numbers is sometimes called a *series*. Thus, a series has the form

$$a_1 + a_2 + \cdots + a_n$$

for some numbers $a_1, a_2, \ldots, a_n$. Each of the numbers $a_1, a_2, \ldots, a_n$ is called a *term* of the series. The series above has n terms. For example,

$$1 + 3 + 5 + 7 + 9$$

is a series with five terms. This is an example of an arithmetic series, as defined below.

Definition of arithmetic series

A series

$$a_1 + a_2 + \cdots + a_n$$

is called an arithmetic series if, and only if, the differences between consecutive terms are all equal, that is,

$$a_2 - a_1 = a_3 - a_2 = a_4 - a_3 = \cdots = a_n - a_{n-1}.$$

The series

$$1 + 3 + 5 + 7 + 9$$

is an arithmetic series having a difference of 2 between consecutive terms.

549

It is easy to find the sum of the arithmetic series above:

$$1 + 3 + 5 + 7 + 9 = 25.$$

However, the sum of the arithmetic series with 50 terms,

$$1 + 3 + 5 + 7 + \cdots + 97 + 99,$$

is not so easily found. We shall presently show that it is 2500.

If the common difference between consecutive terms of an arithmetic series

$$a_1 + a_2 + a_3 + \cdots + a_n$$

is d, then

$$a_2 = a_1 + d,$$
$$a_3 = a_2 + d = a_1 + 2d,$$
$$a_4 = a_3 + d = a_1 + 3d,$$
$$\vdots$$
$$a_n = a_{n-1} + d = a_1 + (n - 1)d.$$

Thus, the series has the form

$$a + (a + d) + (a + 2d) + \cdots + [a + (n - 1)d],$$

where a is the first term and n is the number of terms.

The sum S of an arithmetic series can be found by writing the series twice, once forwards and once backwards, and then adding term by term as illustrated below.

$$
\begin{array}{rl}
S = & 1 + \quad 3 + \quad 5 + \cdots + \quad 99 \\
S = & 99 + \quad 97 + \quad 95 + \cdots + \quad 1 \\
\hline
2S = & 100 + 100 + 100 + \cdots + 100
\end{array}
$$

$$\underbrace{\qquad\qquad\qquad\qquad}_{50 \text{ terms}}$$

Hence, $2S = 50 \cdot 100$, or 5000, and

$$S = 2500.$$

In a similar way, we find the sum S of the arithmetic series with n terms as follows.

$$
\begin{array}{rl}
S = & a \quad + \quad (a + d) \quad + \quad (a + 2d) \quad + \cdots + [a + (n-1)d] \\
S = & [a + (n-1)d] + [a + (n-2)d] + [a + (n-3)d] + \cdots + \quad a \\
\hline
2S = & [2a + (n-1)d] + [2a + (n-1)d] + [2a + (n-1)d] + \cdots + [2a + (n-1)d]
\end{array}
$$

$$\underbrace{\qquad\qquad\qquad\qquad}_{n \text{ terms}}$$

Thus,

$$2S = n[2a + (n - 1)d],$$

and

$$S = \frac{n}{2}[2a + (n - 1)d].$$

Once we realize that $2a + (n - 1)d$ is simply the sum

$$a + [a + (n - 1)d]$$

of the first and last terms of the arithmetic series, we can state the following formula for the sum of any arithmetic series

$$a_1 + a_2 + \cdots + a_n.$$

$$a_1 + a_2 + \cdots + a_n = \frac{n}{2}(a_1 + a_n)$$

Problem 1. Find the sum of the first n positive integers.

Solution. By the formula above,

$$1 + 2 + 3 + \cdots + n = \frac{n}{2}(1 + n) = \frac{n(n + 1)}{2}.$$

For example,

$$1 + 2 + 3 + \cdots + 50 = \frac{50 \cdot 51}{2} = 1275.$$

Problem 2. Find the sum of the first n positive odd integers; then find the sum of the first n positive even integers.

Solution. The nth positive even integer is $2n$; the nth positive odd integer is $2n - 1$. Thus, by the formula,

$$1 + 3 + 5 + \cdots + (2n - 1) = \frac{n}{2}(1 + 2n - 1) = n^2$$

and

$$2 + 4 + 6 + \cdots + 2n = \frac{n}{2}(2 + 2n) = n(n + 1).$$

Problem 3. An arithmetic series starts out $-2 -5 -8 - \ldots$. Find its sum if it has n terms.

Solution. The difference between successive terms is

$$d = -5 - (-2) = -8 - (-5) = \cdots = -3.$$

Since the first term is $a = -2$, the nth term is

$$a + (n - 1)d = -2 + (n - 1)(-3) = -3n + 1.$$

Thus, by the formula,

$$-2 - 5 - 8 - \cdots - 3n + 1 = \frac{n}{2}(-2 - 3n + 1) = \frac{n(-1 - 3n)}{2}.$$

For example, if $n = 6$ we have

$$-2 - 5 - 8 - 11 - 14 - 17 = \frac{6(-1 - 18)}{2} = -57.$$

The terms of an arithmetic series between the first term and the last are called *arithmetic means.*

Problem 4. Find six arithmetic means between 4 and 25.

Solution. The arithmetic series $4 + \cdots + 25$ has 8 terms; the 8th term is $4 + (8 - 1)d = 25$. Thus, $7d = 21$ and $d = 3$. The six arithmetic means are 7, 10, 13, 16, 19, 22.

Exercises

For the specified value of n, find the nth term of each of the arithmetic series which starts as follows.

1. (a) $3 + 8 + 13 + \cdots$, $n = 10$ (b) $-2 - 5 - 8 - \cdots$, $n = 12$
2. (a) $\frac{1}{2} + \frac{3}{4} + 1 + \cdots$, $n = 15$ (b) $1 - \frac{1}{2} - 2 - \cdots$, $n = 9$
3. (a) $3 + 10 + 17 + \cdots$, $n = k$ (b) $8 - 2 - 12 - \cdots$, $n = k$

Find the sum of each arithmetic series.

4. (a) $13 + 20 + 27 + \cdots + 146$ (b) $9 + 15 + 21 + \cdots + 93$
5. (a) $-10 - 5 + 0 + \cdots$, 20 terms   (b) $7 + 11 + 15 + \cdots$, 12 terms
6. (a) $\frac{1}{2} + \frac{1}{4} + 0 + \cdots - 4$ (b) $1 + 1.1 + 1.2 + \cdots + 2$
7. (a) Find one arithmetic mean between -1 and 2.
   (b) Find one arithmetic mean between 5 and 13.
8. (a) Find three arithmetic means between 1 and 5.
   (b) Find four arithmetic means between -2 and -8.
9. (a) Find ten arithmetic means between -3 and -36.
   (b) Find seven arithmetic means between 13 and 29.

10. (a) Find the sum of the integers between 50 and 500 which are divisible by 8.

    (b) Find the sum of the positive integral multiples of 7 which are less than 600.

---

11. If the third term of an arithmetic series is 15, and the seventeenth term is -27, what must the sixth term be?

12. The fifth term of an arithmetic series is -18 and the ninth term is 4. Find the sum of the first twenty terms.

13. If $a + b + c + d + e + f + g + h$ is an arithmetic series, which of the following are also arithmetic series?

    (a) $b + d + f + h$

    (b) $a^2 + b^2 + c^2 + d^2$

    (c) $\dfrac{1}{a} + \dfrac{1}{b} + \dfrac{1}{c} + \dfrac{1}{d} + \dfrac{1}{e}$

    (d) $ka + kb + kc + kd + ke + kf$

14. (a) Find a value of x such that

$$(9x + 7) + (7x + 1) + (3x - 4)$$

    is an arithmetic series of three terms.

    (b) Find another value of x such that the three terms of the series in part (a), arranged in different order, continue to form an arithmetic series.

15. Find the value of x such that $2x - 7$, $6x - 2$, and $8x + 4$ are the first three terms of an arithmetic series.

13–2   GEOMETRIC SERIES

If we deposit $200 in a savings bank that pays 4% interest compounded semiannually, then at the end of one-half year we shall be credited with .02 × 200, or $4, interest. Our account will then total $204. We shall receive .02 × 204, or $4.08, interest the second half of the year, and our account will total $208.08 at the end of 1 year. If we do not draw any money out of our account, how much will it total after 2 years? after 3 years? after 10 years? These questions lead us to the following problem.

Problem 1. If we deposit p dollars in a savings bank paying interest at the rate i for each interest period, and if we leave the principal and accumulated interest in the bank, how much will our account total after n interest periods?

Solution. It is understood that i is the actual interest, in dollars, paid by the bank for each dollar in our account at the end of each interest period. Thus, at the end of the first interest period, we shall be credited with ip dollars interest and the total amount in our account will be

$$p + ip, \quad \text{or } p(1 + i).$$

At the end of the second interest period, the total amount will be

$$[p(1 + i)] + i[p(1 + i)] = [p(1 + i)](1 + i)$$
$$= p(1 + i)^2.$$

At the end of three interest periods, the total amount will be

$$[p(1 + i)^2] + i[p(1 + i)^2] = [p(1 + i)^2](1 + i)$$
$$= p(1 + i)^3.$$

Continuing, after n interest periods our account evidently will total

$$p(1 + i)^n.$$

For example, if we deposit \$200 in a savings bank that pays 4% interest compounded semiannually, then after 5 years we will have (letting $i = .02$ and $n = 10$)

$$200(1 + .02)^{10}$$

in the bank. Since 1.02^{10} is approximately 1.22 (which you can find using logarithms), our account will total approximately 200(1.22), or \$244.

If, as the bank encourages us to do, we save a fixed amount of our salary, then how much will we have in the bank at the end of a certain number of years? To be more explicit, suppose we deposit \$200 in the bank each 6 months. How much money will we have in our account after 5 years, assuming the bank pays 4% interest compounded semi-annually?

The first \$200 will collect interest for 10 periods and will be worth

$$200(1 + .02)^{10}$$

dollars at the end of 5 years. The next \$200, deposited at the start of the second interest period, will be worth

$$200(1 + .02)^9$$

dollars at the end of 5 years. The next \$200, deposited at the start of the third interest period, will be worth

$$200(1 + .02)^8$$

dollars after 5 years, and so on, down to the last \$200 which draws interest for only one period and will be worth

$$200(1 + .02)$$

dollars after 5 years. On adding, we have

$$200(1 + .02)^{10} + 200(1 + .02)^9 + 200(1 + .02)^8 + \cdots + 200(1 + .02)$$

dollars in our account after 5 years. If we reverse the terms in this series,

$$200(1.02) + 200(1.02)^2 + 200(1.02)^3 + \cdots + 200(1.02),^{10}$$

then this is an example of a geometric series as defined below.

Definition of geometric series

A series

$$a_1 + a_2 + \cdots + a_n$$

is called a geometric series if, and only if, the ratios of successive terms are all equal, that is,

$$\frac{a_2}{a_1} = \frac{a_3}{a_2} = \frac{a_4}{a_3} = \cdots = \frac{a_n}{a_{n-1}}.$$

If we let a be the first term and r be the common ratio above, then $a_1 = a$, $a_2/a_1 = r$ and $a_2 = ar$, $a_3/a_2 = r$ and $a_3 = a_2 r = ar^2$, and so on. The geometric series then has the form

$$a + ar + ar^2 + \cdots + ar^{n-1},$$

where n is the number of terms.

For example, the series above,

$$200(1.02) + 200(1.02)^2 + 200(1.02)^3 + \cdots + 200(1.02)^{10}$$

is a geometric series with first term $a = 200(1.02)$, ratio $r = 1.02$, and $n = 10$. The sum S of this series can be found by multiplying each term by r and then subtracting the old series from this new one as follows.

$$1.02S = \qquad\qquad 200(1.02)^2 + 200(1.02)^3 + \cdots + 200(1.02)^{10} + 200(1.02)^{11}$$
$$- \quad S = 200(1.02) + 200(1.02)^2 + 200(1.02)^3 + \cdots + 200(1.02)^{10}$$

$$1.02S - S = -200(1.02) \qquad\qquad\qquad\qquad\qquad\qquad + 200(1.02)^{11}$$

Notice that most of the terms cancel. Thus,

$$.02S = 200(1.02)(1.02^{10} - 1)$$

and

$$S = 10,200(1.02^{10} - 1)$$
$$\doteq 10,200 \times .22, \quad \text{or } \$2244.$$

Similarly, if $S = a + ar + \cdots + ar^{n-1}$ then again we can multiply each term by r and subtract the old series from the new one, as follows.

$$
\begin{aligned}
rS &= \phantom{a + {}} ar + ar^2 + \cdots + ar^{n-1} + ar^n \\
-S &= a + ar + ar^2 + \cdots + ar^{n-1} \\
\hline
rS - S &= -a \phantom{+ ar + ar^2 + \cdots + ar^{n-1}} + ar^n \\
(r-1)S &= a(r^n - 1) \\
S &= \frac{a(r^n - 1)}{r - 1}
\end{aligned}
$$

This proves the following formula for the sum of a geometric series with n terms:

$$a + ar + ar^2 + \cdots + ar^{n-1} = \frac{a(r^n - 1)}{r - 1}, \quad \text{if } r \neq 1.$$

If $r = 1$, the series is simply

$$\underbrace{a + a + \cdots + a}_{n \text{ terms}} = na.$$

For example, $a = 1$, $r = 2$, and $n = 8$, in the geometric series

$$1 + 2 + 4 + 8 + 16 + 32 + 64 + 128 = \frac{1 \cdot (2^8 - 1)}{2 - 1} = 255.$$

Also, $a = 3$, $r = -\frac{1}{3}$, and $n = 5$ in the geometric series

$$3 - 1 + \tfrac{1}{3} - \tfrac{1}{9} + \tfrac{1}{27} = \frac{3 \cdot [(-\frac{1}{3})^5 - 1]}{-\frac{1}{3} - 1} = \tfrac{61}{27}.$$

Problem 2. A savings bank pays interest at the rate i for each interest period. If we deposit p dollars in the bank at the start of each of n successive interest periods, how much money will be in our account at the end of the nth interest period?

Solution. Reasoning as we did above, the amount A in our account at the end of the nth interest period is given by the series

$$A = p(1 + i) + p(1 + i)^2 + p(1 + i)^3 + \cdots + p(1 + i)^n.$$

Since this is a geometric series with first term $a = p(1 + i)$ and ratio $r = (1 + i)$, A is given by

$$A = \frac{p(1 + i)[(1 + i)^n - 1]}{(1 + i) - 1}.$$

If, for example, we deposit $150 every 3 months for 5 years in a bank paying 6% interest compounded quarterly, then the amount A in the bank at the end of 5 years is given by

$$A = \frac{150 \cdot (1 + .015)[(1 + .015)^{20} - 1]}{.015}.$$

Using logarithms, we compute $1.015^{20} \doteq 1.343$. Then A is approximately $3480. (A more accurate table gives $A = 3520.60.)

Exercises

For the specified value of n, find the nth term of each of the geometric series which starts as follows.

1. (a) $2 + 6 + 18 + \cdots$, $n = 7$.
   (b) $5 + 10 + 20 + \cdots$, $n = 9$.

2. (a) $4 + 2 + 1 + \cdots$, $n = 8$.
   (b) $25 - 5 + 1 + \cdots$, $n = 6$.

3. (a) $4 + 6 + 9 + \cdots$, $n = k$.
   (b) $9 + 6 + 4 + \cdots$, $n = k$.

Find the sum of each geometric series.

4. (a) $3^2 + 3^3 + 3^4 + 3^5$
   (b) $1 - \frac{1}{2} + \frac{1}{4} - \frac{1}{8} + \frac{1}{16} - \frac{1}{32}$

5. (a) $1.03 + 1.03^2 + \cdots + 1.03^{12}$
   (b) $1 + 1.04 + 1.04^2 + \cdots + 1.04^{15}$

6. (a) $1 - \sqrt{3} + 3 - \cdots$, 10 terms
   (b) $2 + 2\sqrt{2} + 4 + \cdots$, 14 terms

7. (a) Find the second, third, and fifth terms of a geometric series having first term 8 and fourth term 27.
   (b) The first term of a geometric series is a negative number, the second term is 2, and the fourth term is 4. Find the first and third terms.

8. The terms between any two terms of a geometric series are called *the geometric means* between these two terms.
   (a) Find three geometric means between 15 and $\frac{5}{27}$. Is there more than one way of doing this?
   (b) Find one geometric mean between $\frac{4}{9}$ and $\frac{9}{4}$. This is called the *geometric mean* of the two numbers. Do two numbers have more than one geometric mean?

9. (a) Find the positive geometric mean of 8 and 18.
   (b) Find two positive geometric means between 2 and $\frac{16}{27}$.

10. What are the conditions that have to be imposed on the real numbers x, y, and z for
    (a) $x + y + z$ to be a geometric series?
    (b) $x + y + z$ to be an arithmetic series?
    (c) y to be both the arithmetic and geometric mean of x and z?

11. If t designates the nth term of a geometric series, write a formula for the sum of n terms of the series in terms of a, r, and t instead of a, r, and n.

12. If $a + b + c + d + e + f$ represents a geometric series of six terms, which of the following is also a geometric series?
    (a) $b + d + f$
    (b) $ka + kb + kc + kd + ke + kf$, k any real number
    (c) $(a + k) + (b + k) + (c + k) + (d + k)$, k any real number
    (d) $\sqrt{a} + \sqrt{b} + \sqrt{c} + \sqrt{d} + \sqrt{e} + \sqrt{f}$

13. A newspaper recently reported that a savings account in a bank was now worth \$3738. There had been no deposit since the original deposit of \$26 made 116 years ago. If interest had been added to the account every 6 months, what average rate of interest had the bank paid over this period?

14. Assuming that an automobile depreciates in value 12% every year, find the value, at the end of 4 years, of a car costing \$2500.

15. Find a formula for the sum of the first n positive integral powers of 4.

13–3 INFINITE GEOMETRIC SERIES

The rational number $\frac{1}{3}$ has repeating decimal

$$.3333 \ldots$$

which we can consider to be an infinite sum:

$$\tfrac{1}{3} = .3 + .03 + .003 + .0003 + \cdots.$$

This is an example of an *infinite geometric series* with ratio .1. Thus, $.03 = .3 \times .1$, $.003 = .03 \times .1$, $.0003 = .003 \times .1$, and so on. We define an infinite geometric series in the following way.

Definition of infinite geometric series

An infinite geometric series is an algebraic expression of the form

$$a + ar + ar^2 + \cdots + ar^{n-1} + \cdots.$$

Associated with an infinite geometric series are its *partial sums*

$$S_1 = a,$$
$$S_2 = a + ar,$$
$$S_3 = a + ar + ar^2,$$

and, in general,

$$S_n = a + ar + ar^2 + \cdots + ar^{n-1}.$$

Thus, S_n is the sum of the first n terms of an infinite geometric series. By a previous formula,

$$S_n = \frac{a(1 - r^n)}{1 - r}, \quad r \neq 1, \quad \text{for every positive integer } n.$$

If $0 < r < 1$, then r^n is a small number when n is large. For example, if $r = \frac{1}{2}$ and $n = 10$, then

$$r^n = \frac{1}{2^{10}} = \frac{1}{1024} < .001.$$

Therefore,

$$S_n \doteq \frac{a}{1 - r}, \quad \text{if } 0 < r < 1 \text{ and } n \text{ is large.}$$

In fact, S_n gets closer and closer to $a/(1 - r)$ as n gets larger and larger. For this reason, we call

$$\frac{a}{1 - r}$$

the *sum* of the infinite geometric series.

If $-1 < r \leq 0$, then it is still true that r^n is close to 0 and hence that S_n is close to $a/(1 - r)$ when n is large. Thus, we call $a/(1 - r)$ the sum of the infinite geometric series in this case also. We can unite these two cases into the following formula for the infinite geometric series.

$$a + ar + ar^2 + \cdots + ar^{n-1} + \cdots = \frac{a}{1 - r}, \quad |r| < 1$$

In the example given previously, $.3 + .03 + .003 + \cdots$, we have $a = .3$ and $r = .1$. Therefore, by the formula,

$$.3 + .03 + .003 + \cdots = \frac{.3}{1 - .1}, \quad \text{or } \frac{1}{3}.$$

As another example,

$$1 + \frac{1}{2} + \frac{1}{4} + \cdots + \frac{1}{2^{n-1}} + \cdots = \frac{1}{1 - \frac{1}{2}}, \quad \text{or } 2.$$

If $|r| \geqq 1$, then the infinite geometric series does not have a sum. For example,

$$1 + 2 + 2^2 + \cdots + 2^{n-1} + \cdots \qquad (1)$$

does not have a sum because the partial sum

$$S_n = \frac{1 \cdot (1 - 2^n)}{1 - 2} = 2^n - 1$$

gets very large when n gets large. In fact, there is no limit on how big S_n can get; hence, there is no number assignable as the sum of this infinite series. If we assume that (1) has a sum, we obtain curious results. For example, if

$$S = 1 + 2 + 2^2 + \cdots + 2^{n-1} + \cdots$$

and if the distributive law holds for such sums, then

$$\begin{aligned} 2S &= 2(1 + 2 + 2^2 + \cdots + 2^{n-1} + \cdots) \\ &= 2 + 2^2 + 2^3 + \cdots + 2^n + \cdots \end{aligned}$$

and

$$\begin{aligned} 1 + 2S &= 1 + 2 + 2^2 + 2^3 + \cdots + 2^n + \cdots \\ &= S. \end{aligned}$$

Solving the equation $1 + 2S = S$ for S, we obtain

$$S = -1.$$

Thus, an infinite sum of positive numbers is a negative number. This is nonsense!

Each repeating decimal is an infinite geometric series. Since $a/(1 - r)$ is a rational number if a and r are rational, it follows that each repeating decimal is a rational number. For example, the repeating decimal

$$.\underline{135} = .\boxed{135} \ 135 \ \boxed{135} \ldots$$

is the same as the infinite geometric series

$$.135 + .000 \ 135 + .000 \ 000 \ 135 + \cdots$$

for which

$$a = .135 \quad \text{and} \quad r = 10^{-3}.$$

Therefore,

$$.135 = \frac{.135}{1 - 10^{-3}}, \quad \text{or} \quad \frac{.135}{.999}, \quad \text{or} \quad \frac{15}{111}, \quad \text{or} \quad \frac{5}{37}.$$

Exercises

Find the sum of each of the following infinite geometric series.

1. (a) $1 + \frac{1}{3} + \frac{1}{9} + \cdots$
   (b) $9 - 3 + 1 - \cdots$
2. (a) $0.07 + 0.007 + 0.0007 + \cdots$
   (b) $1 - \frac{1}{2} + \frac{1}{4} \cdots$
3. (a) $12 + (0.3 + 0.03 + 0.003 + \cdots)$
   (b) $\frac{1}{2} + \frac{1}{6} + \frac{1}{18} + \cdots$
4. (a) $9 + 3 + 1 + \frac{1}{3} + \cdots$
   (b) $x + 1 + \frac{1}{x} + \frac{1}{x^2} + \cdots, \quad x > 1$

In Exercises 5–8, find a common fraction for each repeating decimal.

5. (a) 0.5
   (b) 0.062
6. (a) 3.297
   (b) 2.69
7. (a) 12.21
   (b) 0.645
8. (a) 1.254
   (b) 0.0663

---

9. What distance will a golf ball travel if it is dropped from a height of 72 inches and if, after each fall, it rebounds $\frac{9}{10}$ of the distance it fell?

10. A rubber ball falls from a height of 80 feet and on each rebound loses 25% of its previous height. What distance will it have traveled when it strikes the ground for the fifth time? How far will it travel before it comes to rest?

11. In a square of side 12 inches, a second square is inscribed by joining the midpoints of the sides in order. In the second square, a third square is inscribed using the same method. If this process is continued indefinitely, what is the sum of the perimeters of all the squares?

13-4   MATHEMATICAL INDUCTION

The system of integers has a special property that does not belong to the rational, real, or complex number systems. This distinctive property, called the induction axiom, is concerned with the counting of the positive integers. Roughly speaking, it states that every positive integer can be reached by starting with 1 and counting the integers *in order:* 1; 1 + 1, or 2; 2 + 1, or 3; 3 + 1, or 4; 4 + 1, or 5; and so on. Thus, we eventually count to 100, to 1000, to 1,000,000, and to 10^{100}. Although we could not actually count to a number as large as 10^{100} in a lifetime, we can imagine having a machine which could.

INDUCTION AXIOM

If a set S of positive integers contains **1**, *and if whenever S contains an integer k, it also contains the integer k + 1, then S must be the set of all positive integers.*

The only set that can fulfill the conditions stated in the induction axiom is the set of all positive integers. The conditions on S are that

1. S contains only positive integers.
2. S contains 1.
3. if any positive integer k is an element of S, then the next larger integer, $k + 1$, is also an element of S.

Suppose we know that a set P satisfies these conditions and contains 1, 2, and 3. Since set P contains 3, according to the third condition, set P must contain $3 + 1$, or 4. If P contains 4, then it must contain $4 + 1$, or 5, and so on. Thus, P must be the set of all positive integers.

To illustrate how the induction axiom is used, consider the problem of the number of real zeros of a real polynomial. Each real polynomial $ax + b$ of degree 1 has one real zero: $x = -b/a$. However, each real polynomial

$$p(x) = ax^2 + bx + c$$

of degree 2 does not necessarily have two real zeros. In fact, $p(x)$ has no real zeros if its discriminant $b^2 - 4ac$ is less than 0, one real zero if $b^2 - 4ac = 0$, and two real zeros if $b^2 - 4ac > 0$. With this flimsy evidence, we might conjecture the following result.

THEOREM

The number of real zeros of a real polynomial is at most equal to its degree.

The proof is by induction (that is, by use of the induction axiom). We note that the theorem actually consists of an infinite set of statements, or propositions, which we shall designate by $P_1, P_2, \ldots,$ $P_n, \ldots$. They can be stated as follows.

P_1: The number of real zeros of each real polynomial of degree 1 is at most one.

P_2: The number of real zeros of each real polynomial of degree 2 is at most two.

$\vdots$

P_n: The number of real zeros of each real polynomial of degree n is at most n.

$\vdots$

We have already proved that P_1 and P_2 are true propositions. For each positive integer, the proposition P_n is either true or false. Let us consider the set of positive integers n for which P_n is true. We might call this set S. Thus,

$$S = \{n \mid P_n \text{ is true}\}.$$

If we can prove that S is the set of all positive integers, then we shall have proved that every proposition P_n is true. Hence, we shall have proved that the theorem is true. To prove that S is the set of all positive integers, we shall use the induction axiom.

Since P_1 is true, the integer 1 is in set S. Let us now prove that for every integer k in S, the integer $k + 1$ is also in set S. Thus, let k be an element of S, so that the following proposition is true.

P_k: The number of real zeros of each real polynomial of degree k is at most k.

We want to show that $k + 1$ is also in S, that is, that the following proposition is true.

P_{k+1}: The number of real zeros of each real polynomial of degree $k + 1$ is at most $k + 1$.

In attempting to show that P_{k+1} is true, let $p(x)$ be a real polynomial of degree $k + 1$. If $p(x)$ has no real zeros, then the number of real zeros of $p(x)$ is less than $k + 1$. If $p(x)$ has a real zero r, then $x - r$ is a divisor of $p(x)$ by the factor theorem, and

$$p(x) = (x - r)q(x)$$

for some real polynomial $q(x)$ of degree k. If c is another zero of $p(x)$, with $c \neq r$, then $p(c) = 0$, and therefore,

$$(c - r)q(c) = 0.$$

Since $c - r \neq 0$, we must have $q(c) = 0$. Consequently, every zero of $p(x)$ except r is a zero of $q(x)$. It is also true, of course, that every zero of $q(x)$ is a zero of $p(x)$. Thus, the real zeros of $p(x)$ are r and the additional real zeros of $q(x)$.

How many real zeros does $q(x)$ have? Since $q(x)$ has degree k and P_k is true, $q(x)$ has *at most* k real zeros. Now $p(x)$ has at most one more real zero than $q(x)$ does, and therefore, it has *at most* $k + 1$ real zeros. This proves that proposition P_{k+1} is true, and hence, that $k + 1$ is in set S.

We have shown that set S contains the integer 1, and that whenever S contains the integer k, it also contains the integer $k + 1$. Hence, S is the set of all positive integers by the induction axiom. Thus, we have proved that the theorem is true. A proof of this type is called a proof by *mathematical induction*.

We consider below two problems which can be solved by mathematical induction.

Problem 1. Show that for every positive integer n, the sum of the squares of the first n positive integers is $n(n + 1)(2n + 1)/6$.

Solution. We wish to show that the equation

$$E_n: \quad 1^2 + 2^2 + \cdots + n^2 = \tfrac{1}{6}n(n + 1)(2n + 1)$$

is true for every positive integer n. When $n = 1, 2$, and 3, we have the equations

$$E_1: \quad 1^2 = \tfrac{1}{6} \cdot 1 \cdot (1 + 1) \cdot (2 \cdot 1 + 1)$$
$$E_2: \quad 1^2 + 2^2 = \tfrac{1}{6} \cdot 2 \cdot (2 + 1) \cdot (2 \cdot 2 + 1)$$
$$E_3: \quad 1^2 + 2^2 + 3^2 = \tfrac{1}{6} \cdot 3 \cdot (3 + 1) \cdot (2 \cdot 3 + 1)$$

which are easily seen to be true. Let

$$S = \{n \mid E_n \text{ is true}\}.$$

Since E_1, E_2, and E_3 are true, 1, 2, and 3 are in S. Let us prove that for every integer k in S, the integer $k + 1$ is also in S. Thus, assume that the equation

$$E_k: \quad 1^2 + 2^2 + \cdots + k^2 = \tfrac{1}{6}k(k + 1)(2k + 1)$$

is true. We want to show that the equation

$$E_{k+1}: \quad 1^2 + 2^2 + \cdots + (k + 1)^2$$
$$= \tfrac{1}{6}(k + 1)[(k + 1) + 1][2(k + 1) + 1]$$

is also true. The left side of equation E_{k+1} is a series with $k + 1$ terms (incidentally, it is neither an arithmetic nor a geometric series). Since $1^2 + 2^2 + \cdots + (k + 1)^2 = [1^2 + 2^2 + \cdots + k^2] + (k + 1)^2$ and E_k is true, we have the true equations

$$
\begin{aligned}
1^2 + 2^2 + \cdots + (k + 1)^2 &= [\tfrac{1}{6}k(k + 1)(2k + 1)] + (k + 1)^2 \\
&= \tfrac{1}{6}[k(k + 1)(2k + 1) + 6(k + 1)^2] \\
&= \tfrac{1}{6}(k + 1)[k(2k + 1) + 6(k + 1)] \\
&= \tfrac{1}{6}(k + 1)[2k^2 + 7k + 6] \\
&= \tfrac{1}{6}(k + 1)(k + 2)(2k + 3).
\end{aligned}
$$

Thus,

$$1^2 + 2^2 + \cdots + (k + 1)^2 = \tfrac{1}{6}(k + 1)[(k + 1) + 1][2(k + 1) + 1]$$

is true, that is, E_{k+1} is true and $k + 1$ is in S.

We have proved that 1 is in S, and that whenever k is in S then $k + 1$ is also in S. Hence, by the induction axiom, S is the set of all positive integers. Thus, E_n is true for every positive integer n. For example,

$$1^2 + 2^2 + 3^2 + 4^2 + 5^2 + 6^2 + 7^2 = \tfrac{1}{6} \cdot 7 \cdot (7 + 1) \cdot (2 \cdot 7 + 1),$$
$$\text{or } 140.$$

Problem 2. Show that the polynomial $x - y$ is a factor of the polynomial $x^n - y^n$ for every positive integer n.

Solution. Let P_n be the proposition

$$P_n: \quad x - y \text{ is a factor of } x^n - y^n$$

and

$$S = \{n \mid P_n \text{ is true}\}.$$

The integer 1 is in S, because $x - y$ is a factor of $x^1 - y^1$; in fact, $x^1 - y^1 = x - y$. Assume that k is in S. Hence,

P_k: $x - y$ is a factor of $x^k - y^k$

is true. We shall show that

P_{k+1}: $x - y$ is a factor of $x^{k+1} - y^{k+1}$

is also true.

Since P_k is true,

$$x^k - y^k = (x - y)p$$

for some polynomial p. How can we use this true equation to show that $x^{k+1} - y^{k+1} = (x - y)q$ for some polynomial q? The following true equations give us the answer.

$$\begin{aligned}
x^{k+1} - y^{k+1} &= (x^{k+1} - x^k y) + (x^k y - y^{k+1}) \\
&= (x - y)x^k + (x^k - y^k)y \\
&= (x - y)x^k + (x - y)py \\
&= (x - y)(x^k + py)
\end{aligned}$$

Thus, $x^{k+1} - y^{k+1} = (x - y)q$ where q is the polynomial $q = x^k + py$. Thus, P_{k+1} is true whenever P_k is true.

Since 1 is in S, and $k + 1$ is in S whenever k is, S is the set of all positive integers by the induction axiom. Hence, $x - y$ is a factor of $x^n - y^n$ for every positive integer n.

It might seem strange, but Problem 2 can also be solved by using the formula for the sum of a geometric series! Consider the geometric series

$$S = x^{n-1} + x^{n-2}y + x^{n-3}y^2 + \cdots + x^2 y^{n-3} + xy^{n-2} + y^{n-1}$$

having n terms, with first term $a = x^{n-1}$ and ratio $r = y/x$. By the formula on p. 556,

$$S = \frac{x^{n-1}\left[\left(\dfrac{y}{x}\right)^n - 1\right]}{\dfrac{y}{x} - 1}.$$

Thus,

$$S = \frac{x^n\left[\dfrac{y^n - x^n}{x^n}\right]}{y - x}$$

$$= \frac{y^n - x^n}{y - x} = \frac{x^n - y^n}{x - y}$$

and $x^n - y^n = (x - y)S$. This shows that

$$x^n - y^n = (x - y)(x^{n-1} + x^{n-2}y + \cdots + xy^{n-2} + y^{n-1}),$$

which not only shows that $x - y$ is a factor of $x^n - y^n$ but also shows what the other factor is.

For example, if $n = 5$ we have

$$x^5 - y^5 = (x - y)(x^4 + x^3y + x^2y^2 + xy^3 + y^4).$$

Exercises

Show, by mathematical induction, that each of the following equations is true for every positive integer n.

1. (a) $1 + 2 + 3 + \cdots + n = \dfrac{n(n + 1)}{2}$

   (b) $2 + 4 + 6 + \cdots + 2n = n(n + 1)$

2. (a) $1 + 3 + 5 + \cdots + (2n - 1) = n^2$

   (b) $1 + 5 + 9 + \cdots + (4n - 3) = n(2n - 1)$

3. (a) $1 + 2 + 4 + \cdots + 2^{n-1} = 2^n - 1$

   (b) $1 + \dfrac{1}{2} + \dfrac{1}{4} + \cdots + \dfrac{1}{2^{n-1}} = 2\left(1 - \dfrac{1}{2^n}\right)$

4. (a) $1^2 + 3^2 + 5^2 + \cdots + (2n - 1)^2 = \dfrac{n(4n^2 - 1)}{3}$

   (b) $\dfrac{1}{1 \cdot 2} + \dfrac{1}{2 \cdot 3} + \dfrac{1}{3 \cdot 4} + \cdots + \dfrac{1}{n(n + 1)} = \dfrac{n}{n + 1}$

5. Suppose that n boys are entered in a chess tournament. How many games are played if each boy plays one game with each of the other boys? Show that the formula

$$\frac{n(n - 1)}{2}$$

gives the correct number when $n = 2, 3, 4,$ and 5. Use mathematical induction to prove that this formula is true for every positive integer.

6. Devise a formula to determine the number of dominoes in the set that runs from double zero to double n. Prove your formula by mathematical induction.

7. If a convex polygon has n sides, how many diagonals does it have? Prove your formula by mathematical induction.

8. The sum of the measures of the angles of a triangle is $180°$. Generalize this result to give the sum of the measures of the angles of any polygon. Prove your formula by mathematical induction.

---

9. Prove that $n + 1 \leq 2^n$ for every positive integer n. (Hint: If $k + 1 \leq 2^k$ is true, then so is $(k + 1) + 1 \leq 2^k + 1$ and also $2^k + 1 \leq 2^k + 2^k = 2^{k+1}$.)

10. Prove that $n^2 < 4^n$ for every positive integer n.

11. Prove that for every positive integer n,

$$1^3 + 2^3 + 3^3 + \cdots + n^3 = (1 + 2 + 3 + \cdots + n)^2.$$

12. Prove that the product of two consecutive positive integers is always an even integer.

13-5 FURTHER EXAMPLES OF INDUCTION

The formula for the sum of an arithmetic series or a geometric series can be proved by mathematical induction. We illustrate part of this fact below.

Problem 1. Show that if $a_1 + a_2 + \cdots + a_n$ is an arithmetic series with n terms, then

$$E_n: \quad a_1 + a_2 + \cdots + a_n = \frac{n}{2}(a_1 + a_n).$$

Solution. Perhaps the problem should have been stated as follows. Show that for *every* positive integer n and *every* arithmetic series $a_1 + a_2 + \cdots + a_n$ with n terms, E_n is a true equation. Stated this way, E_1 is a true equation: $a_1 = \frac{1}{2}(a_1 + a_1)$. Assume

$$E_k: \quad a_1 + a_2 + \cdots + a_k = \frac{k}{2}(a_1 + a_k)$$

is true for every arithmetic series $a_1 + a_2 + \cdots + a_k$ having k terms. Let $a_1 + a_2 + \cdots + a_k + a_{k+1}$ be any arithmetic series with $k + 1$

terms. Let us prove that

$$E_{k+1}\colon\quad a_1 + a_2 + \cdots + a_k + a_{k+1} = \frac{k+1}{2}(a_1 + a_{k+1})$$

is a true equation.

To this end, we have

$$a_1 + a_2 + \cdots + a_k + a_{k+1} = (a_1 + a_2 + \cdots + a_k) + a_{k+1}$$
$$= \frac{k}{2}(a_1 + a_k) + a_{k+1}.$$

Now $a_{k+1} = a_1 + kd$, where d is the difference between successive terms of the series. Thus,

$$
\begin{aligned}
a_1 + a_2 + \cdots + a_k + a_{k+1} &= \tfrac{1}{2}[k(a_1 + a_k) + 2a_{k+1}]\\
&= \tfrac{1}{2}[k(a_1 + a_k) + a_1 + kd + a_{k+1}]\\
&= \tfrac{1}{2}[k(a_1 + a_k + d) + a_1 + a_{k+1}]\\
&= \tfrac{1}{2}[k(a_1 + a_{k+1}) + (a_1 + a_{k+1})]\\
&= \tfrac{1}{2}(k+1)(a_1 + a_{k+1}).
\end{aligned}
$$

Thus, E_{k+1} is true and the formula is established by mathematical induction.

We can use mathematical induction to prove the five laws of exponents, (LE-1) through (LE-5), for positive integral exponents. Before we begin, let us review the definition of exponents: For each number x, $x^1 = x$, $x^2 = x \cdot x$, and whenever x^k is defined, then x^{k+1} is defined by

$$x^{k+1} = x^k \cdot x.$$

Problem 2. Prove the fourth law of exponents, (LE-4):

$$(x \cdot y)^n = x^n \cdot y^n$$

for all numbers x and y and every positive integer n.

Solution. For each positive integer n, let P_n be the following proposition.

P_n: The equation $(x \cdot y)^n = x^n \cdot y^n$ is true for every pair x, y of numbers.

Next, let

$$S = \{n \mid P_n \text{ is true}\}.$$

Now 1 is in set S, since the equation

$$(x \cdot y)^1 = x^1 \cdot y^1$$

is true for every pair x, y of numbers by the definition of the first power of a number: $(x \cdot y)^1 = x \cdot y$, $x^1 = x$, $y^1 = y$, and therefore, $(x \cdot y)^1 = x^1 \cdot y^1$. If k is an integer in set S, then the following proposition is true.

P_k: The equation $(x \cdot y)^k = x^k \cdot y^k$ is true for every pair x, y of numbers.

To show that $k + 1$ is in S, we must show that the following proposition is true.

P_{k+1}: The equation $(x \cdot y)^{k+1} = x^{k+1} \cdot y^{k+1}$ is true for every pair x, y of numbers.

To show that P_{k+1} is true, we return to the definition of the $(k + 1)$-power of any number. Thus, by definition,

$$(x \cdot y)^{k+1} = (x \cdot y)^k \cdot (x \cdot y), \quad x^{k+1} = x^k \cdot x, \quad y^{k+1} = y^k \cdot y.$$

Hence, each of the following equations is true for every pair x, y of numbers.

$$
\begin{aligned}
(x \cdot y)^{k+1} &= (x \cdot y)^k \cdot (x \cdot y) && \text{(Def-Exp)} \\
&= (x^k \cdot y^k) \cdot (x \cdot y) && \text{(since } P_k \text{ is true)} \\
&= (x^k \cdot x) \cdot (y^k \cdot y) && \text{(R-M)} \\
&= x^{k+1} \cdot y^{k+1} && \text{(Def-Exp)}
\end{aligned}
$$

Since this last equation is true, P_{k+1} is true.

We have proved that 1 is in S, and that whenever k is in S, $k + 1$ is also in S. Hence, by the induction axiom, S is the set of all positive integers. This means that every proposition P_n is true. Thus, we have proved the fourth law of exponents.

Another use of the induction axiom is shown in the problem below.

Problem 3. Prove De Moivre's theorem:

$$[r(\cos \theta + i \sin \theta)]^n = r^n(\cos n\theta + i \sin n\theta)$$

for every positive integer n.

Solution. Let set S contain every positive integer n for which the equation above is true. Since

$$[r(\cos \theta + i \sin \theta)]^1 = r^1[(\cos 1 \cdot \theta) + (i \sin 1 \cdot \theta)]$$

is true, 1 is in S. Let k be an integer in S, so that the equation

$$[r(\cos \theta + i \sin \theta)]^k = r^k(\cos k\theta + i \sin k\theta)$$

is true. We wish to prove that the following equation is also true.

$$[r(\cos \theta + i \sin \theta)]^{k+1} = r^{k+1}[\cos (k + 1)\theta + i \sin (k + 1)\theta]$$

By definition of the $(k + 1)$-power of a number,

$$[r(\cos \theta + i \sin \theta)]^{k+1} = [r(\cos \theta + i \sin \theta)]^k[r(\cos \theta + i \sin \theta)].$$

Using the known value of the kth power of $r(\cos \theta + i \sin \theta)$ and the method of finding a trigonometric form of the product of two complex numbers, we may find the $(k + 1)$-power of $r(\cos \theta + i \sin \theta)$ as follows:

$$
\begin{aligned}
[r(\cos \theta + i \sin \theta)]^{k+1} &= [r(\cos \theta + i \sin \theta)]^k[r(\cos \theta + i \sin \theta)] \\
&= [r^k(\cos k\theta + i \sin k\theta)][r(\cos \theta + i \sin \theta)] \\
&= r^k \cdot r[\cos k\theta \cos \theta - \sin k\theta \sin \theta \\
&\quad + i(\sin k\theta \cos \theta + \cos k\theta \sin \theta)] \\
&= r^k \cdot r[\cos (k\theta + \theta) + i \sin (k\theta + \theta)] \\
&= r^{k+1}[\cos (k + 1)\theta + i \sin (k + 1)\theta].
\end{aligned}
$$

We have proved that $k + 1$ is also in set S.

Since 1 is in set S, and since, whenever the integer k is in S, $k + 1$ is also in S, the set S is the set of all positive integers by the induction axiom. This proves De Moivre's theorem.

Exercises

Show, by mathematical induction, that the following equations are true for every positive integer n.

1. (a) $1 + 3 + 9 + \cdots + 3^{n-1} = \frac{1}{2}(3^n - 1)$

   (b) $1 + \frac{1}{3} + \frac{1}{9} + \cdots + \frac{1}{3^{n-1}} = \frac{3}{2}\left(1 - \frac{1}{3^n}\right)$

2. (a) $1 + 1.03 + 1.03^2 + \cdots + 1.03^{n-1} = \frac{100}{3}(1.03^n - 1)$

   (b) $1 + 1.04 + 1.04^2 + \cdots + 1.04^{n-1} = 25(1.04^n - 1)$

3. (a) $1 + 2 \cdot 2 + 3 \cdot 2^2 + \cdots + n \cdot 2^{n-1} = (n - 1)2^n + 1$

   (b) $1 + 2 \cdot 3 + 3 \cdot 3^2 + \cdots + n \cdot 3^{n-1} = \frac{1}{4}[(2n - 1)3^n + 1]$

4. Prove, by mathematical induction, that the formula for the sum of a geometric series

$$a + ar + ar^2 + \cdots + ar^{n-1} = \frac{a(r^n - 1)}{r - 1}, \quad r \neq 1,$$

is true for every positive integer n.

5. Prove that the equation

$$a + 2ar + 3ar^2 + \cdots + nar^{n-1} = a\left[\frac{(nr - n - 1)r^n + 1}{(r - 1)^2}\right], \quad r \neq 1,$$

is true for every positive integer n.

6. Prove that the first law of exponents,

$$x^m \cdot x^n = x^{m+n},$$

is true for every real number x and all positive integers m and n. (Hint: Prove that, for any given x and m, the equation is true for every positive integer n.)

7. Prove that for every positive integer n, the nth power of the conjugate of a complex number is the conjugate of the nth power of the number; that is, if $\bar{z}$ denotes the conjugate of the complex number z, then $(\bar{z})^n = (\overline{z^n})$.

8. Prove that the equation

$$\frac{1}{1 \cdot 2 \cdot 3} + \frac{1}{2 \cdot 3 \cdot 4} + \frac{1}{3 \cdot 4 \cdot 5} + \cdots + \frac{1}{n(n + 1)(n + 2)}$$
$$= \frac{n(n + 3)}{4(n + 1)(n + 2)}$$

is true for every positive integer n.

---

9. Prove that the integer

$$n^3 + 5n$$

is divisible by 6 for every positive integer n.

10. Prove that

$$(1 + a)^n > 1 + na$$

for every integer $n > 1$ and every number $a > 0$. (Hint: Start the induction with $n = 2$.)

11. Prove by mathematical induction that

$$1 \cdot 2^2 + 2 \cdot 3^2 + 3 \cdot 4^2 + \cdots + n \cdot (n + 1)^2$$
$$= \tfrac{1}{12}n(n + 1)(n + 2)(3n + 5)$$

for every positive integer n.

12. Let $W = \{n \mid 4 + 8 + 12 + \cdots + 4n = 2n(n + 1) + 3\}$.
(a) Is $k + 1$ in W whenever k is in W?
(b) Is W the set of all positive integers?

13. Prove that if x is a nonzero real number and m is an arbitrary positive integer, then

$$\frac{x^m}{x^n} = x^{m-n} \tag{LE-2}$$

is true for every positive integer $n \leq m$.

14. Prove that if x is a real number and m is a positive integer,

$$(x^m)^n = x^{mn} \tag{LE-3}$$

is true for every positive integer n.

15. Prove that if x and y are real numbers, and $y \neq 0$, then

$$\left(\frac{x}{y}\right)^n = \frac{x^n}{y^n} \tag{LE-5}$$

is true for every positive integer n.

EXTRA!

The dichotomy paradox states that it is impossible to cover any distance: to cover a distance, one must first cover one-half the distance, then cover one-half of the remaining distance, then cover one-half of that remaining distance, and so forth. In other words, if a person sets out to walk a mile, first he must walk half of a mile, then a fourth of a mile (half the remaining distance), then an eighth of a mile, and so forth. According to this reasoning, there always remains part of the distance to be covered, and therefore, it is impossible to cover any distance.

Do you see the fallacy in this reasoning? The exercises below will show that this paradox is false.

1. Write a formula for covering a distance, d, according to the dichotomy paradox. (That is, the distance, d, equals half of the distance plus half of the remaining distance, etc.)

2. What kind of series is the formula you wrote in Exercise 1?

3. Write a formula for the sum of the series. Is the sum finite or infinite? Find the sum of the series.

4. What false assumption is made in the dichotomy paradox?

KEY IDEAS AND KEY WORDS

A **series** is an algebraic expression of the form

$$a_1 + a_2 + \cdots + a_n$$

for some numbers $a_1, a_2, \ldots a_n$. Each number $a_1, a_2, \ldots a_n$, is a **term** of the series, and n is the number of terms in the series.

An **arithmetic series** is a series

$$a_1 + a_2 + \cdots + a_n$$

where the differences between consecutive terms are all equal. Letting the common difference be d, an arithmetic series can be expressed in the form

$$a + (a + d) + (a + 2d) + \cdots + [a + (n - 1)d]$$

where a is the first term and n is the number of terms in the series. The **sum** of an arithmetic series is given by

$$S = \frac{n}{2}(a_1 + a_n)$$

where n is the number of terms, a_1 is the first term and a_n is the last term.

A **geometric series** is a series of the form

$$a_1 + a_2 + \cdots + a_n$$

where the ratios of successive terms are all equal. Letting a be the first term and r be the common ratio, a geometric series can be expressed in the form

$$a + ar + ar^2 + \cdots + ar^{n-1}$$

where n is the number of terms. The **sum** of a geometric series is

$$S = \frac{a(r^n - 1)}{r - 1}, \quad r \neq 1$$

where a is the first term, r is the ratio and n is the number of terms.

An **infinite geometric series** is an algebraic expression of the form

$$a + ar + ar^2 + \cdots + ar^{n-1} + \cdots.$$

A **partial sum** of an infinite geometric series is the sum of the first n terms of the series.

$$S_n = a + ar + ar^2 + \cdots + ar^{n-1}.$$

The **sum** of an infinite geometric series is

$$S = \frac{a}{1-r}, \quad |r| < 1$$

The **induction axiom** is a fundamental axiom of the system of positive integers. It can be stated as follows.

If a set S of positive integers contains 1, and if whenever S contains an integer k, it also contains the integer $k + 1$, then S must be the set of all positive integers.

CHAPTER REVIEW

For the specified value of n, find the nth term of each of the following arithmetic series.

1. $-1 + 4 + 9 + \cdots$, $n = 9$
2. $(a - 2) + a + (a + 2) + \cdots$, $n = 10$
3. $a^3 + a(a^2 + a) + a(a^2 + 2a) + \cdots$, $n = 12$

Find the sum of each arithmetic series.

4. $6 + 15 + 24 + \cdots$, 10 terms
5. $-6 - 3 + 0 + \cdots$, 11 terms
6. $-2 - 1.5 - 1 - \cdots$, 10 terms
7. $1 + \frac{4}{3} + \frac{5}{3} + \cdots$, 9 terms
8. Find five arithmetic means between 86 and 14.
9. How many numbers between 50 and 150 are exactly divisible by 7? Find their sum.
10. The sum of the first 15 terms of an arithmetic series is -165. Find the first term and the difference, given that the fifteenth term is -32.
11. If the fifth term of an arithmetic series is 27 and the eleventh term is 48, what is the first term?

For the specified value of n, find the nth term of each of the following geometric series.

12. $4 + 3 + \frac{9}{4} + \cdots$, $n = 9$
13. $1 + 1.1 + 1.21 + \cdots$, $n = 10$
14. $5 + 2 + \frac{4}{5} + \cdots$, $n = 15$

Find the sum of each geometric series.

15. $4 + 1 + \frac{1}{4} + \frac{1}{16} + \frac{1}{64}$
16. $1 - \frac{1}{3} + \frac{1}{9} - \frac{1}{27} + \frac{1}{81}$

17. $1.5 + 1.5^2 + 1.5^3 + \cdots + 1.5^{10}$

18. $1 - \sqrt{5} + 5 - \cdots$, 10 terms

19. If the fourth term of a geometric series is 3, and the ninth term is 729, what are the first three terms?

20. Find five geometric means between $\frac{3}{4}$ and $\frac{16}{243}$.

21. The fifth term of a geometric series is 162, and the ratio is -3. Find the first term and the sum of the first eight terms.

Use the formula given for the nth term to write the first five terms of a series. Tell which series are arithmetic, which are geometric, and which are neither.

22. $3n$ **23.** 3^n

24. $\dfrac{n-1}{n+1}$ **25.** $n(n+3)$

26. $4 - n$ **27.** $3n - 1$

28. (a) For the geometric series

$$\tfrac{2}{3} + \tfrac{1}{3} + \tfrac{1}{6} + \tfrac{1}{12} + \cdots$$

   find the partial sums S_5, S_{10}, and S_{20}.
   (b) Find the sum of the infinite geometric series in part (a).

Find an equivalent common fraction for each repeating decimal.

29. $.\underline{27}$ **30.** $.1\underline{34}$

Use mathematical induction to prove that each of the following formulas is correct for every positive integer n.

31. $2 + 6 + 12 + \cdots + n(n+1) = \dfrac{n(n+1)(n+2)}{3}$

32. $6 + 24 + 60 + \cdots + n(n+1)(n+2) = \dfrac{n(n+1)(n+2)(n+3)}{4}$

33. Show that if $x + y + z$ is a geometric series, then $\log x + \log y + \log z$ is an arithmetic series.

CHAPTER TEST

1. Find a formula for the sum of the arithmetic series

$$20 + 16 + 12 + \cdots + (24 - 4n).$$

2. Find the sum of all the positive integers less than 300 that are divisible by 8.

3. Find the sum of the geometric series

$$6 + 6^2 + 6^3 + \cdots + 6^7.$$

4. Find the sum of the infinite geometric series

$$4 - 2 + 1 - \tfrac{1}{2} + \tfrac{1}{4} - \tfrac{1}{8} + \cdots .$$

5. Find a common fraction equivalent to the repeating decimal $1.2\underline{45}$.

6. The third term of an arithmetic series is $4 + \sqrt{3}$ and the tenth term is $11 + 8\sqrt{3}$. Find the first two terms.

7. Use the given formula for each nth term to write the first five terms of a series. In each case, find the sum of the first ten terms, and name the type of series.
(a) $5 + 2n$ \hspace{4cm} (b) 2^n

8. Given that $n \geq 1$, prove that the sum of the first n powers of 3 is equal to

$$\frac{3(3^n - 1)}{2} .$$

In other words, prove that

$$3 + 3^2 + 3^3 + \cdots + 3^n = \frac{3(3^n - 1)}{2} .$$

CHAPTER 14

Vector Algebra

Objectives . . .

- To compare the structure of the system of vectors with the structure of the real number system.
- To express any vector as a combination of its basis vectors.
- To apply vector techniques to problems in physics.
- To apply the inner product definition to find a condition for perpendicularity.

14–1 VECTORS

The study of geometry usually begins with a list of axioms which relate points, lines, and planes. In such a study, lines and planes are customarily considered to be sets of points. Thus, when we say that point A lies on line L, we mean that point A is an element of the set of points which is L; and when we say that line L lies in plane p, we mean that every point in set L is also in the set p. One of the axioms of euclidean geometry states that there is a unique line L containing any two distinct points A and B. Another axiom states that the points A and B on L separate L into three subsets, indicated by H, K, and $\overline{AB}$ in Fig. 14–1. Sets H and K are called rays, and $\overline{AB}$ is called a *segment* of line L. Segment $\overline{AB}$ consists of points A, B, and all points C on L between A and B. Instead of listing all the axioms, we shall assume that you are familiar with the elementary aspects of plane euclidean geometry. All the points and lines under discussion lie in some given plane.

If our plane has a coordinate system on it, then according to the distance formula, each segment $\overline{AB}$ has a length, which we shall designate by AB. We shall write $AB = CD$ to indicate that the line segments $\overline{AB}$ and $\overline{CD}$ are equal in length, or congruent. It is important to remember that segment $\overline{AB}$ is a part of a line and that AB is a number. If $\overline{AB}$ and $\overline{CD}$ are two segments, then $\overline{AB} \cong \overline{CD}$ if, and only if, $AB = CD$. (The symbol $\cong$ is read "is congruent to.")

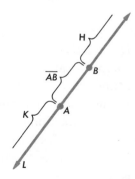

FIGURE 14–1

A direction can be assigned to each segment by arbitrarily calling one of its endpoints the *initial point* and the other the *terminal point*.

The *direction* assigned to the segment begins at the initial point and ends at the terminal point. Such a directed line segment is called a *vector*. If a vector has initial point A and terminal point B, then the vector is designated by

$$\overrightarrow{AB}.$$

Note that if $A \neq B$, then the vector $\overrightarrow{AB}$ is different from the vector $\overrightarrow{BA}$ since the initial point of each vector is the terminal point of the other. Thus, the direction of vector $\overrightarrow{BA}$ is opposite to that of $\overrightarrow{AB}$.

Definition of equal vectors

The vectors $\overrightarrow{AB}$ and $\overrightarrow{CD}$ are said to be equal if, and only if, $AB = CD$ and the vectors $\overrightarrow{AB}$ and $\overrightarrow{CD}$ have the same direction.

If vectors $\overrightarrow{AB}$ and $\overrightarrow{CD}$ do not lie on the same line, then we can decide whether or not $\overrightarrow{AB}$ and $\overrightarrow{CD}$ are equal by looking at the quadrilateral $ABDC$ in Fig. 14-2. Thus, $\overrightarrow{AB} = \overrightarrow{CD}$ if, and only if, $ABDC$ is a parallelogram. If $\overrightarrow{AB}$ and $\overrightarrow{CD}$ lie on the same line L, then $\overrightarrow{AB} = \overrightarrow{CD}$ if, and only if, $AB = CD$ and the direction from A to B is the same as the direction from C to D on the line L.

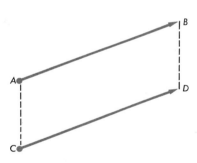

FIGURE 14-2

Several vectors are drawn in Fig. 14-3. Of these vectors, $\overrightarrow{AB} = \overrightarrow{CD}$ since $AB = CD$, each having length $\sqrt{8}$; $\overrightarrow{AB}$ is parallel to $\overrightarrow{CD}$, each having slope 1; and $\overrightarrow{AB}$ has the same direction as $\overrightarrow{CD}$, each being directed upward to the right. On the other hand, $\overrightarrow{AB} \neq \overrightarrow{JK}$ although $\overrightarrow{AB}$ is parallel and congruent to $\overrightarrow{JK}$. The reason that $\overrightarrow{AB}$ is not equal to $\overrightarrow{JK}$ is that the direction of one vector is opposite to the direction of the other. You may check to see that $\overrightarrow{EF} = \overrightarrow{GH}$ and that $\overrightarrow{AB} \neq \overrightarrow{MN}$.

A vector such as $\overrightarrow{AA}$, which has the same initial point and terminal point, is called a *zero vector*. The vector $\overrightarrow{AA}$ consists of a single point. We shall consider every zero vector to have no direction and to be equal to all other zero vectors. For convenience, the symbol **0** will be used to denote a zero vector.

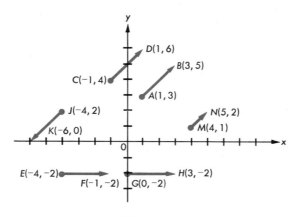

FIGURE 14–3

If we are given a vector $\overrightarrow{AB}$ and a point C, then there exists a *unique* point D such that $\overrightarrow{AB} = \overrightarrow{CD}$. If point C is not on the same line as $\overrightarrow{AB}$, then D is a unique point such that $ABDC$ is a parallelogram. If C is on the same line L as $\overrightarrow{AB}$, then D is selected on L such that $AB = CD$, and the direction from A to B is the same as that from C to D.

Exercises

1. (a) List all nonzero vectors determined by three distinct points A, B, and C.
   (b) Given that $A_1, A_2, \ldots, A_n$ are n distinct points, how many nonzero vectors do they determine?

2. (a) Given that vectors $\overrightarrow{AB}$ and $\overrightarrow{CD}$ are not collinear, what conditions on the quadrilateral containing these points will make the vectors $\overrightarrow{AB}$ and $\overrightarrow{CD}$ of equal length but of opposite direction?
   (b) Given that A, B, C, and D are four points, no three of which are collinear, list all nonzero vectors determined by these points. Are any two of these vectors ever equal?

3. (a) Given points A, B, and C with respective coordinates $(3, 1)$, $(3, 5)$, and $(-1, 1)$, find the coordinates of the points D, E, and F such that each of the following is true.
   (i) $\overrightarrow{AB} = \overrightarrow{CD}$ (ii) $\overrightarrow{AC} = \overrightarrow{BE}$ (iii) $\overrightarrow{BA} = \overrightarrow{AF}$
   (b) Given points A, B, and C with respective coordinates $(0, 0)$, $(2, 2)$, and $(-3, 3)$, find the coordinates of the points D, E, and F such that each of the following is true.
   (i) $\overrightarrow{AC} = \overrightarrow{BD}$
   (ii) $\overrightarrow{BA} = \overrightarrow{CE}$
   (iii) $\overrightarrow{BC} = \overrightarrow{AF}$

4. (a) Given points A and B with respective coordinates $(0, 0)$ and $(4, 4)$, find the coordinates of the points D, E, and F such that each of the following is true.

    (i) $\overrightarrow{AD} = \overrightarrow{DB}$
    (ii) $\overrightarrow{AB} = \overrightarrow{BE}$
    (iii) $\overrightarrow{BA} = \overrightarrow{AF}$

  (b) Given points A and B with respective coordinates $(4, 0)$ and $(0, -4)$, find the coordinates of the points D, E, and F such that each of the following is true.

    (i) $\overrightarrow{BD} = \overrightarrow{DA}$
    (ii) $\overrightarrow{BA} = \overrightarrow{AE}$
    (iii) $\overrightarrow{AB} = \overrightarrow{BF}$

5. (a) Given points A, B, and C with respective coordinates $(4, 1)$, $(-2, 7)$, and $(3, -1)$, find the coordinates of the points D, E, and F such that each of the following is true.

    (i) $\overrightarrow{AB} = \overrightarrow{CD}$
    (ii) $\overrightarrow{AB}$ and $\overrightarrow{CE}$ have equal length and opposite direction
    (iii) $\overrightarrow{AB}$ and $\overrightarrow{CF}$ have the same direction and $CF = AB$

  (b) Given points A, B, and C with respective coordinates $(0, 0)$, $(-5, 1)$, and $(6, -2)$, find the coordinates of the points D, E, and F such that each of the following is true.

    (i) $\overrightarrow{AC} = \overrightarrow{BE}$
    (ii) $AB = 2CD$, and $\overrightarrow{AB}$ and $\overrightarrow{CD}$ have opposite direction
    (iii) $2FC = 3AB$, and $\overrightarrow{FC}$ and $\overrightarrow{AB}$ have the same direction

6. (a) Given points A, B, C, and D with respective coordinates $(-1, 2)$, $(5, 6)$, $(2, -2)$, and $(8, 2)$, determine whether $\overrightarrow{AB} = \overrightarrow{CD}$.

  (b) Given points A, B, C and D with respective coordinates $(2, 3)$, $(-2, -1)$, $(3, -4)$ and $(7, 0)$, determine whether $\overrightarrow{AD} = \overrightarrow{BC}$.

14–2 ADDITION AND SUBTRACTION

Several centuries ago, physicists discovered that a force could conveniently be represented by a vector, with the direction of the vector indicating the direction of application of the force and the length of the vector indicating the size of the force. They also discovered that if two forces were applied to an object, then the resultant force could be found by the *parallelogram law*. Thus, if vectors $\overrightarrow{AB}$ and $\overrightarrow{AC}$ represent two forces applied to an object at A, the resultant force is represented by the diagonal vector $\overrightarrow{AE}$ of the parallelogram $ABEC$ in Fig. 14–4. The resultant force represented by $\overrightarrow{AE}$ has precisely the same effect on the object at A as the two forces represented by $\overrightarrow{AB}$ and $\overrightarrow{AC}$.

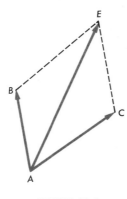

FIGURE 14–4   FIGURE 14–5

We shall define the sum of two vectors in essentially the same way in which the resultant was defined in Fig. 14–4. Thus, the sum of vectors $\overrightarrow{AB}$ and $\overrightarrow{CD}$ is defined in the following manner. (See Fig. 14–5.)

Definition of addition

$$\overrightarrow{AB} + \overrightarrow{CD} = \overrightarrow{AE},$$

where point E is chosen such that $\overrightarrow{BE} = \overrightarrow{CD}$

If vectors $\overrightarrow{AB}$ and $\overrightarrow{CD}$ lie on the same line L, then $\overrightarrow{AE}$, the sum of $\overrightarrow{AB}$ and $\overrightarrow{CD}$, is obtained in the way shown in Fig. 14–6. Perhaps the easiest way to remember the definition of addition is to consider the sum of $\overrightarrow{AB}$ and $\overrightarrow{BC}$, as shown in Fig. 14–7. Then by definition,

$$\overrightarrow{AB} + \overrightarrow{BC} = \overrightarrow{AC}.$$

Thus, in triangle ABC, the sum of the sides $\overrightarrow{AB}$ and $\overrightarrow{BC}$ is the side $\overrightarrow{AC}$.

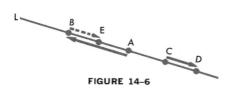

FIGURE 14–6

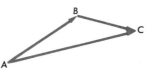

FIGURE 14–7

The following is another property of vector addition.

ADDITIVE PROPERTY

If $\overrightarrow{AB} = \overrightarrow{A'B'}$ and $\overrightarrow{CD} = \overrightarrow{C'D'}$, then $\overrightarrow{AB} + \overrightarrow{CD} = \overrightarrow{A'B'} + \overrightarrow{C'D'}$.

The validity of this property is demonstrated in Fig. 14–8. In this figure, $\overrightarrow{AB} + \overrightarrow{CD} = \overrightarrow{AE}$ and $\overrightarrow{A'B'} + \overrightarrow{C'D'} = \overrightarrow{A'E'}$. To show that $\overrightarrow{AE} = \overrightarrow{A'E'}$, we first observe the equations

$$\overrightarrow{CD} = \overrightarrow{C'D'}, \quad \overrightarrow{CD} = \overrightarrow{BE}, \quad \overrightarrow{C'D'} = \overrightarrow{B'E'}.$$

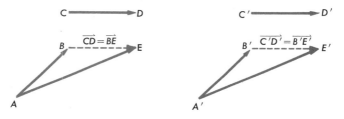

FIGURE 14–8

From these equations we may conclude that

$$\overrightarrow{BE} = \overrightarrow{B'E'}.$$

Triangles ABE and $A'B'E'$ are congruent because $\overrightarrow{AB} = \overrightarrow{A'B'}$, $\overrightarrow{BE} = \overrightarrow{B'E'}$, and the angle at B is equal to the angle at B'. Furthermore, since $\overrightarrow{AB}$ is parallel to $\overrightarrow{A'B'}$ and $\overrightarrow{BE}$ is parallel to $\overrightarrow{B'E'}$, it follows that $\overrightarrow{AE}$ is parallel and equal to $\overrightarrow{A'E'}$. Hence, $\overrightarrow{AE} = \overrightarrow{A'E'}$ so that $\overrightarrow{AB} + \overrightarrow{CD} = \overrightarrow{A'B'} + \overrightarrow{C'D'}$.

Vector addition has all the properties of addition of real numbers. We list these properties below.

COMMUTATIVE LAW

$$\overrightarrow{AB} + \overrightarrow{CD} = \overrightarrow{CD} + \overrightarrow{AB} \quad \textit{for all vectors } \overrightarrow{AB}, \overrightarrow{CD}$$

ASSOCIATIVE LAW

$$\overrightarrow{AB} + (\overrightarrow{CD} + \overrightarrow{EF}) = (\overrightarrow{AB} + \overrightarrow{CD}) + \overrightarrow{EF}$$
$$\textit{for all vectors } \overrightarrow{AB}, \overrightarrow{CD}, \overrightarrow{EF}$$

IDENTITY ELEMENT

$$\overrightarrow{AB} + 0 = 0 + \overrightarrow{AB} = \overrightarrow{AB} \quad \textit{for each vector } \overrightarrow{AB}$$

INVERSE ELEMENT

Each vector $\overrightarrow{AB}$ has an opposite, $-\overrightarrow{AB}$, such that

$$\overrightarrow{AB} + (-\overrightarrow{AB}) = -\overrightarrow{AB} + \overrightarrow{AB} = 0.$$

The additive inverse, or opposite, of $\overrightarrow{AB}$ is $\overrightarrow{BA}$,

$$-\overrightarrow{AB} = \overrightarrow{BA},$$

because by the definition of addition, $\overrightarrow{AB} + \overrightarrow{BA} = \overrightarrow{AA} = 0$ and $\overrightarrow{BA} + \overrightarrow{AB} = \overrightarrow{BB} = 0$.

We have constructed $\overrightarrow{AE} = \overrightarrow{AB} + \overrightarrow{CD}$ and $\overrightarrow{CF} = \overrightarrow{CD} + \overrightarrow{AB}$ in Fig. 14–9. It follows from geometry that $\overrightarrow{AE} = \overrightarrow{CF}$ and, hence, that the commutative law holds. We shall leave the proof of the associative law as an exercise.

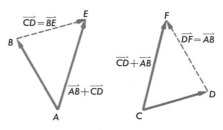

FIGURE 14–9

The following is another property of vector addition, whose proof is the same as that for the cancellation law of addition for numbers given in Section 1–2.

CANCELLATION LAW

$$\textit{If } \overrightarrow{AB} + \overrightarrow{CD} = \overrightarrow{AB} + \overrightarrow{EF}, \textit{ then } \overrightarrow{CD} = \overrightarrow{EF}.$$

Once we have defined the opposite of a vector, we can introduce the operation of subtraction of vectors.

Definition of subtraction

$$\overrightarrow{AB} - \overrightarrow{CD} = \overrightarrow{AB} + (-\overrightarrow{CD}) \textit{ for all vectors } \overrightarrow{AB}, \overrightarrow{CD}$$

Problem. Prove that the diagonals of a parallelogram bisect each other.

Solution. Let $ABCD$ be a parallelogram, as shown in Fig. 14–10, and let E be the point of bisection of diagonal $\overrightarrow{AC}$. Since $\overrightarrow{AB} = \overrightarrow{DC}$ by assumption, and $\overrightarrow{AB} = \overrightarrow{AE} + \overrightarrow{EB}$ and $\overrightarrow{DC} = \overrightarrow{DE} + \overrightarrow{EC}$, we have

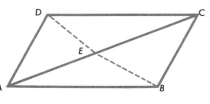

$$\overrightarrow{AE} + \overrightarrow{EB} = \overrightarrow{DE} + \overrightarrow{EC}.$$

FIGURE 14–10

Now $\overrightarrow{AE} = \overrightarrow{EC}$, and hence by the cancellation law, we have that

$$\overrightarrow{DE} = \overrightarrow{EB}.$$

Two nonzero vectors can be equal and have an endpoint in common if, and only if, they lie on the same line. Hence, E must lie on the diagonal $\overrightarrow{DB}$. Furthermore, it is the midpoint of $\overrightarrow{DB}$. This establishes the proof.

Exercises

Each expression in Exercises 1–5 is equal to a vector having its endpoints among the four points A, B, C, and D. For each expression, find the vector determined by these four points.

1. (a) $\overrightarrow{AB} + \overrightarrow{BC} = $ __?__   (b) $\overrightarrow{AB} - \overrightarrow{AC} = $ __?__
2. (a) $\overrightarrow{AB} + (\overrightarrow{BC} + \overrightarrow{CD}) = $ __?__   (b) $(\overrightarrow{AB} + \overrightarrow{BC}) + \overrightarrow{CD} = $ __?__
3. (a) $\overrightarrow{AB} - \overrightarrow{AD} = $ __?__
   (b) $(\overrightarrow{AD} + \overrightarrow{AC}) - \overrightarrow{AD} = $ __?__
4. (a) $\overrightarrow{AB} + (\overrightarrow{CD} - \overrightarrow{AD}) = $ __?__
   (b) $(\overrightarrow{AB} + \overrightarrow{CD}) + (\overrightarrow{BC} + \overrightarrow{DA}) = $ __?__
5. (a) $(\overrightarrow{AB} - \overrightarrow{CB}) + (\overrightarrow{CD} - \overrightarrow{AC}) = $ __?__
   (b) $(\overrightarrow{BD} - \overrightarrow{AC}) + (\overrightarrow{DB} - \overrightarrow{CA}) = $ __?__

Which of the following statements are true for the figure at the right?

6. (a) $\overrightarrow{XY} + \overrightarrow{YZ} = \overrightarrow{XZ}$
   (b) $\overrightarrow{XY} - \overrightarrow{XZ} = \overrightarrow{YZ}$
7. (a) $\overrightarrow{XY} + \overrightarrow{XZ} = \overrightarrow{YZ}$
   (b) $\overrightarrow{XZ} - \overrightarrow{YZ} = \overrightarrow{XY}$

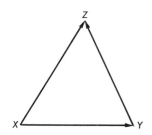

8. (a) Consider the points A, B, and C with respective coordinates $(0, 0)$, $(4, 0)$, and $(-4, 0)$. What can you say about $\overrightarrow{AB} + \overrightarrow{AC}$?
   (b) One vector has length 3; another vector has length 6 and a direction opposite to the first vector. What is the length of their sum? What can you say about the direction of the sum of the vectors?

---

9. Show that if $\overrightarrow{AB} = \overrightarrow{CD}$, then $\overrightarrow{AC} = \overrightarrow{BD}$.

10. Given that $\overrightarrow{AB}$ and $\overrightarrow{AC}$ are not collinear, show that $\overrightarrow{AB} + \overrightarrow{AC}$ and $\overrightarrow{AB} - \overrightarrow{AC}$ are diagonals of the parallelogram having $\overrightarrow{AB}$ and $\overrightarrow{AC}$ as two of its adjacent sides.

11. Given points A, B, and O with respective coordinates $(2, -8)$, $(-5, 10)$, and $(0, 0)$, use the parallelogram law to find the coordinates of point C such that $\overrightarrow{OA} + \overrightarrow{OB} = \overrightarrow{OC}$.

12. Given points Q, R, and O with respective coordinates $(11, 2)$, $(8, 5)$, and $(0, 0)$, use the parallelogram law to determine the coordinates of a point P such that $\overrightarrow{OQ} + \overrightarrow{OR} = \overrightarrow{OP}$.

13. If $\overrightarrow{AB} - \overrightarrow{CD} = \mathbf{0}$, is it necessarily true that $\overrightarrow{AB} = \overrightarrow{CD}$?

14. Given points A, B, C, and D with respective coordinates $(0, 0)$, $(2, 2)$, $(0, 2)$, and $(2, 4)$, graph $\overrightarrow{AB}$ and $\overrightarrow{CD}$. Does $\overrightarrow{AB} = \overrightarrow{CD}$?

15. In the figures, $\overrightarrow{BC}$ and $\overrightarrow{FE}$ are the differences of two vectors. Write the proper subtraction statement for each figure.

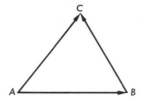 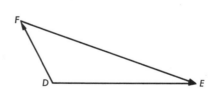

---

16. Given points A, B, and C in the figure, give an argument which shows that $(\overrightarrow{AB} + \overrightarrow{BC}) + \overrightarrow{CA} = \mathbf{0}$.

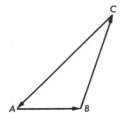

17. Show graphically that $-(\overrightarrow{AB} - \overrightarrow{CD}) = -\overrightarrow{AB} + \overrightarrow{CD}$.

18. Sketch a vector $\overrightarrow{AB}$ that has length 2 inches, is parallel to the lower edge of your paper, and has an arrow on its right-hand end. Sketch a second vector $\overrightarrow{CD}$ that has length 1.5 inches and makes an angle of 30° with $\overrightarrow{AB}$. Now sketch

$$2\overrightarrow{AB}, \quad 3\overrightarrow{CD}, \quad \overrightarrow{AB} + \overrightarrow{CD}, \quad \overrightarrow{AB} - \overrightarrow{CD}, \quad 2\overrightarrow{AB} - 3\overrightarrow{CD}, \quad \frac{\overrightarrow{AB} + \overrightarrow{CD}}{2}.$$

19. Use the figure to show that vector addition is associative.

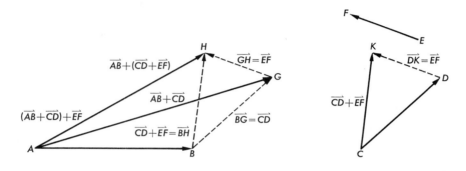

14-3 SCALAR MULTIPLICATION

For a given vector $\overrightarrow{AB}$, let us define

$$1\overrightarrow{AB} = \overrightarrow{AB},$$
$$2\overrightarrow{AB} = \overrightarrow{AB} + \overrightarrow{AB},$$
$$3\overrightarrow{AB} = \overrightarrow{AB} + \overrightarrow{AB} + \overrightarrow{AB},$$

and so on. Whenever $k\overrightarrow{AB}$ has been defined, then we define

$$(k + 1)\overrightarrow{AB} = k\overrightarrow{AB} + \overrightarrow{AB}.$$

In this way, we may define $n\overrightarrow{AB}$ for every positive integer n. Intuitively,

$$n\overrightarrow{AB} = \underbrace{\overrightarrow{AB} + \overrightarrow{AB} + \cdots + \overrightarrow{AB}.}_{n \text{ terms}}$$

How could we define $n\overrightarrow{AB}$, given that n is a negative integer? We would define $(-1)\overrightarrow{AB}$ to be $-\overrightarrow{AB}$, the additive inverse of $\overrightarrow{AB}$. It should then seem natural to define $(-2)\overrightarrow{AB}$ to be $-(2\overrightarrow{AB})$, $(-3)\overrightarrow{AB}$ to be $-(3\overrightarrow{AB})$, and, in general,

$$(-k)\overrightarrow{AB} = -(k\overrightarrow{AB})$$

for every positive integer k. Finally, we define

$$0\overrightarrow{AB} = \mathbf{0}.$$

With the definition above, $n\overrightarrow{AB}$ is defined for every vector $\overrightarrow{AB}$ and every integer n. Some examples are given in Fig. 14–11.

If the plane has a coordinate system on it, so that each vector $\overrightarrow{AB}$ has a length which we shall designate by $|\overrightarrow{AB}|$, then it follows from our definition of $n\overrightarrow{AB}$ that

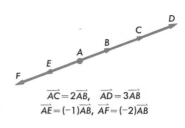

$$\overrightarrow{AC} = 2\overrightarrow{AB}, \quad \overrightarrow{AD} = 3\overrightarrow{AB}$$
$$\overrightarrow{AE} = (-1)\overrightarrow{AB}, \quad \overrightarrow{AF} = (-2)\overrightarrow{AB}$$

FIGURE 14–11

$$|n\overrightarrow{AB}| = |n| \cdot |\overrightarrow{AB}|.$$

In other words, the length of vector $n\overrightarrow{AB}$ is $|n|$ times the length of $\overrightarrow{AB}$. The multiplication of a vector by a number is called *scalar multiplication*. The real number r appearing in a product $r\overrightarrow{AB}$ is often called a *scalar*. With this in mind, let us define $r\overrightarrow{AB}$ for every real number r in the following way.

Definition of scalar multiplication

The vector $r\overrightarrow{AB}$ has length $|r| \cdot |\overrightarrow{AB}|$ and the same direction as $\overrightarrow{AB}$ if $r > 0$, and a direction opposite to that of $\overrightarrow{AB}$ if $r < 0$.

(Def-SM)

In this way, we have defined a vector $r\overrightarrow{AB}$ for every vector $\overrightarrow{AB}$ and every real number r. Some examples are given in Fig. 14–12.

Also, we now have defined a type of multiplication of a vector $\overrightarrow{AB}$ by a real number r, the product $r\overrightarrow{AB}$ being a vector. Some properties of scalar multiplication are given below.

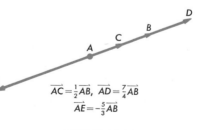

$$\overrightarrow{AC} = \tfrac{1}{2}\overrightarrow{AB}, \quad \overrightarrow{AD} = \tfrac{7}{4}\overrightarrow{AB}$$
$$\overrightarrow{AE} = -\tfrac{5}{3}\overrightarrow{AB}$$

FIGURE 14–12

SCALAR MULTIPLICATIVE PROPERTY

If

$$\overrightarrow{AB} = \overrightarrow{CD},$$

then

$$r\overrightarrow{AB} = r\overrightarrow{CD} \text{ for every real number } r. \qquad (SM\text{-}1)$$

Proof. If $\overrightarrow{AB} = \overrightarrow{CD}$, then $|\overrightarrow{AB}| = |\overrightarrow{CD}|$ and $|r| \cdot |\overrightarrow{AB}| = |r| \cdot |\overrightarrow{CD}|$. Since $\overrightarrow{AB}$ and $\overrightarrow{CD}$ have the same direction, so do $r\overrightarrow{AB}$ and $r\overrightarrow{CD}$. Hence, vectors $r\overrightarrow{AB}$ and $r\overrightarrow{CD}$ are equal, since they have the same length and direction.

ASSOCIATIVE LAW OF SCALAR MULTIPLICATION

$$(rs)\overrightarrow{AB} = r(s\overrightarrow{AB}) \qquad\qquad (SM\text{-}2)$$

for every pair r, s of real numbers and every vector $\overrightarrow{AB}$

DISTRIBUTIVE LAWS OF SCALAR MULTIPLICATION

$$(r + s)\overrightarrow{AB} = r\overrightarrow{AB} + s\overrightarrow{AB}$$

$$r(\overrightarrow{AB} + \overrightarrow{CD}) = r\overrightarrow{AB} + r\overrightarrow{CD} \qquad\qquad (SM\text{-}3)$$

for every pair r, s of real numbers and every pair $\overrightarrow{AB}$, $\overrightarrow{CD}$ of vectors

Property (SM-2) is valid because the vectors $(rs)\overrightarrow{AB}$ and $r(s\overrightarrow{AB})$ have the same length, $|r| \cdot |s| \cdot |\overrightarrow{AB}|$, and the same direction, that of $\overrightarrow{AB}$ if $rs > 0$ and opposite to that of $\overrightarrow{AB}$ if $rs < 0$.

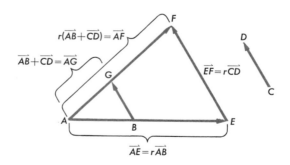

FIGURE 14-13

The second distributive law of (SM-3) is illustrated in Fig. 14–13 for $r > 0$. In this figure, triangles ABG and AEF are similar, with proportionality factor r. Hence, $\overrightarrow{AF} = r\overrightarrow{AG}$, or $r(\overrightarrow{AB} + \overrightarrow{CD})$. On the other hand, $\overrightarrow{AF} = \overrightarrow{AE} + \overrightarrow{EF}$, or $r\overrightarrow{AB} + r\overrightarrow{CD}$. Therefore,

$$r(\overrightarrow{AB} + \overrightarrow{CD}) = r\overrightarrow{AB} + r\overrightarrow{CD}.$$

We shall leave the proof of the first distributive law of scalar multiplication as an exercise.

The set of all vectors in a plane is closed with respect to the operations of addition and scalar multiplication. The properties of these operations should not be hard to remember, since they are very similar to the properties of addition and multiplication of numbers. We shall henceforth speak of *vector algebra*, or the *algebra of vectors*, meaning the set of all vectors in a plane together with the operations of addition and scalar multiplication.

Some practice may be gained in using vector algebra by proving well-known theorems of geometry. Consider, for instance, the following example.

Problem. Prove that the medians of a triangle meet at a point of trisection of each median.

Solution. Let $\overrightarrow{AD}$ be a median of triangle ABC, let E be the midpoint of side $\overrightarrow{AC}$, and let F be the point of trisection of $\overrightarrow{AD}$ nearer D (Fig. 14–14). In vector notation, $\overrightarrow{AE} = \overrightarrow{EC}$, $\overrightarrow{BD} = \overrightarrow{DC}$, and $\overrightarrow{AF} = 2\overrightarrow{FD}$. If we can prove that $\overrightarrow{BF} = 2\overrightarrow{FE}$, then we shall have proved that points B, F, and E are collinear (why?) and that F is a point of trisection of median $\overrightarrow{BE}$. With this in mind, we proceed as follows:

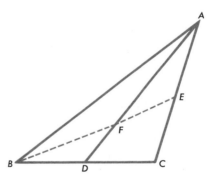

FIGURE 14-14

$$\overrightarrow{BF} + \overrightarrow{FD} = \overrightarrow{BD} \quad \text{and} \quad \overrightarrow{CF} + \overrightarrow{FD} = \overrightarrow{CD}.$$

Therefore,

$$\overrightarrow{BF} + \overrightarrow{FD} = -(\overrightarrow{CF} + \overrightarrow{FD}) \quad \text{since} \quad \overrightarrow{BD} = -\overrightarrow{CD}.$$

Similarly,

$$\overrightarrow{AF} + \overrightarrow{FE} = -(\overrightarrow{CF} + \overrightarrow{FE}) \quad \text{since} \quad \overrightarrow{AE} = -\overrightarrow{CE}.$$

Subtracting, we have

$$\overrightarrow{BF} + \overrightarrow{FD} - \overrightarrow{AF} - \overrightarrow{FE} = -\overrightarrow{FD} + \overrightarrow{FE},$$

or

$$\overrightarrow{BF} = 2\overrightarrow{FE} + \overrightarrow{AF} - 2\overrightarrow{FD}.$$

Since $\overrightarrow{AF} = 2\overrightarrow{FD}$, we have

$$\overrightarrow{BF} = 2\overrightarrow{FE}.$$

We have proved that the point of trisection nearer D of median $\overline{AD}$ is also a point of trisection of any other median. This proves that the medians meet in a point of trisection of each median.

Exercises

Given that $\overrightarrow{AC} = r\overrightarrow{AB}$, describe how point C is related to points A and B for each of the following conditions.

1. (a) $r = \frac{1}{2}$ (b) $r = \frac{2}{3}$

2. (a) $-\frac{1}{2} < r < -\frac{1}{4}$ (b) $\frac{1}{2} < r < \frac{2}{3}$

3. (a) $0 < r < 1$ (b) $-1 < r < 0$

4. Points A, B, and C are on a number line, with points A and B having respective coordinates -1 and 2. Find the coordinate of C, given that $\overrightarrow{AC} = r\overrightarrow{AB}$ and that r has each of the following values.
   (a) $r = \frac{1}{3}$ (b) $r = -1$

Points A, B, and C are on a number line, with points A and B having respective coordinates -2 and 5. Find the coordinate of C, given that $\overrightarrow{AC} = r\overrightarrow{AB}$ and that r has each of the following values.

5. (a) $r = -\frac{1}{2}$ (b) $r = 10$

6. (a) $r = -100$ (b) $r = \frac{3}{4}$

7. (a) $r = \sqrt{3}$ (b) $r = 1 + \sqrt{2}$

---

8. Given points O and P with respective coordinates $(0, 0)$ and $(2, 3)$, find the coordinates of the endpoint of each of the following vectors.
   (a) $2\overrightarrow{OP}$ (b) $-5\overrightarrow{OP}$ (c) $\frac{1}{2}\overrightarrow{OP}$

9. Given points A and B with respective coordinates $(1, 1)$ and $(6, 1)$, find the coordinates of the endpoint of each of the following vectors.
   (a) $3\overrightarrow{AB}$ (b) $-\frac{1}{2}\overrightarrow{AB}$
   Graph the vectors you found in parts (a) and (b).

Let points A, B, and C have respective coordinates $(0, 0)$, $(3, -2)$, and $(4, 3)$, and let $k = 3$ and $l = -2$. Find the coordinates of the endpoint of each of the following vectors.

10. $\overrightarrow{AB} + \overrightarrow{AC}$ **11.** $k\overrightarrow{AB}$ **12.** $l\overrightarrow{AC}$

13. $k\overrightarrow{AB} + l\overrightarrow{AC}$ **14.** $\overrightarrow{AB} - \overrightarrow{AC}$ **15.** $k\overrightarrow{AB} - l\overrightarrow{AC}$

16. Let $ABCD$ be a quadrilateral and E, F, G, and H be the respective midpoints of sides $\overline{AB}$, $\overline{BC}$, $\overline{CD}$, and $\overline{DA}$. Prove that $EFGH$ is a parallelogram.

17. If $PQ = RS$, is it necessarily true that $\overrightarrow{PQ} = \overrightarrow{RS}$?

18. If $\overrightarrow{PQ}$ is a scalar multiple of $\overrightarrow{RS}$, is $\overrightarrow{RS}$ necessarily a scalar multiple of $\overrightarrow{PQ}$?

19. Given that $\overrightarrow{PQ}$ and $\overrightarrow{RS}$ have either the same or opposite direction, with $\overrightarrow{PQ} \neq \mathbf{0}$, explain why there is a unique real number k such that $k\overrightarrow{PQ} = \overrightarrow{RS}$.

20. Prove the first part of (SM–3).

14–4   BASES

In the last section, we saw that for each vector $\overrightarrow{AB}$ and each real number r, the vector $r\overrightarrow{AB}$ lies on the line containing $\overrightarrow{AB}$. Conversely, it is true that for a given nonzero vector $\overrightarrow{AB}$ lying on a line L, every vector $\overrightarrow{CD}$ lying on L or on a line parallel to L is a scalar multiple of $\overrightarrow{AB}$. Thus, if we let

$$ r = \frac{|\overrightarrow{CD}|}{|\overrightarrow{AB}|}, \quad \text{or } r = -\frac{|\overrightarrow{CD}|}{|\overrightarrow{AB}|}, $$

according to whether $\overrightarrow{AB}$ and $\overrightarrow{CD}$ have the same or opposite direction, then $\overrightarrow{CD} = r\overrightarrow{AB}$.

If we are given two nonzero vectors that are not scalar multiples of each other, then every vector in the plane may be expressed as a combination of the two given vectors. To be more explicit, let the two given vectors $\overrightarrow{AB}$ and $\overrightarrow{AC}$ have the same initial point A, and let $\overrightarrow{AD}$ be any other vector having initial point A. Then $\overrightarrow{AD}$ is the diagonal of a

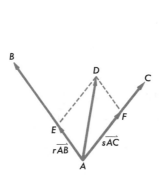

FIGURE 14–15

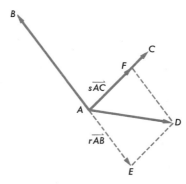

FIGURE 14–16

parallelogram $AEDF$, two of whose sides lie along the lines containing $\overrightarrow{AB}$ and $\overrightarrow{AC}$. Two possible alternatives for the parallelogram $AEDF$ are shown in Fig. 14–15 and 14–16. In any case, $\overrightarrow{AE}$ is collinear with $\overrightarrow{AB}$ so that $\overrightarrow{AE} = r\overrightarrow{AB}$ for some real number r, and $\overrightarrow{AF}$ is collinear with $\overrightarrow{AC}$ so that $\overrightarrow{AF} = s\overrightarrow{AC}$ for some real number s. However, since $\overrightarrow{AD}$ is the diagonal of this parallelogram, $\overrightarrow{AD} = \overrightarrow{AE} + \overrightarrow{AF}$. Consequently,

$$\overrightarrow{AD} = r\overrightarrow{AB} + s\overrightarrow{AC}.$$

A set $\{\overrightarrow{AB}, \overrightarrow{CD}\}$ of two vectors is called a *basis* of our vector algebra if every vector $\overrightarrow{EF}$ may be uniquely expressed as a combination of $\overrightarrow{AB}$ and $\overrightarrow{CD}$ of the form

$$\overrightarrow{EF} = r\overrightarrow{AB} + s\overrightarrow{CD}, \quad r \text{ and } s \text{ scalars.}$$

According to these results, we can make the following statement.

Every set of two nonzero, nonparallel vectors is a basis.

Problem 1. Given vectors $\overrightarrow{AB}$, $\overrightarrow{AC}$, and $\overrightarrow{AD}$ as shown in Fig. 14–17, express $\overrightarrow{AD}$ as a combination of $\overrightarrow{AB}$ and $\overrightarrow{AC}$.

Solution. Clearly, $\overrightarrow{AB}$ and $\overrightarrow{AC}$ are nonzero and nonparallel vectors. Hence, $\{\overrightarrow{AB}, \overrightarrow{AC}\}$ is a basis of vector algebra. To express $\overrightarrow{AD}$ as a combination of $\overrightarrow{AB}$ and $\overrightarrow{AC}$, we first find the coordinates of the vertices of the parallelogram $AEDF$ having $\overrightarrow{AD}$ as a diagonal. The equations of the lines on which the three given vectors lie are

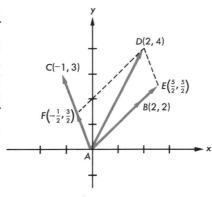

$$\overrightarrow{AB}: y = x,$$
$$\overrightarrow{AC}: y = -3x,$$
$$\overrightarrow{AD}: y = 2x.$$

FIGURE 14–17

The line through point D and parallel to $\overrightarrow{AC}$ has equation

$$y - 4 = -3(x - 2), \quad \text{or } y = -3x + 10.$$

Hence, the solution of the system of linear equations

$$\begin{cases} y = -3x + 10, \\ y = x \end{cases}$$

yields the coordinates of E. We find that $x = \frac{5}{2}$ and $y = \frac{5}{2}$ is the solution of this system, so that E has coordinates $(\frac{5}{2}, \frac{5}{2})$.

The line through point D parallel to $\overrightarrow{AB}$ has equation

$$y - 4 = 1(x - 2), \quad \text{or } y = x + 2.$$

The solution of the system of linear equations

$$\begin{cases} y = x + 2, \\ y = -3x \end{cases}$$

yields the coordinates of F. This solution is given by $x = -\frac{1}{2}$ and $y = \frac{3}{2}$, so that F has coordinates $(-\frac{1}{2}, \frac{3}{2})$. From Fig. 14–17,

$$\overrightarrow{AD} = \overrightarrow{AE} + \overrightarrow{AF}.$$

To express $\overrightarrow{AE}$ as a scalar multiple of $\overrightarrow{AB}$, and $\overrightarrow{AF}$ as a scalar multiple of $\overrightarrow{AC}$, we need to find the lengths of these four vectors. By the distance formula,

$$|\overrightarrow{AB}| = \sqrt{2^2 + 2^2}, \quad \text{or } 2\sqrt{2},$$
$$|\overrightarrow{AE}| = \sqrt{(\tfrac{5}{2})^2 + (\tfrac{5}{2})^2}, \quad \text{or } \tfrac{5}{2}\sqrt{2},$$
$$|\overrightarrow{AC}| = \sqrt{(-1)^2 + 3^2}, \quad \text{or } \sqrt{10},$$
$$|\overrightarrow{AF}| = \sqrt{(-\tfrac{1}{2})^2 + (\tfrac{3}{2})^2}, \quad \text{or } \tfrac{1}{2}\sqrt{10}.$$

Now $\overrightarrow{AB}$ and $\overrightarrow{AE}$ have the same direction, and therefore,

$$\overrightarrow{AE} = r\overrightarrow{AB}, \quad \text{where } r = \frac{|\overrightarrow{AE}|}{|\overrightarrow{AB}|}, \quad \text{or } \frac{5}{4}.$$

Similarly, $\overrightarrow{AC}$ and $\overrightarrow{AF}$ have the same direction, so that

$$\overrightarrow{AF} = s\overrightarrow{AC}, \quad \text{where } s = \frac{|\overrightarrow{AF}|}{|\overrightarrow{AC}|}, \quad \text{or } \frac{1}{2}.$$

Hence,

$$\overrightarrow{AD} = \tfrac{5}{4}\overrightarrow{AB} + \tfrac{1}{2}\overrightarrow{AC}.$$

This is the solution of Problem 1.

Vectors, such as $\overrightarrow{AB}$, $\overrightarrow{AC}$, and $\overrightarrow{AD}$ in Fig. 14–17, whose initial points are at the origin are called *position vectors*. Every vector in the plane is equal to a unique position vector. Given a vector $\overrightarrow{AB}$, we must find the coordinates of the terminal point of the position vector $\overrightarrow{OP}$ for which

$\overrightarrow{AB} = \overrightarrow{OP}$. In other words, if A has coordinates (x_1, y_1) and B has coordinates (x_2, y_2), what are the coordinates of P?

If $\overrightarrow{AB} = \overrightarrow{OP}$ and the segments $\overline{AB}$ and $\overline{OP}$ are not collinear, then $OABP$ is a parallelogram, as shown in Fig. 14–18. Hence, the slopes of the opposite sides of $OABP$ must be equal. Thus, if (x, y) are the coordinates of P, we must have

$$\frac{y}{x} = \frac{y_2 - y_1}{x_2 - x_1}.$$

We can make the following conclusion.

If A has coordinates (x_1, y_1), B has coordinates (x_2, y_2), and $\overrightarrow{AB} = \overrightarrow{OP}$, then P has coordinates

$$(x_2 - x_1, \ y_2 - y_1).$$

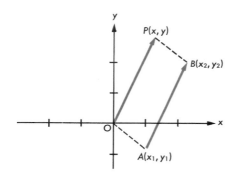

FIGURE 14–18

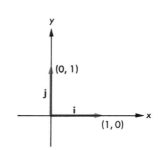

FIGURE 14–19

A particularly useful basis of our vector algebra consists of the set $\{\mathbf{i}, \mathbf{j}\}$, where $\mathbf{i}$ and $\mathbf{j}$ designate the position vectors having terminal points $(1, 0)$ and $(0, 1)$, respectively, as shown in Fig. 14–19. The vectors $\mathbf{i}$ and $\mathbf{j}$ are unit vectors in the sense that each has length 1. If A is the point $(x, 0)$ on the x-axis, then the position vector $\overrightarrow{OA}$ has length $|x|$ and its direction is that of $\mathbf{i}$ if $x > 0$, and is opposite to that of $\mathbf{i}$ if $x < 0$. Thus, $\overrightarrow{OA} = x\mathbf{i}$. Similarly, if B is the point $(0, y)$, then $\overrightarrow{OB} = y\mathbf{j}$. Consequently, if P has coordinates (x, y), then

$$\overrightarrow{OP} = x\mathbf{i} + y\mathbf{j},$$

as shown in Fig. 14–20.

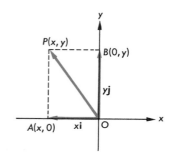

FIGURE 14–20

We saw that if A has coordinates (x_1, y_1) and B has coordinates (x_2, y_2), then $\overrightarrow{AB}$ is equal to the position vector $\overrightarrow{OP}$, where P has coordinates $(x_2 - x_1, y_2 - y_1)$. Hence,

$$\overrightarrow{AB} = (x_2 - x_1)\mathbf{i} + (y_2 - y_1)\mathbf{j}. \tag{1}$$

Problem 2. Express the vectors $\overrightarrow{AB}$ and $\overrightarrow{CD}$ in Fig. 14–21 in terms of $\mathbf{i}$ and $\mathbf{j}$. Also express $\overrightarrow{AB} + \overrightarrow{CD}$ and $\overrightarrow{AB} - \overrightarrow{CD}$ in terms of $\mathbf{i}$ and $\mathbf{j}$.

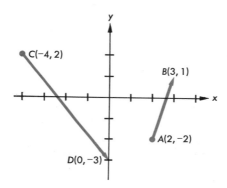

FIGURE 14–21

Solution. In view of equation (1) above,

$$\overrightarrow{AB} = (3 - 2)\mathbf{i} + (1 + 2)\mathbf{j}, \quad \text{or } \overrightarrow{AB} = \mathbf{i} + 3\mathbf{j},$$
$$\overrightarrow{CD} = (0 + 4)\mathbf{i} + (-3 - 2)\mathbf{j}, \quad \text{or } \overrightarrow{CD} = 4\mathbf{i} - 5\mathbf{j}.$$

Hence,

$$\overrightarrow{AB} + \overrightarrow{CD} = 5\mathbf{i} - 2\mathbf{j}, \quad \overrightarrow{AB} - \overrightarrow{CD} = -3\mathbf{i} + 8\mathbf{j}.$$

Exercises

Let points A, B, and C have respective coordinates $(0, 0)$, $(2, 0)$, and $(0, -1)$. Express vector $\overrightarrow{AD}$ as a combination of vectors $\overrightarrow{AB}$ and $\overrightarrow{AC}$, given that D has the following coordinates.

1. (a) $(-3, -5)$ (b) $(1, 0)$

Let points A, B, and C have respective coordinates $(0, 1)$, $(2, 0)$, and $(0, -1)$. Express $\overrightarrow{AD}$ as a combination of $\overrightarrow{AB}$ and $\overrightarrow{AC}$, given that D has the following coordinates.

2. (a) $(1, 0)$ (b) $(0, 2)$
3. (a) $(2, 3)$ (b) $(-1, 1)$

Let points A, B, and C have respective coordinates $(0, 0)$, $(1, -1)$, and $(-1, -1)$. Express vector $\overrightarrow{AD}$ as a combination of vectors $\overrightarrow{AB}$ and $\overrightarrow{AC}$, given that D has the following coordinates.

4. (a) $(0, 0)$ (b) $(1, 1)$

5. (a) $(1, 0)$ (b) $(0, 2)$

6. (a) $(-2, 2)$ (b) $(1, 3)$

Express each of the following vectors in terms of $\mathbf{i}$ and $\mathbf{j}$.

7. (a) $\overrightarrow{AB}$, where $A(0, 0)$ and $B(7, -3)$
   (b) $4\overrightarrow{AB}$, where $A(-1, 1)$ and $B(2, 5)$

8. (a) $\overrightarrow{AB}$, where $A(2, 0)$ and $B(0, 3)$
   (b) $-\overrightarrow{AB}$, where $A(2, 0)$ and $B(0, 3)$

9. (a) $2\overrightarrow{AB}$, where $A(1, 1)$ and $B(-2, 2)$
   (b) $5\overrightarrow{AB}$, where $A(1, 1)$ and $B(-2, 2)$

---

10. Find the length of each of the following vectors.
    (a) $\mathbf{i} + \mathbf{j}$ (b) $4\mathbf{i} + \mathbf{j}$ (c) $-6\mathbf{i}$ (d) $2\mathbf{i} - 3\mathbf{j}$

11. Express the vectors $\overrightarrow{AB}$, $\overrightarrow{CD}$, $\overrightarrow{OE}$ in terms of $\mathbf{i}$ and $\mathbf{j}$, given coordinates

$$A(1, -1), \quad B(3, 2), \quad C(-7, 2), \quad D(0, -4), \quad O(0, 0), \quad E(1, 3).$$

---

12. Solve the equation

$$x\mathbf{i} + y\mathbf{j} = \overrightarrow{AC}, \quad \text{where } A(2, -3) \text{ and } C(-1, -5).$$

13. What conclusions can you draw about the values of x, y, a, and b from each of the following statements?
    (a) $x\mathbf{i} + y\mathbf{j} = \mathbf{0}$ (b) $x\mathbf{i} + y\mathbf{j} = a\mathbf{i} + b\mathbf{j}$

Review for Sections 14–1 through 14–4

Given points A, B, and C with respective coordinates $(-5, 4)$, $(6, -1)$, and $(-2, -5)$, find the following.

1. The coordinates of D such that $\overrightarrow{AB} = \overrightarrow{CD}$

2. The coordinates of E such that $\overrightarrow{AE} = \overrightarrow{CB}$

3. The coordinates of F such that $\overrightarrow{CA} = \overrightarrow{FB}$

4. The coordinates of G such that $\overrightarrow{CB} = 2\overrightarrow{AG}$ and $\overrightarrow{CB}$ and $\overrightarrow{AG}$ have the same direction

5. The coordinates of H such that $\overrightarrow{AC} = 3\overrightarrow{HB}$ and $\overrightarrow{AC}$ and $\overrightarrow{HB}$ have opposite direction

6. Given points $A(2, 1)$, $B(7, 5)$, $C(6, 7)$, and $D(1, 3)$, determine whether $\overrightarrow{AB} = \overrightarrow{CD}$.

Find the vector determined by each of the following.

7. $\overrightarrow{ZX} + \overrightarrow{XY}$ **8.** $\overrightarrow{WZ} + \overrightarrow{ZX}$

9. $\overrightarrow{WX} - \overrightarrow{WZ}$ **10.** $\overrightarrow{ZY} - \overrightarrow{XY}$

11. $\overrightarrow{WZ} + (\overrightarrow{ZX} + \overrightarrow{XY})$ **12.** $\overrightarrow{ZW} + (\overrightarrow{WX} + \overrightarrow{XY})$

13. $\overrightarrow{ZY} + (\overrightarrow{WX} - \overrightarrow{ZX})$ **14.** $\overrightarrow{WZ} + (\overrightarrow{ZY} - \overrightarrow{XY})$

Given points $A(2, 3)$, $B(3, -1)$, and $C(-2, 1)$, find the coordinates of the endpoint of each of the following vectors.

15. $3\overrightarrow{AB}$ **16.** $-2\overrightarrow{BC}$

17. $3\overrightarrow{CB}$ **18.** $\frac{1}{2}\overrightarrow{CA}$

19. $2\overrightarrow{BA} + \overrightarrow{BC}$ **20.** $\overrightarrow{AC} - \frac{1}{2}\overrightarrow{BC}$

Given $A(2, 3)$, $B(-3, 3)$, $C(-5, -2)$, and $D(4, -3)$, express each of the following vectors in terms of **i** and **j**.

21. $\overrightarrow{AB}$ **22.** $\overrightarrow{BC}$

23. $\overrightarrow{DA}$ **24.** $\overrightarrow{CD}$

Find the length of each of the following vectors.

25. $\mathbf{i} - \mathbf{j}$

26. $3\mathbf{i} + 2\mathbf{j}$

Answers to Review for Sections 14–1 through 14–4

1. $(9, -10)$ **2.** $(3, 8)$

3. $(9, -10)$ **4.** $(-1, 6)$

5. $(7, -4)$ **6.** No; $AB = CD$ but $\overrightarrow{AB}$ and $\overrightarrow{CD}$ have opposite direction.

7. $\overrightarrow{ZY}$ **8.** $\overrightarrow{WX}$

9. $\overrightarrow{ZX}$ **10.** $\overrightarrow{ZX}$

11. $\overrightarrow{WY}$ **12.** $\overrightarrow{ZY}$

13. $\overrightarrow{WY}$ **14.** $\overrightarrow{WX}$

15. $(5, -9)$ **16.** $(8, -3)$

17. $(13, -5)$ **18.** $(0, 2)$

19. $(-4, 9)$ **20.** $(\frac{1}{2}, 0)$

21. $-5\mathbf{i}$ **22.** $-2\mathbf{i} - 5\mathbf{j}$

23. $-2\mathbf{i} + 6\mathbf{j}$ **24.** $9\mathbf{i} - \mathbf{j}$

25. $\sqrt{2}$ **26.** $\sqrt{13}$

*14–5   VECTORS IN PHYSICS

Vectors are commonly used in physics to represent forces. The direction of application of the force is indicated by the direction of the vector, and the magnitude of the force is indicated by the length of the vector. For example, vector $\overrightarrow{AB}$ in Fig. 14–22 represents a force of 30 pounds acting in a northeasterly direction.

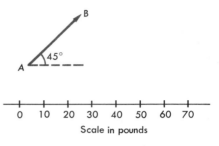

Scale in pounds

FIGURE 14–22

If two or more forces are acting on an object, then the effect of these forces on the object can be attained by a single force, called the *resultant*. When the forces acting on the object are represented by vectors, their resultant is represented by the sum of these vectors. If the object remains at rest under the actions of two or more forces, then it is said to be in *equilibrium*. If an object is in equilibrium, the sum of the vectors representing the forces must be the zero vector. In Fig. 14–23, for example, a 50-pound object suspended in midair by a rope has two forces acting on it. One, a force of 50 pounds which is due to gravity, is represented by vector $\overrightarrow{AB}$, and the other, a force of 50 pounds holding the object up, is represented by vector $\overrightarrow{CD}$. Clearly,

$$\overrightarrow{AB} + \overrightarrow{CD} = \mathbf{0}.$$

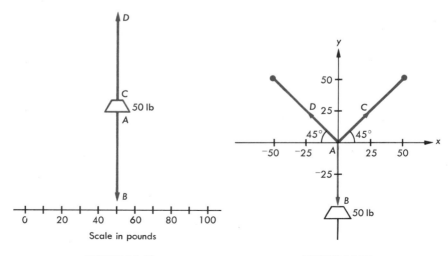

FIGURE 14–23   FIGURE 14–24

If the object is suspended by two ropes, as shown in Fig. 14–24, then we can compute the tension in each rope (that is, the magnitude of the force holding the object up in the direction of each rope). Let vectors $\overrightarrow{AC}$ and $\overrightarrow{AD}$ represent the forces acting in the direction of each rope. If a coordinate system is set up as in Fig. 14–24, then

$$\overrightarrow{AC} = r(\mathbf{i} + \mathbf{j}), \quad \overrightarrow{AD} = s(-\mathbf{i} + \mathbf{j}), \quad \overrightarrow{AB} = -50\mathbf{j},$$

where r and s are positive numbers to be determined. Since the object is in equilibrium,

$$r(\mathbf{i} + \mathbf{j}) + s(-\mathbf{i} + \mathbf{j}) - 50\mathbf{j} = \mathbf{0}$$

and

$$(r - s)\mathbf{i} + (r + s - 50)\mathbf{j} = \mathbf{0}.$$

Hence, $r - s = 0$ and $r + s - 50 = 0$, so that $r = 25$ and $s = 25$. Thus, $\overrightarrow{AC} = 25(\mathbf{i} + \mathbf{j})$ and $\overrightarrow{AD} = 25(-\mathbf{i} + \mathbf{j})$. Now $|\overrightarrow{AC}|$, or $25\sqrt{2}$, and $|\overrightarrow{AD}|$, or $25\sqrt{2}$, are the magnitudes of the forces acting along the two ropes. Therefore, the tension in each rope is $25\sqrt{2}$ pounds, or approximately 35.3 pounds.

Exercises

Each of the figures in Exercises 1–6 shows an object in equilibrium. Give the direction and magnitude of each force acting on the object.

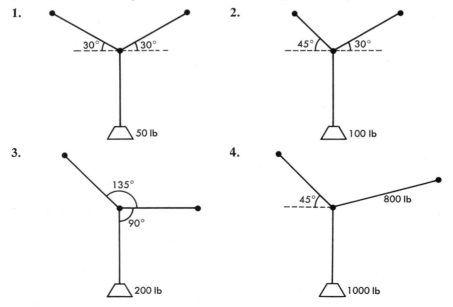

1.

30° 30°

50 lb

2.

45° 30°

100 lb

3.

135°

90°

200 lb

4.

45° 800 lb

1000 lb

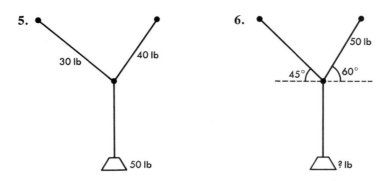

14–6 VECTOR COMPONENTS

In Section 14–4, we saw that each vector $\overrightarrow{AB}$ is equal to a unique vector of the form $x\mathbf{i} + y\mathbf{j}$. The numbers x and y are called the *components* of the vector $\overrightarrow{AB}$. In Fig. 14–21, for example, vector $\overrightarrow{AB}$ has components 1 and 3 and vector $\overrightarrow{CD}$ has components 4 and -5.

The notation $[x, y]$ will be used to designate the components of a vector. For example, the vector $2\mathbf{i} + 7\mathbf{j}$ has components $[2, 7]$. If vector $\overrightarrow{AB}$ has components $[x_1, y_1]$ and $\overrightarrow{CD}$ has components $[x_2, y_2]$, then $\overrightarrow{AB} + \overrightarrow{CD}$ has components $[x_1 + x_2, y_1 + y_2]$. This is true because

$$(x_1\mathbf{i} + y_1\mathbf{j}) + (x_2\mathbf{i} + y_2\mathbf{j}) = (x_1 + x_2)\mathbf{i} + (y_1 + y_2)\mathbf{j}.$$

If vector $\overrightarrow{AB}$ has components $[x, y]$, then vector $r\overrightarrow{AB}$ has components $[rx, ry]$. This is so because

$$\overrightarrow{AB} = x\mathbf{i} + y\mathbf{j} \quad \text{and} \quad r\overrightarrow{AB} = r(x\mathbf{i} + y\mathbf{j}) = rx\mathbf{i} + ry\mathbf{j}.$$

The length of the vector with components $[x, y]$ is $\sqrt{x^2 + y^2}$.

Problem 1. Given points A and B with respective coordinates (x_1, y_1) and (x_2, y_2), and r a real number, find the coordinates of the point C on the line containing A and B such that $\overrightarrow{AC} = r\overrightarrow{AB}$.

Solution. We know that in terms of the basis $\{\mathbf{i}, \mathbf{j}\}$,

$$\overrightarrow{AB} = (x_2 - x_1)\mathbf{i} + (y_2 - y_1)\mathbf{j}.$$

Therefore, $\overrightarrow{AB}$ has components $[x_2 - y_1, y_2 - y_1]$ and $r\overrightarrow{AB}$ has components $[r(x_2 - x_1), r(y_2 - y_1)]$. If point C has coordinates (x, y), then

$$\overrightarrow{AC} = (x - x_1)\mathbf{i} + (y - y_1)\mathbf{j},$$

and $\overrightarrow{AC}$ has components $[x - x_1, y - y_1]$. The vectors $\overrightarrow{AC}$ and $r\overrightarrow{AB}$ are equal if, and only if, they have the same components. Hence,

$$\overrightarrow{AC} = r\overrightarrow{AB}$$

if, and only if,

$$x - x_1 = r(x_2 - x_1) \quad \text{and} \quad y - y_1 = r(y_2 - y_1).$$

Thus, $x = x_1 + r(x_2 - x_1)$, $y = y_1 + r(y_2 - y_1)$, and point C has coordinates

$$(x_1 + r(x_2 - x_1), \ y_1 + r(y_2 - y_1)).$$

For example, if $r = 0$, then C and A are the same point, and if $r = 1$, C and B are the same point. If $r = \frac{1}{2}$ so that C is the midpoint of $\overline{AB}$, then the x-coordinate of C is

$$x_1 + \tfrac{1}{2}(x_2 - x_1), \quad \text{or } x_1 + \tfrac{1}{2}x_2 - \tfrac{1}{2}x_1, \quad \text{or } \tfrac{1}{2}x_1 + \tfrac{1}{2}x_2.$$

Similarly, $\tfrac{1}{2}y_1 + \tfrac{1}{2}y_2$ may be shown to be the y-coordinate of C when C is the midpoint of $\overline{AB}$. Thus, the segment with endpoints (x_1, y_1) and (x_2, y_2) has midpoint

$$\left(\frac{x_1 + x_2}{2}, \frac{y_1 + y_2}{2}\right).$$

Problem 2. Given the nonzero vectors $\overrightarrow{AB}$ and $\overrightarrow{CD}$ with respective components $[x_1, y_1]$ and $[x_2, y_2]$, prove that $\overrightarrow{AB}$ and $\overrightarrow{CD}$ are parallel or collinear if, and only if, $x_1y_2 = x_2y_1$.

Solution. We know that $\overrightarrow{AB}$ and $\overrightarrow{CD}$ are parallel or collinear if, and only if,

$$\overrightarrow{CD} = r\overrightarrow{AB}$$

for some nonzero real number r. Thus, we must prove that

$$\overrightarrow{CD} = r\overrightarrow{AB} \text{ for some } r \text{ if, and only if, } x_1y_2 = x_2y_1.$$

Let us first assume that $\overrightarrow{CD} = r\overrightarrow{AB}$ for some number r. Then $\overrightarrow{CD}$ must have components $[rx_1, ry_1]$, that is,

$$x_2 = rx_1, \quad y_2 = ry_1.$$

Hence,

$$x_2y_1 = rx_1y_1, \quad x_1y_2 = rx_1y_1, \quad x_2y_1 = x_1y_2.$$

This proves that if $\overrightarrow{CD} = r\overrightarrow{AB}$, then $x_2y_1 = x_1y_2$.

To prove the converse, let us assume that $x_1 y_2 = x_2 y_1$. Since the vector $\overrightarrow{AB}$ is not $\mathbf{0}$, either $x_1 \neq 0$ or $y_1 \neq 0$. If $x_1 \neq 0$, then we may solve the equation $x_1 y_2 = x_2 y_1$ for y_2, obtaining $y_2 = (x_2 y_1)/x_1$. Hence,

$$y_2 = \left(\frac{x_2}{x_1}\right) y_1,$$

and since it immediately follows that

$$x_2 = \left(\frac{y_2}{y_1}\right) x_1,$$

we have that $\overrightarrow{CD} = r\overrightarrow{AB}$, where the real number $r = x_2/x_1$. If $x_1 = 0$, we may let $r = y_2/y_1$ to obtain the same result. This proves that if $x_1 y_2 = x_2 y_1$, then $\overrightarrow{CD} = r\overrightarrow{AB}$ for some real number r, which concludes the proof of Problem 2.

For example, the vectors $\overrightarrow{AB}$ and $\overrightarrow{CD}$ with components $[-1, 3]$ and $[2, -6]$ are parallel or collinear, since $-1 \times -6 = 3 \times 2$. If vector $\overrightarrow{EF}$ has components $[-3, 7]$, then $\overrightarrow{AB}$ and $\overrightarrow{EF}$ are not parallel since $-1 \times 7 \neq -3 \times 3$.

Exercises

Given points A and B with respective coordinates $(3, -1)$ and $(-3, 3)$, find the coordinates of point C on the line containing A and B such that $\overrightarrow{AC} = r\overrightarrow{AB}$ for each of the following values of r.

1. (a) $r = -1$
   (b) $r = \frac{1}{2}$
2. (a) $r = 2$
   (b) $r = 10$
3. (a) $r = -3$
   (b) $r = 0$

Sketch the following pairs of vectors, and find their sum.

4. (a) $2\mathbf{i} + 3\mathbf{j}$, $\mathbf{i} + \mathbf{j}$
   (b) $2\mathbf{i} + 3\mathbf{j}$, $-4\mathbf{i} + 2\mathbf{j}$
5. (a) $-\mathbf{i} - \mathbf{j}$, $-\mathbf{i} + 3\mathbf{j}$
   (b) $4\mathbf{i} + 2\mathbf{j}$, $2\mathbf{i} + 3\mathbf{j}$

What are the components of each of the following vectors?

6. (a) $\mathbf{r} = (x - 1)\mathbf{i} + (y + 2)\mathbf{j}$ (b) $\mathbf{v} = x\mathbf{i} - y\mathbf{j} + 5\mathbf{i} + 3\mathbf{j}$

7. (a) $\frac{1}{2}(b\mathbf{i} - 4\mathbf{j})$ (b) $\frac{1}{3}(2\mathbf{i} + \mathbf{j} - a\mathbf{i} - b\mathbf{j})$

---

8. Solve each of the following equations for x and y.
  (a) $x\mathbf{i} + (-4)\mathbf{j} = 7\mathbf{i} + y\mathbf{j}$
  (b) $5(\mathbf{i} + \mathbf{j}) - \mathbf{i} + y\mathbf{j} = x\mathbf{i} - 4\mathbf{j}$

9. Determine the real numbers k and s such that

$$4\mathbf{i} + 3\mathbf{j} = k(\mathbf{i} - \mathbf{j}) + s(2\mathbf{i} + 5\mathbf{j}).$$

10. In the figure, $PQ = 6$ and $\theta = 30°$. Determine the components of $\overrightarrow{PQ}$.

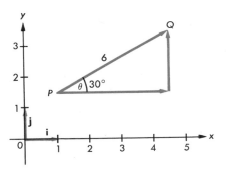

---

11. An object P is moving on a plane in such a way that t seconds after it starts, the position vector $\overrightarrow{OP}$ has components $[t + 2, -3t + 3]$. Describe the path of the object between $t = 0$ and $t = 10$ seconds. At what time does the object cross the x-axis?

12. If the object P of Exercise 11 is moving so that t seconds after it starts, the position vector $\overrightarrow{OP}$ has components $[2\sqrt{t}, t]$, describe the path of the object. At what times does the object cross the line $y = 3x - 8$? When is the object 20 units away from its starting point?

13. Given that points E and F are chosen on sides $\overline{AC}$ and $\overline{BC}$, respectively, of triangle ABC in such a way that $\overrightarrow{AE} = r\overrightarrow{AC}$ and $\overrightarrow{BF} = s\overrightarrow{BC}$, and that D is the point of intersection of lines containing $\overline{BE}$ and $\overline{AF}$, prove that

$$\overrightarrow{AD} = t\overrightarrow{AF} \quad \text{and} \quad \overrightarrow{BD} = u\overrightarrow{BE},$$

where $t = r/(r + s - rs)$ and $u = s/(r + s - rs)$. Use this result to prove that the three medians of a triangle meet at a point of trisection of each median.

14–7   INNER PRODUCTS

Given two nonzero vectors $\overrightarrow{AB}$ and $\overrightarrow{AC}$ with the same initial point, the *angle between* $\overrightarrow{AB}$ *and* $\overrightarrow{AC}$ is defined to be the smallest angle θ having its vertex at A and containing sides $\overrightarrow{AB}$ and $\overrightarrow{AC}$. Several examples of θ are given in Fig. 14–25. We may define the angle between two nonzero vectors even if they do not have the same initial point. If $\overrightarrow{AB}$ and $\overrightarrow{CD}$ are the given vectors, then there exists a unique vector $\overrightarrow{AE}$ such that $\overrightarrow{CD} = \overrightarrow{AE}$. The angle θ between $\overrightarrow{AB}$ and $\overrightarrow{AE}$, as shown in Fig. 14–26, is defined to be the angle between $\overrightarrow{AB}$ and $\overrightarrow{CD}$. From its definition, the angle between two vectors always has measure between $0°$ and $180°$ inclusive.

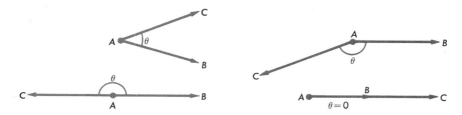

FIGURE 14–25

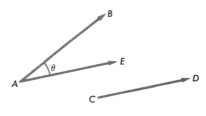

FIGURE 14–26

Definition of the inner product of two vectors

The inner product of two vectors is defined by

$$\overrightarrow{AB} \cdot \overrightarrow{CD} = |\overrightarrow{AB}|\,|\overrightarrow{CD}|\,\cos\theta,$$

where θ is the angle between $\overrightarrow{AB}$ and $\overrightarrow{CD}$. If either $\overrightarrow{AB} = 0$ or $\overrightarrow{CD} = 0$, then $\overrightarrow{AB} \cdot \overrightarrow{CD}$ is zero.

Problem 1. If vectors $\overrightarrow{AB}$ and $\overrightarrow{AC}$ are as shown in Fig. 14–27, find $\overrightarrow{AB} \cdot \overrightarrow{AC}$.

Solution. According to the definition,

$$\overrightarrow{AB} \cdot \overrightarrow{AC} = |\overrightarrow{AB}| |\overrightarrow{AC}| \cos 45°$$

$$= 3 \cdot 4 \cdot \frac{\sqrt{2}}{2}, \quad \text{or } 6\sqrt{2}.$$

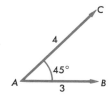

FIGURE 14-27

As this problem illustrates, the *inner product of two vectors is a number, not a vector.*

Two nonzero vectors are said to be perpendicular if the lines on which they lie are perpendicular. Evidently two nonzero vectors are perpendicular if, and only if, the angle between them is a right angle.

PERPENDICULARITY PROPERTY

The nonzero vectors $\overrightarrow{AB}$ and $\overrightarrow{CD}$ are perpendicular if, and only if,

$\overrightarrow{AB} \cdot \overrightarrow{CD}$ is equal to zero.

If $\overrightarrow{AB}$ and $\overrightarrow{CD}$ are perpendicular, then the angle θ between them is a right angle, and therefore $\cos \theta = 0$. Hence,

$$\overrightarrow{AB} \cdot \overrightarrow{CD} = 0.$$

Conversely, if $\overrightarrow{AB} \cdot \overrightarrow{CD} = 0$, then $|\overrightarrow{AB}| |\overrightarrow{CD}| \cos \theta = 0$. Since $|\overrightarrow{AB}| \neq 0$ and $|\overrightarrow{CD}| \neq 0$ by assumption, we must have $\cos \theta = 0$. By definition, $0° \leq \theta \leq 180°$. Now there is precisely one angle between $0°$ and $180°$ whose cosine is zero: $90°$. Hence, $\overrightarrow{AB}$ and $\overrightarrow{CD}$ are perpendicular.

The inner product of two vectors is easily computed if the components of the vectors are known. For convenience, let us henceforth denote vectors by such symbols as **a, b, v,** and so on, when it is not important to know the endpoints of the vectors. The formula for the inner product of two vectors whose components are known is the following.

*If vectors **a** and **b** have components $[x_1, y_1]$ and $[x_2, y_2]$, respectively, then*

$$\mathbf{a} \cdot \mathbf{b} = x_1 x_2 + y_1 y_2.$$

To prove this formula, let $\mathbf{a} = \overrightarrow{OA}$ and $\mathbf{b} = \overrightarrow{OB}$, as shown in Fig. 14-28. By what is given, we know that point A has coordinates

(x_1, y_1) and B has coordinates (x_2, y_2). If θ is the angle between **a** and **b**, then by the law of cosines,

$$|\overrightarrow{AB}|^2 = |\mathbf{a}|^2 + |\mathbf{b}|^2 - 2|\mathbf{a}| \, |\mathbf{b}| \cos \theta.$$

Using the distance formula as well as the known formula for the inner product and the formula for the length of a vector, we obtain the equivalent equation

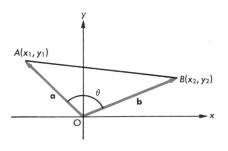

FIGURE 14-28

$$(x_1 - x_2)^2 + (y_1 - y_2)^2 = (x_1^2 + y_1^2) + (x_2^2 + y_2^2) - 2\mathbf{a} \cdot \mathbf{b},$$

or

$$x_1^2 - 2x_1x_2 + x_2^2 + y_1^2 - 2y_1y_2 + y_2^2 = x_1^2 + y_1^2 + x_2^2 + y_2^2 - 2\mathbf{a} \cdot \mathbf{b}.$$

Hence,

$$-2x_1x_2 - 2y_1y_2 = -2\mathbf{a} \cdot \mathbf{b}$$

and

$$\mathbf{a} \cdot \mathbf{b} = x_1x_2 + y_1y_2.$$

This proves the formula.

Problem 2. Given that vectors **a**, **b**, and **c** are as shown in Fig. 14–29, find $\mathbf{a} \cdot \mathbf{b}$, $\mathbf{a} \cdot \mathbf{c}$, and $\mathbf{b} \cdot \mathbf{c}$.

Solution. The components of **a** are $[-1 - 2, 4 - 1]$, or $[-3, 3]$; those of **b** are $[0 + 1, -1 - 4]$, or $[1, -5]$; and those of **c** are $[2 - 0, 1 + 1]$, or $[2, 2]$. Hence, by the formula above,

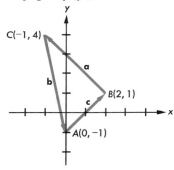

FIGURE 14-29

$$\mathbf{a} \cdot \mathbf{b} = (-3 \cdot 1) + [3 \cdot (-5)], \quad \text{or } -18,$$
$$\mathbf{a} \cdot \mathbf{c} = (-3 \cdot 2) + (3 \cdot 2), \quad \text{or } 0,$$
$$\mathbf{b} \cdot \mathbf{c} = (1 \cdot 2) + (-5 \cdot 2), \quad \text{or } -8.$$

Incidentally, we note that vectors **a** and **c** are perpendicular, since $\mathbf{a} \cdot \mathbf{c} = 0$. Thus, ABC is a right triangle with right angle at B.

The inner-product operation has some of the properties of multiplication of real numbers, as you can see by looking at the properties of the inner product listed below.

$$\mathbf{a} \cdot \mathbf{b} = \mathbf{b} \cdot \mathbf{a} \qquad\qquad \text{(commutative law)} \qquad \text{(IP-1)}$$

$$(\mathbf{a} + \mathbf{b}) \cdot \mathbf{c} = (\mathbf{a} \cdot \mathbf{c}) + (\mathbf{b} \cdot \mathbf{c}) \qquad \text{(distributive law)} \qquad \text{(IP-2)}$$

$$\left.\begin{array}{l}(k\mathbf{a}) \cdot \mathbf{b} = k(\mathbf{a} \cdot \mathbf{b}) \\ \mathbf{a} \cdot (k\mathbf{b}) = k(\mathbf{a} \cdot \mathbf{b})\end{array}\right\} \; k \text{ a real number} \qquad \text{(IP-3)}$$

$$\mathbf{a} \cdot \mathbf{a} = |\mathbf{a}|^2 \qquad\qquad\qquad\qquad \text{(IP-4)}$$

The equations above are true for all vectors $\mathbf{a}, \mathbf{b}, \mathbf{c}$.

Each of these properties may be proved by means of components. For example, to prove (IP-2), let $\mathbf{a}, \mathbf{b}$, and $\mathbf{c}$ have components $[x_1, y_1]$, $[x_2, y_2]$, and $[x_3, y_3]$, respectively. Then $\mathbf{a} + \mathbf{b}$ has components $[x_1 + x_2, y_1 + y_2]$ and

$$\begin{aligned}(\mathbf{a} + \mathbf{b}) \cdot \mathbf{c} &= (x_1 + x_2)x_3 + (y_1 + y_2)y_3 \\ &= x_1x_3 + x_2x_3 + y_1y_3 + y_2y_3\end{aligned}$$

by our formula above. Next,

$$\mathbf{a} \cdot \mathbf{c} = x_1x_3 + y_1y_3, \quad \mathbf{b} \cdot \mathbf{c} = x_2x_3 + y_2y_3,$$

so that

$$(\mathbf{a} \cdot \mathbf{c}) + (\mathbf{b} \cdot \mathbf{c}) = x_1x_3 + y_1y_3 + x_2x_3 + y_2y_3.$$

Therefore,

$$(\mathbf{a} + \mathbf{b}) \cdot \mathbf{c} = (\mathbf{a} \cdot \mathbf{c}) + (\mathbf{b} \cdot \mathbf{c}).$$

We shall leave the proofs of (IP-1), (IP-3), and (IP-4) as exercises.

Problem 3. Are the diagonals of a parallelogram ever perpendicular?

Solution. If $\mathbf{a}$ and $\mathbf{b}$ designate non-parallel sides of a parallelogram, as shown in Fig. 14–30, then $\mathbf{a} - \mathbf{b}$ and $\mathbf{a} + \mathbf{b}$ are the two diagonals. Hence, the diagonals of the parallelogram are perpendicular if, and only if,

$$(\mathbf{a} - \mathbf{b}) \cdot (\mathbf{a} + \mathbf{b}) = 0.$$

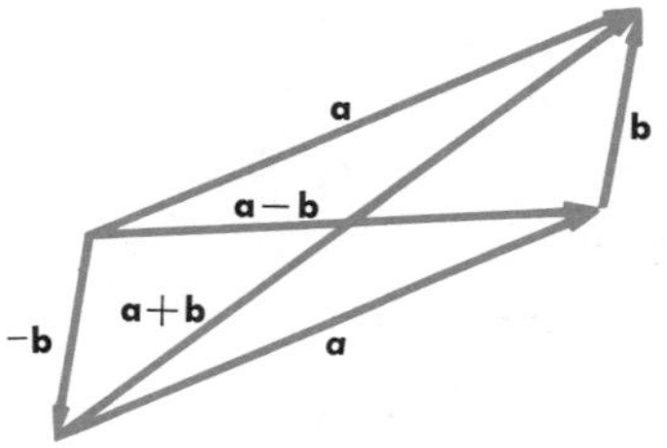

FIGURE 14–30

Using the properties (IP-1) through (IP-4), we have

$$\begin{aligned}(\mathbf{a} - \mathbf{b}) \cdot (\mathbf{a} + \mathbf{b}) &= (\mathbf{a} - \mathbf{b}) \cdot \mathbf{a} + (\mathbf{a} - \mathbf{b}) \cdot \mathbf{b} \\ &= (\mathbf{a} \cdot \mathbf{a}) + (-\mathbf{b} \cdot \mathbf{a}) + (\mathbf{a} \cdot \mathbf{b}) + (-\mathbf{b} \cdot \mathbf{b}) \\ &= (\mathbf{a} \cdot \mathbf{a}) - (\mathbf{b} \cdot \mathbf{a}) + (\mathbf{b} \cdot \mathbf{a}) - (\mathbf{b} \cdot \mathbf{b}) \\ &= |\mathbf{a}|^2 - |\mathbf{b}|^2.\end{aligned}$$

Therefore, the diagonals are perpendicular if, and only if, $|\mathbf{a}|^2 = |\mathbf{b}|^2$, or $|\mathbf{a}| = |\mathbf{b}|$. In other words, the diagonals of a parallelogram are perpendicular if, and only if, the parallelogram is a rhombus or a square, that is, if it is equilateral.

Exercises

Find $\mathbf{a} \cdot \mathbf{b}$.

1. (a) $\mathbf{a} = \mathbf{i}, \quad \mathbf{b} = \mathbf{j}$ (b) $\mathbf{a} = \mathbf{i}, \quad \mathbf{b} = \mathbf{i}$

2. (a) $\mathbf{a} = \mathbf{j}, \quad \mathbf{b} = \mathbf{j}$ (b) $\mathbf{a} = 2\mathbf{i} - \mathbf{j}, \quad \mathbf{b} = \mathbf{i} - 3\mathbf{j}$

3. (a) $\mathbf{a} = \mathbf{i} + 3\mathbf{j}, \quad \mathbf{b} = \mathbf{j} - 3\mathbf{i}$ (b) $\mathbf{a} = 5\mathbf{i}, \quad \mathbf{b} = 2\mathbf{j} + 7\mathbf{i}$

Tell whether the pairs of vectors are perpendicular. Graph the vectors.

4. (a) $\mathbf{v} = 2\mathbf{i}, \quad \mathbf{u} = 4\mathbf{j}$ (b) $\mathbf{v} = -3\mathbf{i}, \quad \mathbf{u} = -2\mathbf{j}$

5. (a) $\mathbf{v} = \mathbf{i}, \quad \mathbf{u} = -\frac{1}{2}\mathbf{j}$ (b) $\mathbf{v} = -3\mathbf{i}, \quad \mathbf{u} = \frac{2}{3}\mathbf{j}$

6. (a) $\mathbf{v} = 2\mathbf{i}, \quad \mathbf{u} = 0$ (b) $\mathbf{v} = 0, \quad \mathbf{u} = 3\mathbf{i}$

7. (a) A triangle has vertices $(-2, 0)$, $(2, 0)$, and $(0, 4)$. Find its area.
    (b) A triangle has vertices $(0, 0)$, $(6, 0)$, and $(3, 6)$. Find its area.

In each of the following exercises, vectors $\mathbf{a}$, $\mathbf{b}$, and $\mathbf{c}$ are sides of a triangle. Tell whether the triangle is right, isosceles, equilateral, or none of these.

8. (a) $\mathbf{a} = \mathbf{i}, \quad \mathbf{b} = \mathbf{j}, \quad \mathbf{c} = \mathbf{i} - \mathbf{j}$
    (b) $\mathbf{a} = \mathbf{i} + 3\mathbf{j}, \quad \mathbf{b} = \mathbf{j} - \mathbf{i}, \quad \mathbf{c} = -2(\mathbf{i} + \mathbf{j})$

9. (a) $\mathbf{a} = 3\mathbf{j}, \quad \mathbf{b} = \mathbf{i} + 2\mathbf{j}, \quad \mathbf{c} = \mathbf{i} + 5\mathbf{j}$
    (b) $\mathbf{a} = \mathbf{i} + \sqrt{3}\,\mathbf{j}, \quad \mathbf{b} = -\mathbf{i} + \sqrt{3}\,\mathbf{j}, \quad \mathbf{c} = -2\mathbf{i}$

10. (a) $\mathbf{a} = 2\mathbf{i} + \mathbf{j}, \quad \mathbf{b} = 3\mathbf{j} - 2\mathbf{i}, \quad \mathbf{c} = 2\mathbf{j} - 4\mathbf{i}$
    (b) $\mathbf{a} = -3\mathbf{j}, \quad \mathbf{b} = -2(\mathbf{i} + \mathbf{j}), \quad \mathbf{c} = -2\mathbf{i} - 5\mathbf{j}$

11. Find the inner product of each of the following pairs of vectors.
    (a) $\mathbf{v} = x\mathbf{i} + y\mathbf{j}, \quad \mathbf{r} = 3\mathbf{i} - 2\mathbf{j}$
    (b) $\mathbf{v} = 2\mathbf{i}, \quad \mathbf{r} = 3\mathbf{j}$

---

12. Prove (IP-1).   **13.** Prove (IP-3).   **14.** Prove (IP-4).

---

15. Given that $\mathbf{a} = r[(\cos \theta)\mathbf{i} + (\sin \theta)\mathbf{j}]$ and $\mathbf{b} = s[(\cos \phi)\mathbf{i} + (\sin \phi)\mathbf{j}]$ are nonzero vectors, prove that $\mathbf{a}$ and $\mathbf{b}$ are perpendicular if, and only if, $\theta - \phi = n\pi/2$ for some odd integer n.

16. In triangle ABC, select point D on side $\overline{BC}$ and point E on side $\overline{AC}$ so that $\overline{AD}$ is perpendicular to $\overline{BC}$ and $\overline{BE}$ is perpendicular to $\overline{AC}$. If F is the point of intersection of $\overline{AD}$ and $\overline{BE}$, then show that the line through points C and F is perpendicular to side $\overline{AB}$. (Hint: Show that $\overrightarrow{CF} \cdot \overrightarrow{AB} = 0$ by letting $\overrightarrow{CF} = \overrightarrow{CA} + \overrightarrow{AF}$ and $\overrightarrow{AB} = \overrightarrow{AF} + \overrightarrow{FB}$.)

17. Prove that each of the following expressions is true for every pair of vectors **a, b**.

(a) $|\mathbf{a} + \mathbf{b}|^2 = |\mathbf{a}|^2 + |\mathbf{b}|^2 + 2\mathbf{a} \cdot \mathbf{b}$

(b) $|\mathbf{a} - \mathbf{b}|^2 = |\mathbf{a}|^2 + |\mathbf{b}|^2 - 2\mathbf{a} \cdot \mathbf{b}$

(c) $(\mathbf{a} \cdot \mathbf{b})^2 \leq |\mathbf{a}|^2 \cdot |\mathbf{b}|^2$ When does the inequality sign hold?

EXTRA!

Logarithms are useful in determining the magnitude of earthquakes. An earthquake of magnitude 6 is considered a major earthquake. Those with magnitude 2 are usually the smallest felt by humans. The largest recorded earthquakes have magnitudes between 8 and 9.

Instruments called "seismographs" trace zig-zag lines which show the amplitude of an earthquake. The amplitude is used to measure the magnitude of the earthquake. The formula for this (popularly called the Richter scale*) is

$$M = \log A - \log A_0.$$

M is the magnitude. A is the recorded trace amplitude (in millimeters) from the seismograph. A_0 is a standard amplitude; this is sometimes called the "zero shock" since if $A = A_0$, $M = 0$.

Standard values of A_0 have been established as a function of the distance from the recording seismograph to the epicenter (the point on the earth's surface directly above the point where the earthquake's energy originates). Some of these values are as follows.

Distance (in kilometers)	$-\log A_0$
0	1.4
10	1.5
20	1.7
30	2.1
40	2.4
50	2.6
100	3.0
150	3.3
200	3.5
300	4.0

---

* C. F. Richter, *Elementary Seismology* (San Francisco: W. H. Freeman & Co., 1958) pp. 340–342.

There are corrections applied to each seismographic station and instrument, but we shall not take these into consideration here. Using the formula for magnitude and the standard values for A_0 given above, find the magnitudes for the following earthquakes.

1. Amplitude 3.5 mm, distance 10 km

2. Amplitude 3.5 mm, distance 20 km

3. Amplitude 26.1 mm, distance 50 km

4. Amplitude 37.8 mm, distance 30 km

5. Amplitude 7.5 mm, distance 100 km

6. Amplitude 5.0 mm, distance 100 km

7. Amplitude 2.25 mm, distance 150 km

8. Amplitude 1.5 mm, distance 200 km

9. Amplitude 0.9 mm, distance 300 km

10. What is the ratio of the amplitude of an earthquake having magnitude of 6 to the amplitude of an earthquake having magnitude of 2?

KEY IDEAS AND KEY WORDS

A **vector** is a line segment having an **initial point** A, a **terminal point** B, and a **direction** from A to B. This vector is denoted by $\overrightarrow{AB}$, and its length is denoted by $|\overrightarrow{AB}|$. We call the vector $\overrightarrow{AA}$ of zero length the **zero vector, 0.** Vectors $\overrightarrow{AB}$ and $\overrightarrow{CD}$ are defined to be equal if, and only if, the quadrilateral $ABCD$ is a parallelogram. That is, $\overrightarrow{AB}$ and $\overrightarrow{CD}$ have the same length, and the same direction.

The **sum of two vectors** is defined by

$$\overrightarrow{AB} + \overrightarrow{BC} = \overrightarrow{AC},$$

which is the resultant law of physics. Each vector has an **additive inverse,**

$$-\overrightarrow{AB} = \overrightarrow{BA}.$$

Each vector $\overrightarrow{AB}$ may be multiplied by a **scalar r,** which is a real number, thereby giving another vector $r\overrightarrow{AB}$, of length $|r|$ times the length of $\overrightarrow{AB}$.

The basic properties of addition and multiplication in the real number system are also valid in the **algebra of vectors.**

The vectors **i** and **j** are defined in a **cartesian coordinate system** by

$$\mathbf{i} = \overrightarrow{OA} \quad \text{and} \quad \mathbf{j} = \overrightarrow{OB},$$

where O is the origin, A is the point $(1, 0)$, and B is the point $(0, 1)$. Each vector in the plane has the unique form

$$x\mathbf{i} + y\mathbf{j}$$

for some real numbers x and y; x and y are called the **components** of the vectors.

The **inner product** of vectors $\overrightarrow{AB}$ and $\overrightarrow{CD}$ is denoted by $\overrightarrow{AB} \cdot \overrightarrow{CD}$ and is defined by

$$\overrightarrow{AB} \cdot \overrightarrow{CD} = |\overrightarrow{AB}|\,|\overrightarrow{CD}| \cos \theta$$

where θ is the angle between $\overrightarrow{AB}$ and $\overrightarrow{CD}$. Two nonzero vectors, $\overrightarrow{AB}$ and $\overrightarrow{CD}$ are **perpendicular** if, and only if, $\overrightarrow{AB} \cdot \overrightarrow{CD} = 0$.

CHAPTER REVIEW

In Exercises 1–14, tell which of the statements are true and which are false. Correct the ones which are false.

1. If $A_1, A_2, \ldots, A_k$ are k distinct points, then they determine k nonzero vectors.

2. $\overrightarrow{AB} = \overrightarrow{CD}$ if, and only if, $|\overrightarrow{AB}| = |\overrightarrow{CD}|$

3. $\overrightarrow{AB} - \overrightarrow{CD} = \overrightarrow{AB} + \overrightarrow{CD}$

4. If A has coordinates $(4, 9)$, B has coordinates $(9, -4)$, O has coordinates $(0, 0)$, and $\overrightarrow{AB} = \overrightarrow{OP}$, then P has coordinates $(13, 5)$.

5. The product of a vector and a scalar is a scalar.

6. The nonparallel vectors $\overrightarrow{KL}$ and $\overrightarrow{MN}$ with lengths 2 and 10, respectively, form a basis.

7. Subtraction of vectors is not commutative.

8. In triangle ABC, $\overrightarrow{AB} + \overrightarrow{BC} = \overrightarrow{CA}$.

9. For any four points R, S, T, and U, $(\overrightarrow{RS} + \overrightarrow{TU}) - (\overrightarrow{TS} + \overrightarrow{RU}) = \mathbf{0}$.

10. The vectors $\overrightarrow{AB}$ and $\overrightarrow{CD}$ with components $[6, -3]$ and $[4, -8]$ are parallel or collinear.

11. If $\overrightarrow{AB} \cdot \overrightarrow{AC} = 8$, where $|\overrightarrow{AB}| = 2$ and $|\overrightarrow{AC}| = 4$, then $\overrightarrow{AB}$ and $\overrightarrow{AC}$ are parallel or collinear.

12. If vectors $\mathbf{a}$ and $\mathbf{b}$ have components $[3, 1]$ and $[-2, 2]$, respectively, then $\mathbf{a} \cdot \mathbf{b} = 4$.

13. The inner product of two nonzero vectors is a vector.

14. If $\mathbf{a} = \mathbf{i}$ and $\mathbf{b} = 2\mathbf{j}$, then $\mathbf{a} \cdot \mathbf{b} = 0$.

15. Can every point be considered to be a zero vector? Explain your answer.

16. Given that θ is the angle between $\overrightarrow{AB}$ and $\overrightarrow{CD}$ and that $|\overrightarrow{AB}| = 6$, $|\overrightarrow{CD}| = 3$,and $\overrightarrow{AB} \cdot \overrightarrow{CD}$ has the values below, find the measure of θ.
(a) 0
(b) 18
(c) 9

17. Find $\overrightarrow{AB} \cdot \overrightarrow{CD}$ given that $|\overrightarrow{AB}| = 5$, $|\overrightarrow{CD}| = 7$ and θ has each of the following values.
(a) 30°
(b) 45°

18. Given points M and N with respective coordinates $(2, 11)$ and $(3, 4)$, find the length of $\overrightarrow{MN}$. Graph $\overrightarrow{MN}$.

Find each of the vectors in Exercises 19 and 20 which has its endpoints among the four points A, B, C, and D.

19. $(\overrightarrow{BA} + \overrightarrow{CB}) + \overrightarrow{DC}$

20. $(\overrightarrow{CA} - \overrightarrow{BA}) - (\overrightarrow{DB} - \overrightarrow{DA})$

21. Given points S and T with respective coordinates $(7, 3)$ and $(1, 5)$, find the coordinates of point P such that $\overrightarrow{OS} + \overrightarrow{OP} = \overrightarrow{OT}$.

In Exercises 22 and 23, solve the equations for x and y.

22. $(3x)\mathbf{i} + (2y)\mathbf{j} = 6\overrightarrow{PQ}$ where $P(-1, 2)$ and $Q(3, 4)$

23. $(2x + 3y)\mathbf{i} - (5y)\mathbf{j} = 6\mathbf{i} + 25\mathbf{j}$

24. Given points A and B with respective coordinates $(0, 11)$ and $(4, 2)$, find the coordinates of point C on the line containing A and B such that $\overrightarrow{AC} = r\overrightarrow{AB}$ for each of the following values of r.
(a) $r = 6$ (b) $r = 2$

In each of the following exercises, vectors **a**, **b**, and **c** are sides of a triangle. Tell whether the triangle is right, isosceles, or equilateral.

25. $\mathbf{a} = 2\mathbf{i}$, $\mathbf{b} = 4\mathbf{j}$, $\mathbf{c} = 2(\mathbf{i} - 2\mathbf{j})$

26. $\mathbf{a} = 2\mathbf{i}$, $\mathbf{b} = \mathbf{i} + \mathbf{j}$, $\mathbf{c} = \mathbf{i} - \mathbf{j}$

27. $\mathbf{a} = 2\mathbf{j}$, $\mathbf{b} = 2\mathbf{i} + \mathbf{j}$, $\mathbf{c} = 2\mathbf{i} - \mathbf{j}$

Find the sum of each of the following pairs of vectors.

28. $\mathbf{i} + \mathbf{j}$, $3\mathbf{i} + 2\mathbf{j}$

29. $-\mathbf{i} - \mathbf{j}$, $-\mathbf{i} + 2\mathbf{j}$

In Exercises 30–33, what are the components of each of the vectors?

30. $\mathbf{r} = x \cos \theta\mathbf{i} + y \sin \theta\mathbf{j}$

31. $\mathbf{s} = \mathbf{i} + \mathbf{j}$

32. $\mathbf{v} = 2\mathbf{i}$

33. $\mathbf{s} = -x\mathbf{i} + 3\mathbf{i} + y\mathbf{j} - \mathbf{j}$

34. Find the length of the vector $3\mathbf{i} - 2\mathbf{j}$.

35. Find the length of the vector $\mathbf{i} + \mathbf{j}$.

In Exercises 36–41, express each of the vectors in terms of $\mathbf{i}$ and $\mathbf{j}$.

36. $\overrightarrow{AB}$, where $A(0, 0)$ and $B(14, -6)$

37. $2\overrightarrow{AB}$, where $A(-2, 2)$ and $B(4, 10)$

38. $\overrightarrow{AB} + \overrightarrow{CD}$, where $A(4, 0)$, $B(0, 6)$, $C(0, 0)$, and $D(-8, -2)$

39. $\overrightarrow{AC} - \overrightarrow{BD}$, where $A(4, 0)$, $B(0, 6)$, $C(0, 0)$, and $D(-8, -2)$

40. $4\overrightarrow{AB} + 5\overrightarrow{CD}$, where $A(1, 1)$, $B(-1, 2)$, $C(1, -2)$, and $D(-5, -2)$

41. Find the inner product of the two vectors $\overrightarrow{OA}$ and $\overrightarrow{OB}$, given that

$$O(0, 0), \quad A(2, 3), \quad B(-2, 3).$$

CHAPTER TEST

1. Given points R and S with respective coordinates $(3, 1)$ and $(5, 3)$, determine the length of the vector $\overrightarrow{RS}$.

Each of the vectors in Exercises 2 and 3 is equal to a vector having its endpoints among the four points A, B, C, and D. Find the indicated vector.

2. $\overrightarrow{BA} - \overrightarrow{DA}$

3. $(\overrightarrow{AC} + \overrightarrow{CD}) + \overrightarrow{DB}$

4. Given points A and B with respective coordinates $(3, 4)$ and $(6, 3)$, find the coordinates of point C such that $\overrightarrow{OA} + \overrightarrow{OB} = \overrightarrow{OC}$.

5. Given points A and B with respective coordinates $(-4, 2)$ and $(3, -2)$, find the coordinates of the point C on the line containing A and B such that $\overrightarrow{AC} = r\overrightarrow{AB}$ for each of the following values of r.
   (a) $r = \frac{1}{4}$ (b) $r = -5$

6. Express each of the following vectors in terms of $\mathbf{i}$ and $\mathbf{j}$.
   (a) $2\overrightarrow{AB}$, where $A(-3, 2)$ and $B(3, 3)$
   (b) $\overrightarrow{AC} - \overrightarrow{BD}$, where $A(3, 0)$, $B(0, 4)$, $C(0, 0)$, and $D(4, 7)$

7. What are the components of each of the following vectors?
   (a) $\mathbf{k} = x\mathbf{i}$ (b) $\mathbf{m} = (3x)\mathbf{i} + 2\mathbf{j} - (2y)\mathbf{i}$

8. Given that $|\overrightarrow{AB}| = 2$, $|\overrightarrow{CD}| = 8$, and $\theta = 60°$, where θ is the angle between $\overrightarrow{AB}$ and $\overrightarrow{CD}$, find $\overrightarrow{AB} \cdot \overrightarrow{CD}$.

9. Given that $|\overrightarrow{AB}| = 2$, $|\overrightarrow{CD}| = 8$, and $\overrightarrow{AB} \cdot \overrightarrow{CD} = 16$, find the measure of angle θ between $\overrightarrow{AB}$ and $\overrightarrow{CD}$.

10. Given that $\mathbf{a} = \mathbf{i} - \mathbf{j}$, $\mathbf{b} = \mathbf{i} + 2\mathbf{j}$, find $\mathbf{a} \cdot \mathbf{b}$.

11. Given points O, A, and B with respective coordinates $(0, 0)$, $(4, 4)$, and $(-4, 4)$, prove that $\overrightarrow{OA}$ and $\overrightarrow{OB}$ are perpendicular.

CUMULATIVE REVIEW IV

1. If a and b are real numbers, then $ab = 0$ if, and only if, either $a = 0$ or $b = 0$. Make use of this fact in drawing the graph of each of the following equations.
   (a) $(x + y - 1)(x - y + 1) = 0$
   (b) $(x^2 + y^2 - 4)(x + y - 2) = 0$
   (c) $(xy - 4)(xy + 4) = 0$

2. Graph each of the following.
   (a) $y = 2|x|$
   (b) $y > 2|x|$
   (c) $y = 2|x| + 1$
   (d) $y < 2|x| + 1$

3. Show that $1 - i$ is a zero of the polynomial

   $$f(x) = x^4 - 6x^3 + 12x - 20,$$

   and find the other zeros of $f(x)$.

4. Prove that it is impossible to double a two-digit positive integer by reversing its digits.

5. Draw the graph of the equation

   $$|x - 1| + |x + 1| + |y - 1| + |y + 1| = 4.$$

6. Draw the graph of the equation

   $$|x - 1| + |x + 1| + |y - 1| + |y + 1| = 2\sqrt{2} + 4.$$

7. Describe the graph of the following equation, and sketch it.

   $$x^2 - y^2 + 3x - y + 2 = 0$$

8. A closed rectangular box has a volume of 60 cubic feet and a surface area of 94 square feet. If the height of the box were doubled, the surface area would increase to 148 square feet. What are the dimensions of the box?

9. An ant can crawl around the base of a cubical room in 10 minutes. By taking a path of least length, how long does it take the ant to crawl from a corner of the floor to the diametrically opposite corner of the ceiling?

10. In how many ways can the letters of the word *prom* be rearranged so that
    (a) the resulting rearrangement does not begin with the letter p?
    (b) no letter is in its original position?

11. In each of the following exercises, find a formula for the sum of the series and use mathematical induction to prove that your formula is true for every positive integer n.
    (a) $1 + 5 + 9 + \cdots + (4n - 3)$
    (b) $14 + 19 + 24 + \cdots + (9 + 5n)$

12. Let $S_n = \dfrac{1}{1 \cdot 2} + \dfrac{1}{2 \cdot 3} + \cdots + \dfrac{1}{n(n + 1)}$.
    (a) Find S_1, S_2, S_3, and S_4.
    (b) Guess a formula for S_n.
    (c) Prove by mathematical induction that your formula in part (b) is true for every positive integer n.

13. In the following way, P_n is defined as a product for every positive integer $n \geq 2$.

$$P_n = \left(1 - \frac{1}{4}\right)\left(1 - \frac{1}{9}\right)\left(1 - \frac{1}{16}\right) \cdot \ldots \cdot \left(1 - \frac{1}{n^2}\right)$$

    (a) Find P_2, P_3, P_4, P_5, and P_6.
    (b) Give a formula for P_n.
    (c) Prove by mathematical induction that your formula in part (b) is correct for every positive integer $n \geq 2$.

14. Given a geometric series with a, the first term, equal to 3, and r, the ratio, equal to $\frac{1}{2}$, find the partial sums S_2, S_5, S_6, and S_{10}.

15. Find the sum of the infinite geometric series

$$1 + \frac{1}{2} + \frac{1}{4} + \cdots + \frac{1}{2^{n-1}} \cdots$$

16. Find the sum of the infinite geometric series

$$3 - .3 + .03 - \cdots + 3(-.1)^{n-1} + \cdots$$

17. Let S_n denote the sum of the first n terms of the arithmetic series that starts out $a + (a + d) + (a + 2d) + \cdots$. Prove that

$$3S_{2n} = 3S_n + S_{3n}.$$

18. Two cyclists started out at the same time, one going from town P to town Q and the other from town Q to town P. Each cyclist traveled at a constant speed and, on arriving at his destination, immediately turned around and returned. They met for the first time 6 miles from P and 48 minutes later, they met for the second time 2 miles from P. Find the speed of each cyclist and the distance between the towns P and Q.

19. Prove by mathematical induction that the equation

$$\frac{1}{2} + \frac{2}{2^2} + \frac{3}{2^3} + \cdots + \frac{n}{2^n} = 2 - \frac{n+2}{2^n}$$

is true for every positive integer n.

20. (a) Given the formula

$$1^2 + 2^2 + 3^2 + \cdots + n^2 = \frac{n(n+1)(2n+1)}{6},$$

find a summation formula for

$$2^2 + 4^2 + 6^2 + \cdots + (2n)^2 = S(n),$$

and prove your result by mathematical induction.

(b) Using the formulas of part (a), find a summation formula for

$$1^2 + 3^2 + 5^2 + \cdots + (2n-1)^2 = T(n),$$

and prove your result by mathematical induction.

21. In a geometric series, the second term is 4 more than the first term, and the sum of the second and third terms is 24. Find the sum of the first six terms of the series (two solutions).

22. Find all possible values of x and y such that 3, x, and y will form the first three terms of an arithmetic series, and x, y, and 8 will form the first three terms of a geometric series.

23. Find a summation formula for

$$1 \cdot 3 + 2 \cdot 4 + 3 \cdot 5 + \cdots + n(n+2),$$

and prove your result by mathematical induction.

24. Find each of the following sums.
(a) $-2 - 5 - 8 - 11 - 14 - \cdots - 62$
(b) $1 + 2 + 2^2 + 2^3 + \cdots + 2^9$
(c) $1 - 3 + 3^2 - 3^3 + 3^4 - 3^5$

In each of the following exercises, find the sum and the inner product of the pairs of vectors.

25. $3\mathbf{i} + 7\mathbf{j}, \quad -2\mathbf{i} + 5\mathbf{j}$

26. $-10\mathbf{i} - 8\mathbf{j}, \quad -4\mathbf{i} - 3\mathbf{j}$

In each of the following exercises, find the sum and the inner product of vectors $\overrightarrow{AB}$ and $\overrightarrow{CD}$.

27. $A(-3, 5), \; B(2, 8), \; C(1, 3), \text{ and } D(4, 7)$

28. $A(-7, -1), \; B(2, -8), \; C(-2, 5), \text{ and } D(1, -6)$

In each of the following exercises, vectors **a**, **b**, and **c** are sides of a triangle. Tell whether the triangle is right, isosceles, or equilateral.

29. $\mathbf{a} = 2\mathbf{i}, \quad \mathbf{b} = 2\mathbf{j}, \quad \mathbf{c} = 2(\mathbf{i} + \mathbf{j})$

30. $\mathbf{a} = -2\mathbf{i}, \quad \mathbf{b} = -2\mathbf{j}, \quad \mathbf{c} = -2\mathbf{i} - 2\mathbf{j}$

Logic

Objectives . . .

- To analyze a concept in terms of its basic statement components.
- To make truth tables to test the truth or falsity of a compound statement.
- To relate the conditional connective to statements of theorems in mathematics.
- To build direct and indirect arguments on the elements of symbolic logic.
- To write contrapositive and converse statements for a given statement.

15–1 STATEMENTS AND CONNECTIVES

Although the content of mathematics is both important and useful, the essence of mathematics is its structure and logical development. In this chapter, we shall study *symbolic logic* in order to examine some of the common forms of argument used in mathematics.

A sentence that is either true or false, but not both, is called a *statement*. For example, the following two statements can be made about any given quadrilateral $ABCD$.

> Quadrilateral $ABCD$ is a square.
>
> Quadrilateral $ABCD$ is a parallelogram.

In the same way that we use symbols to denote numbers, sets, and other objects, we shall use symbols, such as p and q, to denote statements. For example, in the statements above, we might let p denote the first statement and q denote the second statement.

> p: Quadrilateral $ABCD$ is a square.
>
> q: Quadrilateral $ABCD$ is a parallelogram.

We shall combine simple statements, such as q and p, to form *compound statements*, such as the following.

> Quadrilateral $ABCD$ is a parallelogram and
> quadrilateral $ABCD$ is a square.

To make compound statements from simple ones, we shall use certain words called *connectives*. The common connectives are *and*, which is denoted by $\wedge$; *or*, which is denoted by $\vee$; and *not*, which is denoted by $\sim$. The table on the next page shows the ways in which these connectives are used with statements.

Statement	Symbolic form	Name
p and q	$p \wedge q$	conjunction
p or q	$p \vee q$	disjunction
not p	$\sim p$	negation

For example, if p and q are the two given statements about the quadrilateral $ABCD$, then $p \wedge q$, $p \vee q$, and $\sim p$ are the following statements.

$p \wedge q$:   Quadrilateral $ABCD$ is a square and a parallelogram.

$p \vee q$:   Quadrilateral $ABCD$ is a square or a parallelogram.

$\sim p$:   Quadrilateral $ABCD$ is not a square.

We can combine the statements shown at the top of this page to make more complicated statements. For example, the statement $q \wedge \sim p$ denotes the following.

$q \wedge \sim p$:   Quadrilateral $ABCD$ is a parallelogram and not a square.

The operations of *conjunction* and *disjunction* of statements in logic are analogous to the operations of *intersection* and *union* in set theory. The operation of *negation* can be compared to finding the *complement* of a set. In fact, logic and set theory are closely related subjects.

Let us now make another compound statement which relates p and q. If quadrilateral $ABCD$ is a square, then it is a parallelogram. This is a *conditional statement*, rather than an assertion. The symbol $\rightarrow$ is used for the *if–then* connective.

Statement	Symbolic form	Name
if p, then q	$p \rightarrow q$	conditional statement

In the following problem, we give further illustrations of the use of these four connectives.

Problem. Assign letters to the simple statements in each of the following compound statements, and then express the compound statement in symbolic form.

(a) The grass is wet and it has rained.
(b) If the grass is wet, it has rained.
(c) The grass is wet but it has not rained.
(d) It has not rained and the grass is not wet.
(e) The statement that it has rained and the grass is not wet is false.

Solution. Let p denote the statement "The grass is wet" and q the statement "It has rained." Then (a) becomes $p \wedge q$ and (b) becomes $p \rightarrow q$, although the word *then* in the *if–then* statement has been omitted as it frequently is in ordinary discourse. In (c), the word *but* has the same logical meaning as *and*, although it has more descriptive force. Thus, (c) becomes $p \wedge \sim q$. The statement in (d) that it has *not* rained *and* the grass is *not* wet becomes $\sim q \wedge \sim p$. In (e), the *negation* of "It has rained and the grass is not wet" is $\sim(q \wedge \sim p)$. Notice the use of parentheses to enclose the statement that is being negated.

Exercises

1. (a) Use p for "It is snowing" and q for "It is cold outside." Write each of the following in symbolic form.
   (i) It is snowing but it is not cold outside.
   (ii) It is snowing and it is cold outside.
   (iii) If it is snowing, it is cold outside.
   (iv) It is snowing or it is cold outside.
   (v) It is snowing and it is not cold outside.
   (vi) The statement that it is snowing and it is cold outside is false.

   (b) Use p for "Tomorrow is a holiday" and q for "I am going skiing." Write each of the following in symbolic form.
   (i) Tomorrow is a holiday and I am going skiing.
   (ii) If tomorrow is a holiday, I am going skiing.
   (iii) Tomorrow is not a holiday.
   (iv) I am going skiing but tomorrow is not a holiday.
   (v) Tomorrow is not a holiday or I am going skiing.
   (vi) It is false that tomorrow is a holiday and I am not going skiing.

2. (a) Use p for "I eat apples" and q for "I eat cake." Give verbal translations of each of the following.
   (i) $p \rightarrow \sim q$
   (ii) $p \wedge \sim q$
   (iii) $\sim(p \wedge q)$
   (iv) $\sim p \vee \sim q$
   (v) $(p \wedge \sim q) \vee (\sim p \wedge q)$

   (b) Use p for "I am tall" and q for "I am athletic." Give verbal translations for each of the following.
   (i) $q \rightarrow p$
   (ii) $p \wedge \sim q$
   (iii) $q \vee \sim p$
   (iv) $\sim(p \rightarrow q)$
   (v) $(p \wedge q) \vee (\sim p \wedge \sim q)$

3. (a) Assign letters to the three simple statements which are common to the following group of statements. Write each statement in symbolic form.

   (i) If a person has a car, he buys gasoline.

   (ii) A person has a car and a power lawn mower.

   (iii) If a person buys gasoline, then he has a car or a power mower.

   (iv) A person buys gasoline or he does not have a car.

   (v) A person does not have a car, but if he owns a power mower, he buys gasoline.

   (vi) The statement that a person does not have a car and does not own a power mower and buys gasoline is false.

(b) Write the following statements in symbolic form, letting p be "Mary plays the piano well," q be "Mary practices the piano faithfully" and r be "Mary plays tennis."

   (i) Mary plays the piano well but she does not play tennis.

   (ii) If Mary plays tennis, she practices the piano faithfully and also plays the piano well.

   (iii) It is false that Mary does not practice the piano faithfully and still plays the piano well.

   (iv) Mary does not play the piano well but she practices it faithfully and also plays tennis.

   (v) The statement that if Mary plays tennis, she does not play the piano well is false.

15-2 TRUTH TABLES AND EQUIVALENT STATEMENTS

In this section, we shall develop methods for testing the truth or falsity of *compound* statements for all possible cases of the truth or falsity of their simple components. To do this, we shall give a *truth table* for each of the connectives, using "T" to indicate a true statement and "F," a false statement.

Suppose that we make a statement p which is either true or false, but not both. If p is a true statement, then $\sim p$ is false; if p is false, then $\sim p$ must be true. This gives us the *truth table* for negation.

p	$\sim p$
T	F
F	T

Truth Table for Negation

Construction of the truth table for conjunction requires that we first list all possible combinations for the truth and falsity of two statements p and q. This is an elementary counting problem. Since we have the two possibilities T and F for p, and the two possibilities T and F for q, we have $2 \cdot 2$, or 4 cases, as listed in the truth table below.

p	q	$p \wedge q$
T	T	T
T	F	F
F	T	F
F	F	F

Truth Table for Conjunction

According to this table, *p and q* is a true statement if both p and q are true. Otherwise, the statement *p and q* is false.

Before constructing the truth table for the connective *or*, we must face the problem of the ambiguity of the use of the word *or* in ordinary discourse. Probably it is used most frequently in the sense of *one or the other but not both*. For example,

I shall have ice cream or sherbet for dessert

illustrates this use of the *exclusive or*.

Another usage of *or* is illustrated by the following property of the system of real numbers.

$$\text{If } ab = 0, \text{ then } a = 0 \text{ or } b = 0. \qquad \text{(F-0)}$$

Stated in words, it says that if the product of two numbers is zero, then *at least* one of the numbers is zero. This use of the connective *or* to mean *one or the other or possibly both* is called the *inclusive or*. The *inclusive or* is sometimes indicated in business documents by *and/or*.

In logic, we agree to use the *inclusive or* for disjunction. Consequently, the following is the truth table for disjunction.

p	q	$p \vee q$
T	T	T
T	F	T
F	T	T
F	F	F

Truth Table for Disjunction

According to this table, $p \vee q$ is true in all cases except the one in which both p and q are false. As we shall presently see, the *exclusive or* can be given in terms of the three connectives $\vee$, $\wedge$, and $\sim$.

Finally, the following truth table represents the conditional statement *if p, then q.*

p	q	$p \rightarrow q$
T	T	T
T	F	F
F	T	T
F	F	T

Truth Table for the Conditional

Stated in words, this means that $p \rightarrow q$ is always true *unless p* is true and *q* is false.

You will probably agree with the first two rows of the truth table above. Our reason for labelling the last two cases true is somewhat similar to our reason for defining zero and negative exponents as we do. In other words, the set of labels for the two last cases in this table produces useful results. We shall return to this point later, after we have illustrated the use of truth tables in analyzing more complicated statements.

Problem 1. Compare the truth table for $q \vee \sim p$ with that for $p \rightarrow q$.

Solution.

p	q	$q \vee \sim p$			$p \rightarrow q$		
T	T	T	T	F	T	T	T
T	F	F	F	F	T	F	F
F	T	T	T	T	F	T	T
F	F	F	T	T	F	T	F
		1	2	1	1	2	1

The numbers below the columns indicate the order of events, and the final results are in color.

From our work above, we see that the truth tables of the statements $p \rightarrow q$ and $q \vee \sim p$ are the same. Statements which have the same truth tables are called *logically equivalent statements.* Thus, the statement *if p, then q* is logically equivalent to *either q or not p.* Both statements are true except when *p* is true and *q* is false. We could have defined *if p, then q* to be the same as *q or not p.* Then we would have obtained the truth table for $p \rightarrow q$ from that of $q \vee \sim p$.

Problem 2. Find truth tables for $p \vee \sim p$ and $p \wedge \sim p$.

Solution. Since each of these statements involves only one statement, the tables need just two rows.

p	$p \lor \sim p$		
T	T	T	F
F	F	T	T
	1	2	1

p	$p \land \sim p$		
T	T	F	F
F	F	F	T
	1	2	1

Thus, the statement $p \lor \sim p$ is true for every value of p and the statement $p \land \sim p$ is false for every value of p. These two statements are examples of *logically true* and *logically false* statements, respectively. In other words, they are examples of statements whose truth tables have a T in every row or an F in every row of the final column.

Problem 3. Find the truth table for the statement

$$(p \land \sim q) \lor (q \land \sim p).$$

Solution. This statement can be expressed in the following way:

$$p \text{ and not } q \quad \text{or} \quad q \text{ and not } p.$$

We proceed as shown in Tables 1, 2, and 3. Notice that the column headings represent p, q, and the substatements within the given statement.

p	q	$(p \land \sim q)$		$\lor$	$(q \land \sim p)$	
T	T	T	F		T	F
T	F	T	T		F	F
F	T	F	F		T	T
F	F	F	T		F	T
		1	1		1	1

Table 1

In Table 1, we have listed the four possible cases for statements p and q. We have copied these cases in the columns under the symbols p and q in the compound statements. We have also used the truth table for negation to write values in color under the columns for $\sim q$ and $\sim p$.

p	q	p	$\wedge$	$\sim q$	$\vee$	q	$\wedge$	$\sim p$
T	T	T	F	F		T	F	F
T	F	T	T	T		F	F	F
F	T	F	F	F		T	T	T
F	F	F	F	T		F	F	T
		1	2	1		1	2	1

Table 2

In Table 2, the first column in color shows the values found by forming the conjunction of the values of p and $\sim q$. The second column in color shows the values found by forming the conjunction of the values of q and $\sim p$.

p	q	p	$\wedge$	$\sim q$	$\vee$	q	$\wedge$	$\sim p$
T	T	T	F	F	F	T	F	F
T	F	T	T	T	T	F	F	F
F	T	F	F	F	T	T	T	T
F	F	F	F	T	F	F	F	T
		1	2	1	3	1	2	1

Table 3

In Table 3, the column in color shows the values found by forming the disjunction of the values of the two columns in color in Table 2.

In practice, we usually show this sequence of three steps in one table, as shown below.

p	q	$(p$	$\wedge$	$\sim q)$	$\vee$	$(q$	$\wedge$	$\sim p)$
T	T	T	F	F	F	T	F	F
T	F	T	T	T	T	F	F	F
F	T	F	F	F	T	T	T	T
F	F	F	F	T	F	F	F	T
		1	2	1	3	1	2	1

Table 4

Now let us consider the verbal interpretation of the *exclusive or: p or q but not both p and q.* The truth table for the compound sentence $(p \wedge \sim q) \vee (q \wedge \sim p)$ has a T in the two cases in which one statement is true and the other false, and an F in the cases in which both statements are true and both are false. This is the set of truth values we would assign to the verbal statement of the *exclusive or*. We could invent a new symbol for the *exclusive or* (the symbol $\underline{\vee}$ is used by some logicians), and assign values F, T, T, F to the truth table of this new symbol. We shall not do this because we can express statements involving the *exclusive or* in terms of the connectives, $\wedge$, $\vee$, and $\sim$ as we have just shown in Problem 3.

Exercises

Construct a truth table for each of the following statements.

1. (a) $p \rightarrow \sim q$ (b) $(p \vee q) \vee \sim p$
2. (a) $p \wedge \sim q$ (b) $p \rightarrow (q \vee p)$
3. (a) $\sim(p \wedge q)$ (b) $\sim(p \vee q)$
4. (a) $\sim p \vee \sim q$ (b) $\sim p \wedge \sim q$
5. (a) $(p \wedge \sim q) \vee (\sim p \wedge q)$ (b) $\sim[(p \vee q) \wedge (\sim p \vee \sim q)]$
6. (a) Are there any pairs of statements in Exercises 1(a), 2(a), 3(a), 4(a), and 5(a) which are logically equivalent?
   (b) Are there any pairs of statements in Exercises 1(b), 2(b), 3(b), 4(b), and 5(b) which are logically equivalent?
7. (a) Suppose that a is a real number and let p be the following statement.

$$p: \quad a \text{ is positive.}$$

   Give a verbal statement of the following.
   (i) $\sim p$
   (ii) $p \wedge \sim p$
   (iii) $p \vee \sim p$
   (b) Suppose that n is an integer and let p be the following statement.

$$p: \quad n \text{ is even}$$

   Give a verbal statement of the following.
   (i) $\sim p$
   (ii) $p \wedge \sim p$
   (iii) $p \vee \sim p$
8. (a) Show that $[p \wedge (p \rightarrow q)] \rightarrow q$ is logically true.
   (b) Show that $[(p \rightarrow q) \wedge \sim q] \rightarrow \sim p$ is logically true.

---

9. Show that $\sim(p \wedge \sim p)$ is a logically true statement and that $\sim(p \vee \sim p)$ is logically false.

10. (a) Show that $p \lor q$ is logically equivalent to $q \lor p$.
(b) Show that $p \land q$ is logically equivalent to $q \land p$.
(c) Consider disjunction and conjunction as *operations* on pairs of statements, and tell which of the five fundamental properties of numbers can be used to describe the logical equivalences in parts (a) and (b).

11. Are $p \to q$ and $q \to p$ logically equivalent statements?

12. Use truth tables to prove the following equivalences, which are called De Morgan's laws.
(a) $\sim(p \land q)$ is logically equivalent to $\sim p \lor \sim q$
(b) $\sim(p \lor q)$ is logically equivalent to $\sim p \land \sim q$
(c) Make up examples of statements for p and q to illustrate these laws.

13. (a) Construct a truth table for $\sim(\sim p)$. This is usually written as $\sim\sim p$ and is called the *double negative* of p.
(b) Find a simpler statement which is logically equivalent to $\sim\sim p$.
(c) Let p be the following statement.

$$p: \quad \text{It is snowing.}$$

State the double negative of p.

14. Show that the statement $p \to q$ is logically equivalent to the statement $\sim(p \land \sim q)$. Stated in words, this equivalence means that the verbal statement *if p, then q* is the same as the statement,

$$\text{It is false that we have } p \text{ and not } q.$$

15. Let p and q be the following statements.

$$p: \quad a = 0$$

and

$$q: \quad b = 0.$$

Find a verbal statement that is logically equivalent to each of the following statements.
(a) $\sim(p \lor q)$
(b) $\sim(\sim p \land \sim q)$

16. Construct a truth table for

$$(p \lor q) \land [\sim(p \land q)],$$

and compare this truth table with that in Problem 3 on page 627.
(b) Give a verbal statement of this symbolic statement in which you take specific examples of statements p and q.

15-3 VARIATIONS OF THE CONDITIONAL

Many theorems and related statements in mathematics have the *if–then* form. Therefore, it is worthwhile for us to study the conditional connective in some detail. For convenience, let us call p the *hypothesis* and q the *conclusion* in the conditional statement $p \rightarrow q$.

First, let us consider the truth tables of the four related statements below.

Statement	Converse	Inverse	Contrapositive
$p \rightarrow q$	$q \rightarrow p$	$\sim p \rightarrow \sim q$	$\sim q \rightarrow \sim p$

We see from the truth table below that the following statements are equivalent.

$$p \rightarrow q \quad \text{and} \quad \sim q \rightarrow \sim p$$
$$q \rightarrow p \quad \text{and} \quad \sim p \rightarrow \sim q$$

The statement $q \rightarrow p$ is called the *converse* of the statement $p \rightarrow q$. According to the table, a conditional statement and its converse are *not logically equivalent*. You probably know from experience that the truth of a statement does not insure the truth of its converse.

p	q	$p \rightarrow q$			$q \rightarrow p$			$\sim p \rightarrow \sim q$			$\sim q \rightarrow \sim p$		
T	T	T	T	T	T	T	T	F	T	F	F	T	F
T	F	T	F	F	F	T	T	F	T	T	T	F	F
F	T	F	T	T	T	F	F	T	F	F	F	T	T
F	F	F	T	F	F	T	F	T	T	T	T	T	T

For example, the general statement

> If a quadrilateral is a square, then it is a parallelogram,

is true, but its converse,

> If a quadrilateral is a parallelogram, then it is a square,

is false.

The statement $\sim q \rightarrow \sim p$ is called the *contrapositive* of the statement $p \rightarrow q$. To form the contrapositive of an *if–then* statement, we negate the hypothesis and conclusion, and then form the converse statement. Since an *if–then* statement and its contrapositive are logically equivalent, the assertion of the truth or falsity of a particular statement $p \rightarrow q$ is equivalent to the assertion of the truth or falsity of its contrapositive statement, $\sim q \rightarrow \sim p$. In a later section, we shall see that this is a basis for a particular form of mathematical proof.

Sometimes we wish to combine an *if–then* statement with its converse by using the connective *and* to form the statement $p \rightarrow q$ *and* $q \rightarrow p$. A shorter way of writing this statement is

$$p \leftrightarrow q,$$

which is read *p if, and only if, q*. Let us determine the truth table for $p \leftrightarrow q$. Since $p \leftrightarrow q$ is defined as $(p \rightarrow q) \wedge (q \rightarrow p)$, we obtain the following truth table.

p	q	$(p \rightarrow q)$	$\wedge$	$(q \rightarrow p)$			
T	T	T	T	T	T	T	T
T	F	T	F	F	F	F	T	T
F	T	F	T	T	F	T	F	F
F	F	F	T	F	T	F	T	F
		1	2	1	3	1	2	1

Thus, the statement *p if, and only if, q* is true unless p and q have different truth values, that is, unless one is true and the other false.

A closer look at the words in the statement *p, if and only if, q* suggests a slightly different interpretation from that used in the definition of $p \leftrightarrow q$. The statement seems to contain the compound statements *p if q* and *p only if q*. The first statement gives us $q \rightarrow p$ but the second statement, literally translated, suggests $\sim q \rightarrow \sim p$. However, since $\sim q \rightarrow \sim p$ is the contrapositive of $p \rightarrow q$, we see that our definition of *if and only if* as $(p \rightarrow q) \wedge (q \rightarrow p)$ is consistent with the ordinary usage of words.

Still another logically equivalent form of $p \leftrightarrow q$ is the type of statement seen frequently in geometry, *if p, then q, and conversely*. In fact, this last form is probably most suggestive of the double arrow in $p \leftrightarrow q$.

We shall not be concerned about these different verbal statements for $p \leftrightarrow q$ because they are all logically equivalent to the compound statement

$$(p \rightarrow q) \wedge (q \rightarrow p).$$

You probably remember that the proof of a geometric or algebraic theorem of the form $p \leftrightarrow q$ requires the proof of two statements, one of the form $p \rightarrow q$ and the other its converse, $q \rightarrow p$.

Exercises

1. (a) Let p denote "The weather is bad" and q denote "The plane is late." Write each of the following in symbolic form.
    (i) If the weather is bad, the plane is late.
    (ii) The plane is late if, and only if, the weather is bad.
    (iii) The weather is bad if the plane is late.
    (iv) The plane is late only if the weather is bad.
   (b) Let p denote "I wear a raincoat" and q denote "the sun is shining." Write each of the following in symbolic form.
    (i) If the sun is not shining, I wear a raincoat.
    (ii) The sun is shining if, and only if, I do not wear a raincoat.
    (iii) I wear a raincoat but the sun is shining.
    (iv) I wear a raincoat only if the sun is not shining.

2. (a) State the converse, contrapositive, and inverse of the statement in part i of Exercise 1(a), and express each in symbolic form.
   (b) State the converse, contrapositive, and inverse of the statement in part i of Exercise 1(b) and express each in symbolic form.

3. (a) Form the contrapositive of the contrapositive of $p \to q$. To what statement is your resulting statement logically equivalent?
   (b) Construct the truth table for $\sim(p \to q)$. Find an equivalent statement which uses only the connectives $\sim$ and $\wedge$. Is $\sim(p \to q)$ equivalent to $\sim p \to \sim q$?

---

4. Why is $\sim p \leftrightarrow \sim q$ logically equivalent to $p \leftrightarrow q$? Give your answer without using truth tables.

5. Using the results of Exercise 4, find a statement which is logically equivalent to $p \leftrightarrow (q \vee r)$ and involves only the connectives $\sim$ and $\wedge$ used with $\leftrightarrow$. (Hint: You will need to use De Morgan's laws of Exercise 12 on Page 630.)

6. Using Exercises 4 and 5, give a verbal statement which is logically equivalent to the statement

   $$ab = 0 \text{ if, and only if, } a = 0 \text{ or } b = 0.$$

7. Give a verbal statement concerning odd integers which is logically equivalent to the following statement.

   The product of two integers is even if, and only if, at least one of the integers is even.

15–4 LOGICAL IMPLICATION AND VALID ARGUMENT

In the truth table for the conditional $p \rightarrow q$, where statements p and q are assigned all four possible pairs of truth values, there is an F in the second row for the case where p is true and q is false and a T in all other rows. Thus, the conditional statement $p \rightarrow q$ is not logically true. In Problem 1, we consider a more complex conditional statement.

Problem 1. Construct the truth table for the statement

$$[(p \rightarrow q) \wedge p] \rightarrow q.$$

Solution.

p	q	$[(p \rightarrow q) \wedge p] \rightarrow q$
T	T	T T T T T T T
T	F	T F F F T T F
F	T	F T T F F T T
F	F	F T F F F T F
		1 2 1 3 1 4 1

Thus, the conditional statement with hypothesis $(p \rightarrow q) \wedge p$ and conclusion q is a *logically true statement.*

When a conditional statement is logically true, we say that the hypothesis logically *implies* the conclusion, or that the conclusion *follows from* the hypothesis. For example, in any true mathematical theorem, the hypothesis *implies* the conclusion. The truth table in Problem 1 shows that $(p \rightarrow q) \wedge p$ logically *implies* the statement q.

Since the truth table for any conditional has T's in the rows where the hypothesis is *false*, we need look only at cases in which the hypothesis is *true* to test a conditional statement for implication. Thus, we could say the following.

Statement p implies q if, whenever p is true, q is also true.

It is this notion that most people have in mind when they make a conditional, or *if–then*, statement. This accounts for their initial shock when they see the last two rows of the truth table for $p \rightarrow q$. For example, a person asserting, "If you drink coffee, you won't sleep" really means to assert that drinking coffee implies lack of sleep and, of course, sees no point in saying this to a person who does *not* drink coffee (the case of false hypothesis).

The hypothesis and conclusion of a logically true conditional statement are related. They cannot take on all four pairs of truth values, since it is impossible to have a *true* hypothesis and *false* conclusion. This relationship is called a *logical implication.*

To *prove* a mathematical theorem, we must show that the hypothesis of the theorem logically *implies* the conclusion. In constructing a mathematical proof or in making a verbal argument, we usually form a chain of statements, prefacing the last of these with the word *therefore.* The statements in the chain are not all independent, and we rely strongly on notions of implication. We illustrate this with a simple example.

Problem 2. Symbolize the following argument.

> If it is raining, I will take an umbrella.
> It is raining. *Therefore,* I will take an umbrella.

Solution. Let p be the statement, "It is raining" and q the statement "I will take an umbrella." We write this argument in the form

$$\begin{array}{c} p \rightarrow q \\ \underline{p \qquad\qquad} \\ q \end{array}$$

Using the notation of the mathematician David Hilbert, who made outstanding contributions to the field of mathematical logic in the early twentieth century, we have drawn a horizontal line under the first two statements to denote the word *therefore.* Each statement which lies above such a horizontal line is called a premise, and each statement below the line is called a conclusion of the argument.

An argument is said to be valid according to the following definition.

Definition of a valid argument

An argument is valid if, and only if, the conjunction of (all) the premises implies the conclusion.

Now return to the truth table used in Problem 1. Note that it contains the two premises and the conclusion of the argument in Problem 2 and, furthermore, that it shows that the conjunction of these true premises implies the conclusion. In other words, this truth table establishes the validity of the argument of Problem 2.

You may have learned from experience that the argument in the next problem is *invalid.*

Problem 3. Test the following argument for validity.

> If John studies hard, he will pass the course.
> John passes the course. Therefore, he studied hard.

Solution.

> p: John studies hard.
> q: John passes the course.

The symbolized argument and its truth table are given below.

	p	q	$[(p \to q) \land q] \to p$
$p \to q$	T	T	T T T T T T T
q	T	F	T F F F F T T
p	F	T	F T T T T F F
	F	F	F T F F F T F
			1 2 1 3 1 4 1

The colored column shows that the argument is *invalid* since the conjunction of the premises does *not* imply the conclusion (we do not have all T's in column 4). Note that the case in which both premises are true and yet the conclusion is false is that of John not studying hard and passing the course. This case destroys the validity of the argument.

Exercises

Show that the first statement in each of the following pairs *implies* the second.

1. (a) $p \land q$, p (Hint: Use a truth table to show that $(p \land q) \to p$ is logically true.)

(b) p, $p \lor q$ (Hint: Use a truth table to show that $p \to (p \lor q)$ is logically true.)

2. (a) $p \land q$, q

(b) q, $p \lor q$

3. (a) $p \leftrightarrow q$, $p \to q$

(b) $p \land q$, $\sim p \lor q$

4. (a) $p \leftrightarrow q$, $q \to p$

(b) $p \land q$, $q \to p$

5. (a) $p \land q$, $p \to q$

(b) $q \leftrightarrow p$, $q \to p$

6. (a) In Exercises 1(a), 2(a), 3(a), 4(a), and 5(a), show that the second member of each pair does *not* imply the first.

   (b) In Exercises 1(b), 2(b), 3(b), 4(b), and 5(b), show that the second member of each pair does *not* imply the first.

In Exercises 7–10, test each argument for validity.

7. (a) $p \vee q$ (b) $p \rightarrow q$
      $\dfrac{\sim p}{q}$ $\dfrac{\sim q}{\sim p}$

8. (a) $p \vee q$ (b) $p \rightarrow q$
      $\dfrac{p}{\sim q}$ $\dfrac{\sim p}{\sim q}$

9. (a) $p \wedge q$ (b) $p \leftrightarrow q$
      $\dfrac{\sim p \rightarrow q}{\sim q}$ $\dfrac{p}{q}$

10. (a) $p \leftrightarrow q$ (b) $(p \vee q) \rightarrow r$
      $\dfrac{\sim p}{\sim q}$ $\dfrac{q \rightarrow \sim r}{p}$

---

11. Show that $p \wedge \sim p$ implies any statement q.   (Hint: Remember that $p \wedge \sim p$ is logically false.)

Write each of the following arguments in symbolic language. Then test each argument for validity.

12. If a candidate does not win the party's nomination, he will not be elected. A candidate wins the party's nomination. Therefore, he is elected.

13. If the sky is not cloudy, it will not rain. It is raining. Therefore, the sky is cloudy.

14. Only the brave deserve the fair. You deserve the fair. Therefore, you are brave.

15. If I work diligently, I finish by noon. Either the clock is fast or I do not finish by noon. But the clock is not fast. Therefore, I do not work diligently.

16. If a person is sane, he can do logic. An insane person is not fit to serve on a jury. Jones cannot do logic. Therefore, Jones is not fit to serve on a jury.

17. If I do not make good grades I will not win a scholarship. If I have not studied I will not make good grades. I do not win a scholarship. Therefore, I did not study.

15-5 PROOF SCHEMA AND INDIRECT ARGUMENT

In the previous section, we have tested the validity of *particular* arguments. However, the configuration of each of these arguments, called by Hilbert a *proof schema,* can be applied to all arguments of that form. Consider, for example, the proof schema displayed below. It is shown in the valid argument in Problem 2 on page 635, and is called the *rule of detachment* (*modus ponens*).

$$p \rightarrow q$$
$$\underline{p}$$
$$q$$

The rule of detachment is one of the patterns of reasoning used repeatedly in constructing proofs of mathematical theorems.

Another useful proof schema, called the *transitivity property of the conditional* (*transitivity of* $\rightarrow$), is given below.

$$p \rightarrow q$$
$$\underline{q \rightarrow r}$$
$$p \rightarrow r$$

The following truth table establishes the validity of this argument.

p	q	r	$[(p \rightarrow q)$	$\wedge$	$(q \rightarrow r)]$	$\rightarrow$	$(p \rightarrow r)$
T	T	T	T	T	T	T	T
T	T	F	T	F	F	T	F
T	F	T	F	F	T	T	T
T	F	F	F	F	T	T	F
F	T	T	T	T	T	T	T
F	T	F	T	F	F	T	T
F	F	T	T	T	T	T	T
F	F	F	T	T	T	T	T
			1	2	1	3	1

The use of the transivity property of the conditional is illustrated in the following problem.

Problem 1. Show that the following is a valid argument.

$$p \rightarrow q$$
$$q \rightarrow r$$
$$r \rightarrow s$$
$$\underline{p}$$
$$s$$

Solution.

$p \rightarrow q$	(given) (premise)
$q \rightarrow r$	(given)
$p \rightarrow r$	(transitivity of $\rightarrow$)
$r \rightarrow s$	(given)
$p \rightarrow s$	(transitivity of $\rightarrow$)
p	(given)
s	(rule of detachment)

The proofs of many mathematical theorems follow this pattern. However, in the *statement* of the theorem, the hypothesis may not contain all of the premises used in the proof. Some premises are introduced as the proof develops. Then the reason cited is an axiom or a previously proved theorem which asserts the truth of the premise. The theorem proved, then, actually has these axioms or previously proved theorems as additional premises.

It should be clear that if we replace a statement or any component of a statement by a logically equivalent statement, the original statement is *logically true* if, and only if, the statement containing the replacement is *logically true*. The reason for this is that logically equivalent statements have the same truth table.

In Section 15–3, we showed that the statement $p \rightarrow q$ is logically equivalent to its contrapositive, $\sim q \rightarrow \sim p$. Hence, *a proof of the contrapositive of a theorem constitutes (automatically) a proof of the theorem itself.* This principle is the basis of one of the proof forms called *proof by indirect reasoning,* which we illustrate in Problem 2.

Problem 2. Suppose that the property of multiplication by zero has been established: If $a = 0$ or $b = 0$, then $ab = 0$. Prove the following theorem.

$$\text{If } ab \neq 0, \text{ then } a \neq 0 \text{ and } b \neq 0.$$

Solution. To prove this theorem we first denote the statements $a = 0$, $b = 0$, and $ab = 0$ by p, q, and r, respectively. We are to prove that the following is logically true.

$$\sim r \rightarrow (\sim p \wedge \sim q)$$

The contrapositive of this statement is

$$\sim(\sim p \wedge \sim q) \rightarrow \sim(\sim r).$$

By applying one of De Morgan's laws (see Exercise 12 on page 630) and the double negative (see Exercise 13 on page 630), we determine that $\sim(\sim p \wedge \sim q)$ is equivalent to $p \vee q$ and that $\sim\sim r$ is equivalent to r. Thus, the contrapositive becomes

$$(p \vee q) \rightarrow r.$$

Stated in words, this says that if $a = 0$ or $b = 0$, then $ab = 0$. This is the statement of the theorem previously established, and hence, our original theorem is true.

The proof of this theorem as it is given in mathematics texts usually proceeds in the following way.

1. Given $ab \neq 0$.
2. Suppose it is false that $a \neq 0$ and $b \neq 0$.
3. Then at least one of a, b is 0.
4. But then $ab = 0$ by the zero multiplication property.
5. This contradicts the hypothesis that $ab \neq 0$ and hence, our *supposition* is false.

Therefore, if $ab \neq 0$, then $a \neq 0$ and $b \neq 0$.

We can facilitate the interpretation of the supposition in step 2 by noticing that it is logically equivalent to the statement in step 3, since $\sim(\sim p \wedge \sim q)$ is equivalent to $p \vee q$.

Another form of proof is called *reductio ad absurdum*, or proof by contradiction, which you encountered in your study of geometry. The following is an example.

Problem 3. Prove that if two different lines intersect, their intersection contains only one point.

Solution. Suppose that the two lines intersect in two different points, P and Q. Then two different lines contain points P and Q. However, this contradicts the *line postulate:* For every two different points, there is exactly one line that contains both points. Therefore, the theorem stated in the problem is true.

The above argument for p implies q has the form $(p \wedge \sim q)$ which implies $(r \wedge \sim r)$, as we now show. Let p, q be the following statements.

p: The two intersecting lines are different.

q: The two intersecting lines meet in only one point.

Let r be the line postulate. We show that whenever both premises p and $\sim q$ are true, the conclusion $r \wedge \sim r$ is true. Of course r is true by assumption. Therefore, we have to show only that whenever both p and $\sim q$ are true, $\sim r$ is true. This is done in the above verbal argument.

We shall let you verify that the two statements

$$p \rightarrow q \quad \text{and} \quad (p \wedge \sim q) \rightarrow (r \wedge \sim r)$$

are logically equivalent for any statements p, q, and r. This verification establishes the validity of the *reductio ad absurdum* reasoning.

Exercises

Use truth tables to test the arguments in Exercises 1 and 2 for validity.

1. (a) The murderer either fled through the skylight or disguised himself as a visiting policeman. He did not flee through the skylight. Therefore, he disguised himself as a visiting policeman.
   (b) If he has subversive ideas, he will vote against the bill. He will vote against the bill. Therefore, he has subversive ideas.

2. (a) Potatoes will make a heavy crop, if and only if, they are planted at the full moon. If the potato crop is light, wheat prices are high. Therefore, if potatoes are planted at the full moon, wheat prices will be high.
   (b) If the speaker is well-known, his lecture is worth attending. His lecture is short or it is not worth attending. But his lecture is not short. Therefore, the speaker is not well-known.

3. (a) Show that $p \vee q$ is logically equivalent to $\sim p \rightarrow q$. Use this to show that the valid argument of Exercise 1(a) has the proof schema of the law of detachment, or *modus ponens*.
   (b) In the sequence of proof schemas given below, we reduce the original proof schema for the valid argument in Exercise 2(b) to a simpler one in successive steps. Supply the missing rules of logic used in this process. (The symbol $\Rightarrow$ is used here to mean *logically implies*.)

$$
\begin{array}{l}
p \rightarrow q \\
r \vee \sim q \\
\hline
\sim r \\
\hline
\sim p
\end{array}
\quad
\begin{array}{c}
\text{Exercise 3(a)} \\
\xLongrightarrow{\hspace{1cm}}
\end{array}
\quad
\begin{array}{l}
p \rightarrow q \\
\sim r \rightarrow \sim q \\
\hline
\sim r \\
\hline
\sim p
\end{array}
\quad
\overset{?}{\Rightarrow}
\quad
\left.\begin{array}{l}
p \rightarrow q \\
q \rightarrow r
\end{array}\right\} \overset{?}{\Rightarrow}
\quad
\begin{array}{l}
p \rightarrow r \\
\\
\sim r \\
\hline
\sim p
\end{array}
$$

$$
\overset{?}{\Rightarrow}
\quad
\begin{array}{l}
\sim r \rightarrow \sim p \\
\sim r \\
\hline
\sim p
\end{array}
$$

Exercises 4–6 are adapted from problems posed by Lewis Carroll. Find a chain of conditional statements for each of these arguments, and supply the missing conclusion.

4. If fruit is unripe, it is unwholesome. If fruit is grown in the shade, it is unripe. This fruit is wholesome. *Therefore, __?__.*

5. If one hogs the conversation, one appears conceited. One is well-informed only if one is good company. If one appears conceited, one is not good company. *Therefore, __?__.*

6. If a kitten loves fish, he is teachable. A kitten with no tail will not play with a gorilla. If a kitten has whiskers, he loves fish. If a kitten has green eyes, he is unteachable. If a kitten has no whiskers, he has no tail. *Therefore, __?__.*

7. Show that $p \to q$ is logically equivalent to $(p \wedge \sim q) \to (r \wedge \sim r)$.

8. (a) An even integer is a number of the form $2n$, with n an integer. Show that a product of two integers x and y, with x even, is an even integer.
   (b) Use indirect argument and the theorem of part (a) to prove that if the product of two integers is odd, then both integers are odd.

9. Suppose that a group of 367 people are in a room. Use indirect argument to prove that at least two of these people have the same birthday.

10. Test for validity of the arguments in parts (a) and (b), each of which uses the following premise:

    A person will live to be 80 only if he has a sensible diet.

    (a) Mr. Smith dies before he is 80. *Therefore,* Mr. Smith did not have a sensible diet.
    (b) Mr. Jones has a sensible diet. *Therefore,* Mr. Jones will live to be 80 or over.

KEY IDEAS AND KEY WORDS

In logic, a **statement** is a sentence which is either true or false, but is not both true and false.

If p and q are statements, we use the **connectives** described below.

negation	$\sim p$	not p
conjunction	$p \wedge q$	p and q
disjunction	$p \vee q$	p or q
conditional	$p \to q$	if p, then q

The following are truth tables for these connectives.

p	$\sim p$
T	F
F	T

p	q	$p \wedge q$	$p \vee q$	$p \to q$
T	T	T	T	T
T	F	F	T	F
F	T	F	T	T
F	F	F	F	T

A statement is **logically true** or **logically false** if there is a T or an F, respectively, in every row of the final column of its truth table.

Two statements are **logically equivalent** if they have the same final column in their truth tables. Examples of logically equivalent pairs of statements are the following.

$$\sim\sim p \text{ (double negative) } \text{ and } p$$

$$\left. \begin{array}{ll} \sim(p \wedge q) & \text{and} \quad \sim p \vee \sim q \\ \sim(p \vee q) & \text{and} \quad \sim p \wedge \sim q \end{array} \right\} \text{ De Morgan's Laws}$$

The **statement** $p \rightarrow q$ has three related statements.

converse	$q \rightarrow p$
inverse	$\sim p \rightarrow \sim q$
contrapositive	$\sim q \rightarrow \sim p$

A statement and its contrapositive form a **logically equivalent pair.** In other words,

$$p \rightarrow q \text{ is logically equivalent to } \sim q \rightarrow \sim p.$$

If a conditional statement $p \rightarrow q$ is logically true, we say that the hypothesis p **implies** the conclusion q.

An argument is written in symbolic form by listing vertically the various premises and by separating the conclusion from the premises by a horizontal line.

$$\begin{array}{ll} p \rightarrow q & (1) \\ \underline{p} & \\ q & \end{array} \qquad\qquad \begin{array}{ll} p \rightarrow q & (2) \\ \underline{q} & \\ p & \end{array}$$

The argument is **valid** if the conjunction of all the premises **implies** the conclusion. Argument (1) above is valid, whereas argument (2) is invalid.

The symbolic form of a valid argument is called a **proof schema.** The proof schema in argument (1) is known as the **law of detachment,** or *modus ponens.* Another proof schema, called the **transitivity of the conditional,** is

$$\begin{array}{l} p \rightarrow q \\ \underline{q \rightarrow r} \\ p \rightarrow r. \end{array}$$

One form of proof by **indirect argument** is based on the logical equivalence of a statement and its contrapositive. Thus, the proof of a theorem of the form $\sim q \rightarrow \sim p$ automatically gives a proof of the theorem $p \rightarrow q$.

Another form of indirect argument is called *reductio ad absurdum.* To prove the theorem $p \rightarrow q$, one shows that $p \wedge \sim q$ implies a contradiction or a logically false conclusion, $r \wedge \sim r$.

CHAPTER REVIEW

Make a truth table for each of the statements in Exercises 1–4.

1. $\sim(p \wedge \sim q)$ **2.** $[(p \to q) \wedge q] \to p$

3. $(p \wedge q) \vee r$ **4.** $[(p \wedge q) \vee (p \wedge r)] \to [p \wedge (r \vee q)]$

5. Which of the following statements are logically equivalent to the statement, "It is false that at least one of the two dice is loaded."
  (a) Neither of the dice is loaded.
  (b) At least one die is fair.
  (c) Both dice are fair.
  (d) Neither of the dice is fair.
  (e) Both dice are loaded.

6. For any three statements p, q, and r, use truth tables to show that $p \to q$ and $q \to r$ cannot both be false at the same time.

7. Let p denote the statement, "A person is musically inclined"; q, the statement, "A person can do mathematics"; and r, the statement, "A person is good at debate." By using truth tables or the application of various logical principles (for example, transitivity of the conditional), show that the following is a valid argument.
  If a person can do mathematics, he is musically inclined. If a person cannot do mathematics, he is not good at debate. Tom is not musically inclined. *Therefore*, Tom is not good at debate.

8. Form a chain of conditional statements for the argument given below, and supply the missing conclusion.
  If the game is cancelled, the tie will not be broken. If it rains, the game will be cancelled. The tie is broken. *Therefore*, __?__.

9. (a) Using the definition of an even integer as an integer which can be written in the form $2n$ for some integer n, show that the square of an even integer is even.
  (b) Prove by indirect argument that if the square of an integer is odd, then that integer is odd.

10. Suppose that each individual in a town of 17,577 inhabitants has exactly three initials in his name. Prove that at least two individuals must have the same set of initials.

CHAPTER TEST

1. Using a truth table, determine whether the following statement is logically true, logically false, or neither logically true nor logically false.

$$(p \vee q) \vee (\sim p)$$

2. Let p denote "Mary passed the course" and q denote "John passed the course." Which of the following are logically equivalent to the statement,

  "It is not the case that Mary and John both failed the course"?

(a) $\sim(\sim p \vee \sim q)$ (b) $\sim(\sim p \wedge \sim q)$ (c) $(\sim p) \wedge (\sim q)$
(d) $p \vee q$ (e) $p \wedge q$

3. Using a truth table, test the following argument for validity.

$$p \vee q$$
$$\underline{q \to p}$$
$$q$$

4. Find a chain of conditional statements for the following argument, and supply the missing conclusion.

A person is successful in playing the organ only if he has studied piano. If one is unwilling to practice an hour a day, one cannot study piano. Susie plays the organ successfully. *Therefore,* __?__.

Table of Squares and Square Roots

N	N^2	$\sqrt{N}$	N	N^2	$\sqrt{N}$
1	1	1	51	2,601	7.141
2	4	1.414	52	2,704	7.211
3	9	1.732	53	2,809	7.280
4	16	2	54	2,916	7.348
5	25	2.236	55	3,025	7.416
6	36	2.449	56	3,136	7.483
7	49	2.646	57	3,249	7.550
8	64	2.828	58	3,364	7.616
9	81	3	59	3,481	7.681
10	100	3.162	60	3,600	7.746
11	121	3.317	61	3,721	7.810
12	144	3.464	62	3,844	7.874
13	169	3.606	63	3,969	7.937
14	196	3.742	64	4,096	8
15	225	3.873	65	4,225	8.062
16	256	4	66	4,356	8.124
17	289	4.123	67	4,489	8.185
18	324	4.243	68	4,624	8.246
19	361	4.359	69	4,761	8.307
20	400	4.472	70	4,900	8.367
21	441	4.583	71	5,041	8.426
22	484	4.690	72	5,184	8.485
23	529	4.796	73	5,329	8.544
24	576	4.899	74	5,476	8.602
25	625	5	75	5,625	8.660
26	676	5.099	76	5,776	8.718
27	729	5.196	77	5,929	8.775
28	784	5.292	78	6,084	8.832
29	841	5.385	79	6,241	8.888
30	900	5.477	80	6,400	8.944
31	961	5.568	81	6,561	9
32	1,024	5.657	82	6,724	9.055
33	1,089	5.745	83	6,889	9.110
34	1,156	5.831	84	7,056	9.165
35	1,225	5.916	85	7,225	9.220
36	1,296	6	86	7,396	9.274
37	1,369	6.083	87	7,569	9.327
38	1,444	6.164	88	7,744	9.381
39	1,521	6.245	89	7,921	9.434
40	1,600	6.325	90	8,100	9.487
41	1,681	6.403	91	8,281	9.539
42	1,764	6.481	92	8,464	9.592
43	1,849	6.557	93	8,649	9.644
44	1,936	6.633	94	8,836	9.695
45	2,025	6.708	95	9,025	9.747
46	2,116	6.782	96	9,216	9.798
47	2,209	6.856	97	9,409	9.849
48	2,304	6.928	98	9,604	9.899
49	2,401	7	99	9,801	9.950
50	2,500	7.071	100	10,000	10

Table of Values of Trigonometric Functions

deg	rad	sin	cos	tan	deg	rad	sin	cos	tan
0	.000	.000	1.000	.000					
1	.017	.017	1.000	.017	46	.803	.719	.695	1.036
2	.035	.035	.999	.035	47	.820	.731	.682	1.072
3	.052	.052	.999	.052	48	.838	.743	.669	1.111
4	.070	.070	.998	.070	49	.855	.755	.656	1.150
5	.087	.087	.996	.087	50	.873	.766	.643	1.192
6	.105	.105	.995	.105	51	.890	.777	.629	1.235
7	.122	.122	.993	.123	52	.908	.788	.616	1.280
8	.140	.139	.990	.141	53	.925	.799	.602	1.327
9	.157	.156	.988	.158	54	.942	.809	.588	1.376
10	.175	.174	.985	.176	55	.960	.819	.574	1.428
11	.192	.191	.982	.194	56	.977	.829	.559	1.483
12	.209	.208	.978	.213	57	.995	.839	.545	1.540
13	.227	.225	.974	.231	58	1.012	.848	.530	1.600
14	.244	.242	.970	.249	59	1.030	.857	.515	1.664
15	.262	.259	.966	.268	60	1.047	.866	.500	1.732
16	.279	.276	.961	.287	61	1.065	.875	.485	1.804
17	.297	.292	.956	.306	62	1.082	.883	.470	1.881
18	.314	.309	.951	.325	63	1.100	.891	.454	1.963
19	.332	.326	.946	.344	64	1.117	.899	.438	2.050
20	.349	.342	.940	.364	65	1.134	.906	.423	2.145
21	.367	.358	.934	.384	66	1.152	.914	.407	2.246
22	.384	.375	.927	.404	67	1.169	.921	.391	2.356
23	.401	.391	.921	.424	68	1.187	.927	.375	2.475
24	.419	.407	.914	.445	69	1.204	.934	.358	2.605
25	.436	.423	.906	.466	70	1.222	.940	.342	2.747
26	.454	.438	.899	.488	71	1.239	.946	.326	2.904
27	.471	.454	.891	.510	72	1.257	.951	.309	3.078
28	.489	.470	.883	.532	73	1.274	.956	.292	3.271
29	.506	.485	.875	.554	74	1.292	.961	.276	3.487
30	.524	.500	.866	.577	75	1.309	.966	.259	3.732
31	.541	.515	.857	.601	76	1.326	.970	.242	4.011
32	.559	.530	.848	.625	77	1.344	.974	.225	4.331
33	.576	.545	.839	.649	78	1.361	.978	.208	4.705
34	.593	.559	.829	.675	79	1.379	.982	.191	5.145
35	.611	.574	.819	.700	80	1.396	.985	.174	5.671
36	.628	.588	.809	.727	81	1.414	.988	.156	6.314
37	.646	.602	.799	.754	82	1.431	.990	.139	7.115
38	.663	.616	.788	.781	83	1.449	.993	.122	8.144
39	.681	.629	.777	.810	84	1.466	.995	.105	9.514
40	.698	.643	.766	.839	85	1.484	.996	.087	11.430
41	.716	.656	.755	.869	86	1.501	.998	.070	14.301
42	.733	.669	.743	.900	87	1.518	.999	.052	19.081
43	.751	.682	.731	.933	88	1.536	.999	.035	28.636
44	.768	.695	.719	.966	89	1.553	1.000	.017	57.290
45	.785	.707	.707	1.000	90	1.571	1.000	.000	—

Table of Common Logarithms

N	0	1	2	3	4	5	6	7	8	9
10	.0000	.0043	.0086	.0128	.0170	.0212	.0253	.0294	.0334	.0374
11	.0414	.0453	.0492	.0531	.0569	.0607	.0645	.0682	.0719	.0755
12	.0792	.0828	.0864	.0899	.0934	.0969	.1004	.1038	.1072	.1106
13	.1139	.1173	.1206	.1239	.1271	.1303	.1335	.1367	.1399	.1430
14	.1461	.1492	.1523	.1553	.1584	.1614	.1644	.1673	.1703	.1732
15	.1761	.1790	.1818	.1847	.1875	.1903	.1931	.1959	.1987	.2014
16	.2041	.2068	.2095	.2122	.2148	.2175	.2201	.2227	.2253	.2279
17	.2304	.2330	.2355	.2380	.2405	.2430	.2455	.2480	.2504	.2529
18	.2553	.2577	.2601	.2625	.2648	.2672	.2695	.2718	.2742	.2765
19	.2788	.2810	.2833	.2856	.2878	.2900	.2923	.2945	.2967	.2989
20	.3010	.3032	.3054	.3075	.3096	.3118	.3139	.3160	.3181	.3201
21	.3222	.3243	.3263	.3284	.3304	.3324	.3345	.3365	.3385	.3404
22	.3424	.3444	.3464	.3483	.3502	.3522	.3541	.3560	.3579	.3598
23	.3617	.3636	.3655	.3674	.3692	.3711	.3729	.3747	.3766	.3784
24	.3802	.3820	.3838	.3856	.3874	.3892	.3909	.3927	.3945	.3962
25	.3979	.3997	.4014	.4031	.4048	.4065	.4082	.4099	.4116	.4133
26	.4150	.4166	.4183	.4200	.4216	.4232	.4249	.4265	.4281	.4298
27	.4314	.4330	.4346	.4362	.4378	.4393	.4409	.4425	.4440	.4456
28	.4472	.4487	.4502	.4518	.4533	.4548	.4564	.4579	.4594	.4609
29	.4624	.4639	.4654	.4669	.4683	.4698	.4713	.4728	.4742	.4757
30	.4771	.4786	.4800	.4814	.4829	.4843	.4857	.4871	.4886	.4900
31	.4914	.4928	.4942	.4955	.4969	.4983	.4997	.5011	.5024	.5038
32	.5051	.5065	.5079	.5092	.5105	.5119	.5132	.5145	.5159	.5172
33	.5185	.5198	.5211	.5224	.5237	.5250	.5263	.5276	.5289	.5302
34	.5315	.5328	.5340	.5353	.5366	.5378	.5391	.5403	.5416	.5428
35	.5441	.5453	.5465	.5478	.5490	.5502	.5514	.5527	.5539	.5551
36	.5563	.5575	.5587	.5599	.5611	.5623	.5635	.5647	.5658	.5670
37	.5682	.5694	.5705	.5717	.5729	.5740	.5752	.5763	.5775	.5786
38	.5798	.5809	.5821	.5832	.5843	.5855	.5866	.5877	.5888	.5899
39	.5911	.5922	.5933	.5944	.5955	.5966	.5977	.5988	.5999	.6010
40	.6021	.6031	.6042	.6053	.6064	.6075	.6085	.6096	.6107	.6117
41	.6128	.6138	.6149	.6160	.6170	.6180	.6191	.6201	.6212	.6222
42	.6232	.6243	.6253	.6263	.6274	.6284	.6294	.6304	.6314	.6325
43	.6335	.6345	.6355	.6365	.6375	.6385	.6395	.6405	.6415	.6425
44	.6435	.6444	.6454	.6464	.6474	.6484	.6493	.6503	.6513	.6522
45	.6532	.6542	.6551	.6561	.6571	.6580	.6590	.6599	.6609	.6618
46	.6628	.6637	.6646	.6656	.6665	.6675	.6684	.6693	.6702	.6712
47	.6721	.6730	.6739	.6749	.6758	.6767	.6776	.6785	.6794	.6803
48	.6812	.6821	.6830	.6839	.6848	.6857	.6866	.6875	.6884	.6893
49	.6902	.6911	.6920	.6928	.6937	.6946	.6955	.6964	.6972	.6981
50	.6990	.6998	.7007	.7016	.7024	.7033	.7042	.7050	.7059	.7067
51	.7076	.7084	.7093	.7101	.7110	.7118	.7126	.7135	.7143	.7152
52	.7160	.7168	.7177	.7185	.7193	.7202	.7210	.7218	.7226	.7235
53	.7243	.7251	.7259	.7267	.7275	.7284	.7292	.7300	.7308	.7316
54	.7324	.7332	.7340	.7348	.7356	.7364	.7372	.7380	.7388	.7396

Table of Common Logarithms (*Continued*)

N	0	1	2	3	4	5	6	7	8	9
55	.7404	.7412	.7419	.7427	.7435	.7443	.7451	.7459	.7466	.7474
56	.7482	.7490	.7497	.7505	.7513	.7520	.7528	.7536	.7543	.7551
57	.7559	.7566	.7574	.7582	.7589	.7597	.7604	.7612	.7619	.7627
58	.7634	.7642	.7649	.7657	.7664	.7672	.7679	.7686	.7694	.7701
59	.7709	.7716	.7723	.7731	.7738	.7745	.7752	.7760	.7767	.7774
60	.7782	.7789	.7796	.7803	.7810	.7818	.7825	.7832	.7839	.7846
61	.7853	.7860	.7868	.7875	.7882	.7889	.7896	.7903	.7910	.7917
62	.7924	.7931	.7938	.7945	.7952	.7959	.7966	.7973	.7980	.7987
63	.7993	.8000	.8007	.8014	.8021	.8028	.8035	.8041	.8048	.8055
64	.8062	.8069	.8075	.8082	.8089	.8096	.8102	.8109	.8116	.8122
65	.8129	.8136	.8142	.8149	.8156	.8162	.8169	.8176	.8182	.8189
66	.8195	.8202	.8209	.8215	.8222	.8228	.8235	.8241	.8248	.8254
67	.8261	.8267	.8274	.8280	.8287	.8293	.8299	.8306	.8312	.8319
68	.8325	.8331	.8338	.8344	.8351	.8357	.8363	.8370	.8376	.8382
69	.8388	.8395	.8401	.8407	.8414	.8420	.8426	.8432	.8439	.8445
70	.8451	.8457	.8463	.8470	.8476	.8482	.8488	.8494	.8500	.8506
71	.8513	.8519	.8525	.8531	.8537	.8543	.8549	.8555	.8561	.8567
72	.8573	.8579	.8585	.8591	.8597	.8603	.8609	.8615	.8621	.8627
73	.8633	.8639	.8645	.8651	.8657	.8663	.8669	.8675	.8681	.8686
74	.8692	.8698	.8704	.8710	.8716	.8722	.8727	.8733	.8739	.8745
75	.8751	.8756	.8762	.8768	.8774	.8779	.8785	.8791	.8797	.8802
76	.8808	.8814	.8820	.8825	.8831	.8837	.8842	.8848	.8854	.8859
77	.8865	.8871	.8876	.8882	.8887	.8893	.8899	.8904	.8910	.8915
78	.8921	.8927	.8932	.8938	.8943	.8949	.8954	.8960	.8965	.8971
79	.8976	.8982	.8987	.8993	.8998	.9004	.9009	.9015	.9020	.9025
80	.9031	.9036	.9042	.9047	.9053	.9058	.9063	.9069	.9074	.9079
81	.9085	.9090	.9096	.9101	.9106	.9112	.9117	.9122	.9128	.9133
82	.9138	.9143	.9149	.9154	.9159	.9165	.9170	.9175	.9180	.9186
83	.9191	.9196	.9201	.9206	.9212	.9217	.9222	.9227	.9232	.9238
84	.9243	.9248	.9253	.9258	.9263	.9269	.9274	.9279	.9284	.9289
85	.9294	.9299	.9304	.9309	.9315	.9320	.9325	.9330	.9335	.9340
86	.9345	.9350	.9355	.9360	.9365	.9370	.9375	.9380	.9385	.9390
87	.9395	.9400	.9405	.9410	.9415	.9420	.9425	.9430	.9435	.9440
88	.9445	.9450	.9455	.9460	.9465	.9469	.9474	.9479	.9484	.9489
89	.9494	.9499	.9504	.9509	.9513	.9518	.9523	.9528	.9533	.9538
90	.9542	.9547	.9552	.9557	.9562	.9566	.9571	.9576	.9581	.9586
91	.9590	.9595	.9600	.9605	.9609	.9614	.9619	.9624	.9628	.9633
92	.9638	.9643	.9647	.9652	.9657	.9661	.9666	.9671	.9675	.9680
93	.9685	.9689	.9694	.9699	.9703	.9708	.9713	.9717	.9722	.9727
94	.9731	.9736	.9741	.9745	.9750	.9754	.9759	.9763	.9768	.9773
95	.9777	.9782	.9786	.9791	.9795	.9800	.9805	.9809	.9814	.9818
96	.9823	.9827	.9832	.9836	.9841	.9845	.9850	.9854	.9859	.9863
97	.9868	.9872	.9877	.9881	.9886	.9890	.9894	.9899	.9903	.9908
98	.9912	.9917	.9921	.9926	.9930	.9934	.9939	.9943	.9948	.9952
99	.9956	.9961	.9965	.9969	.9974	.9978	.9983	.9987	.9991	.9996

LIST OF ABBREVIATIONS
AND SYMBOLS

ABBREVIATIONS

$(A>), (A<)$ Additive property of inequalities

(A-1) First addition formula

(A-2) Second addition formula

(A-3) Third addition formula

(A-4) Fourth addition formula

(A-A) Associative axiom of addition

(A-M) Associative axiom of multiplication

(Add-A) Additive axiom

(C-A) Commutative axiom of addition

(C-M) Commutative axiom of multiplication

(Can-A) Cancellation law of addition

(Can-M) Cancellation law of multiplication

(Clos-A) Closure of P under addition

(Clos-M) Closure of P under multiplication

(D) Distributive axiom

(D-1) First double-angle formula

(D-2) Second double-angle formula

$(Def >)$ Definition of greater than

$(Def <)$ Definition of less than

$(Def \geq)$ Definition of greater than or equal to

$(Def \leq)$ Definition of less than or equal to

(Def-Div) Definition of division

(Def-Neg. Exp.) Definition of negative exponents

(Def-nth Rt.) Definition of nth root

(Def-Rat. Exp.) Definition of rational exponents

(Def-SM) Definition of scalar multiplication

(Def-Sub) Definition of subtraction

$(Def |x|)$ Definition of absolute value

(F-0) Factors of zero

(FI-1) First fundamental identity

(FI-2) Second fundamental identity

(FI-3) Third fundamental identity

(FI-4) Fourth fundamental identity

(FI-5) Fifth fundamental identity

(FI-6) Sixth fundamental identity

(FI-7) Seventh fundamental identity

(FI-8) Eighth fundamental identity

(FI-9) Ninth fundamental identity

(FI-10) Tenth fundamental identity

(FI-11) Eleventh fundamental identity

(FI-12) Twelfth fundamental identity

(FI-13) Thirteenth fundamental identity

(FI-14) Fourteenth fundamental identity

(FI-15) Fifteenth fundamental identity

(H-1) First half-angle formula

(H-2) Second half-angle formula

(Id-A) Additive identity axiom

(Id-M) Multiplicative identity axiom

(Inv-A) Additive inverse axiom

(Inv-M) Multiplicative inverse axiom

(LE-1) First law of exponents

(LE-2) Second law of exponents

(LE-3) Third law of exponents

(LE-4) Fourth law of exponents

(LE-5) Fifth law of exponents

(LL-1) First law of logarithms

(LL-2) Second law of logarithms

(LL-3) Third law of logarithms

(LR-1) First law of radicals

(LR-2) Second law of radicals

$(M>), (M<)$ Positive multiplicative property of inequalities

$(-M>), (-M<)$ Negative multiplicative property of inequalities

(Mult-A) Multiplicative axiom

(Neg-M) Negative multiplication

(R-A) Rearrangement property of addition

(R-M) Rearrangement property of multiplication

(Ref-A)	Reflexive axiom
(SM-1)	Scalar multiplicative property
(SM-2)	Associative law of scalar multiplication
(SM-3)	Distributive laws of scalar multiplication
(Sym-A)	Symmetric axiom
(T >) (T <)	Transitive law of inequalities
(Trans-A)	Transitive axiom
(Tri)	Trichotomy axiom
(Zero-M)	Zero multiplication

SYMBOLS

$=$	Equal to
$\neq$	Not equal to
$\doteq$	Approximately equal to
$[x]$	Greatest-integer function
$>$	Greater than
$<$	Less than
$\{\,\}$	Set
$\subset$	Subset
$\cap$	Intersection
$\cup$	Union
$\emptyset$	Empty set
$\geqq$	Greater than or equal to
$\leqq$	Less than or equal to
$\not>$	Not greater than
$\not<$	Not less than
$|x|$	Absolute value
AB	Distance between the points A and B
$d(AB)$	Directed distance
$\overline{AB}$	Segment $\overline{AB}$
i	$i^2 = -1$
$\bar{r}$	Conjugate of the complex number r
$\overparen{AB}$	Arc $\overparen{AB}$
$_nP_r$	Number of permutations of r objects from a set of n objects
$_nC_r$ or $\binom{n}{r}$	Number of combinations of r objects from a set of n objects
$n!$	n factorial
$\overrightarrow{AB}$	Vector $\overrightarrow{AB}$
a	Vector **a**
0	Zero vector
i, j	Unit vectors
$\wedge$	And (conjunction)
$\vee$	Or (disjunction)
$\sim$	Not (negation)
$\rightarrow$	If-then (conditional statement)
$\leftrightarrow$	If and only if

GLOSSARY

Absolute value. $|a| = a$ if $a \geq 0$ and $|a| = -a$ if $a < 0$.

Additive identity. The additive identity element is 0.

Additive inverse. Each real number x has a unique opposite, $-x$.

Arithmetic series. An algebraic expression of the form

$$a + (a + d) + (a + 2d) + \cdots + [a + (n - 1)d].$$

Associative axiom of addition. $(a + b) + c = a + (b + c)$.

Associative axiom of multiplication. $(ab) \cdot c = a \cdot (bc)$.

Binomial distribution theorem. In a sequence of n Bernoulli trials with probability of success p, the probability of exactly k successes in the n trials is given by

$$\binom{n}{k} p^k (1 - p)^{n-k}$$

for $k = 0, 1, 2, \ldots, n$.

Binomial theorem. For every pair x, y of real numbers and every positive integer n,

$$(x + y)^n = \binom{n}{0} x^n + \binom{n}{1} x^{n-1}y + \cdots + \binom{n}{k} x^{n-k}y^k + \cdots + \binom{n}{n} y^n.$$

Cancellation law of addition. It $a + c = b + c$, then $a = b$.

Cancellation law of multiplication. If $ac = bc$ and $c \neq 0$, then $a = b$.

Characteristic. The greatest integer contained in $\log_{10} N$.

Circle. The set of all points in a plane at a given distance from a fixed point. The equation

$$(x - h)^2 + (y - k)^2 = r^2$$

denotes the circle with radius r and center coordinates (h, k).

Combination. A subset of r elements chosen from a set of n elements, $n \geq r$.

Commutative axiom of addition. $a + b = b + a$.

Commutative axiom of multiplication. $ab = ba$.

Complement. $\overline{A}$ is the set of all elements that are not in A.

Complex number. Every number of the form $a + bi$ where a and b are real numbers and $i = \sqrt{-1}$.

Conjugate. The conjugate of a complex number of the form $a + bi$ is $a - bi$.

Conjunction. The statement $p \wedge q$ meaning p and q.

Contrapositive. The related statement $\sim q \rightarrow \sim p$ of the statement $p \rightarrow q$.

Converse. The related statement $q \rightarrow p$ of the statement $p \rightarrow q$.

Determinant.   A real number associated with a square matrix.

Discriminant of a quadratic equation.   The discriminant is $b^2 - 4ac$ for the quadratic equation $ax^2 + bx + c = 0$.

Disjunction.   The statement $p \lor q$ meaning p or q.

Distance formula.   The distance between points $P(x_1, y_1)$ and $Q(x_2, y_2)$ is

$$PQ = \sqrt{(x_2 - x_1)^2 + (y_2 - y_1)^2}.$$

Distributive axiom. $a(b + c) = ab + ac$.

Domain of a function.   *See* Function.

Ellipse.   Given two points A and B in a plane and a positive number k greater than AB, the set consisting of all points P in a plane such that $AP + BP = k$.

Empty set.   A set with no elements. It is denoted by $\emptyset$.

Exponential function.   The function f, defined by $f(x) = b^x$, $b > 0$, $b \neq 1$ and x real.

Factor Theorem.   The theorem states that the polynomlal $x - r$ is a divisor, or factor, of a polynomial $f(x)$ if, and only if, $f(r) = 0$.

Function.   If to each value of a variable, there corresponds a unique value of a second variable, the correspondence between these two variables is called a function. If to each value of a variable x, there corresponds a unique value of a variable y, then we say that y is a function of x. The set of values of x is called the *domain of the function*, and the set of values of y is called the *range of the function*.

Geometric series.   An algebraic expression of the form

$$a + aq + aq^2 + \cdots + aq^{n-1}.$$

Greater than. $x > y$ if, and only if, $x - y$ is positive.

Half-plane.   Each of two regions into which a line divides a plane.

Hyperbola.   Given two points A and B in a plane and a positive number k less than AB, the set consisting of every point P in the plane such that either $AP - BP = k$ or $BP - AP = k$.

Induction axiom.   If a set S of positive integers contains 1, and if whenever S contains the integer k, it also contains the integer $k + 1$, then the set S must be the set of all positive integers.

Infinite geometric series.   A geometric series with an infinite number of terms, $a + aq + aq^2 + \cdots + aq^{n-1} + \cdots$

Inner product. $\overrightarrow{AB} \cdot \overrightarrow{CD} = |AB|\,|\overrightarrow{CD}| \cos \theta$ where θ is the angle between $\overrightarrow{AB}$ and $\overrightarrow{CD}$.

Intersection of A and B.   All elements common to both A and B, denoted by $A \cap B$.

Inverse.   The related statement $\sim p \rightarrow \sim q$ of the statement $p \rightarrow q$.

Inverse trigonometric functions.

$$\arcsin x = s, \text{ where } \sin s = x \text{ and } -\frac{\pi}{2} \leqq s \leqq \frac{\pi}{2}$$

$$\arccos x = s, \text{ where } \cos s = x \text{ and } 0 \leqq s \leqq \pi$$

$$\arctan x = s, \text{ where } \tan s = x \text{ and } -\frac{\pi}{2} < s < \frac{\pi}{2}$$

Law of cosines.   If α, β, and γ are the angles and a, b, and c are the lengths of the respective opposite sides of a triangle, then

$$a^2 = b^2 + c^2 - 2bc \cos \alpha.$$

Law of sines.

$$\frac{\sin \alpha}{a} = \frac{\sin \beta}{b}$$

Less than. $x < y$ if, and only if, $y - x$ is positive.

Logarithm functions.   The logarithm function to the base b, $\log_b$, is given by $\log_b s = r$, where $b^r = s$ (assuming $b > 0$ and $b \neq 1$).

Mantissa.   The fractional part of $\log_{10} N$.

Matrix.   A rectangular array of numbers.

Mean proportional.   If the means of a proportion are equal, their common value is called a mean proportional between the extremes.

Multiplicative identity.   The multiplicative identity element is 1.

Multiplicative inverse.   If the product of two numbers is 1, each number is a multiplicative inverse, or reciprocal, of the other.

Mutually exclusive events.   If $A \cap B = \emptyset$, A and B are said to be mutually exclusive events.

Negation.   The statement $\sim p$ meaning *not p*.

Open ray.   A ray without its endpoint.

Order.   The set P of positive numbers is closed under addition and under multiplication. The trichotomy law holds.

Parabola.   If F is a point and L is a line not containing F, a parabola is the set of all points P in the plane containing F and L such that $PF = PQ$, where Q is at the foot of the perpendicular drawn from P to L.

Permutation.   An arrangement of symbols, in which repetition of symbols is not allowed.

Polynomial.   An algebraic expression of the form
$$a_n x^n + a_{n-1} x^{n-1} + \cdots + a_1 x + a_0$$
where n is an integer and $n \geq 0$, x is a variable and $a_n, a_{n-1}, \ldots, a_1, a_0$ are real or complex numbers.

Probability.   A measure of the likelihood of an event occurring.

Pythagorean theorem.   If a and b are the lengths of the legs and c is the length of the hypotenuse of a right triangle, then $a^2 + b^2 = c^2$.

Quadratic equation.   A second-degree polynomial equation.

Quadratic formula.   If $ax^2 + bx + c = 0$, then
$$x = \frac{-b \pm \sqrt{b^2 - 4ac}}{2a}.$$

Range of a function.   *See* Function.

Rational exponents.
$$x^{\frac{m}{n}} = \sqrt[n]{x^m} = (\sqrt[n]{x})^m.$$

Ray.   Each of the two pieces into which a point P divides a line. The ray includes P.

Rearrangement property of addition.   The addends of a sum may be rearranged in any order.

Rearrangement property of multiplication.   The multiplicands of a product may be rearranged in any order.

Reciprocal.   *See* Multiplicative inverse.

Solution set.   The set of all solutions of an equation or an inequality.

Transitive law.   If $x > y$ and $y > z$, then $x > z$.

Trichotomy axiom.   Every real number is either a positive number, a negative number, or 0.

Trigonometric functions.   If α is an acute angle of the right triangle ABC, a is the side opposite α, b the side adjacent to α, and c the hypotenuse, then
$$\sin \alpha = \frac{a}{c}, \ \cos \alpha = \frac{b}{c}, \ \tan \alpha = \frac{a}{b}.$$

Union.   The union of sets A and B consists of all the elements in either set A or set B. It is denoted by $A \cup B$.

Vector.   A line segment having an initial point A, a terminal point B, and a direction from A to B. This vector is denoted by $\overrightarrow{AB}$.

INDEX

Absolute value, 16
  of complex number, 209, 473
  function, 266
Addend, 6
Addition
  associative axiom of, 2
  cancellation law of, 7
  closure under, 11
  commutative axiom of, 2
  of complex numbers, 191
  of functions, 284
  of imaginary numbers, 186
  of polynomials, 340–341
  rearrangement property of, 7
  solution of equations by, 98, 112
  theorem of probabilities, 525
  of vectors, 584–585
Addition formulas, 448, 449
Additive
  axiom, 1
  identity axiom, 3
  identity of polynomials, 341
  inverse axiom, 3
  inverse of polynomials, 341
  inverse of vectors, 585
  property of inequalities, 12
  property of vectors, 584
Algebra
  of functions, 284
  of polynomials, 339, 358
  of vectors, 582
Algebraic numbers, 49
Alternative cases principle, 489
Amplitude, of trigonometric
  functions, 464
Angle(s), 426
  double-angle formulas, 452
  half-angle formulas, 453
  radian measure of, 426
  trigonometric functions of, 399,
  428
Antilogarithm, 317
Approximations,
  of radical expressions, 26, 153
  of irrational zeros, 381
Arccosine, 468–469
Arcsine, 468,470
Arctangent, 470–471
Arithmetic mean(s), 47–48, 552

Arithmetic series, 549
Arrangements, 493
Associative axioms of addition and
  multiplication, 2
Associative law
  of addition of complex numbers,
  192
  of addition of polynomials, 341
  of addition of vectors, 584
  of multiplication of polynomials,
  343
  of scalar multiplication of vectors,
  590
Asymptotes, 462
Axiom(s)
  additive and multiplicative
  identity, 3
  additive and multiplicative
  inverse, 3
  associative, 2
  commutative, 2
  distributive, 2
  of equality, 1, 2, 3
  for integers, 19
  of order, 11
  of the real number system, 1
  trichotomy, 11
Axis(es)
  of ellipse, 237, 240
  of hyperbola, 247
  imaginary, 208
  major and minor, 240
  of parabola, 256
  real, 208
  of symmetry, 157, 161, 164, 237,
  249
  transverse, 251

Base, of a logarithm, 294, 296
Bases, of vector algebra, 594
Bernoulli trials, 534
Between, 16
Binomial
  coefficients, 507, 512
  distribution theorem, 533,537
  theorem, 509

Cancellation law
  of addition and multiplication, 7
  of vectors, 585
Cartesian coordinate system, 78, 221

SELECTED ANSWERS FOR EXERCISES

In the side headings below, the hyphenated numerals (**1-1**, for example) refer to chapter and section numbers and the final numeral (*4*, for example) refers to the first page of an exercise for which answers are given.

1–1, *4*   **1.** (a) 3   **3.** (a) 7   **5.** (a) No   **7.** (a) No   **9.** (a) Additive
11. (a) Multiplicative   **13.** (a) Neither   **15.** (a) (A-A)   **17.** (a) (C-A), (A-A)
19. (a) (C-M)   **21.** (a) (Trans-A)   **23.** (A-A)   **25.** (D), (C-M)
27. (C-M), (A-M)

1–2, *9*   **1.** (a) -5 **3.** (a) $2\frac{2}{5}$ **5.** (a) -1 **7.** (a) 8   **9.** (a) 0   **11.** (a) -42
13. (a) 16   **15.** (a) (Add-A)   **17.** (a) (Mult-A)   **19.** (a) (Mult-A), (D) or (D),
(Can-M)   **21.** (a) 29, (Add-A): $3x - 12 + 12 = 17 + 12$, or
(Can-A): $3x - 12 = 29 - 12$ **23.** (a) 0, (Mult-A), (Zero-M)   **25.** (a) Signs
alike: add number keeping same sign; signs different: subtract numbers keeping
sign of larger.   **27.** $-x, - [-(-3)] = -[3] = -3$ **29.** Yes   **31.** (a) 7, 2, 0
(b) 7, 2, 1   (c) No

1–3, *13*   **1.** (a) T, since $3 - (-4) = 7$ and $7 > 0$ **3.** (a) F, $-\frac{1}{7} > -\frac{2}{7}$ **5.** (a) $-12, -3$
7. (a) $5 > 3$ and $5 + (-3) > 3 + (-3), (2 > 0)$ **9.** (a) $4 > 1$ and
$4 \cdot 2 > 1 \cdot 2, (8 > 2)$ **11.** (a) (Def $>$)   **18.** (c) If x and y are positive real
numbers, then $x^2 > y^2$ if, and only if, $x > y$.   **19.** S is closed under "δ";
this operation is commutative and associative; 0 is the identity element; no
element except 0 has an inverse.

1–4, *17*   **1.** (a) T   **3.** (a) F, $|3 - \pi| = \pi - 3$ **5.** (a) T   **7.** (a) 1   **9.** (a) $\sqrt{2} - 1.41$
11. (a) 3   **13.** $\{-4, 4\}$ **15.** $\{-3, 15\}$ **17.** $\{-4, -3, -2, -1, 0, 1, 2, 3, 4\}$
19. $\{-4, -3, -2, -1, 0, 1, 2, 3, 4, 5, 6\}$ **21.** $\{-11, -10, -9, -8, -7, -6,$
$-5, -4, -3, -2, -1, 0, 1, 2, 3, 4, 5, 6, 7, 8, 9, 10\}$ **23.** $\{10, 9, 8, 7, 6, 5, 4, 3, 2\}$
25. $\{-5, -4, -3, -2, -1, 0, 1, 2, 3, 4, 5, 6, 7, 8, 9\}$ **27.** $\{-9, -8, -7, -6,$
$-5, -4, 4, 5, 6, 7, 8, 9\}$ **29.** Equal   **31.** Equal   **33.** Always equal
35. $|-8| + |6| > |-8 + 6|$ **37.** $|0| + |12| = |0 + 12|$ **39.** (a) x and $y > 0$,
x and $y < 0$ (b) x and y having opposite signs   (c) No   (d) For all real
numbers x and y, $|x| + |y| \geq |x + y|$

1–5, *21*   **1.** (a) $\frac{3}{8}$ **3.** (a) $\frac{1}{12}$ **5.** (a) $-\frac{9}{8}$ **7.** (a) $-\frac{9}{5}$ **9.** (a) 0   **11.** Yes, the difference of
two integers is an integer.   **13.** No, the product of two negative integers is not
a negative integer.   **15.** Yes, the quotient of two positive rational numbers is a
positive rational number.   **17.** Yes   **19.** Yes   **21.** No   **23.** Yes   **25.** (a) 2
(b) 3   (c) 2   **27.** Yes, multiplication   **29.** Yes, multiplication

1–6, *27*   **1.** (a) $\sqrt{15}$ **3.** (a) $3\sqrt{5}$ **5.** (a) $2\sqrt{3}$ **7.** (a) $7\sqrt{2}$ **9.** (a) $15\sqrt{11}$
11. (a) $\frac{1}{11}\sqrt{22}$ **13.** (a) $\frac{2}{5}\sqrt{10}$ **15.** (a) $\frac{7}{12}\sqrt{6}$ **17.** (a) 22   **19.** (a) $54\sqrt{2}$
21. (a) 4   **23.** (a) $1 < \sqrt{3} < 2$. Therefore, either 1 or 2 is an integral
approximation.   (b) $17 < 10\sqrt{3} < 18$. Therefore, either 1.7 or 1.8 is a
one-decimal approximation.   (c) $173 < 100\sqrt{3} < 174$. Therefore, either 1.73

or 1.74 is a two-decimal-place approximation.   **25.** Any number less than $n + \frac{1}{2}n$ and greater than or equal to n. (i.e., $n \le x < n + \frac{1}{2}n$) $[2.4] = 2$ and nearest integer is also 2.

1–7, 31   **1.** (a) 3^7 **3.** (a) 1   **5.** (a) 7^9, (LE-1)   **7.** (a) $5^2 \cdot 2^1 = 50$, (LE-2)

9. (a) $\dfrac{2^2 x^{33}}{10^3 y^{12}}$ (LE-5), (LE-3)   **11.** (a) 81   **13.** (a) $3\frac{1}{3}$ **15.** (a) $-125x^3 y^3$

17. (a) $\dfrac{2y^2}{3x^3}$ **19.** (a) $2^8 \cdot 10^5$ **21.** (a) 3^{18} **23.** (a) 256

25. $x^n \cdot x^0 = x^{n+0} = x^n$, thus x^0 acts as the multiplicative identity and is equal to 1   **27.** (a) No; no   (b) No   (c) Yes   **29.** $\dfrac{x^2 y^2 - 1}{y^2}$

31. $\dfrac{1}{4x^2 - y^2}$ **33.** $-xy$

1–8, 37   **1.** (a) $5\sqrt{7}$ **3.** (a) $3x^2 y\sqrt{3y}$ **5.** (a) $-5x^2 y^2 \sqrt[3]{2y^2}$ **7.** (a) $15ab$;

$\dfrac{2a}{5b^2}\sqrt{15ab}$ **9.** (a) $3\sqrt{2}$ **11.** (a) $\dfrac{\sqrt{2}}{2}$ **13.** (a) 2   **15.** (a) 22

17. $(12 - 15x)\sqrt{3x}$ **19.** (a) $\dfrac{x\sqrt{10x}}{5}$ **21.** $2\sqrt{3} + 1$ **23.** $4(\sqrt{7} + \sqrt{3})$

25. $\dfrac{x + 6\sqrt{xy} + 9y}{x - 9y}$ **27.** $-\dfrac{\sqrt{2}}{2}$ **29.** $\dfrac{25\sqrt{2}}{6}$ **31.** $(2 + x)\sqrt{2x}$

33. $\dfrac{1 - 2x + x^2}{x}$ **35.** $\sqrt[6]{9} < \sqrt{3} < \sqrt[4]{27}$ **37.** Let $x = 25$, $y = 16$

1–9, 42   **1.** (a) 3   **3.** (a) $2^5 = 32$ **5.** (a) $3^2 = 9$ **7.** (a) $3 \cdot 2^{\frac{1}{2}} x^{\frac{3}{4}} y^{\frac{1}{4}}$

9. (a) $\sqrt[5]{(2x)^4} = \sqrt[5]{16x^4}$ **11.** (a) $\sqrt[3]{x} - \sqrt[3]{y}$ **13.** 100.01   **15.** 32   **17.** $\dfrac{1}{(6x)^3}$

19. $e^{2x} - 2 + e^{-2x}$ **21.** $\frac{1}{2}$; $\frac{1}{3}$; 3, 9; 4, 2; 7, 11; xy **23.** $\dfrac{\sqrt[6]{ab^5}}{b^2}$

25. 0   **27.** $\sqrt[6]{72}$ **29.** $\sqrt{2}$ **31.** $\sqrt[5]{4}$ **33.** $\sqrt[6]{x^3} = (x^3)^{\frac{1}{6}} = x^{\frac{1}{2}} = x^{\frac{2}{4}} = \sqrt[4]{x^2}$; $\sqrt{x}$

1–10, 48   **1.** (a) -4 **3.** (a) $(-4 - 3) + [8 - (-4)] = 5$ **5.** (a) $\frac{1}{2}(0 + 8) = 4$
7. (a) -4 **9.** (a) 4   **13.** (a) $x = \frac{1}{3}(2b + 2)$ (b) $x = \frac{1}{4}(3b + a)$
(c) $x = \frac{1}{5}(3b + 2a)$ (d) $x = \dfrac{1}{r + s}(rb + sa)$

Chapter   **1.** (C-A), (C-M)   **3.** (D)   **5.** (Can-A)   **7.** (Add-A)   **9.** (M>)   **11.** 0   **13.** -17
Review,
53   **15.** $\frac{1}{2}$ **17.** $-\frac{5}{2}$ **19.** $\frac{6}{5}$ **21.** $5\sqrt{14}$ **23.** $-\frac{109}{30}$ **25.** $\dfrac{4x^2}{9y^4}$ **27.** $\dfrac{10\sqrt{42}}{21}$

29. $\dfrac{2b^4}{5x^3}$ **31.** (a) $\dfrac{1 + x^2 y^2}{x^2}$ (b) $\dfrac{y^2 - x^2}{x^2 y^2}$ **33.** $\dfrac{\sqrt[6]{14}}{2}$ **35.** $\dfrac{4\sqrt{15} - 17}{7}$

37. $\dfrac{22\sqrt{3} - 23}{71}$ **39.** $\left(\dfrac{2p^2 + 3q}{3q}\right)(\sqrt[4]{6pq^2})$ **41.** $\dfrac{(9 - 2x)^2}{18x}$ **43.** 3^7

45. $-(2x + 3x^2)\sqrt[3]{3x}$
51. $1\frac{1}{2}$ **53.** $16\frac{1}{2}$ **55.** 14   **57.** (a) 6   (b) 1   (c) $-\frac{15}{4}$ (d) 16   **59.** No, for example, $\frac{14}{21} = \frac{1}{7}$ which is not a multiple of 7.   **61.** Yes

2–1, 61   **1.** (a) Equivalent   **3.** (a) $\{4\}$ **5.** (a) $\{-\frac{16}{11}\}$ **7.** (a) $\{\frac{11}{10}\}$ **9.** Equivalent
11. Not equivalent, change second equation to $3x - 6 - 5 = 8 - 2x + 8$

13. $\{2\}$ **15.** $\{5\}$ **17.** $\{-4\}$ **19.** $\{-\frac{21}{10}\}$ **21.** $\{\frac{1}{8}\}$ **23.** $\{-4\}$ **25.** (a) $0, 0$; $12, 12; 6, 6; 5, 5$ (b) Infinite number of values

2–2, 65 **1.** (a) $4x + 6$ **3.** (a) $6x$ **5.** (a) $6x + 10(100 - x)$ **7.** (a) $|2\frac{1}{2}h - 3\frac{1}{2}(h - 3)|$ mi **9.** (a) $2(x + 3)$ **11.** (a) $.65x + .75(15)$ (in ounces) **13.** $40, 42, 44$ **15.** -6 **17.** 12 quarters, 16 dimes, 34 nickels **19.** 7 yrs, 37 yrs **21.** 15 lbs **23.** $3\frac{3}{4}$ hr; $13\frac{1}{8}$ mi **25.** 2.4 gal

Preparation **1.** $3 > 1$ **2.** $-3 > -5$ **3.** $-21 < -5$ **4.** $10 > 7$ **5.** $-7 < 3$
Exercises, 67 **6.** $2 < 12$

2–3, 71 **1.** (a) $8, 3, 10, 1.6$ **3.** (a) 5 **5.** (a) $x > -1$ **7.** (a) $x \geqq -6$ **9.** (a) $x > -\frac{14}{3}$ **17.** (b) $x < 3$ and $-2x > -6$ **19.** $x > 5, x > 1$, $\{x \mid x > 5\}$ **21.** $x > 4, x < \frac{4}{5}, \emptyset$ **23.** E.g., $A = \{0, 1, 2\}, B = \{-1, -2, -3\}$; $A \cup B =$ number line **25.** E.g., $A = \{2, 3, 3.5\}, B = \{1, 0, -2\}$; $A \cup B =$ number lines **27.** $x \geqq 2$

2–4, 75 **1.** (a) $(\frac{1}{3}, -4), (0, -5), (\frac{5}{3}, 0)$ **3.** (a) $x = \frac{1}{4}(7y + 5)$ **5.** (a) E.g., $(0, -4)$, $(2, -3), (8, 0)$ **7.** (a) $y = -\frac{8}{5}x + \frac{6}{5}$ **9.** (a) Yes **11.** (a) Yes, no, yes (f) $M = R \cup S$ **13.** $2x - 3y = 10, 2x - 3y = -10$ **15.** (a) $x \leqq 2; y \leqq 2$ (b) $x + y = 2$ (c) $-x - y = 2$ (d) $-x + y = 2$ (e) $x - y = 2$

2–5, 83 **1.** (a) $\frac{4}{3}$ **3.** (a) $\frac{3}{4}$ **5.** (a) No. Use of the formula would entail division by zero. **7.** (a) $-\frac{2}{5}, 2$ **9.** (a) No slope, no y-intercept **11.** (b) They are parallel with slope 2 (c) Each, solved for y, has a coefficient of 2 for x. **13.** $7, y = 7x + 47$ **15.** $y + 2 = -\frac{1}{3}(x + 3)$ **17.** $y = 3$ **21.** $y = -4x - 4$ **23.** $y = \frac{3}{2}$ **25.** $y = -\frac{2}{3}x + 2$ **27.** (a) No, different slopes. **29.** (b) The graphs will be symmetrical about $y = x$. The first has slope r and y-intercept s. The second has slope $1/r$ and x-intercept s. **31.** (c) In common: same slope, lines are parallel; Differ: y-intercept. **33.** (a) $y = \frac{1}{2}x + 3$ (b) $y = \frac{1}{2}x + b$ (c) $y - 3 = \frac{1}{2}(x - 2)$ **35.** $y = mx - 5$

2–6, 90 **1.** (a) $0, 3$ **3.** (a) $-1, 2$ **5.** (a) $\{(x, y) \mid y > 3x - 2\}$ **7.** (a) $\{(x, y) \mid y < \frac{x}{3}\}$ **9.** $y \leqq 2$ **11.** $y > -4x$ **13.** (b) $(2, 0), (4, 1)$, and $(-2, -2)$ lie to the left of the line $x = 2y + 3$ **15.** $-1 \geqq -3b + 6, 3b \geqq 7$

2–7, 96 **1.** (a) $\{(3, 4)\}$ **3.** (a) $\{(-1, 3)\}$ **5.** Inconsistent **7.** Dependent **9.** Independent **11.** $\{(\frac{39}{7}, \frac{1}{7})\}$ **13.** $\{(1, 1)\}$ **15.** $\{(5, 10)\}$ **17.** $\{(0, 0)\}$ **19.** (b) $0 = 0$. For any k, the two equations are equivalent and thus, any solution of the first equation is a solution of the second one also.

2–8, 100 **1.** (a) $\{(\frac{21}{7}, 5)\}$ **3.** (a) $\{(8, 17)\}$ **5.** (a) $\begin{cases} 8x - 20y = 36 \\ 15x + 20y = 40 \end{cases}$ **7.** (a) $\{(0, 4)\}$ **9.** (a) $\{(3, 2)\}$ **11.** (a) $\{(\frac{1}{2}, \frac{1}{3})\}$

2–9, 105 **1.** (a) 2650 mi and back **3.** (a) 15 quarters **5.** (a) The numbers l and p will both be integers if, and only if, $d + s$ and $s - d$ are both even. **7.** (a) $a = 5$ and $b = 3$ **9.** (a) $\{(8, 2)\}$ **11.** A: 50 items per hour; B: 40 items per hour. ***13.** The bullet travels 750 yd/sec and sound 375 yd/sec.

2–10, 110 **1.** (a) Quarter-plane **3.** (a) Infinite strip **5.** (a) $(1, 1), (1, 2)$ **7.** $\begin{cases} x - 2y + 6 > 0, \\ x - 2y < 4. \end{cases}$ **9.** Pentagon, $(8, 22), (3, 22), (15, 15), (3, 0), (15, 0)$ **11.** Pentagon, $(0, 8), (9, 8), (2, 4), (6, 1), (9, 0)$ **13.** Quadrilateral, $(-7, 5)$, $(-3, 3), (-3, -3), (\frac{3}{2}, -\frac{3}{2})$ **15.** (e) Triangle, $(0, 4), (0, -8), (3, -2)$ **17.** $S = \{(x, y) \mid 5x - 3y - 9 < 0\} \cap \{(x, y) \mid 2x + 3y - 12 > 0\}$ Quarter-plane; No, because the graph is a quarter-plane with no edge.

2–11, 114 **1.** (a) $(3, 5, -4)$ **3.** (a) $(3, 2, 1)$ **5.** (a) $(-2, 1, 4)$ **7.** 9 nickels, 8 dimes, 7 quarters **9.** $A = 32°, B = 64°, C = 84°$ **11.** No, there is not a unique set. Three sets are $(-5, 53, 24), (90, -42, 24), (\sqrt{7}, 48 - \sqrt{7}, 24)$. **13.** No solution. **15.** (a) No (b) $(0, 0, 0)$ (c) Yes; yes; any real number

2–12, 126 **1.** $(-3, 2)$ **3.** $(11, -7)$ **5.** $(\frac{17}{31}, \frac{2}{31})$ **7.** $(-3, -7, 5)$ **9.** $(\frac{1}{2}, \frac{3}{2}, -\frac{1}{2})$ **11.** $(\frac{19}{11}, -\frac{23}{11}, -\frac{20}{11})$ **13.** $(-3, -1, 2, 1)$

2–13, 129 **1.** (a) $C = 820 + x + 2y$ **3.** (a) $50x + 40y \geq 1000; x + y \leq 24$ (c) $(4, 20)$ (d) $(20, 0)$ **5.** $b =$ number of acres to be planted in B. $c =$ number of acres to be planted in C. (a) $b + c \leq 50$ (b) $4b + c \leq 185$ (c) $2b + 5c \leq 205$ (d) $b \geq 0, c \geq 0$ (f) Profit $= 15b + 6.5c$ (g) 45 acres of B, 5 acres of C

Chapter **1.** (a) $\{4\}$ **3.** (a) Slope: -3; x-intercept: $\frac{1}{3}$; y-intercept: 1; no solution in
Review, positive integers. (b) Slope: -5; x-intercept: 2; y-intercept: 10; solution in
133 positive integers $(1, 5)$ **5.** (a) $(1, 4)$ (b) $(8, 2)$ **7.** Inconsistent **9.** $y > \frac{2}{3}x - 4$ **11.** 39 dimes, 13 quarters **13.** Jane must earn \$60 and Joe \$90; Jane must earn at least \$80 and Joe at least \$130. **15.** (17 dimes, 7 nickels), $(19, 8), (21, 9), (23, 10)$

3–1, 140 **1.** (a) $(x + 9)(x + 6)$ **3.** (a) $(a - 2)(a - 6)$ **5.** (a) $(x + 9)(x + 9)$, or $(x + 9)^2$ **7.** (a) $(x - 1)(x - 12)$ **9.** (a) $(5 - x)(5 + x)$ **11.** (a) $(y + 7)(y - 6)$ **13.** (a) Not factorable **15.** (a) Not factorable **17.** (a) $(3x - 4)(x - 4)$ **19.** (a) $(2x + 1)(x + 2)$ **21.** $y(y - 4)(y + 4)$ **23.** $2(5x - 3)(3x - 2)$ **25.** $6(x - 2)(x - 7)$ **27.** $(x^4 + 4)(x^2 + 2)(x^2 - 2)$ **29.** $x(x + 1)(x - 1)(x^2 + 1)$

3–2, 144 **1.** (a) $\{-\frac{1}{2}, \frac{2}{3}\}$ **3.** (a) $\{9, -5\}$ **5.** (a) $\{\pm\frac{7}{3}\}$ **7.** (a) $\{-\frac{5}{4}\}$ **9.** (a) $\{\frac{3}{2}, -4\}$ **11.** (a) $\{-2\}$ **13.** $\{13, -13\}$ **15.** $\{-\frac{1}{5}, 3\}$ **17.** $\{\frac{4}{3}, -\frac{23}{17}\}$ **19.** $\{\frac{2}{3}, -\frac{4}{5}\}$ **21.** $\{0, -\frac{1}{4}\}$ **23.** (a) 2, 80; 10, 8; 10, 8; -10, 8 (b) 8, 10; 8, -10 **25.** $\{\frac{3}{4}\}$ **27.** $\{10, -8\}$ **29.** $\{\frac{1}{5}, -\frac{31}{5}\}$ **31.** $\{6, -8\}$ **33.** $\{\frac{7}{2}, -4\}$ **35.** $\{3, 0\}$

3–3, 146 **1.** 20 ft **3.** 12 in. by 18 in. **5.** 6 in. by 9 in. **7.** 8, 15; No **9.** 12, 13, 14 **11.** 14, 16, and $-14, -16$ **13.** 7 ft, 24 ft, 25 ft **15.** $-8, -9$, and 8, 9

Preparation **1.** $1^2x^2 + 2 \cdot 1 \cdot 1 \cdot x + 1^2$ **3.** $2^2x^2 + 2 \cdot 2 \cdot 3 \cdot x + 3^2$
Exercises, 147 **5.** $1^2x^2 + 2 \cdot 1 \cdot \frac{1}{2}x + (\frac{1}{2})^2$ **7.** $(x + 6)^2$ **9.** $(2x - 5)^2$ **11.** $(x - \frac{1}{4})^2$

3–4, 150 **1.** (a) 25, 5 **3.** (a) 64, 8 **5.** (a) 81 **7.** (a) -28 or 28 **9.** $\{\pm\frac{7}{4}\}$ **11.** $\{\frac{4}{3}, -\frac{2}{3}\}$ **13.** $\{3 \pm 3\sqrt{2}\}$ **15.** $\{8, -2\}$ **17.** $\{16, -1\}$ **19.** $\{2 \pm \sqrt{7}\}$ **21.** $\left\{\dfrac{3 \pm \sqrt{7}}{2}\right\}$ **23.** $\left\{\dfrac{3 \pm \sqrt{149}}{10}\right\}$ **25.** $\left\{\dfrac{7 \pm \sqrt{17}}{4}\right\}$ **27.** $\{-\frac{1}{2}, -\frac{5}{2}\}$ **29.** $\{-p + \sqrt{p^2 - q}, -p - \sqrt{p^2 - q}\}$

3–5, 153 **1.** (a) $\{\sqrt{6} \pm 2\}$; sum $2\sqrt{6}$; product: 2 **3.** (a) $\{\sqrt{2}, -2\sqrt{2}\}$; sum: $-\sqrt{2}$; product: -4 **5.** (a) No real solutions. **7.** (a) No real solutions. **9.** $\emptyset$ **11.** $\emptyset$ **13.** $\emptyset$ **15.** 5 ft by 15 ft **17.** 12 cm and 18 cm pieces **19.** (a) $A = \frac{1}{2}x(300 - 3x)$ or $A = \frac{1}{3}y(300 - 2y)$ **21.** (a) $k = 16$ (b) $k = 2\sqrt{10}$ **23.** $4(1 + \sqrt{2})$ in.

3–6, 158 **5.** (a) $a > 0$: first and second quadrants $a < 0$: third and fourth quadrants (b) The opening narrows **7.** (a) $y = 3x^2 + 4$ (b) $y = -2x^2 + 4$ **9.** The graph is parabolic with axis of symmetry at $t = 0$, vertex at $(0,400)$, opening downward. **11.** (a) $4 = a + c$; infinitely many solutions (b) $y = x^2 + 3$, $y = 2x^2 + 2, y = 3x^2 + 1$ **13.** Both graphs have the same shape, direction of opening, and axis of symmetry. The first has $(0, 0)$ as its vertex, the second, $(0, 3)$.

3–7, 166 **1.** (a) 9, 1, 0, 1, 9 **3.** (a) $x = 1$; (1, 0) (b) $x = 1$; (1, −4) **5.** (a) Vertex:
(2, 0); axis: $x = 2$; opens upward. (b) Vertex: (2, 4); axis: $x = 2$; opens
upward. **7.** (a) $y = 3(x^2 − 10x + 25) = 3(x − 5)^2$. Axis: $x = 5$; vertex:
(5, 0) **9.** (a) $y = x^2 + 4x + (4 − 4) + 1$; $y = (x + 2)^2 − 3$ (b) $x = −2$
(c) (−2, −3) (e) −3.6 and −.4 (f) $x = −2 + \sqrt{3}$ or $x = −2 − \sqrt{3}$;
$x \doteq −.3$ or $x \doteq −3.7$ **11.** $y = −9(x − \frac{1}{3})^2$; $(\frac{1}{3}, 0)$; $x = \frac{1}{3}$
13. $y = −2(x + 3)^2 + 3$; (−3, 3); $x = −3$ **15.** (b) No (c) There exist no
real solutions. **17.** $a = 0$, $b = 2$, $c = −1$; No, a straight line.
19. (a) $y = x^2 + (30 − x)^2$ (b) 15 and 15 (c) No (unless x is restricted to
positive numbers) **21.** (a) $y = x(35 − x)$ (d) $306\frac{1}{4}$ sq ft

3–8, 174 **1.** (a) On the graph, Inside, On, Inside, Outside, Outside. **3.** (a) Inside:
$2y < −x^2 + 8x − 12$. Outside: $2y > −8x^2 + 8x − 12$. **5.** (a) The parabola
and all points inside. **7.** Maximum value of 10 when $x = 10$; no minimum
value. **9.** (a) −1 **11.** (a) $\{t \mid 0 \leq t < 100 − 50\sqrt{2}\}$ (b) $\{t \mid 50 < t \leq 100\}$
(c) $t = 100$ **13.** (a) $\{x \mid 0 < x < 4\}$ (b) $\{x \mid x < 0$ or $x > 4\}$ (c) 12 when
$x = 2$ **15.** $\{x \mid x \neq 2\}$ **17.** $\{x \mid x \leq −1$ or $x \geq 6\}$ **19.** (a) 5
(b) $\{x \mid −2.6 < x < .6\}$ (c) $x = −1 \pm \frac{1}{2}\sqrt{10} \doteq −2.58, +.58$; yes

3–9, 178 **1.** (a) $\{5\}$ **3.** (a) $\{2, 5\}$ **5.** (a) $\{1, 2, 4, 5\}$ **7.** (a) $\emptyset$ **9.** Here, 1 and 6 are
their own multiplicative inverses; 2 and 4 are multiplicative inverses of each
other; and 3 and 5 are multiplicative inverses of each other.

EXTRA! **181** **1.** (b) 175 **2.** (b) 369

Chapter **1.** $\{\frac{1}{2}, −3\}$ **3.** $\{\frac{1}{2}, −\frac{1}{2}\}$ **5.** $\{\frac{5}{2}\}$ **7.** $\{2, \frac{5}{2}\}$ **9.** $\{2\sqrt{2}, −2\sqrt{2}, 4, −4\}$
Review, **11.** $2\frac{1}{2}$ ft **13.** 20 mph **15.** (a) No real solution (b) No real solution
182 **17.** (a) Axis: $x = −3$; vertex: (−3, 1) (b) Axis: $x = 1$; vertex: (1, −1)
(c) Axis: $x = −1$; vertex: (−1, −2) (d) Axis: $x = 3$; vertex: (3, 0)
19. (a) $\{x \mid x \leq −1$ or $x \geq 3\}$ (b) $\{x \mid −1 \leq x \leq 9\}$
21. $y = 2x^2 + 3x − 4$

4–1, 189 **1.** (a) $−\frac{3}{4}$ **3.** (a) 1 **5.** (a) −32 **7.** (a) 0 **9.** −1; $i^{4k+2} = −1$
11. $−i$, $i^{4k+3} = −i$ **13.** −1 **15.** 1 **17.** −1 **21.** $−i$ **23.** $\frac{1}{2}i$ **25.** $\frac{3}{2}$
27. $(x^2 + 4)(x^2 − 4) = (x + 2i)(x − 2i)(x + 2)(x − 2)$
29. $(x + \sqrt{7})(x − \sqrt{7})$ **31.** $(3x + 1)(3x − 1)(3x − i)(3x + i)$ **33.** $\{−6, 6\}$
35. $\{−\sqrt{5}i, \sqrt{5}i\}$ **37.** $\{2, −2, 2i, −2i\}$ **39.** $\{3\sqrt{2}, −3\sqrt{2}\}$
41. $\{2, −2, 2i, −2i\}$

4–2, 193 **1.** (a) $−4i$ **3.** (a) $6 − 3i$ **5.** (a) 3 **7.** (a) $(2 + \sqrt{3}i)^2 − 4(2 + \sqrt{3}i) + 7 =$
$4 + 4\sqrt{3}i − 3 − 8 − 4\sqrt{3}i + 7 = 0$ **9.** 1 **11.** $p(a^2 + b^2)$ **13.** 0
15. $1 − \sqrt{3}i$ **17.** $1 + \frac{10}{9}i$ **19.** $\{2, −1 − \sqrt{3}i\}$ **21.** (Def-MC), (C-A), (C-M),
(Def-MC)

4–3, 196 **1.** (a) $4 − 2i$; 8; 20 **3.** (a) $\frac{1}{2} + \frac{1}{2}\sqrt{3}i$; 1; 1 **5.** (a) $\frac{1}{2} − \frac{1}{2}i$ **7.** (a) $−\frac{2}{29} + \frac{5}{29}i$
9. i **11.** $−\frac{32}{85} − \frac{9}{85}i$ **13.** $\frac{5}{7} + \frac{6}{7}\sqrt{3}i$ **15.** $\frac{1}{5} + \frac{2}{5}i$ **17.** $\frac{33}{85} − \frac{89}{85}i$
19. $−\frac{1}{5} − \frac{9}{10}i$ **21.** (a) $a − bi$, $c − di$; $(ac − bd) − i(bc + ad)$
(b) $(ac − bd) + i(bc + ad)$; $(ac − bd) − i(bc + ad)$ (c) Equal

23. (a) $\dfrac{(ac + bd)}{c^2 + d^2} − \dfrac{i(bc − ad)}{c^2 + d^2}$ (b) $\dfrac{(ac + bd)}{c^2 + d^2} − \dfrac{i(bc − ad)}{c^2 + d^2}$ (c) Equal

25. $x = −5$, $y = 4$ **27.** $x = 5$, $y = 2$ **29.** (a) Equal (b) 13; 2; 26
(c) $a^2c^2 + a^2d^2 + b^2c^2 + b^2d^2$; $a^2c^2 + a^2d^2 + b^2c^2 + b^2d^2$ (d) Equal

4–4, 201 **1.** (a) $\{3 + i, 3 − i\}$ **3.** (a) $\{2 + 5i, 2 − 5i\}$ **5.** (a) $\{\sqrt{3} + i, \sqrt{3} − i\}$
9. (a) $x^2 − \frac{1}{6}x − \frac{1}{6} = 0$ **11.** (a) $x^2 + 6x + 25 = 0$
13. $\{−2 + 4i, −2 − 4i\}$; $(x + 2 − 4i)(x + 2 + 4i)$

15. $\{1 + \sqrt{3}i, 1 - \sqrt{3}i\}$ $(x - 1 - \sqrt{3}i)(x - 1 + \sqrt{3}i)$
17. $\{\frac{2}{3} + \frac{1}{3}i, \frac{2}{3} - \frac{1}{3}i\}$; $(2 + i - 3x)(3x - 2 + i)$

4–5, 206   **3.** (a) $D = -3$; nonreal   **5.** (a) $\{3i, -3i\}$ **7.** (a) $\{-\frac{1}{6} \pm \frac{1}{6}\sqrt{13}\}$
9. (a) $\{\frac{2}{3} \pm \frac{1}{3}\sqrt{14}i\}$ **11.** (a) $\{4, 5\}$ **13.** $x^2 - 2x - 2 = 0$
15. $2x^2 - x - 6 = 0$ **17.** $x^2 - x - 1 = 0$ **19.** $x^2 + x + 1 = 0$
23. Tangent: $9 - 4m = 0$; $m = \frac{9}{4}$ **25.** $k = 8$ or $k = -4$ **31.** $p < -3, p > 3$
33. $k = 8$ **35.** $\sqrt{a} \cdot \sqrt{b} = (i\sqrt{-a})(i\sqrt{-b}) = i^2(\sqrt{-a})(-b) = -\sqrt{ab}$

4–6, 212   **5.** (a) 10, $\sqrt{2}$, 10, 5; $6 + 8i$, -10; $1 - i$; yes, $6 + 8i$ and -10 **7.** (a) 1
9. (a) 5 **11.** (b) D has coordinate $3 + 6i$ (c) $(2 + i) + (1 + 5i) = 3 + 6i$;

same   **13.** (a) slope of $\overline{EF} = \dfrac{b}{a}$; slope of $\overline{GH} = \dfrac{b}{a}$ (b) slope of $\overline{FG} = \dfrac{d}{c}$;

slope of $\overline{EH} = \dfrac{d}{c}$ (c) Since both pairs of opposite sides are parallel, $EFGH$ is

a parallelogram.   **15.** (a) $2 + 7i$ **17.** (a) $\dfrac{d - b}{c - a}$; $\dfrac{d - b}{c - a}$ **19.** Not true
21. Not true   **23.** Not true

Chapter   **1.** $-2\sqrt{2}i$ **3.** $34 - 13i$ **5.** $\frac{3}{4}$ **7.** $\frac{7}{11} - \frac{6}{11}\sqrt{2}i$ **9.** (a) $-\sqrt{2} - 7i$; $-2\sqrt{2}$; 51
Review,   (b) $-\frac{3}{25} - \frac{4}{25}i$ **11.** $\{\frac{3}{2}, \frac{2}{3}\}$ **13.** $\{\frac{3}{2}\}$ **15.** $x^2 + 4 = 0$
217   **17.** $2x^2 + 5x - 3 = 0$

Cumulative   **1.** $6\sqrt{35}$ **3.** $\frac{5}{4}\sqrt{6}$ **5.** $\frac{1}{7}\sqrt{70}$ **7.** $-3 - 2\sqrt{2}$ **9.** $\frac{1}{2}$ **11.** 2 **13.** $\emptyset$
Review I,   **15.** $\{x \mid x \leq -4$ or $x \geq 12\}$ **17.** (a) $\{x \mid x < \frac{7}{4} - \frac{1}{4}\sqrt{577}$ or $x > \frac{7}{4} + \frac{1}{4}\sqrt{577}\}$
218   **19.** $r = \dfrac{a - s}{L - s}$ **23.** (b) $\{x \mid x > 3$ or $x < -1\}$ (c) $\{x \mid x > 3$ or $x < -1\}$
25. $\{2, -2\}$ **27.** 1.1 in.   **29.** (a) $1 < x < 2$ (b) $\emptyset$

5–1, 223   **1.** (a) 5 **3.** (a) $x^2 + y^2 \geq 16$ **5.** (a) $(-1, 1)$, $(0, 1)$, $(-3, 0)$, $(-3, 1)$,
$(-3, -1)$, etc.   **7.** Outside, Inside, On, Outside, Outside   **9.** For $k = 10^6, 10^2$,
$5^2, 10, 5, 1$: circle, center $(0, 0)$ with radius $\sqrt{k}$; $k = 0$: $(0, 0)$; $k = -1$: an
imaginary circle; $k > 0$

Preparation   **1.** $\{(6, 2)\}$ **2.** Systems of equations which have the same solution set.
Exercises, 224   **3.** $\{3, -4\}$ **4.** It does not cross the x-axis.

5–2, 226   **1.** (a) $(3, 0)$, $(0, 3)$ **3.** (a) $\{(2, -4)\}$; line tangent to circle.
5. (a) $\{(-\frac{9}{2} - \frac{3}{2}i, -\frac{9}{2} + \frac{3}{2}i)\}$ **7.** There are two points on the circle for which
the abscissa is -4, but only one of those is also on the line. The same is true
for 3.   **9.** $x^2 + y^2 = 20$; $x + y = 6$; $\{(4, 2), (2, 4)\}$ **15.** $k = 2\sqrt{5}$ or
$k = -2\sqrt{5}$

Preparation   **1.** (a) If $x < 0$ $x = -|x|$ (b) If $x = 0$ $x = |x|$ (c) If $x > 0$ $x = |x|$
Exercises, 228   **2.** (a) If $x < 0$ $x^2 = |x|^2$ (b) If $x \geq 0$ $x^2 = |x|^2$ **3.** 4 **4.** 5 **5.** 5

5–3, 231   **1.** (a) $3\sqrt{10}$ **3.** (a) $p = \sqrt{13} + \sqrt{26}$; isosceles; $\angle A$ and $\angle B$ **5.** (a)
$AM = \sqrt{80}$; $BM = \sqrt{80}$. Hence, $AM = BM$ and $(3, -2)$ is the midpoint.
7. (a) $RS = \sqrt{10}$, $ST = 3\sqrt{10}$, $RT = 4\sqrt{10}$, $RS + ST = \sqrt{10} + 3\sqrt{10} =$
$4\sqrt{10} = RT$ so R, S, and T are collinear.   **9.** Center: $(-5, 2)$; radius: 3
11. (a) $3\sqrt{5}$ **13.** (a) $(x - 1)^2 + (y - 3)^2 = 4$; $(1, 3)$; 2
(b) $(x + 2)^2 + (y + 1)^2 = 1$; $(-2, -1)$; 1 (c) $(x - 3)^2 + y^2 = 8$; $(3, 0)$;
$2\sqrt{2}$ (d) $7x^2 + (y - \frac{1}{2})^2 = \frac{4}{9}$; $(0, \frac{1}{2})$; $\frac{2}{3}$ **15.** $(6, 6)$ **17.** $5x - 11y = 3$

5–4, 242   **1.** (a) (i) 2 and -2; $\sqrt{3}$ and $-\sqrt{3}$ (iii) If (x, y) is on the ellipse, then so are
$(x, -y)$, $(-x, y)$, and $(-x, -y)$.   **3.** (a) $\dfrac{x^2}{9} + \dfrac{y^2}{5} = 1$ **7.** (a) All points

inside the ellipse which is the graph of $\dfrac{x^2}{4} + \dfrac{y^2}{3} = 1$; integral solutions: $(-1, 1)$, $(-1, 0)$, $(-1, -1)$, $(0, 1)$, $(0, 0)$, $(0, -1)$, $(1, 1)$, $(1, 0)$, $(1, -1)$ **9.** None; $(-\sqrt{3}, 0)$; $(1, \frac{1}{2}\sqrt{6})$; $(1, -\frac{1}{2}\sqrt{6})$; $(\sqrt{3}, 0)$; none **11.** (a) Circle with center $(0, 0)$ and radius $\sqrt{13}$; ellipse with center $(0, 0)$, major axis horizontal
13. (a) $\dfrac{x^2}{4} + \dfrac{y^2}{1} = 1$

Preparation Exercises, 245
1. $d = \sqrt{(x + 5)^2 + y^2}$ **2.** $d = \sqrt{(x - 5)^2 + y^2}$
3. $\sqrt{(x + 5)^2 + y^2} - \sqrt{(x - 5)^2 + y^2}$
4. $\sqrt{(x + 5)^2 + y^2} - \sqrt{(x - 5)^2 + y^2} = 8$ **5.** $9x^2 - 16y^2 = 144$
6. $\sqrt{(x - 5)^2 + y^2} - \sqrt{(x + 5)^2 + y^2}$
7. $\sqrt{(x - 5)^2 + y^2} - \sqrt{(x + 5)^2 + y^2} = 8$ **8.** $9x^2 - 16y^2 = 144$
9. They are the same; yes, all are equivalent

5–5, 252 **1.** (a) (i) $(5, 0)$, $(-5, 0)$. If $x = 0$, $y^2 = -16$, hence there are no y-intercepts.
(ii) $(\sqrt{41}, 0)$, $(-\sqrt{41}, 0)$ (iii) $(\sqrt{14}, \frac{16}{5})$, $(\sqrt{41}, -\frac{16}{5})$, $(-\sqrt{41}, \frac{16}{5})$, $(-\sqrt{14}, -\frac{16}{5})$ (iv) $\pm\frac{4}{5}\sqrt{11}$, $\pm\frac{8}{5}\sqrt{6}$, $\pm 4\sqrt{3}$ **3.** (a) $7x^2 - 9y^2 = 63$
5. (a) $12x^2 - 4y^2 = 3$ **7.** (a) $(0, 3)$, $(0, -3)$ **9.** $\{(\frac{5}{3}\sqrt{5}, \frac{8}{3}), (\frac{5}{3}\sqrt{5}, -\frac{8}{3}),$
$(-\frac{5}{3}\sqrt{5}, \frac{8}{3}), (-\frac{5}{3}\sqrt{5}, -\frac{8}{3})\}$ **11.** $\{(4, 0), (-4, 0)\}$ **13.** $\dfrac{x^2}{a^2} - \dfrac{y^2}{c^2 - a^2} = 1$;
$\dfrac{x^2}{a^2} - \dfrac{y^2}{b^2} = 1$

Preparation Exercises, 254
2. $(\frac{5}{2}, -\frac{49}{4})$ **3.** (a) $\{6, -1\}$ (b) $\{7, -2\}$ (c) $\{1, 5\}$
4. $d = \sqrt{(x - 3)^2 + y^2}$ **5.** $d = x + 3$ **6.** $y^2 = 12x$

5–6, 258 **1.** (a) $x^2 = -12y$ **3.** (a) Focus: $(0, 4)$; end points: $(8, 4)$, $(-8, 4)$; length: 16
5. (a) Vertex: $(0, 0)$; focus: $(0, 2)$; end points: $(4, 2)$, $(-4, 2)$; directrix: $y = -2$; axis: $x = 0$ **7.** (a) $(0, 0)$; $(0, 5)$; $(10, 5)$, $(-10, 5)$; $y = -5$; $x = 0$
9. (a) $x^2 = 2y$ **11.** No; no; no **13.** (a) $\begin{cases} x = -2 + 2\sqrt{2} \text{ or } -2 - 2\sqrt{2} \\ y = 3 - 2\sqrt{2} \text{ or } 3 + 2\sqrt{2} \end{cases}$
15. $(-3, -9)$, $(1, -1)$ **17.** None **21.** (a) $x^2 = 8(y + 2)$; $(0, -2)$
(b) $x^2 = -4(y - 1)$; $(0, 1)$ (c) $x^2 = 4(y - 2)$; $(0, 2)$ (d) $x^2 = -2(y + \frac{3}{2})$; $(0, -\frac{3}{2})$

Chapter Review, 262
1. (b) $(\frac{3}{2}, \frac{3}{2}\sqrt{3})$, $(\frac{9}{2}, \frac{3}{2}\sqrt{3})$ (c) $\overline{M_1 M_2} = 3$ **3.** (a) Ellipse; intercepts: $(5, 0)$, $(-5, 0)$, $(0, 2)$, $(0, -2)$; foci: $(\sqrt{21}, 0)$, $(-\sqrt{21}, 0)$; major axis: x-axis **5.** (a) Hyperbola, intercepts: $(0, 2)$, $(0, -2)$; foci: $(0, \sqrt{5})$, $(0, -\sqrt{5})$
(b) Region outside branches of hyperbola of (a) **7.** $\{(0, 1), (0, -1)\}$
9. (a) $x^2 = 8y$ (b) $y^2 = -4x$ **13.** (c) Parabola: vertex $(-5, 1)$
(d) Ellipse: center $(2, -\frac{3}{2})$

6–1, 266 **1.** (a) $D = \{n \mid n,$ a nonnegative integer$\}$ **3.** (a) $D = \{t \mid 0 \leq t \leq 2\}$
5. (a) $D = \{x \mid x = 7, 8, 9\}$; $R = \{y \mid y = -3, 2, 0\}$ **7.** (a) (i) $y = -\frac{5}{2}x + 5$ (ii) Yes (iii) $x = -\frac{2}{5}y + 2$ (iv) Yes **9.** (a) $(2, 3)$ and $(2, 4)$
have the same first element. **11.** (a) $D = \{n \mid 0 < n \leq 16\}$ **13.** $A = x(x + 3)$;
$D = \{x \mid x > 0\}$; $R = \{A \mid A > 0\}$ **15.** $B = \dfrac{100}{h}$; $D = \{h \mid h > 0\}$;
$R = \{B \mid B > 0\}$ **17.** $A = (12 - 2x)(14 - 2x)$; $D = \{x \mid 0 < x < 6\}$;
$R = \{A \mid 0 < A < 168\}$

6–2, 271 **1.** (a) 0, $1 - 5\sqrt{2}$, $-\frac{49}{8} - 3$ **3.** (a) $x \neq -4$ **5.** (a) $x \neq 2$ **7.** (a) $\frac{5}{6}, \frac{5}{3}, \frac{10}{11}$;
$\sqrt{3}, 0, \frac{1}{2}\sqrt{5}$; indeterminant, -1, -6; $4, 4, 4$ **9.** (a) $3, 4, 1, \sqrt{2}$;

$R = \{y \mid y \geqq 1\}$ **11.** (a) 9, 25, 225; equal **13.** (a) $k = 132$ (b) $N(p) = \dfrac{132}{p}$; $D = \{p \mid p$ integer, $p > 0\}$ (c) 12, 22, 33 **15.** (a) $O(x) = 10x$ (b) $O(x) = x + 7$ (c) $O(x) = \dfrac{x}{3}$ (d) $O(x) = x$ (e) $O(x) = 1$ **17.** $g(x) = \dfrac{1}{\sqrt{x+2}}$, $x > 0$

Preparation Exercise, 274 **1.** (a) 2; -3 (b) $x = \frac{3}{2}$ (c) Yes, no, yes, yes, no, yes

6–3, 276 **4.** (a) $D = \{x \mid -3 \leqq x \leqq 3\}$ **5.** (a) $D = \{v \mid v > 0\}$ **8.** $-3, -6,$ $-12, -30, 3, 6, 12, 30, .3, .03, .003, -3, -.03, -.003$

Preparation **1.** $\frac{1}{8}, \frac{1}{2}, \frac{1}{5}, 3, 216, \frac{1}{32}, 8$ **2.** .18, .35, .71, 1.41, 2.83, 5.66 **3.** $(2^4)^{\frac{1}{8}} = 2^{\frac{1}{2}} = \sqrt{2}$; *Exercise,* 279 $(3^2)^{\frac{1}{4}} = \sqrt{3}$; $(3^3)^{-\frac{1}{9}} = 3^{-\frac{1}{3}} = \dfrac{1}{\sqrt[3]{3}}$

6–4, 282 **3.** (a) 150; 37.5; $t = 1500$; No, since $2^{-.002t} > 0$ for all real t. **5.** 1 hr **7.** 212.1 mg **9.** (a) $\{x \mid x \leqq 4\}$ (b) $\{x \mid x > \frac{3}{2}\}$ (c) $\{x \mid x < \frac{3}{2}\}$ (d) $\{x \mid x > 0\}$

6–5, 285 **1.** (a) $4x - 1$; $3x^2 - 7x - 6$; both domains all reals **3.** (a) $x + \dfrac{1}{x}$; 1; both: $\{x \mid x \neq 0\}$ **5.** (a) $\sqrt{16 - x^2} + 4 - x$; $(4 - x)\sqrt{16 - x^2}$; both: $\{x \mid -4 \leqq x \leqq 4\}$ **9.** F **11.** T **13.** F **15.** F **17.** F **19.** 12, 13

Chapter **1.** (a) $F(C) = \frac{9}{5}C + 32$ (b) 32, 212, -40 (c) Linear *Review,* **3.** (a) $D = \{x \mid x \neq -2\}$ (b) $D = \{x \mid -4 \leqq x \leqq 4\}$ (c) $D = \{$all reals$\}$ 288 (d) $D = \{x \mid x \geqq 0\}$ **7.** $0, 0, 0, \frac{7}{4}, \sqrt{5}, 6, \pi$ **9.** 500 yrs

7–1, 292 **1.** (a) 1,048,576 **3.** (a) 262,144 **5.** (a) $\frac{1}{1024}$ **7.** (a) 1,048,576 **9.** (a) 4096 **11.** (a) $\frac{23}{2}$ **13.** 1,594,323 **15.** 243 **17.** 81 **19.** $x = 8$ **21.** $x = \frac{7}{2}$ **23.** $x = \frac{9}{4}$ **25.** (a) 7776 (b) 20,736 (c) 104,976

Preparation Exercises, 293 **1.** $8, \frac{1}{8}$ **2.** Yes, $a = 5$ **3.** Positive

7–2, 296 **1.** (a) $\log_2 32 = 5$ **3.** (a) $\log_{16} \frac{1}{64} = -\frac{3}{2}$ **5.** (a) $10^2 = 100$ **7.** (a) $8^0 = 1$ **9.** (a) $n^4 = 9$ **11.** (a) 4 **13.** (a) -2 **15.** (a) -2 **17.** $\frac{1}{216}$ **19.** -3 **21.** 100 **23.** 128 **25.** 0 **27.** $\frac{1}{64}$ **29.** $\frac{3}{2}$

7–3, 298 **1.** (a) $y = x$. By interchanging x and y. **3.** (a) $-1 < \log_{10} .375 < 0$ **5.** If $M > N$, $\log_{10} M > \log_{10} N$. **15.** (b) For $x < 0$ **17.** $x > -1$; $y = \log_2 x$ is one unit to the right.

Preparation Exercises, 299 **1.** $b^r = x$ **2.** $b^s = y$ **3.** b^{r+s} **4.** $\log_b xy = \log_b x + \log_b y$

7–4, 303 **1.** (a) $\frac{5}{3}$ **3.** (a) 5 **5.** (a) $\frac{11}{2}$ **7.** (a) $\log_3 400$ **9.** $p - q$ **11.** $-p$ **13.** $-q$ **15.** $s - r$ **17.** $3s - 2r$ **19.** $3rs - 3r$ **21.** $\frac{1}{2}(s - r)$ **23.** $x = 42$ **25.** $x = \frac{9}{2}$ **27.** $x = \dfrac{12 + 5^{20}}{8}$ **32.** $x = 2$ **34.** (a) 6 (b) 12 (c) 20 (d) -56

7–5, 310 **1.** (a) 5.87×10^{12} mi **3.** (a) 2.6990 **5.** (a) 10^3; 2 **7.** (a) $0 < \log 1.56 < 1$ **9.** (a) -2 **11.** (a) 2.051×10^1; 1 **13.** (a) 3.1875; $10^{3.1875}$ **15.** (a) -3.3947; $10^{-3.3947}$ **17.** $-.5918$ **19.** -1.5918 **21.** -3.5918 **23.** 1.5105 **25.** 6.5105 **27.** .9304 **29.** 3.3139 **31.** 4.3139 **33.** (a) -1 and 0; -1 (b) -2 and -1; -2 (c) -3 (d) $-k$

Preparation **1.** $\log a + \log b$ **2.** $\log a - \log b$ **3.** $\log a + \log b - (\log c + \log d)$ *Exercises, 312* **4.** $\frac{1}{2} \log a$ **5.** $\frac{1}{3}(\log a + \log b)$ **6.** $\frac{1}{5}(\log a - \log b)$

7–6, 315 **1.** (a) .9360, .1614, .3160, 1.4134 + 2 = 3.4134 **3.** −1.0615 **5.** 1.2282
7. −6.8928 **9.** −.0421 **11.** .5398 **13.** 6.1918 **15.** 2.3662

7–7, 321 **1.** (a) 324 **3.** (a) 1080 **5.** (a) .705 **7.** (a) 29.9 **9.** (a) .00145 **11.** 18.0
13. 4.03 **15.** 9.40 **17.** 617 **19.** 82,800 **21.** 1.85 **23.** 1.92 sec **25.** (a) $2210
(b) $2210 (c) $1200 **27.** 415 mg **29.** 1180 sq in.

7–8, 326 **1.** (a) 1.8157 **3.** (a) 2.0806 **5.** (a) .8746 − 1 **7.** (a) .4071 **9.** 36.67
11. 1.9113 **13.** .06789 **15.** 1115 **17.** 24 **19.** $\frac{1}{3}$ **21.** .5274 **23.** 44.54
25. 2.772 **27.** 3.146 **29.** −.4682 **31.** 12.76 **33.** 30.65 **35.** .6399
37. −5.115 **39.** (a) .4786 − 1 (b) .8911 − 1 (c) .2342 (d) .3868
(e) .0792 + 1 (f) .0906 **41.** 1792 sq in. **43.** 3778 sq in. **45.** 2.185 in.
47. 17.72 ft

7–9, 330 **1.** (a) 2.096 **3.** (a) 3.465 **5.** 2 **7.** −2 **9.** 2.399 **11.** 10,000 **14.** $x > 2.322$
15. $x \le 1.222$ **16.** $x > 6.644$

EXTRA!, 330 **1.** 3.2757 acid **3.** 1.5575 acid **5.** 8.4318 alkaline **7.** 9 **9.** 9.8 **11.** 10.4

Chapter **1.** F, $2^r > 2^s$ **3.** F, $\log rs = \log r + \log s$ **5.** T **7.** F, $\log x^n = n \log x$
Review, **9.** T **11.** 20 **13.** $\frac{1}{3}$ or 1 **15.** $\frac{8}{3}$ **17.** 16 **19.** .05259 **21.** 16.55 **23.** $x > 0$
333 **25.** $x > -2$ **27.** (a) .8993 (b) .09434 **29.** 1.46×10^3 cm

Cumulative **1.** (a) $x = \pm 1, y \ne 0$ **7.** $(-1, -3), (-1, 5)$ **9.** (a) 2, 2.25, 2.37, 2.44, 2.49,
Review II,
335 2.52 (b) $\left(1 + \dfrac{1}{x}\right)^x$ approaches 2.72 **11.** (a) $(-a, b)$ (b) $(-a, -b)$
(c) $(-a, b), (b, a)$ **13.** (a) $x = 0$ (b) $x > 0$ (c) $x < 0$
15. $\dfrac{1}{x}(1 + \sqrt{x+1})$ **17.** (a) 16 (b) 15 **19.** D: all reals; R: all
non-negative reals; $f(x) = |x|$.

8–1, 345 **3.** (a) $x^2 + 5x + 3$ **5.** (a) $-x^3 + 4x^2 - 2$ **7.** (a) 0 **9.** (a)
$-5x^6 + x^5 + 10x^4 - 23x^3 + 4x^2 + 2x - 4$ **11.** The degree of the
polynomial of higher degree. **13.** The degree of the product of three
polynomials is the sum of their degrees.

8–2, 349 **1.** (a) $(4x^2 - 9x + 12)(x + 1) - 14$ **3.** (a) $1 \cdot (x^2 + x - 2) + (-3x + 5)$
5. (a) $(5x + 25)(x^3 - 5x^2 + 2x - 1) + (115x^2 - 48x + 33)$
7. (a) $(-x^3 - x^2)(1 - x) + 1$ (b) $(x^3 - x^2)(x + 1) x + 1$
9. $(x^2 + 2x + 1)(x^2 + 4) = (x + 1)^2(x^2 + 4)$ **11.** $(x + 1)(x + 2)^2$
13. $(x + 2)(x^2 - 2x + 4)(x + 3)^2$ **15.** (a) R = 0 (b) $f(1) = 0$
17. (a) $f(3) = 11$ (b) R = 11

8–3, 352 **1.** (a) $(x + 2)(2x^2 - 5x + 14) - 33$ **3.** (a) $(x^2 - 4x + 8)(x + 1)$
5. (a) $(x^4 + x^3 + x^2 + x + 1)(x - 1) + 2$
7. (a) $(3x^3 - 3x^2 + 6)(x - \frac{1}{3}) + 19$ **9.** $a = -5, b = 10$
11. (a) $(x - 2)(x - 1) - x$

Preparation **1.** $-4; -8; \sqrt{3} - 6; -7; -5\frac{1}{2}$ **2.** 13; 1; $3\sqrt{3} + 7$; 4; $8\frac{1}{2}$ **3.** 3; 3; 2; 0; $-\frac{3}{4}$
Exercises, **4.** 17; 5; $10 + 3\sqrt{3}$; 5; $8\frac{3}{4}$ **5.** 18; 6; $7 + 3\sqrt{3}$; -6; $-5\frac{1}{4}$ **6.** $25 - 2\sqrt{2}$;
353 $25 + 2\sqrt{2}$; 23 + $\sqrt{6}$; $19 + \sqrt{2}$; $17\frac{1}{2} - \frac{1}{2}\sqrt{2}$ **7.** 31; 11; $17 + 4\sqrt{3}$; 7; $6\frac{5}{8}$
8. -1; 27; $6 - 4\sqrt{3}$; -4; $-\frac{13}{16}$

8–4, 357 **1.** (a) $-3, -39, 192, -195$ **3.** (a) $-1, 0, 1$ **5.** (a) $-3, -1, 1$ **7.** (a) $(x - 1)$,
$(x + 3), (x - 4)$ **9.** (a) $\pm\sqrt{2}$ **11.** (a) 8, 8; 32, 32; $k^4 + 3k^2 + 4$,
$k^4 + 3k^2 + 4$; even function **13.** (a) 1, -3; 60, -68; $2k^5 - k^2, -2k^5 - k^2$;
neither **15.** (a) No **17.** No; yes

8–5, 362 **1.** (a) Possible: $\pm 1, \pm 2, \pm 3, \pm 6$; actual: $-2, 3$ **3.** (a) -2 **5.** (a) 4, 9
7. 1, 2, 3, 4 **9.** $-1, 2$ **11.** $\{-3, 2\}$; $(x + 3)(x - 2)(x^2 + 4)$ **13.** $\{5\}$;
$(x - 5)(x^2 + x + 12)$ **15.** $\{-4, -2\}$; $(x + 4)(x + 2)(6x^2 - 13x + 6)$
18. (a) $-1, 3, -\frac{2}{3}$ (b) $-2, 3$ (c) $9, \frac{1}{2}(-1 + \sqrt{3}i), \frac{1}{2}(-1 - \sqrt{3}i)$
(d) $-10, \frac{1}{2}, -i, i$

8–6, 368 **1.** (a) $\pm 1, \pm \frac{1}{2}; \frac{1}{2}$ **3.** (a) $\pm 1, \pm 2, \pm \frac{1}{2}, \pm \frac{1}{4}, \pm \frac{1}{5}, \pm \frac{2}{5}, \pm \frac{1}{10}, \pm \frac{1}{20}; -\frac{2}{5}, \frac{1}{2}$
5. (a) $\frac{3}{2}$ **7.** (a) -4 **9.** (a) None **11.** (a) $-2, -\frac{3}{2}, 1$ (b) $-\frac{1}{2}, -\frac{2}{3}, 1$
(c) They are reciprocals of each other. (d) $-\frac{1}{2}, -\frac{4}{3}, \frac{1}{2}$

8–7, 373 **1.** (a) $x^3 - 3x^2 - 4x + 12$ **3.** (a) $6x^3 - 11x^2 - 12x + 5$
5. (a) $24x^4 - 50x^3 + 35x^2 - 10x + 1$
7. (a) $ax^4 + bx^3 - 4ax^2 - 4bx, a \neq 0$ **9.** (a) $x^2 - 6x + 4$
11. (a) $2x^2 - 2x - 1$ **13.** (a) $x^2 - 6$ (b) $x^3 - 13$ (c) $x^n - 2$
(d) $x^3 - 6x^2 + 12x - 5$ (e) $2x^5 - 1$

8–8, 376 **1.** (a) $(2x - 3)(x + 2)$ **3.** (a) $(x - 1)(x^2 + x + 1)$ **5.** (a) $(3x - 1)^2(x + 3)$
7. (a) $(x + 1)^3$ **9.** (a) $x^3 + x^2 - 3$ **11.** $(3x - 5)(x^2 - x + 2)$
13. $(x^2 - 3)(x^2 - 2)$ **15.** $x(x - 6)(3x^2 - 2x + 1)$ **17.** $3(5x^2 - 2)(x^2 + 1)$
19. $(2x - 1)(2x + 1)(4x^2 + 2x + 1)(4x^2 - 2x + 1)$

8–9, 378 **1.** (a) $(x^2 + 3x + 1)(x^2 + 3)$ **3.** (a) $(x^2 + x + 1)^2$
5. (a) $(x^2 + 5)(x - 3)(x + 7)$ **7.** (a) $(x^2 - 2x - 4)(x^2 - x + 6)$

Preparation Exercises, 379 **1.** 2, 3 **2.** 1, -7 **3.** 4, $-\frac{1}{3}$ **4.** $\frac{3}{2}, -5$ **5.** $-\frac{1}{3}, -\frac{1}{2}$ **6.** $\frac{3}{2}, -2$

8–10, 381 **1.** (a) $1 < r_1 < 2, -2 < r_2 < -1, 2 < r_3 < 3$ **3.** (a) $-.9; .7; 3.1$
5. (a) 1.3 **7.** 3.71 **9.** (a) -1 and -2 (b) No (c) 0, 0, No

Preparation **1.** $5 - 8i$ **2.** $3 - i$ **3.** $4 + 5i$ **4.** $7 + i$ **5.** $2 - i$ **6.** $5 + 2i$ **7** $8 - 3i$
Exercises, 382 **8.** $-13 - i$ **9.** $25 + 25i$ **10.** $-11 + 7i$

8–11, 389 **1.** (a) $1 + 2i, 2$; $(x - 2)(x^2 - 2x + 5)$ **3.** (a) $-\dfrac{3}{2} - \dfrac{\sqrt{3}}{2}i, \dfrac{1 \pm \sqrt{7}i}{4}$;
$(x^2 + 3x + 3)(2x^2 - x + 1)$ **5.** (a) $\frac{1}{2} - \frac{5}{2}i, \pm\sqrt{2}$;
$(2x^2 - 2x + 13)(x - \sqrt{2})(x + \sqrt{2})$ **7.** (a) $x - 1 - \sqrt{2}$
9. (a) $2x^3 - 19x^2 + 42x + 26$
13. $(x^2 + 1)(x^4 - x^2 + 1) = (x^2 + 1)(x^2 + 1 + \sqrt{3}x)(x^2 + 1 - \sqrt{3}x)$

EXTRA!, **1.** 109; 111 **3.** 49; 49 **5.** 33; 37 **7.** 116; 120 **9.** 108; 100
391 **11.** (a) $(n + 3)^2 - n^2 = 6n + 9$ (b) $(n + 3)^2 - n^2 = 6n + 9$;
$(n + 4)^2 - (n + 1)^2 = 6n + 15$; $(n + 5)^2 - (n + 2)^2 = 6n + 21$

Chapter **1.** (a) $4x^2 + 8x + 11$; 23 **3.** (a) $\{-1, -\frac{1}{2}, \frac{5}{3}\}$ **5.** (a) $6x^3 - 17x^2 - 5x + 6$
Review, (b) $x^4 - 2x^3 + 2x^2 - 8x - 8$ **7.** (a) $(x - 2)(x + 3)(x - 4)(x + 5)$
394 (b) $(x^2 + x - 1)(x^2 - x + 2)$ **11.** $x^3 + 3x^2 + 7x + 1$
13. $9x^5 + 15x^4 + 3x^3 + 13x^2 - 40x + 16$ **15.** $c = -5, d = 10$
17. $(2x - 2), (2x + 2)$ **19.** $(2x - 8)$ **21.** None
23. $(4x^2 - 1)(x - 1)(ax + b), a \neq 0, a$ and b integers
25. $x^4 - 2x^3 - 5x^2 + 6x$ **27.** $\{0, -\frac{1}{2}\}$
29. $(x^2 - 3)^2(x^2 + 1)(x + 1)(x - 1)$

9–1, 400 **1.** (a) sin: $\frac{1}{2}$; cos: $\frac{1}{2}\sqrt{3}$; tan: $\frac{1}{3}\sqrt{3}$ **3.** (a) sin: $\frac{12}{145}\sqrt{145}$; cos: $\frac{1}{145}\sqrt{145}$;
tan: 12 **5.** (a) sin: .99; cos: $\frac{1}{100}\sqrt{199}$; tan: $\frac{99}{199}\sqrt{199}$ **7.** (a) $16, 4\sqrt{7}$

9–2, 406 **1.** (a) $\left(\dfrac{\sqrt{3}}{2}, \dfrac{1}{2}\right), \left(\dfrac{\sqrt{2}}{2}, \dfrac{\sqrt{2}}{2}\right), \left(\dfrac{1}{2}, \dfrac{\sqrt{3}}{2}\right)$ **3.** (a) $\pi, \dfrac{3\pi}{2}, 0, \dfrac{3\pi}{2}, \pi, 0$ **5.** (a) $\dfrac{7\pi}{6}$

7. (a) $\left(\dfrac{\sqrt{3}}{2},\dfrac{1}{2}\right)$; $\left(-\dfrac{\sqrt{3}}{2},-\dfrac{1}{2}\right)$; $\left(-\dfrac{1}{2},\dfrac{\sqrt{3}}{2}\right)$ **9.** $\left(\dfrac{1}{2},-\dfrac{\sqrt{3}}{2}\right)$

11. $\left(\dfrac{\sqrt{2}}{2},\dfrac{\sqrt{2}}{2}\right)$ **13.** $\left(\dfrac{\sqrt{3}}{2},-\dfrac{1}{2}\right)$ **15.** $(0,1)$ **17.** $\left(-\dfrac{\sqrt{2}}{2},-\dfrac{\sqrt{2}}{2}\right)$

19. $\left(-\dfrac{1}{2},-\dfrac{\sqrt{3}}{2}\right)$

9–3, 409

1. (a) $\left(-\dfrac{\sqrt{2}}{2},\dfrac{\sqrt{2}}{2}\right)$ **3.** (a) $\left(-\dfrac{\sqrt{3}}{2},-\dfrac{1}{2}\right)$ **5.** (a) $(1,0)$ **7.** $(1,0)$,

$\left(\dfrac{\sqrt{3}}{2},-\dfrac{1}{2}\right),\left(\dfrac{\sqrt{2}}{2},-\dfrac{\sqrt{2}}{2}\right),\left(\dfrac{1}{2},-\dfrac{\sqrt{3}}{2}\right),\dfrac{\pi}{2},\dfrac{2\pi}{3},\dfrac{3\pi}{4},\dfrac{5\pi}{6},(0,1)$,

$\left(-\dfrac{1}{2},\dfrac{\sqrt{3}}{2}\right),\left(-\dfrac{\sqrt{2}}{2},\dfrac{\sqrt{2}}{2}\right),\left(-\dfrac{\sqrt{3}}{2},\dfrac{1}{2}\right),\left(-\dfrac{1}{2},\dfrac{\sqrt{3}}{2}\right),\left(-\dfrac{\sqrt{3}}{2},\dfrac{1}{2}\right)$,

$\left(-\dfrac{\sqrt{2}}{2},\dfrac{\sqrt{2}}{2}\right),(0,-1),\left(-\dfrac{1}{2},-\dfrac{\sqrt{3}}{2}\right),\left(-\dfrac{\sqrt{3}}{2},-\dfrac{1}{2}\right),\left(-\dfrac{\sqrt{2}}{2},-\dfrac{\sqrt{2}}{2}\right)$,

$\pi,\dfrac{7\pi}{6},\dfrac{4\pi}{3},\dfrac{5\pi}{4},(-1,0),\left(-\dfrac{\sqrt{3}}{2},-\dfrac{1}{2}\right),\left(-\dfrac{1}{2},-\dfrac{\sqrt{3}}{2}\right),\left(-\dfrac{\sqrt{2}}{2},-\dfrac{\sqrt{2}}{2}\right)$

13. $(-x,y)$

9–4, 415

1. (a) $\left(\dfrac{\sqrt{2}}{2},\dfrac{\sqrt{2}}{2}\right)$, sin: $\dfrac{\sqrt{2}}{2}$, cos: $\dfrac{\sqrt{2}}{2}$ **3.** (a) $\dfrac{\sqrt{2}}{2}$ **5.** (a) 0 **7.** (a) $-\dfrac{1}{2}$

9. (a) One point only: $(0,1)$ (b) $s=0$ **11.** (a) Positive   (b) $-\dfrac{4}{5}$

9–5, 420

1. (a) $\dfrac{\sqrt{2}}{2}$ **3.** (a) $\dfrac{\sqrt{3}}{2}$ **5.** (a) $-\dfrac{\sqrt{3}}{2}$ **7.** (a) $-\dfrac{\sqrt{3}}{2}$ **9.** (a) $\dfrac{1}{2}$ **11.** Even

13. Neither   **17.** (a) Odd polynomial functions have only odd powers of x appearing.   (c) Polynomial functions which have both odd and even powers of x are neither odd nor even.

9–6, 424

1. (a) sin: $\dfrac{2\sqrt{5}}{5}$, tan: 2, cot: $\dfrac{1}{2}$, sec: $\sqrt{5}$, csc: $\dfrac{\sqrt{5}}{2}$ **3.** (a) sin: $\dfrac{2\sqrt{5}}{5}$,

cos: $\dfrac{\sqrt{5}}{5}$, cot: $-\dfrac{1}{2}$, sec: $\sqrt{5}$, csc: $-\dfrac{\sqrt{5}}{2}$ **5.** (a) sin: $-\dfrac{\sqrt{2}}{2}$, cos: $\dfrac{-\sqrt{2}}{2}$,

cot: 1; sec: $-\sqrt{2}$; csc: $-\sqrt{2}$ **7.** (a) $-,-,+$ **9.** (a) All real numbers

11. $\sin s$ **13.** $2\tan s$ **15.** $\cos s$

9–7, 429   **1.** (a) $120°$ **3.** (a) $160°$ **5.** (a) $-\dfrac{\pi}{2}$ radians   **7.** (a) $\dfrac{10\pi}{9}$ **9.** $\dfrac{1}{2},\dfrac{\sqrt{3}}{2},\dfrac{\sqrt{3}}{3}$

11. $-1,0$, undefined   **13.** $\dfrac{\sqrt{3}}{2},-\dfrac{1}{2},-\sqrt{3}$ **15.** $-\dfrac{1}{2},-\dfrac{\sqrt{3}}{2},\dfrac{\sqrt{3}}{3}$ **17.** $0,1,0$

19. .985, .174, 5.671   **21.** .588, .809   **23.** .719, .695   **25.** .259, .966

9–8, 432   **1.** (a) $\dfrac{\sqrt{3}}{2}$ **3.** (a) $\dfrac{\sqrt{2}}{2}$ **5.** (a) $.-391$ **7.** (a) -57.290 **9.** (a) -2.356

11. (a) 1   **13.** (a) $42°$ **15.** (a) $\dfrac{\pi}{6}$ **17.** (12a) .951, (12b) 1.154, (13a) 1.111,

(13b) .643, (14a) $\dfrac{1}{2}\sqrt{2}$, (14b) .510, (15a) 2, (15b) $\dfrac{1}{3}\sqrt{3}$, (16a) 1.391, (16b) .946

19. .524; sin: .866, cos: .500, sin: .500; cos: .866   **20.** $1.571-1.309=.262$

21. 1.257; $\sin .314=\cos 1.257=.309$; $\cos .314=\sin 1.257=.951$ **23.** .140;

$\sin 1.431=\cos .140=.990$; $\cos 1.431=\sin .140=.139$

Chapter Review, 434   **1.** 0   **3.** 0   **5.** 0   **7.** -1 **9.** -1 **11.** 1   **13.** -1 **15.** $\dfrac{\sqrt{3}}{2}$ **17.** $\left(\dfrac{\sqrt{2}}{2}, \dfrac{\sqrt{2}}{2}\right)$
21. $\sin^2 s$ **23.** $\cos^2 s$ **25.** $\tan^2 s$ **31.** $\cos(-60°) = \frac{1}{2}$ **33.** $\tan(-135°) = 1$
35. $\cos s$ **37.** $-\sin s$ **39.** $-\sin s$ **41.** $\tan s$ **43.** Even   **45.** Odd

10–1, 439   **1.** (a) 5.57   **3.** (a) 5   **5.** (a) 29°   **7.** 105 ft   **9.** 61°

10–2, 445   **1.** (a) 10   **3.** (a) 126°   **5.** (a) 33.95 or 9.66   **7.** (a) 77.77   **9.** (a) 99.7
11. (a) 48.1   **13.** 1496 ft   **17.** 4.44; 7.40; 67°; 113°   **19.** 60   **21.** 690 lbs; 19°

10–3, 450   **1.** (a) $\frac{1}{4}(\sqrt{6} - \sqrt{2})$ **3.** (a) $2 + \sqrt{3}$ **5.** (a) $\frac{1}{4}(\sqrt{2} - \sqrt{6})$
7. (a) $-\frac{1}{21}(3\sqrt{5} + 4\sqrt{10})$, $\frac{2}{21}(3 - 5\sqrt{2})$, $\frac{2}{115}(49\sqrt{5} - 25\sqrt{10})$
9. (a) $-\sin u$ **11.** (a) $-\cos u$

10–4, 454   **1.** (a) $\frac{4}{5}$ **3.** (a) $-\frac{24}{7}$ **5.** (a) $-\frac{12}{13}$ **7.** (a) $-\frac{24}{25}$ **9.** (a) $-\frac{2}{7}\sqrt{6}$
11. (a) sin: $\frac{1}{2}\sqrt{2 - \sqrt{3}}$, cos: $\frac{1}{2}\sqrt{2 + \sqrt{3}}$, tan: $2 - \sqrt{3}$, cot: $2 + \sqrt{3}$,
sec: $2\sqrt{2 - \sqrt{3}}$, csc: $2\sqrt{2 + \sqrt{3}}$

10–5, 459   **1.** (a) $\left\{\dfrac{\pi}{6}, \dfrac{5\pi}{6}\right\}$ **3.** (a) $\left\{\dfrac{\pi}{12}, \dfrac{5\pi}{12}, \dfrac{13\pi}{12}, \dfrac{17\pi}{12}\right\}$ **5.** (a) $\left\{\dfrac{5\pi}{6}, \dfrac{7\pi}{6}\right\}$
7. (a) $\left\{\dfrac{\pi}{3}, \dfrac{5\pi}{3}, \pi\right\}$ **9.** (a) $\left\{\dfrac{\pi}{3}, \dfrac{5\pi}{3}, \dfrac{3\pi}{4}, \dfrac{7\pi}{4}\right\}$ **11.** (a) $\left\{\dfrac{\pi}{24}, \dfrac{5\pi}{24}, \dfrac{7\pi}{24}, \dfrac{11\pi}{24}, \dfrac{13\pi}{24}, \right.$
$\left. \dfrac{17\pi}{24}, \dfrac{19\pi}{24}, \dfrac{23\pi}{24}, \dfrac{25\pi}{24}, \dfrac{29\pi}{24}, \dfrac{31\pi}{24}, \dfrac{35\pi}{24}, \dfrac{37\pi}{24}, \dfrac{41\pi}{24}, \dfrac{43\pi}{24}, \dfrac{47\pi}{24}\right\}$
13. (a) $\left\{\dfrac{\pi}{9}, \dfrac{2\pi}{9}, \dfrac{4\pi}{9}, \dfrac{5\pi}{9}, \dfrac{7\pi}{9}, \dfrac{8\pi}{9}, \dfrac{10\pi}{9}, \dfrac{11\pi}{9}, \dfrac{13\pi}{9}, \dfrac{14\pi}{9}, \dfrac{16\pi}{9}, \dfrac{17\pi}{9}\right\}$
15. $\left\{\dfrac{\pi}{4}, \dfrac{5\pi}{4}\right\}$ **17.** $\left\{\dfrac{\pi}{9}, \dfrac{7\pi}{9}, \dfrac{13\pi}{9}\right\}$ **19.** $\left\{\left(\dfrac{\pi}{6}, -\dfrac{1}{2}\right), \left(\dfrac{5\pi}{6}, -\dfrac{1}{2}\right)\right\}$

10–6, 463   **3.** $1, 0, -1, -\sqrt{2}, -1, 0, 1$ **5.** Shift π units to the left.

10–7, 467   **1.** (a) 2π; 4   **3.** (a) 3π; 4   **5.** (a) 2π; 3   **7.** (a) 2π; 2   **9.** 2π
14. $2\sin\left(x + \dfrac{\pi}{6}\right)$ **15.** $\sqrt{2}\sin\left(x - \dfrac{\pi}{4}\right)$

10–8, 471   **1.** (a) $\dfrac{\pi}{3}$ **3.** (a) 0   **5.** (a) $\dfrac{\pi}{6}$ **7.** (a) $\dfrac{2\pi}{3}$ **9.** (a) .925   **11.** (a) $\dfrac{\pi}{4}$ **13.** (a) $-\dfrac{\pi}{4}$
15. (a) $-\frac{3}{4}$ **17.** (a) 2   **19.** $\left\{s \;\middle|\; -\dfrac{\pi}{2} < s < \dfrac{\pi}{2}\right\}$ **21.** $\{x \mid x \text{ is real}\}$
25. $\{\frac{1}{3}, -1\}$

10–9, 477   **1.** (a) $2(\cos 120° + i\sin 120°)$ **3.** (a) $5(\cos 270° + i\sin 270°)$
5. (a) $\dfrac{\pi}{2}(\cos 0° + i\sin 0°)$ **7.** (a) -20 **9.** $8i$ **11.** -64 **13.** $24\sqrt{3}i$
15. $64\sqrt{2} - 64\sqrt{2}i$ **17.** $-3i, -\frac{3}{2}\sqrt{3} + \frac{3}{2}i, \frac{3}{2}\sqrt{3} + \frac{3}{2}i$
19. $\sqrt{2}, 1 + i, \sqrt{2}i, -1 + i, -\sqrt{2}, -1 - i, -\sqrt{2}i, 1 - i$ **21.** $.924 + .383i$;
$-.383 + .924i$; $-.924 - .383i$; $.383 - .924i$ **23.** (a) $1, \frac{1}{2} + \frac{1}{2}\sqrt{3}i$,
$-\frac{1}{2} + \frac{1}{2}\sqrt{3}i, -1, -\frac{1}{2} - \frac{1}{2}\sqrt{3}i, \frac{1}{2} - \frac{1}{2}\sqrt{3}i$

Chapter Review, 480   **1.** 4.36   **3.** $5\sqrt{2}$ **5.** $\frac{1}{77}(-21\sqrt{5} + 12\sqrt{2})$ **7.** $\dfrac{14 + 18\sqrt{10}}{12\sqrt{2} - 21\sqrt{5}}$
9. $\dfrac{-51 + 10\sqrt{91}}{10\sqrt{389}}$ **11.** sin: $\frac{1}{2}\sqrt{2 - \sqrt{2}}$, cos: $\frac{1}{2}\sqrt{2 + \sqrt{2}}$, tan: $\sqrt{2} - 1$

13. sin: $\dfrac{\sqrt{3}}{2}$, cos: $-\frac{1}{2}$, tan: $-\sqrt{3}$ **15.** $\dfrac{-4\sqrt{5}}{9}$ **17.** $\cos x - \sin x$ **19.** 1

21. $\left\{\dfrac{7\pi}{6}, \dfrac{11\pi}{6}\right\}$ **23.** $\left\{0, \dfrac{\pi}{4}, \pi, \dfrac{5\pi}{4}\right\}$ **25.** π; 3 **27.** Does not exist **29.** $-\dfrac{\pi}{4}$

31. π **33.** $\frac{2}{3}\sqrt{3}$ **41.** $2, 1 + \sqrt{3}i, -1 + \sqrt{3}i, -2, 1 - \sqrt{3}i, -1 - \sqrt{3}i$

43. 5 ft **44.** 260 mi **45.** $d \doteq 132, \alpha = 19°$

11–1, 487 **1.** (a) 20, 60, 120, 120 **3.** (a) 133,225; 132,860 **5.** (a) 243 **7.** (a) 8 **9.** 72
11. 3024 **13.** 13,776 **15.** 1200

11–2, 490 **1.** (a) 15; 39; 10 (no repetition) or 16 (repetition) **3.** (a) 676; 17,576; 18,252
5. 6 **7.** 8 **9.** $26^2 \cdot 9 \cdot 10^3$ **11.** $26 \cdot 25 \cdot 10 \cdot 9 \cdot 8 \cdot 7$

11–3, 495 **1.** (a) *abc, acd, abd, bcd, acb, adc, adb, bdc, bac, cad, bad, cbd, bca, cda, bda, cdb, cab, dac, dab, dbc, cba, dca, dba, dcb,* Same **3.** (a) 67, 68, 69, 76, 78, 79, 86, 87, 89, 96, 97, 98; 678, 698, 768, 798, 786, 796, 876, 896, 976, 986, 968, 978; {7698, 9678, 7896, 9876, 6789, 6987, 8769, 8967} **5.** (a) $\{\{K, P\}, \{O, H, V\}\}$, $\{\{K, O\}, \{P, H, V\}\}$, $\{\{K, H\}, \{P, O, V\}\}$, $\{\{K, V\}, \{P, O, H\}\}$, $\{\{P, O\}, \{K, H, V\}\}$, $\{\{P, H\}, \{K, O, V\}\}$, $\{\{P, V\}, \{K, O, H\}\}$, $\{\{O, H\}, \{K, P, V\}\}$, $\{\{O, V\}, \{K, P, H\}\}$, $\{\{H, V\}, \{K, P, O\}\}$
7. (a) Permutations (b) Combinations (c) Combinations (d) Permutations
(e) Combinations (f) Neither (g) Permutations (h) Permutations

11–4, 499 **1.** (a) 720 **3.** (a) 1 **5.** (a) 256 **7.** (a) 16 **9.** (a) 720 **11.** (a) 210
13. (a) $n = 6$ **15.** 10,080 **17.** (a) 24 **19.** 6 **21.** 1440 **23.** (a) 15 **25.** 3

11–5, 505 **1.** (a) 60 **3.** (a) $\frac{34191}{45451}$ **5.** (a) $(n + 3)(n + 2)(n + 1)$
7. (a) $2^n(2n - 1)(2n - 3) \cdots 5 \cdot 3 \cdot 1$ **11.** 40,320 **13.** 12 **15.** 2520
17. $\dfrac{n(n - 1)}{2}$

11–6, 510 **1.** (a) $x^8 - 8x^7y + 28x^6y^2 - 56x^5y^3 + 70x^4y^4 - 56x^3y^5 + 28x^2y^6 - 8xy^7 + y^8$
3. (a) $1 + 5x + 10x^2 + 10x^3 + 5x^4 + x^5$ **5.** (a) $1 + 3x^2 + 3x^4 + x^6$
7. (a) Fourth; $-1792a^5b^3$; $112a^2b^6$ **9.** (a) 70
11. (a) $x^7\sqrt{x} + 10x^6 + 40x^4\sqrt{x}$ **13.** (a) .951 (b) 1.26528 (c) .9506; 1.265

11–7, 513 **1.** (a) $16a^4 + 96a^3b + 216a^2b^2 + 216ab^3 + 81b^4$ **3.** (a) \$104.06
7. (b) $1 - 1 = 0$; $1 - 2 + 1 = 0$; $1 - 3 + 3 - 1 = 0$;
$1 - 4 + 6 - 4 + 1 = 0$; $1 - 5 + 10 - 10 + 5 - 1 = 0$; and so on.

Chapter **1.** $1000 \cdot 999 \cdot 998 \cdot \ldots \cdot 989$ **3.** 225 **5.** 28 **7.** 4950 **9.** 107 **11.** (a) 48
Review, (b) 100 (c) 60 **13.** $8x^3 + 60x^2y + 150xy^2 + 125y^3$
515 **15.** $x^7 - 7x^6y + 21x^5y^2 - 35x^4y^3 + 35x^3y^4 - 21x^2y^5 + 7xy^6 - y^7$
17. $\dfrac{x^5}{y^5} - 5\dfrac{x^4}{y^4} + 10\dfrac{x^3}{y^3} - 10\dfrac{x^2}{y^2} + 5\dfrac{x}{y} - 1$
19. $243x^5 - \frac{405}{2}x^4y + \frac{135}{2}x^3y^2 - \frac{45}{4}x^2y^3 + \frac{15}{16}xy^4 - \frac{1}{32}y^5$
21. $x^5 + \frac{5}{2}x^4y + \frac{5}{2}x^3y^2 + \frac{5}{4}x^2y^3 + \frac{5}{16}xy^4 + \frac{1}{32}y^5$ **23.** $x^{10} + 10x^9\sqrt{y} + 45x^8y + 120x^7y\sqrt{y} + 210x^6y^2 + 252x^5y^2\sqrt{y} + 210x^4y^3 + 120x^3y^3\sqrt{y} + 45x^2y^4 + 10xy^4\sqrt{y} + y^5$ **25.** $-48, 384x^5y^6$ **27.** $810x^4y$ **29.** $6x^4y^4$ **31.** y

12–1, 521 **1.** (a) $\frac{1}{36}$ **3.** (a) $\frac{1}{18}$ **5.** (a) $\frac{1}{13}; \frac{1}{4}; \frac{1}{52}$ **7.** (a) $\frac{1}{25}; \frac{2}{5}$

12–2, 523 **1.** (a) $\frac{1}{8}, \frac{3}{8}, \frac{3}{8}, \frac{1}{8}$ **3.** (a) 1326; $\frac{1}{221}; \frac{8}{663}$ **5.** (a) 60 **7.** $\frac{1}{8}; \frac{3}{8}; \frac{3}{8}; \frac{3}{8}$ **9.** $\frac{1}{20}; \frac{1}{5}$
11. $\frac{2}{9}$

12–3, 527 **1.** (a) $\frac{5}{6}$ **3.** (a) (ii) $\frac{3}{5}; \frac{2}{5}$ **5.** $\frac{5}{6}$ **7.** 32; $\frac{31}{32}; \frac{3}{16}$ **9.** (a) $\frac{6}{25}$ (b) $\frac{1}{5}$

12–4, 531   **1.** (a) (ii) Independent   **3.** (a) 216, 108, 108, 36, 54, 18, 18, 9; yes   **7.** No

12–5, 536   **1.** (a) $\frac{5}{32}; \frac{31}{32}$ **3.** (a) $\frac{27}{128}; \frac{175}{256}$ **5.** (a) .05   **7.** (a) .35   (b) .65   (c) .74

12–6, 539   **1.** (a) .055   (b) 0   (c) 0   (d) .070   (e) .474   **3.** (a) .004; .776; .22   (b) .776; .004; .22

EXTRA!, 541   **1.** .04   **2.** (a) $1 - (\frac{364}{365})^5$ (b) $n \geq 251$

Chapter Review, 543   **1.** (a) $\frac{1}{4}$ **3.** $\frac{3}{8}$ **5.** $P(A) = \frac{1}{2}$, $P(B) = \frac{1}{3}$, or $P(A) = \frac{1}{3}$, $P(B) = \frac{1}{2}$ **7.** (a) 3003   (b) $\frac{1}{3}$ (c) $\frac{82}{143}$ **9.** $\frac{671}{1296}; \frac{125}{324}$ **11.** $\frac{1}{25}$

Cumulative Review III, 545   **1.** $-1 - i\sqrt{3}; \frac{5}{4}; a = 6, b = -20$ **5.** (a) $\{-1, 2, 3\}$; $(x + 1)(x - 2)(x - 3)$ (b) $\{\frac{1}{2}, \frac{1}{2}(-3 \pm \sqrt{5})\}$; $(2x - 1)(2x + 3 + \sqrt{5})(2x + 3 - \sqrt{5})$ (c) $\{3, \pm i\}$; $(x - 3)^2(x^2 + 1)$ (d) $\{\frac{1}{2}, \frac{1}{2}(-1 \pm \sqrt{3}i)\}$; $(2x - 1)^2(x^2 + x + 1)$ **7.** 2.1   **9.** $a = -22, b = -24$; use synthetic division   **11.** $32i$ **15.** (a) $0, 2 \pm i, -\sqrt{3}$ (b) $x^3 - 6x^2 - 5x + 22$ **17.** (a) 120   (b) 64   **19.** $m = -1, n = 16$ **25.** $ad = bc$

13–1, 552   **1.** (a) 48   **3.** (a) $7k - 4$ **5.** (a) 750   **7.** (a) $\frac{1}{2}$ **9.** (a) $-6, -9, -12, -15, -18, -21, -24, -27, -30, -33$ **11.** 6   **13.** a and d **15.** $x = \frac{1}{2}$

13–2, 557   **1.** (a) 1458   **3.** (a) $\dfrac{3^{k-1}}{2^{k-3}}$ **5.** (a) 14.6   **7.** (a) 12, 18, $\frac{81}{2}$ **9.** (a) 12   **11.** $\dfrac{a - rt}{1 - r}$ **13.** 4.4%, approximately   **15.** $\frac{4}{3}(4^n - 1)$

13–3, 561   **1.** (a) $\frac{3}{2}$ **3.** (a) $12\frac{1}{3}$ **5.** (a) $\frac{5}{9}$ **7.** (a) $\frac{403}{33}$ **9.** 1368 in.   **11.** $48(2 + \sqrt{2})$

13–4, 567   **6.** $\dfrac{(n + 1)(n + 2)}{2}, n \geq 1$ **7.** $\dfrac{n(n - 3)}{2}, n \geq 3$ **8.** $[(n - 2)180]°$

EXTRA! 573   **1.** $d = \dfrac{d}{2} + \dfrac{d}{4} + \dfrac{d}{8} + \dots$ **3.** $S = d$; The sum is finite.

Chapter Review, 575   **1.** 39   **3.** $a^3 + 11a^2$ **5.** 99   **7.** 21   **9.** 14; 1421   **11.** 13   **13.** $(1.1)^9$ **15.** $\frac{341}{64}$ **17.** $3[(1.5)^{10} - 1]$ **19.** $\frac{1}{9}, \frac{1}{3}, 1$ **21.** $a = 2, S_n = -3280$ **23.** $3 + 9 + 27 + 81 + 243$; geometric   **25.** 4, 10, 18, 28, 40; neither   **27.** $2 + 5 + 8 + 11 + 14$; arithmetic   **29.** $\frac{3}{11}$

14–1, 581   **1.** (a) $\overrightarrow{AB}, \overrightarrow{BA}, \overrightarrow{AC}, \overrightarrow{CA}, \overrightarrow{BC}, \overrightarrow{CB}$ **3.** (a) (i) $(-1, 5)$ (ii) $(-1, 5)$ (iii) $(3, -3)$ **5.** (a) (i) $(-3, 5)$ (ii) $(9, -7)$ (iii) $(-3, 5)$

14–2, 586   **1.** (a) $\overrightarrow{AC}$ **3.** (a) $\overrightarrow{DB}$ **5.** (a) $\overrightarrow{CD}$ **7.** (a) F   **11.** $(-3, 2)$ **13.** Yes   **15.** $\overrightarrow{BC} = \overrightarrow{AC} - \overrightarrow{AB}$; $\overrightarrow{FE} = \overrightarrow{DE} - \overrightarrow{DF}$

14–3, 592   **1.** (a) C is midpoint of $\overline{AB}$ **3.** (a) C is any point between A and B **5.** (a) $-\frac{11}{2}$ **7.** (a) $7\sqrt{3} - 2$ **9.** (a) $(16, 1)$ **11.** $(9, -6)$ **13.** $(1, -12)$ **15.** $(17, 0)$ **17.** No

14–4, 597   **1.** (a) $-\frac{3}{5}\overrightarrow{AB} + 5\overrightarrow{AC}$ **3.** (a) $\overrightarrow{AB} - \frac{3}{2}\overrightarrow{AC}$ **5.** (a) $\frac{1}{2}\overrightarrow{AB} - \frac{1}{2}\overrightarrow{AC}$ **7.** (a) $7i + 3j$ **9.** (a) $-6i + 2j$ **11.** $\overrightarrow{AB} = 2i + 3j$; $\overrightarrow{CD} = 7i - 6j$; $\overrightarrow{OE} = i + 3j$ **13.** (a) $x = 0, y = 0$ (b) $x = a, y = b$

14–5, 601   **1.** 50 lb, 50 lb   **3.** 283 lb, 200 lb   **5.** 37°, 53°

14–6, 604   **1.** (a) $(9, -5)$ **3.** (a) $(21, -13)$ **5.** (a) $-2i + 2j$ **7.** (a) $[\frac{1}{2}b, -2]$ **9.** $s = 1, k = 2$ **11.** $t = 1$

14–7, 610   **1.** (a) 0   **3.** (a) 0   **5.** (a) Yes   **7.** (a) 8 sq units   **9.** (a) None
11. (a) $3x - 2y$ (b) 0

EXTRA!, 612   **1.** 2.04   **3.** 4.02   **5.** 3.88   **7.** 3.65   **9.** 3.95

Chapter   **1.** F, $k(k - 1)$ nonzero vectors   **3.** F, $= \overrightarrow{AB} + \overrightarrow{DC}$ **5.** F, product is a vector
Review,   **7.** T   **9.** T   **11.** T   **13.** F, inner product is a number   **15.** Yes
613   **17.** (a) $\dfrac{35\sqrt{3}}{2}$ (b) $\dfrac{35\sqrt{2}}{2}$ **19.** $\overrightarrow{DA}$ **21.** $(-6, 2)$ **23.** $x = \frac{21}{2}, y = -5$
25. Right   **27.** Isosceles   **29.** $-2i + j$ **31.** $[1, 1]$ **33.** $[3 - x, y - 1]$
35. $\sqrt{2}$ **37.** $12i + 16j$ **39.** $4i + 8j$ **41.** 5

Cumulative   **9.** $\dfrac{5\sqrt{5}}{2}$ min   **11.** (a) $n(2n - 1)$ (b) $\dfrac{n}{2}(5n + 23)$ **13.** (a) $\frac{3}{4}, \frac{2}{3}, \frac{5}{8}, \frac{3}{5}, \frac{7}{12}$
Review IV,
616   (b) $\frac{1}{2} \cdot \dfrac{n + 1}{n}$ **15.** 2   **21.** 728 or 252   **23.** $\dfrac{n(n + 1)(2n + 7)}{6}$ **25.** $i + 12j$; 29
27. $[8, 7]$; 27   **29.** Right and isosceles

15–1, 623   **1.** (a) (i) $p \wedge \sim q$ (ii) $p \wedge q$ (iii) $p \rightarrow q$ (iv) $p \vee q$ (v) $p \wedge \sim q$
(vi) $\sim(p \wedge q)$ **3.** (a) (i) $p \rightarrow q$ (ii) $p \wedge r$ (iii) $q \rightarrow (p \vee r)$ (iv) $q \vee \sim p$
(v) $\sim p \wedge (r \rightarrow q)$ (vi) $\sim(\sim p \wedge \sim r \wedge q)$

15–2, 629   **7.** (a) (i) a is not positive   (ii) a is positive and a is not positive   (iii) a is
positive or a is not positive   **11.** No   **13.** (b) p (c) It is not true that it is not
snowing.   **15.** (a) It is not true that $a = 0$ or $b = 0$.   (b) It is not true that
$a \neq 0$ and $b \neq 0$.

15–3, 633   **1.** (a) (i) $p \rightarrow q$ (ii) $q \leftrightarrow p$ (iii) $q \rightarrow p$ (iv) $q \rightarrow p$ **3.** (a) $\sim(\sim p) \rightarrow \sim(\sim q)$;
$p \rightarrow q$ **5.** $\sim p \leftrightarrow (\sim q \wedge \sim r)$ **7.** The product of two integers is odd if, and only
if, both the integers are odd.

15–4, 636   **7.** (a) Valid   **9.** (a) Invalid   **13.** $q \rightarrow p$ Valid   **15.** $p \rightarrow q$ Valid
$$\frac{q}{p}$$
$$\frac{r \wedge \sim q}{\sim r}$$
$$\overline{\sim p}$$

17. $\sim p \rightarrow \sim q$ Invalid
$\sim r \rightarrow \sim p$
$$\frac{\sim q}{\sim r}$$

15–5, 641   **1.** (a) Valid   **3.** (b) Contrapositive; Contrapositive; Transitivity of the
conditional   **10.** (a) Invalid   (b) Invalid

Chapter   **5.** (a) and (c)   **7.** $q \rightarrow p$ Valid
Review, $\sim q \rightarrow \sim r$
644 $$\frac{\sim p}{\sim r}$$